Preface

The first edition of *Medical Neurosciences,* published in 1978, presented a way to organize knowledge of the nervous system that is based on the physician's approach to clinical problems. For medical students and residents alike, this organizational framework served as an effective foundation on which to build knowledge, and it required only an updating in the second edition.

In the last 15 years, our understanding of the normal function and pathophysiology of the nervous system has rapidly increased, adding immeasurably to the range and depth of information vital to comprehending neural function. This change has required reorganization of the text as well as the addition of a new chapter in the third edition. Nonetheless, the basic framework remains valid, and systems and levels continue to be the book's guiding principles. In fact, our expanded knowledge of underlying organizational principles has led to the introduction of another unifying concept in the text: one that relates the basic organization of the nervous system to a core, or inner tube, of phylogenetically older structures surrounded by an outer tube of newer structures. We believe that this concept makes knowledge of the nervous system more accessible than it has been in the past. We sincerely hope these additions and changes will allow *Medical Neurosciences* to better serve as an introduction to the neurosciences for new students, as a review and update of the knowledge of basic neuroscience for more experienced students, and as a framework for an organized approach to the principles of neurologic diagnosis for all who attempt to evaluate clinical problems.

This edition, like its predecessors, is the product of the authors. However, many others have contributed significantly to its development and evolution, and we are grateful to the students and faculty, both at the Mayo Clinic and elsewhere, who have taken the time to share their suggestions with us. In particular, we acknowledge the faculty consultants at Mayo who contributed to this edition: Charles F. Abboud, M.D., Division of Endocrinology, Metabolism, and Internal Medicine; Arnold D. Aronson, Ph.D., Section of Speech Pathology; Robert C. Benassi, Section of Visual Information; Shelley A. Cross, M.D., Department of Neurology; Clifford R. Jack, M.D., Department of Diagnostic Radiology; Terrence D. Lagerlund, M.D., Department of Neurology; Jay W. McLaren, Ph.D., Section of Ophthalmology Research; O. Eugene Millhouse, Ph.D., Section of Publications; Ronald C. Petersen, M.D., Department of Neurology; Michael H. Silber, M.B.Ch.B., F.C.P. (SA), Department of Neurology; and Jerry W. Swanson, M.D., Department of Neurology. We also thank Roberta J. Schwartz, Mary Jane I. Badker, and Dorothy L. Tienter of the Section of Publications, and Jeanette K. Connaughty, Secretary, Section of Electroencephalography, for their help preparing the manuscript.

This is an exciting time in the world of neuroscience; we hope our readers will be stimulated to explore it further.

B. F. W.
E. E. B.
J. R. D.
T. J. R.
B. A. S.

Medical Neurosciences

— 1 —

Integrated Neuroscience for the Clinician

Neurologic disorders are common, and clinicians must be capable of dealing confidently with them. Many steps are required in accomplishing this task. Patients seldom present to their physician with a well-defined diagnosis for which appropriate therapy can be readily dispensed. Instead they arrive with a vast array of symptoms and signs that constitute a clinical problem the physician must attempt to resolve.

In solving problems, one generally approaches them by using one of two well-known methods. First, if the problem is similar to or identical to one encountered previously and the person is able to recall the answer or solution, he or she may move quickly and rapidly to an answer. This method is called *problem solving by pattern recognition.* A second approach is that of *logical analysis,* or *inductive reasoning.* In using this method, one traces the problem to its source by a series of steps based on knowledge of the underlying structure and function. Both methods have a critical step in common that will be used throughout your medical career — hypothesis testing. When a problem looks like one seen before, one can hypothesize that the solution is likely to be the same and develop a scheme to test the hypothesis. When a problem is not clearly understood or familiar, but some of the underlying components are understood, one can propose a hypothesis about the mechanism of the problem based on an analysis of that knowledge.

The solution of a clinical problem in neurology, as in any area of medicine, requires a knowledge of anatomy, physiology, and pathophysiology. This book is an attempt to organize the body of information contained in the basic neurologic sciences into the format used by clinicians in dealing with diseases of the nervous system.

The process used by a clinician who examines a patient with a neurologic disorder (that is, one involving the brain, spinal cord, nerves, or muscles) may involve either pattern recognition or inductive reasoning. The latter is a familiar process in which a number of distinct pieces of information are put together to reach a general conclusion. For example, if a woman has a 1-year history of slowly progressive numbness and weakness of the left side of her face, left arm, and left leg, the physician concludes that the patient may have a neoplastic lesion at the supratentorial level on the right side. The physician uses the data obtained by interviewing and examining the patient to produce a history that is a chronologic account of the patient's symptoms and their evolution with time (the temporal profile). The specific symptoms in the history can be categorized into broad groups and related to particular anatomical structures and certain disease categories. In a patient with neurologic disease, these symptoms often are identified with changes in sensation, activity, movement, thinking, or consciousness. Often the physical examination of a patient with neurologic disease allows an even more precise definition of abnormal function, which, based on the clinician's knowledge of anatomical structure and function, can be related to specific areas of the nervous system.

Throughout the interview and the examination, the clinician is constantly organizing and reorganizing the collected data to arrive at hypotheses about the nature of the disorder. In the previous example, the hypothesis of a right cerebral tumor was reached because the temporal profile of slow progression is common with neoplastic disorders, and weakness and numbness on the left side of the body often are due to disease of structures that are controlled at the supratentorial level on the right.

The physician must answer three questions. Is there disease involving the nervous system? If so, where is the disease located? And what kind of disease is it (that is, what is the pathologic nature of the disease)? The first question is often one of the most difficult to answer, because an answer depends not only on the knowledge to be presented in this book but also on experience with disease involving all other body systems. This book focuses primarily on answering the two simpler questions: "Where is the lesion located?" and "What is its pathologic nature?"

Objectives

Neurologic diseases include all the major pathologic categories seen in other organ systems and can involve one or several areas in the complex human nervous system. However, adequate management of neurologic problems can be based on answering the questions: "Where is the problem?" and "What is the problem?" The elaboration and analysis of these specific questions form the major objectives in the study of neuroscience. The answers to these questions are based on a knowledge of the gross anatomical structures of the nervous system (Fig. 1-1), their function, the usual patterns of disease, and the forms of treatment available. This simplified approach to neurologic disease is the one customarily used by many neurologists, and it includes four questions:

1. Is the responsible lesion located at
   a. The supratentorial level
   b. The posterior fossa level
   c. The spinal level
   d. The peripheral level
   e. More than one level
2. Is the responsible lesion

Fig. 1-1. Levels of the neuraxis. Supratentorial level includes cerebral hemispheres and portions of cranial nerves I and II within the skull. Posterior fossa level includes brain stem, cerebellum, and portions of cranial nerves III through XII within the skull. Spinal level includes spinal cord and portions of nerve roots contained within the vertebral column. Peripheral level includes portions of both cranial and peripheral nerves that lie outside the skull and spinal column and structures innervated by these nerves.

   a. Focal, and located on the right side of the nervous system
   b. Focal, and located on the left side of the nervous system
   c. Focal, but involving midline and contiguous structures on both sides of the nervous system
   d. Diffuse, and involving homologous, symmetric, noncontiguous areas on both sides of the nervous system

3. Is the responsible lesion
   a. Some form of mass lesion
   b. Some form of nonmass lesion
4. Is the lesion most likely
   a. Vascular
   b. Degenerative
   c. Inflammatory-immunologic
   d. Neoplastic
   e. Toxic-metabolic
   f. Traumatic
   g. Congenital-developmental

The major objective of this text therefore is to provide the information necessary to answer these questions for any clinical problem involving the nervous system and to provide a description of the mechanism by which the patient's symptoms and findings are produced by the underlying disorder.

Organization

The solution of a neurologic problem requires three levels of knowledge; therefore, this text is organized into three sections. Section I provides general information necessary to understand how neurologic disorders are diagnosed. The remainder of the text is organized to enable a precise topographic and etiologic diagnosis. Topographic localization initially requires relating the patient's functional impairment to one of the major longitudinal systems (Section II) and then localizing the lesion at a well-defined level of the nervous system (Section III).

Each chapter begins with an introduction and overview and ends with a listing of objectives and clinical problems for self-assessment. Additional readings are provided.

Survey of the Neurosciences

The clinician must first have an understanding of the methods utilized in diagnosing a neurologic disorder. How is a lesion localized, and to what do the general anatomical terms used to describe localization refer? How is a pathologic or etiologic diagnosis determined, and what do the terms used to describe them mean? These questions require a general knowledge of the diagnostic principles of neurologic disorders as these principles relate to

the anatomy, physiology, and pathology of the nervous system. Chapters 2 through 5 provide the basic vocabulary and the background knowledge necessary to begin solving clinical problems. These chapters cover the following subjects:

Chapter 2: Developmental Organization of the Nervous System: Neuroembryology
Chapter 3: Diagnosis of Neurologic Disorders: Anatomical Localization
Chapter 4: Diagnosis of Neurologic Disorders: Neurocytology and the Pathologic Reactions of the Nervous System
Chapter 5: Diagnosis of Neurologic Disorders: Transient Disorders and Neurophysiology

Longitudinal Systems

Increasingly detailed knowledge of the anatomy and physiology of the nervous system is required for a precise diagnosis of a neurologic disorder. The clinician usually first identifies the patient's symptoms and signs as indicative of disease involving one or more of the major longitudinal subdivisions of the nervous system. These longitudinally organized groups of structures are called *systems* within the nervous system, each subserving a specific function. In this section the anatomy, physiology, and clinical expression of disease as it affects the following major longitudinal systems are described:

Chapter 6: The Cerebrospinal Fluid System
Chapter 7: The Sensory System
Chapter 8: The Motor System
Chapter 9: The Internal Regulation System
Chapter 10: The Consciousness System
Chapter 11: The Vascular System
Chapter 12: The Neurochemical Systems

The name of each system characterizes its function. Correlation of the symptoms and signs with the appropriate system permits localization of the disease process in one dimension.

Chapter 12 (The Neurochemical Systems) examines the functional organization of the systems in terms of the chemical agents used for the transmission and modulation of neural activity and provides an additional method of classifying neurologic function.

Levels of the Neuraxis

The final step in localizing a lesion requires identification of an additional dimension — determining its location along the length of the systems involved. Although a precise localization can be made in many cases, most clinicians classify the disorder according to one of four major regions defined by the bony structures surrounding much of the nervous system. The final part of the text explores the ways in which functions in each major system are integrated and modified at each of the following levels:

Chapter 13:   The Peripheral Level
Chapter 14:   The Spinal Level
Chapter 15:   The Posterior Fossa Level
Chapter 16:   The Supratentorial Level

In all these sections, there is repetition of material, with each subsequent section building on the basic information presented earlier to provide amplification and reemphasis. This approach to clinical neurologic problems can be used with any of the problems that may be encountered and is particularly useful in problems that are new, unfamiliar, or unusual to the clinician. Although the identification of diseases by recognition of a particular syndrome sometimes can be very efficient, the method of hypothesis testing and inductive reasoning presented herein is consistently more accurate and more reliable.

Objectives

1. Define: problem solving, pattern recognition, inductive reasoning, and hypothesis.

2. Given any clinical problem, develop a series of hypotheses that will allow you to understand its cause. Identify and describe the type of reasoning used to generate and test these hypotheses.

Clinical Problems

1. You walk into a room and find your friend lying limp and motionless on the floor. As you approach and attempt to assess the situation further and offer aid, several thoughts go through your mind about what might have happened. Describe the thoughts and the reasoning that contributed to each of them.

2. You sit quietly in a chair with your legs crossed and begin to notice a "numb-tingling feeling" in your right lower leg. On attempting to rise from the chair, you are unable to move the right leg normally. What hypotheses have you developed about the possible cause of this dysfunction?

Additional Reading

Albanese, M. A., and Mitchell, S. Problem-based learning: A review of literature on its outcomes and implementation issues. *Acad. Med.* 68:52, 1993.

Barrows, H. S., and Tamblyn, R. M. *Problem-Based Learning: An Approach to Medical Education.* New York: Springer, 1980.

Eddy, D. M., and Clanton, C. H. The art of diagnosis: Solving the clinicopathological exercise. *N. Engl. J. Med.* 306:1263, 1982.

Engel, G. L. Clinical observation: The neglected basic method of medicine. *JAMA* 192:849, 1965.

Kassirer, J. P., and Gorry, G. A. Clinical problem solving: A behavioral analysis. *Ann. Intern. Med.* 89:245, 1978.

Larkin, J., et al. Expert and novice performance in solving physics problems. *Science* 208:1335, 1980.

— I —

Survey of the Neurosciences

— 2 —

Developmental Organization of the Nervous System: Neuroembryology

The study of neuroscience begins with a survey of neuroembryology, because it provides a framework and background for understanding the anatomy of the nervous system in the adult. The eventual location of the structures in the brain is not a random occurrence but is a reflection of the orderly development of the primitive nervous system. Neuroembryology also serves as an aid in understanding the pathogenesis of developmental neurologic abnormalities that are encountered not only in the newborn and pediatric periods but also in later life.

Overview

The formation of the neural tube begins on the eighteenth day of gestation. By this day of embryonic development, the early stage of gastrulation is completed. The two-layered embryo consisting of ectoderm and endoderm is transformed into a three- layered structure by the outgrowth of mesoderm from the midline primitive streak into the area between the original layers. The notochord, a specialized column of mesodermal cells, grows forward from the anterior end of the primitive streak (Hensen's node). The ectoderm overlying the notochord is induced to form the neural plate, which thickens and folds into the neural tube. The entire central nervous system develops from this tube. Cell columns, called the neural crest, derived from the junction of skin ectoderm and neuroectoderm separate from the neural tube and form a major portion of the peripheral nervous system.

Throughout the length of the neural tube, primitive neuroectodermal cells proliferate, differentiate into neurons and supporting cells (ependyma, astrocytes, and oligodendrocytes), migrate to their genetically coded location, and develop specific intercellular connections and relationships. The cells of the neural crest differentiate into dorsal root ganglia, autonomic ganglia, and Schwann cells.

The neural tube undergoes transverse differentiation (Fig. 2-1), with formation of a dorsal region, the alar plate, which subserves sensory functions, and a ventral region, the basal plate, which subserves motor functions. Also, at all levels, structures that develop in close proximity to the cavity of the neural tube — that is, in the inner tube or core — give rise to phylogenetically older and more primitive functional systems (the consciousness system and the internal regulation system). Structures that develop in the outer regions of the tube (outer tube), at a greater distance from the neural canal, generally belong to phylogenetically newer and higher level functional systems (the motor system and the sensory system). Even within systems, such as the motor system, this concentric relationship pertains, with older and less discrete components of the system located in the inner tube and newer and more highly developed components in the outer regions of the tube. The neurochemical system develops in parallel with the development of functional systems as outlined above, with different sets of excitatory and inhibitory neurotransmitters acting as synapses in different systems.

The cavity of the tube forms the central canal at the spinal cord level and more complex fluid-filled spaces, the ventricular system, at cephalic levels. Mesodermal tissues surround

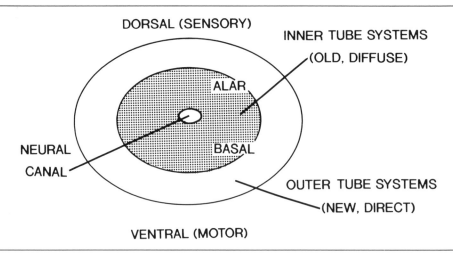

Fig. 2-1. Functional organization of the neural tube.

the neural tube and form the meninges, which in conjunction with the ventricular system form the cerebrospinal fluid system. Mesoderm that surrounds and grows into the neural tube forms the vascular system.

The neural tube undergoes longitudinal differentiation into six regions: telencephalon (cerebral hemispheres), diencephalon (thalamus and hypothalamus), mesencephalon (midbrain), metencephalon (pons and cerebellum), myelencephalon (medulla), and spinal cord. These subdivisions of the neural tube are the precursors of three of the four major anatomical levels in the adult: supratentorial (telencephalon and diencephalon), posterior fossa (mesencephalon, metencephalon, and myelencephalon), and spinal (spinal cord). The fourth, or peripheral level, is composed of a combination of efferent fibers growing outward from the posterior fossa and spinal levels and neural crest derivatives, including somatic and visceral afferent neurons and postganglionic autonomic neurons.

Disorders of development of the nervous system may occur at any embryonic step. They generally are classified according to the dominant process occurring at the time they are thought to arise. The most common are failures of fusion (dorsal induction) of the neural tube (for example, spina bifida and meningomyelocele) and failures of proliferation and migration (for example, pachygyria and microgyria).

Formation of the Neural Tube

The nervous system is commonly divided into central and peripheral components. The central nervous system is that part located within the spinal column and skull. It is formed from the neural tube between the eighteenth and the twenty-fifty day of gestation. Before these structures are formed, at the end of the second week of gestation, gastrulation has been completed. The longitudinal axis of the two-layered embryonic disk is established by the formation of an area of rapidly proliferating cells, the *primitive streak*. The midline of the embryo is defined by the growth of the *notochord,* a group of mesodermal cells that grow forward from one end of the primitive streak (Hensen's node) in a plane between the ectoderm and the endoderm. The mesoderm of the remainder of the embryonic disk is formed by the outgrowth of mesodermal cells from the lateral margins of the primitive streak. As the notochord and mesodermal tissues grow forward, the primitive streak becomes incorporated into the tailbud, and a three-layered embryo with a clearly delineated longitudinal axis is formed. These early changes set the stage for the subsequent events that establish the *neural tube,* the morphologic substrate of the adult nervous system.

The neural tube is formed in approximately 1 week, beginning on the eighteenth

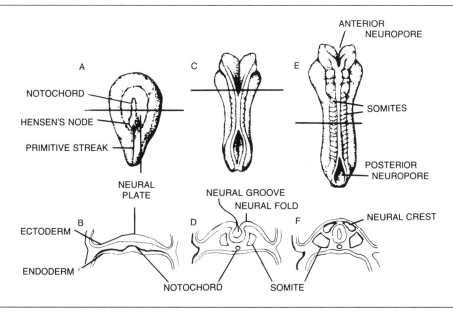

Fig. 2-2. Formation of neural tube (eighteenth to twenty-fifth day). A. Dorsal view of neural plate forming over notochord, which has grown forward from Hensen's node between ectoderm and endoderm. B. Cross section through neural plate shown in A. C. Dorsal view of early closure of neural tube. D. Cross section through neural tube shown in C. E. Dorsal view of almost complete closure of neural tube, and formation of well-defined somites. F. Cross section through E.

day. The initial step in its formation is a thickening of the ectoderm in the dorsal midline overlying the notochord to form the *neural plate* (Fig. 2-2A, B). The lateral edges of the neural plate thicken more rapidly than the center and begin to roll toward the midline, creating the *neural groove,* which has lateral margins, the *neural folds.* With continued growth, the neural folds meet in the midline to form a hollow tube, the neural tube, which closes first in the middle of the embryo (Fig. 2-2C, D) (the future cervical region) and then proceeds toward the head (cephalad) and toward the tail (caudad), until the entire tube is closed. The unfused areas at the two ends of the tube before complete closure are *neuropores* (Fig. 2-2E). As the neural tube is being formed by the fusion of the margins of the neural folds, the skin ectoderm also fuses and covers its dorsal surface. Ultimately, the two ectodermal derivatives, neural tube and skin, become further separated by the growth of intervening mesodermal derivatives, bone and muscle. Cell columns derived from the original junction of skin and

neuroectoderm form the neural crests, which later differentiate into important components of the peripheral nervous system.

Even before the neural tube is entirely closed, longitudinal differentiation begins. Parallel to the neural tube, the mesodermal cells on each side segment into aggregates, the *somites,* from which bone and muscle arise (Fig. 2-2E, F). At the same time, the cephalic, or head, end of the neural tube becomes larger than the caudal end, resulting in an irregularly shaped tubal structure. Continued differential growth along the length of the neural tube results in the formation of three cavities at the cephalic end of the tube. These are the primary brain vesicles: the *prosencephalon,* the *mesencephalon,* and the *rhombencephalon* (Fig. 2-3A, B). These three vesicles further differentiate into five subdivisions, which persist in the brain of the mature nervous system (Fig. 2-3C, D). The remaining caudal end of the neural tube undergoes much less modification as it forms the spinal cord. A central remnant of the internal cavity of the tube remains in each of these derivatives.

Fig. 2-3. Formation of major brain vesicles of neural tube (twenty-fifth to thirtieth day) in horizontal section (*left*) and dorsal view (*right*). A, B. Stage of three primary vesicles. C, D. Stage of five major vesicles. E, F. Differentiation of specific structures by cell migration and overgrowth.

Table 2-1. Major Elements in Adult Nervous System Derived from the Neural Tube

Level	Primary divisions	Subdivisions	Major derivatives	Cavities
Supratentorial	Prosencephalon	Telencephalon	Rhinencephalon Basal ganglia Cerebral cortex	Lateral ventricles
		Diencephalon	Thalamus Hypothalamus Optic nerves Neurohypophysis Pineal	Third ventricle
Posterior fossa	Mesencephalon	Mesencephalon	Midbrain	Aqueduct of Sylvius
	Rhombencephalon	Metencephalon	Cerebellum Pons	Fourth ventricle
		Myelencephalon	Medulla	Fourth ventricle
Spinal	Primitive neural tube	Neural tube	Spinal cord	Central canal
Peripheral		Neural crest	Peripheral nerve Ganglia	None

The subdivisions of the primitive neural tube evolve, through the processes of cellular proliferation, migration, and differentiation (described in the next section), into the major elements in the adult nervous system listed in Table 2-1.

Differentiation of the Central Nervous System

Cytologic Differentiation

The wall of the primitive neural tube consists of multipotential neuroepithelial cells derived from ectoderm. These cells undergo multiplication, migration, and differentiation to establish concentric layers of the neural tube. Cell division occurs primarily in the innermost layer bordering the neural canal. In some texts, this is called the ependymal layer in accordance with a convention established in the early part of the century. However, most anatomists now reserve this term for the single layer of fully differentiated ciliated cells that line the ventricular system in mature brains (Fig. 2-4). The primitive innermost layer, before ependymal maturation, is more properly called the *ventricular zone*. It consists of a single layer of pseudostratified epithelium in which nuclei move in toward the canal to divide and out toward the periphery during the intermitotic phases of the cell cycle.

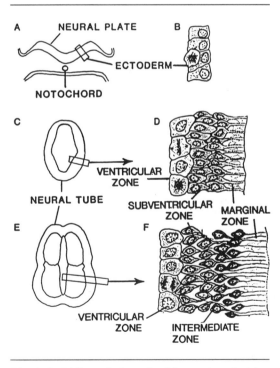

Fig. 2-4. Differentiation of cell layers in primitive neural tube, with high-power view on the right and cross section of tube shown on the left. A, B. Early neural plate is a single layer of cells. C, D. Formation of layers of cells by outward migration of cells proliferating in ventricular zone. E, F. Formation of outer acellular marginal zone by growth of processes (axons) peripherally from cells.

Fig. 2-5. Process of myelination of nerve fibers in central and peripheral nervous system. Layer of cytoplasm wraps around an axon (A) and then encircles it repeatedly (B). Condensation of layers of cytoplasm forms myelin (C).

Cytoplasmic processes of the cells of the ventricular layer establish the outermost layer of the neural tube, the *marginal zone.* This zone increases in width and definition at all levels of the developing nervous system because of the increasing number and complexity of the neuronal processes (axons and dendrites) that compose it. Some glial cells migrate into this zone, but it remains relatively acellular throughout development.

Between the ventricular and marginal zones are two other cellular zones that previously were lumped together as the mantle layer. These are called the *subventricular zone* and the *intermediate zone* (Fig. 2-4). Their relative prominence varies at different levels of the nervous system. Both receive immature neurons from the ventricular zone. However, those that migrate directly into the intermediate zone are postmitotic and do not divide further. Those remaining in the subventricular zone continue to divide as primitive neuroblasts. Eventually these cells stop dividing and migrate into or through the intermediate zone to their programmed destination.

In the prosencephalon, many of the postmitotic cells migrate to the outer limits of the intermediate zone, where they accumulate in what sometimes is described at this level as a fifth zone, the *cortical plate.* After migrating to their definitive location, the immature neurons begin the final stages of maturation, with the development of synaptic connections with numerous other neurons, setting the stage for their primary function in central nervous system information processing.

The subventricular zone is also the reposi-

tory of the spongioblasts, which give rise to the major supporting cells of the central nervous system: astrocytes, oligodendrocytes, and ependymal cells. Ependymal cells mature in the innermost layer of the ventricular zone and form the continuous layer of ependyma that lines the cavities of the brain. The astrocytes and oligodendroglia migrate from the subventricular zone to all areas of the central nervous system, where they undergo further growth and functional maturation. Astrocytes provide mechanical support and maintain the chemical environment of neurons. Oligodendroglia form the insulation of axons, *myelin sheaths,* by wrapping layers of their cytoplasmic membranes around the axons (Fig. 2-5).

In addition to the neuroectodermal elements described above, cells of mesodermal origin make significant contributions to the structural and functional support of the nervous system. Mesodermal tissue gives rise to the covering layers of the central nervous system, the *meninges.* The extensive vascular system of the central nervous system, like the vascular system of all organs, is also of mesodermal origin. Finally, in the later stages of embryonic development, monocytes migrate into the brain and spinal cord, where they reside as potential phagocytic cells called *microglia.*

The events described above do not occur randomly. Each event — down to the last detail, including establishment of the ultimate number and location of neurons in each area of the nervous system and of each synaptic connection of the dendritic trees of neurons — is precisely programmed in the genetic

Preface

The first edition of *Medical Neurosciences,* published in 1978, presented a way to organize knowledge of the nervous system that is based on the physician's approach to clinical problems. For medical students and residents alike, this organizational framework served as an effective foundation on which to build knowledge, and it required only an updating in the second edition.

In the last 15 years, our understanding of the normal function and pathophysiology of the nervous system has rapidly increased, adding immeasurably to the range and depth of information vital to comprehending neural function. This change has required reorganization of the text as well as the addition of a new chapter in the third edition. Nonetheless, the basic framework remains valid, and systems and levels continue to be the book's guiding principles. In fact, our expanded knowledge of underlying organizational principles has led to the introduction of another unifying concept in the text: one that relates the basic organization of the nervous system to a core, or inner tube, of phylogenetically older structures surrounded by an outer tube of newer structures. We believe that this concept makes knowledge of the nervous system more accessible than it has been in the past. We sincerely hope these additions and changes will allow *Medical Neurosciences* to better serve as an introduction to the neurosciences for new students, as a review and update of the knowledge of basic neuroscience for more experienced students, and as a framework for an organized approach to the principles of neurologic diagnosis for all who attempt to evaluate clinical problems.

This edition, like its predecessors, is the product of the authors. However, many others have contributed significantly to its development and evolution, and we are grateful to the students and faculty, both at the Mayo Clinic and elsewhere, who have taken the time to share their suggestions with us. In particular, we acknowledge the faculty consultants at Mayo who contributed to this edition: Charles F. Abboud, M.D., Division of Endocrinology, Metabolism, and Internal Medicine; Arnold D. Aronson, Ph.D., Section of Speech Pathology; Robert C. Benassi, Section of Visual Information; Shelley A. Cross, M.D., Department of Neurology; Clifford R. Jack, M.D., Department of Diagnostic Radiology; Terrence D. Lagerlund, M.D., Department of Neurology; Jay W. McLaren, Ph.D., Section of Ophthalmology Research; O. Eugene Millhouse, Ph.D., Section of Publications; Ronald C. Petersen, M.D., Department of Neurology; Michael H. Silber, M.B.Ch.B., F.C.P. (SA), Department of Neurology; and Jerry W. Swanson, M.D., Department of Neurology. We also thank Roberta J. Schwartz, Mary Jane I. Badker, and Dorothy L. Tienter of the Section of Publications, and Jeanette K. Connaughty, Secretary, Section of Electroencephalography, for their help preparing the manuscript.

This is an exciting time in the world of neuroscience; we hope our readers will be stimulated to explore it further.

B. F. W.
E. E. B.
J. R. D.
T. J. R.
B. A. S.

Medical Neurosciences

Notice

The indications and dosages of all drugs in this book have been recommended in the medical literature and conform to the practices of the general medical community. The medications described do not necessarily have specific approval by the Food and Drug Administration for use in the diseases and dosages for which they are recommended. The package insert for each drug should be consulted for use and dosage as approved by the FDA. Because standards for usage change, it is advisable to keep abreast of revised recommendations, particularly those concerning new drugs.

— 1 —

Integrated Neuroscience for the Clinician

Neurologic disorders are common, and clinicians must be capable of dealing confidently with them. Many steps are required in accomplishing this task. Patients seldom present to their physician with a well-defined diagnosis for which appropriate therapy can be readily dispensed. Instead they arrive with a vast array of symptoms and signs that constitute a clinical problem the physician must attempt to resolve.

In solving problems, one generally approaches them by using one of two well-known methods. First, if the problem is similar to or identical to one encountered previously and the person is able to recall the answer or solution, he or she may move quickly and rapidly to an answer. This method is called *problem solving by pattern recognition*. A second approach is that of *logical analysis,* or *inductive reasoning*. In using this method, one traces the problem to its source by a series of steps based on knowledge of the underlying structure and function. Both methods have a critical step in common that will be used throughout your medical career — hypothesis testing. When a problem looks like one seen before, one can hypothesize that the solution is likely to be the same and develop a scheme to test the hypothesis. When a problem is not clearly understood or familiar, but some of the underlying components are understood, one can propose a hypothesis about the mechanism of the problem based on an analysis of that knowledge.

The solution of a clinical problem in neurology, as in any area of medicine, requires a knowledge of anatomy, physiology, and pathophysiology. This book is an attempt to organize the body of information contained in the basic neurologic sciences into the format used by clinicians in dealing with diseases of the nervous system.

The process used by a clinician who examines a patient with a neurologic disorder (that is, one involving the brain, spinal cord, nerves, or muscles) may involve either pattern recognition or inductive reasoning. The latter is a familiar process in which a number of distinct pieces of information are put together to reach a general conclusion. For example, if a woman has a 1-year history of slowly progressive numbness and weakness of the left side of her face, left arm, and left leg, the physician concludes that the patient may have a neoplastic lesion at the supratentorial level on the right side. The physician uses the data obtained by interviewing and examining the patient to produce a history that is a chronologic account of the patient's symptoms and their evolution with time (the temporal profile). The specific symptoms in the history can be categorized into broad groups and related to particular anatomical structures and certain disease categories. In a patient with neurologic disease, these symptoms often are identified with changes in sensation, activity, movement, thinking, or consciousness. Often the physical examination of a patient with neurologic disease allows an even more precise definition of abnormal function, which, based on the clinician's knowledge of anatomical structure and function, can be related to specific areas of the nervous system.

Throughout the interview and the examination, the clinician is constantly organizing and reorganizing the collected data to arrive at hypotheses about the nature of the disorder. In the previous example, the hypothesis of a right cerebral tumor was reached because the temporal profile of slow progression is common with neoplastic disorders, and weakness and numbness on the left side of the body often are due to disease of structures that are controlled at the supratentorial level on the right.

The physician must answer three questions. Is there disease involving the nervous system? If so, where is the disease located? And what kind of disease is it (that is, what is the pathologic nature of the disease)? The first question is often one of the most difficult to answer, because an answer depends not only on the knowledge to be presented in this book but also on experience with disease involving all other body systems. This book focuses primarily on answering the two simpler questions: "Where is the lesion located?" and "What is its pathologic nature?"

Objectives

Neurologic diseases include all the major pathologic categories seen in other organ systems and can involve one or several areas in the complex human nervous system. However, adequate management of neurologic problems can be based on answering the questions: "Where is the problem?" and "What is the problem?" The elaboration and analysis of these specific questions form the major objectives in the study of neuroscience. The answers to these questions are based on a knowledge of the gross anatomical structures of the nervous system (Fig. 1-1), their function, the usual patterns of disease, and the forms of treatment available. This simplified approach to neurologic disease is the one customarily used by many neurologists, and it includes four questions:

1. Is the responsible lesion located at
   a. The supratentorial level
   b. The posterior fossa level
   c. The spinal level
   d. The peripheral level
   e. More than one level
2. Is the responsible lesion

Fig. 1-1. Levels of the neuraxis. Supratentorial level includes cerebral hemispheres and portions of cranial nerves I and II within the skull. Posterior fossa level includes brain stem, cerebellum, and portions of cranial nerves III through XII within the skull. Spinal level includes spinal cord and portions of nerve roots contained within the vertebral column. Peripheral level includes portions of both cranial and peripheral nerves that lie outside the skull and spinal column and structures innervated by these nerves.

   a. Focal, and located on the right side of the nervous system
   b. Focal, and located on the left side of the nervous system
   c. Focal, but involving midline and contiguous structures on both sides of the nervous system
   d. Diffuse, and involving homologous, symmetric, noncontiguous areas on both sides of the nervous system

3. Is the responsible lesion
   a. Some form of mass lesion
   b. Some form of nonmass lesion
4. Is the lesion most likely
   a. Vascular
   b. Degenerative
   c. Inflammatory-immunologic
   d. Neoplastic
   e. Toxic-metabolic
   f. Traumatic
   g. Congenital-developmental

The major objective of this text therefore is to provide the information necessary to answer these questions for any clinical problem involving the nervous system and to provide a description of the mechanism by which the patient's symptoms and findings are produced by the underlying disorder.

Organization

The solution of a neurologic problem requires three levels of knowledge; therefore, this text is organized into three sections. Section I provides general information necessary to understand how neurologic disorders are diagnosed. The remainder of the text is organized to enable a precise topographic and etiologic diagnosis. Topographic localization initially requires relating the patient's functional impairment to one of the major longitudinal systems (Section II) and then localizing the lesion at a well-defined level of the nervous system (Section III).

Each chapter begins with an introduction and overview and ends with a listing of objectives and clinical problems for self-assessment. Additional readings are provided.

Survey of the Neurosciences

The clinician must first have an understanding of the methods utilized in diagnosing a neurologic disorder. How is a lesion localized, and to what do the general anatomical terms used to describe localization refer? How is a pathologic or etiologic diagnosis determined, and what do the terms used to describe them mean? These questions require a general knowledge of the diagnostic principles of neurologic disorders as these principles relate to

the anatomy, physiology, and pathology of the nervous system. Chapters 2 through 5 provide the basic vocabulary and the background knowledge necessary to begin solving clinical problems. These chapters cover the following subjects:

Chapter 2: Developmental Organization of the Nervous System: Neuroembryology

Chapter 3: Diagnosis of Neurologic Disorders: Anatomical Localization

Chapter 4: Diagnosis of Neurologic Disorders: Neurocytology and the Pathologic Reactions of the Nervous System

Chapter 5: Diagnosis of Neurologic Disorders: Transient Disorders and Neurophysiology

Longitudinal Systems

Increasingly detailed knowledge of the anatomy and physiology of the nervous system is required for a precise diagnosis of a neurologic disorder. The clinician usually first identifies the patient's symptoms and signs as indicative of disease involving one or more of the major longitudinal subdivisions of the nervous system. These longitudinally organized groups of structures are called *systems* within the nervous system, each subserving a specific function. In this section the anatomy, physiology, and clinical expression of disease as it affects the following major longitudinal systems are described:

Chapter 6: The Cerebrospinal Fluid System
Chapter 7: The Sensory System
Chapter 8: The Motor System
Chapter 9: The Internal Regulation System
Chapter 10: The Consciousness System
Chapter 11: The Vascular System
Chapter 12: The Neurochemical Systems

The name of each system characterizes its function. Correlation of the symptoms and signs with the appropriate system permits localization of the disease process in one dimension.

Chapter 12 (The Neurochemical Systems) examines the functional organization of the systems in terms of the chemical agents used for the transmission and modulation of neural activity and provides an additional method of classifying neurologic function.

Levels of the Neuraxis

The final step in localizing a lesion requires identification of an additional dimension — determining its location along the length of the systems involved. Although a precise localization can be made in many cases, most clinicians classify the disorder according to one of four major regions defined by the bony structures surrounding much of the nervous system. The final part of the text explores the ways in which functions in each major system are integrated and modified at each of the following levels:

Chapter 13:   The Peripheral Level
Chapter 14:   The Spinal Level
Chapter 15:   The Posterior Fossa Level
Chapter 16:   The Supratentorial Level

In all these sections, there is repetition of material, with each subsequent section building on the basic information presented earlier to provide amplification and reemphasis. This approach to clinical neurologic problems can be used with any of the problems that may be encountered and is particularly useful in problems that are new, unfamiliar, or unusual to the clinician. Although the identification of diseases by recognition of a particular syndrome sometimes can be very efficient, the method of hypothesis testing and inductive reasoning presented herein is consistently more accurate and more reliable.

Objectives

1. Define: problem solving, pattern recognition, inductive reasoning, and hypothesis.

2. Given any clinical problem, develop a series of hypotheses that will allow you to understand its cause. Identify and describe the type of reasoning used to generate and test these hypotheses.

Clinical Problems

1. You walk into a room and find your friend lying limp and motionless on the floor. As you approach and attempt to assess the situation further and offer aid, several thoughts go through your mind about what might have happened. Describe the thoughts and the reasoning that contributed to each of them.

2. You sit quietly in a chair with your legs crossed and begin to notice a "numb-tingling feeling" in your right lower leg. On attempting to rise from the chair, you are unable to move the right leg normally. What hypotheses have you developed about the possible cause of this dysfunction?

Additional Reading

Albanese, M. A., and Mitchell, S. Problem-based learning: A review of literature on its outcomes and implementation issues. *Acad. Med.* 68:52, 1993.

Barrows, H. S., and Tamblyn, R. M. *Problem-Based Learning: An Approach to Medical Education.* New York: Springer, 1980.

Eddy, D. M., and Clanton, C. H. The art of diagnosis: Solving the clinicopathological exercise. *N. Engl. J. Med.* 306:1263, 1982.

Engel, G. L. Clinical observation: The neglected basic method of medicine. *JAMA* 192:849, 1965.

Kassirer, J. P., and Gorry, G. A. Clinical problem solving: A behavioral analysis. *Ann. Intern. Med.* 89:245, 1978.

Larkin, J., et al. Expert and novice performance in solving physics problems. *Science* 208:1335, 1980.

I

Survey of the Neurosciences

— 2 —

Developmental Organization of the Nervous System: Neuroembryology

The study of neuroscience begins with a survey of neuroembryology, because it provides a framework and background for understanding the anatomy of the nervous system in the adult. The eventual location of the structures in the brain is not a random occurrence but is a reflection of the orderly development of the primitive nervous system. Neuroembryology also serves as an aid in understanding the pathogenesis of developmental neurologic abnormalities that are encountered not only in the newborn and pediatric periods but also in later life.

Overview

The formation of the neural tube begins on the eighteenth day of gestation. By this day of embryonic development, the early stage of gastrulation is completed. The two-layered embryo consisting of ectoderm and endoderm is transformed into a three- layered structure by the outgrowth of mesoderm from the midline primitive streak into the area between the original layers. The notochord, a specialized column of mesodermal cells, grows forward from the anterior end of the primitive streak (Hensen's node). The ectoderm overlying the notochord is induced to form the neural plate, which thickens and folds into the neural tube. The entire central nervous system develops from this tube. Cell columns, called the neural crest, derived from the junction of skin ectoderm and neuroectoderm separate from the neural tube and form a major portion of the peripheral nervous system.

Throughout the length of the neural tube, primitive neuroectodermal cells proliferate, differentiate into neurons and supporting cells (ependyma, astrocytes, and oligodendrocytes), migrate to their genetically coded location, and develop specific intercellular connections and relationships. The cells of the neural crest differentiate into dorsal root ganglia, autonomic ganglia, and Schwann cells.

The neural tube undergoes transverse differentiation (Fig. 2-1), with formation of a dorsal region, the alar plate, which subserves sensory functions, and a ventral region, the basal plate, which subserves motor functions. Also, at all levels, structures that develop in close proximity to the cavity of the neural tube — that is, in the inner tube or core — give rise to phylogenetically older and more primitive functional systems (the consciousness system and the internal regulation system). Structures that develop in the outer regions of the tube (outer tube), at a greater distance from the neural canal, generally belong to phylogenetically newer and higher level functional systems (the motor system and the sensory system). Even within systems, such as the motor system, this concentric relationship pertains, with older and less discrete components of the system located in the inner tube and newer and more highly developed components in the outer regions of the tube. The neurochemical system develops in parallel with the development of functional systems as outlined above, with different sets of excitatory and inhibitory neurotransmitters acting as synapses in different systems.

The cavity of the tube forms the central canal at the spinal cord level and more complex fluid-filled spaces, the ventricular system, at cephalic levels. Mesodermal tissues surround

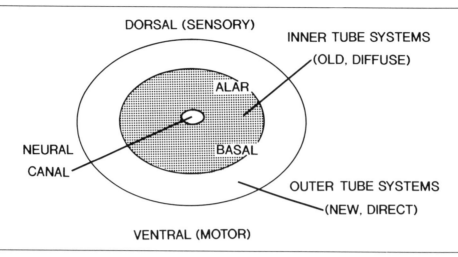

Fig. 2-1. Functional organization of the neural tube.

the neural tube and form the meninges, which in conjunction with the ventricular system form the cerebrospinal fluid system. Mesoderm that surrounds and grows into the neural tube forms the vascular system.

The neural tube undergoes longitudinal differentiation into six regions: telencephalon (cerebral hemispheres), diencephalon (thalamus and hypothalamus), mesencephalon (midbrain), metencephalon (pons and cerebellum), myelencephalon (medulla), and spinal cord. These subdivisions of the neural tube are the precursors of three of the four major anatomical levels in the adult: supratentorial (telencephalon and diencephalon), posterior fossa (mesencephalon, metencephalon, and myelencephalon), and spinal (spinal cord). The fourth, or peripheral level, is composed of a combination of efferent fibers growing outward from the posterior fossa and spinal levels and neural crest derivatives, including somatic and visceral afferent neurons and postganglionic autonomic neurons.

Disorders of development of the nervous system may occur at any embryonic step. They generally are classified according to the dominant process occurring at the time they are thought to arise. The most common are failures of fusion (dorsal induction) of the neural tube (for example, spina bifida and meningomyelocele) and failures of proliferation and migration (for example, pachygyria and microgyria).

Formation of the Neural Tube

The nervous system is commonly divided into central and peripheral components. The central nervous system is that part located within the spinal column and skull. It is formed from the neural tube between the eighteenth and the twenty-fifty day of gestation. Before these structures are formed, at the end of the second week of gestation, gastrulation has been completed. The longitudinal axis of the two-layered embryonic disk is established by the formation of an area of rapidly proliferating cells, the *primitive streak.* The midline of the embryo is defined by the growth of the *notochord,* a group of mesodermal cells that grow forward from one end of the primitive streak (Hensen's node) in a plane between the ectoderm and the endoderm. The mesoderm of the remainder of the embryonic disk is formed by the outgrowth of mesodermal cells from the lateral margins of the primitive streak. As the notochord and mesodermal tissues grow forward, the primitive streak becomes incorporated into the tailbud, and a three-layered embryo with a clearly delineated longitudinal axis is formed. These early changes set the stage for the subsequent events that establish the *neural tube,* the morphologic substrate of the adult nervous system.

The neural tube is formed in approximately 1 week, beginning on the eighteenth

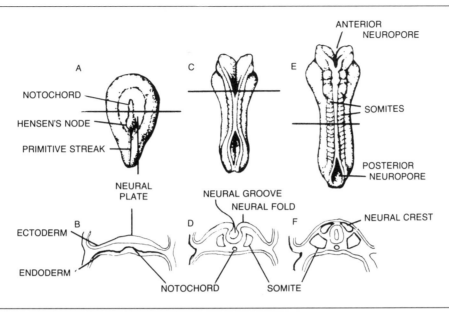

Fig. 2-2. Formation of neural tube (eighteenth to twenty-fifth day). A. Dorsal view of neural plate forming over notochord, which has grown forward from Hensen's node between ectoderm and endoderm. B. Cross section through neural plate shown in A. C. Dorsal view of early closure of neural tube. D. Cross section through neural tube shown in C. E. Dorsal view of almost complete closure of neural tube, and formation of well-defined somites. F. Cross section through E.

day. The initial step in its formation is a thickening of the ectoderm in the dorsal midline overlying the notochord to form the *neural plate* (Fig. 2-2A, B). The lateral edges of the neural plate thicken more rapidly than the center and begin to roll toward the midline, creating the *neural groove,* which has lateral margins, the *neural folds.* With continued growth, the neural folds meet in the midline to form a hollow tube, the neural tube, which closes first in the middle of the embryo (Fig. 2-2C, D) (the future cervical region) and then proceeds toward the head (cephalad) and toward the tail (caudad), until the entire tube is closed. The unfused areas at the two ends of the tube before complete closure are *neuropores* (Fig. 2-2E). As the neural tube is being formed by the fusion of the margins of the neural folds, the skin ectoderm also fuses and covers its dorsal surface. Ultimately, the two ectodermal derivatives, neural tube and skin, become further separated by the growth of intervening mesodermal derivatives, bone and muscle. Cell columns derived from the original junction of skin and

neuroectoderm form the neural crests, which later differentiate into important components of the peripheral nervous system.

Even before the neural tube is entirely closed, longitudinal differentiation begins. Parallel to the neural tube, the mesodermal cells on each side segment into aggregates, the *somites,* from which bone and muscle arise (Fig. 2-2E, F). At the same time, the cephalic, or head, end of the neural tube becomes larger than the caudal end, resulting in an irregularly shaped tubal structure. Continued differential growth along the length of the neural tube results in the formation of three cavities at the cephalic end of the tube. These are the primary brain vesicles: the *prosencephalon,* the *mesencephalon,* and the *rhombencephalon* (Fig. 2-3A, B). These three vesicles further differentiate into five subdivisions, which persist in the brain of the mature nervous system (Fig. 2-3C, D). The remaining caudal end of the neural tube undergoes much less modification as it forms the spinal cord. A central remnant of the internal cavity of the tube remains in each of these derivatives.

Fig. 2-3. Formation of major brain vesicles of neural tube (twenty-fifth to thirtieth day) in horizontal section (*left*) and dorsal view (*right*). A, B. Stage of three primary vesicles. C, D. Stage of five major vesicles. E, F. Differentiation of specific structures by cell migration and overgrowth.

Table 2-1. Major Elements in Adult Nervous System Derived from the Neural Tube

Level	Primary divisions	Subdivisions	Major derivatives	Cavities
Supratentorial	Prosencephalon	Telencephalon	Rhinencephalon Basal ganglia Cerebral cortex	Lateral ventricles
		Diencephalon	Thalamus Hypothalamus Optic nerves Neurohypophysis Pineal	Third ventricle
Posterior fossa	Mesencephalon	Mesencephalon	Midbrain	Aqueduct of Sylvius
	Rhombencephalon	Metencephalon	Cerebellum Pons	Fourth ventricle
		Myelencephalon	Medulla	Fourth ventricle
Spinal	Primitive neural tube	Neural tube	Spinal cord	Central canal
Peripheral		Neural crest	Peripheral nerve Ganglia	None

The subdivisions of the primitive neural tube evolve, through the processes of cellular proliferation, migration, and differentiation (described in the next section), into the major elements in the adult nervous system listed in Table 2-1.

Differentiation of the Central Nervous System

Cytologic Differentiation

The wall of the primitive neural tube consists of multipotential neuroepithelial cells derived from ectoderm. These cells undergo multiplication, migration, and differentiation to establish concentric layers of the neural tube. Cell division occurs primarily in the innermost layer bordering the neural canal. In some texts, this is called the ependymal layer in accordance with a convention established in the early part of the century. However, most anatomists now reserve this term for the single layer of fully differentiated ciliated cells that line the ventricular system in mature brains (Fig. 2-4). The primitive innermost layer, before ependymal maturation, is more properly called the *ventricular zone*. It consists of a single layer of pseudostratified epithelium in which nuclei move in toward the canal to divide and out toward the periphery during the intermitotic phases of the cell cycle.

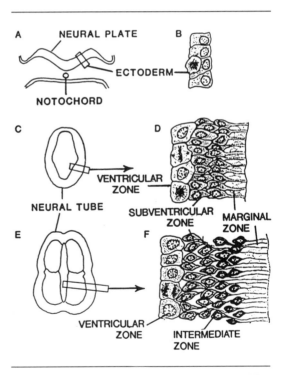

Fig. 2-4. Differentiation of cell layers in primitive neural tube, with high-power view on the right and cross section of tube shown on the left. A, B. Early neural plate is a single layer of cells. C, D. Formation of layers of cells by outward migration of cells proliferating in ventricular zone. E, F. Formation of outer acellular marginal zone by growth of processes (axons) peripherally from cells.

Fig. 2-5. Process of myelination of nerve fibers in central and peripheral nervous system. Layer of cytoplasm wraps around an axon (A) and then encircles it repeatedly (B). Condensation of layers of cytoplasm forms myelin (C).

Cytoplasmic processes of the cells of the ventricular layer establish the outermost layer of the neural tube, the *marginal zone*. This zone increases in width and definition at all levels of the developing nervous system because of the increasing number and complexity of the neuronal processes (axons and dendrites) that compose it. Some glial cells migrate into this zone, but it remains relatively acellular throughout development.

Between the ventricular and marginal zones are two other cellular zones that previously were lumped together as the mantle layer. These are called the *subventricular zone* and the *intermediate zone* (Fig. 2-4). Their relative prominence varies at different levels of the nervous system. Both receive immature neurons from the ventricular zone. However, those that migrate directly into the intermediate zone are postmitotic and do not divide further. Those remaining in the subventricular zone continue to divide as primitive neuroblasts. Eventually these cells stop dividing and migrate into or through the intermediate zone to their programmed destination.

In the prosencephalon, many of the postmitotic cells migrate to the outer limits of the intermediate zone, where they accumulate in what sometimes is described at this level as a fifth zone, the *cortical plate*. After migrating to their definitive location, the immature neurons begin the final stages of maturation, with the development of synaptic connections with numerous other neurons, setting the stage for their primary function in central nervous system information processing.

The subventricular zone is also the reposi-tory of the spongioblasts, which give rise to the major supporting cells of the central nervous system: astrocytes, oligodendrocytes, and ependymal cells. Ependymal cells mature in the innermost layer of the ventricular zone and form the continuous layer of ependyma that lines the cavities of the brain. The astrocytes and oligodendroglia migrate from the subventricular zone to all areas of the central nervous system, where they undergo further growth and functional maturation. Astrocytes provide mechanical support and maintain the chemical environment of neurons. Oligodendroglia form the insulation of axons, *myelin sheaths,* by wrapping layers of their cytoplasmic membranes around the axons (Fig. 2-5).

In addition to the neuroectodermal elements described above, cells of mesodermal origin make significant contributions to the structural and functional support of the nervous system. Mesodermal tissue gives rise to the covering layers of the central nervous system, the *meninges*. The extensive vascular system of the central nervous system, like the vascular system of all organs, is also of mesodermal origin. Finally, in the later stages of embryonic development, monocytes migrate into the brain and spinal cord, where they reside as potential phagocytic cells called *microglia*.

The events described above do not occur randomly. Each event — down to the last detail, including establishment of the ultimate number and location of neurons in each area of the nervous system and of each synaptic connection of the dendritic trees of neurons — is precisely programmed in the genetic

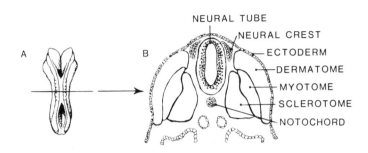

Fig. 2-13. Formation of myotome, sclerotome, and dermatome from somites in embryo of 4 weeks, in whole embryo (A) and transverse section (B).

to carry this information to the central nervous system. Therefore, these neurons are the initial transmitters of sensory information and are *primary sensory neurons.*

The *autonomic ganglia* are collections of cell bodies of visceral neurons in the trunk and head that send out axons to innervate all the internal organs. They receive connections from axons of visceral neurons in the central nervous system and from sensory neurons in the internal organs. These ganglia mediate motor and sensory activities of the visceral organs.

Schwann cells form the myelin, or insulation, surrounding the axons in the peripheral nervous system, just as the oligodendroglia do in the central nervous system (see Fig. 2-5). Schwann cells are located serially along the length of all peripheral axons and envelop them. Neural crest cells also give rise to an endocrine organ, the adrenal medulla.

Somites

As the neural tube closes, the embryonic mesoderm lateral to the tube becomes segmented into cell masses known as *somites* (see Fig. 2-13). These masses differentiate into three components: the sclerotome, myotome, and dermatome. The ventromedial portion of the somite forms the *sclerotome,* which differentiates into cartilage and bone, forming the vertebrae of the spinal column and base of the skull surrounding the central nervous system. The notochord becomes incorporated into the ventromedial extensions of the sclerotome and thus remains ventral to the tube. The notochordal remnant within the vertebral column is the nucleus pulposis in the intervertebral disk. The dorsomedial portion of the somite forms the *myotome,* which gives rise to the striated skeletal muscle of the body, with the exception of that muscle formed from the branchial arches in the head and neck. The primordial muscle cells of the myotome migrate peripherally, reaching their eventual location in the trunk and limbs. The lateral portion of the somite forms the *dermatome.* Cells from the dermatome migrate peripherally to form the dermis, the connective tissue layer of the skin.

Peripheral Nerves

Connections between the central nervous system and the peripheral structures derived from the somites and the neural crest are established by growth of axons from the dorsal root ganglia into the alar plate of the neural tube and by outgrowth of axons from neurons in the basal plate. These distally growing motor axons join the peripherally growing sensory axons of the dorsal root ganglia to form a nerve that innervates the somite at the same level (Fig. 2-14). The nerves formed in this fashion at the spinal level are the *spinal nerves;* those formed at the posterior fossa and supratentorial levels are the *cranial nerves.* Both types are composed of mixtures of sensory and motor axons. In these nerves, the motor axons from cells in the central nervous system innervate the myotomal derivatives and autonomic ganglia, while the sensory axons innervate the dermatomes and endoderm derivatives. As the embryo develops and the cells forming the muscles, skin, and internal organs migrate to their adult locations, these neural processes are pulled along with

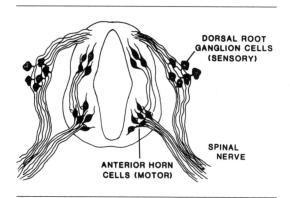

Fig. 2-14. Formation of spinal nerves by combination of axons from basal plate and dorsal root ganglia.

them to establish the pattern of innervation of peripheral nerves.

The functions of the axons in peripheral nerves are classified into systems, just as are those in the central nervous system. *Afferent* fibers are those that conduct information toward the central nervous system (sensory), and *efferent* fibers are those that carry information away from the central nervous system. Axons are also subdivided on the basis of the type of structure they innervate. Fibers that innervate tissues derived from somites (muscles and skin) are designated *somatic;* fibers that innervate endodermal or other mesodermal derivatives (internal organs) are called *visceral.* Thus, afferent axons that carry sensations such as pain, temperature, touch, and joint movement from the body surface and supporting structures are *general somatic afferent* (GSA). Affer-

ent axons that carry sensations such as pain, fullness, and blood chemical levels from the internal organs are *general visceral afferent* (GVA). Motor axons to skeletal muscle of somite origin are *general somatic efferent* (GSE). Motor axons that innervate smooth muscle of viscera, glands, and blood vessels are *general visceral efferent* (GVE).

Each of these types of fibers is found in the spinal and cranial nerves. The cranial nerves also have fibers that mediate special sensations and fibers that innervate branchial arch derivatives. Those to the branchial arch derivatives, especially facial muscles, are *special visceral efferent* (SVE); those mediating sensations of taste and smell are *special visceral afferent* (SVA). The fibers that carry the other special sensory information of vision, hearing, and balance are *special somatic afferent* (SSA). The somatic afferent fibers are considered in detail in the discussion of the sensory system; the somatic efferent fibers are considered in the discussion of the motor system; and the visceral afferent and efferent fibers are considered in the discussion of the visceral system. Other special functions are presented in the discussion of the posterior fossa and supratentorial levels. Table 2-2 summarizes the classification of the functional components of nerves on the basis of embryologic origin and destination.

Clinical Correlations

Although some developmental processes occur more or less simultaneously, they may be

Table 2-2. Classification of the Functional Components of Nerves on Basis of Embryologic Origin and Destination

Type	Category	Tissue innervated	Tissue origin	Abbreviation*
Afferent (sensory)	General	Skin, muscle, bone, joints	Somites	GSA
		Visceral organs	Endoderm	GVA
	Special	Ear, eye, balance	External receptors (ectoderm)	SSA
		Taste, smell	Visceral receptors (endoderm)	SVA
Efferent (motor)	General	Somatic striated muscle	Somites	GSE
		Glands, smooth muscle, visceral organs	Nonsomite (mesoderm and endoderm)	GVE
	Special	Head and neck muscle	Branchial arches	SVE

*GSA = general somatic afferent; GVA = general visceral afferent; SSA = special somatic afferent; SVA = special visceral afferent; GSE = general somatic efferent; GVE = general visceral efferent; and SVE = special visceral efferent.

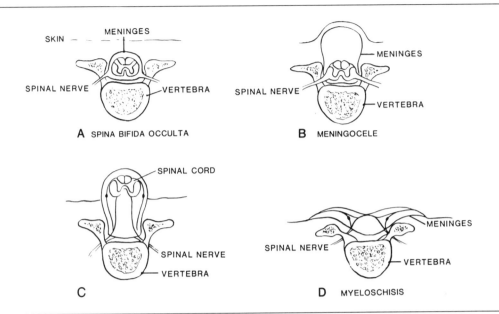

Fig. 2-15. Examples of failure of fusion at spinal level. A. Spina bifida occulta with incomplete vertebral arch. B. Meningocele with outpouching of fluid-filled sac of meninges and skin. C. Meningomyelocele with sac containing abnormal neural tissue. D. Myeloschisis with no closure and a deformed neural plate open to the surface. (Redrawn from B. Pansky and E. L. House. *Review of Gross Anatomy* [3rd ed.]. New York: Macmillan, 1975.)

thought of as occurring in six stages, according to the process that is dominant at different stages of embryogenesis.

The *first stage* is *neural tube formation,* sometimes called *dorsal induction* because of the important influence the notochord and other underlying mesodermal structures have on inducing the formation of the neural plate and its derivatives. This process dominates approximately the third and fourth weeks of embryogenesis. Injury (genetic or acquired) to the embryo during this stage produces defects in the dorsal midline, often obvious on the surface. The various degrees of severity of these defects in the caudal (lumbosacral) region are illustrated in Figure 2-15. Thus, *spina bifida occulta,* a defect only in the vertebral arch (Fig. 2-15A), *meningocele,* protrusion of a meningeal sac through the bone defect (Fig. 2-15B), meningomyelocele, inclusion of herniated spinal cord in the sac (Fig. 2-15C), and myeloschisis, a completely open spinal cord through an overlying bone and skin defect (Fig. 2-15D) are viewed as increasingly severe manifestations of the same disorder. Similar

defects occur at the rostral end of the neural tube and cause malformations, analogous to those at the caudal end, termed *cranium bifidium, cranial meningocele, meningoencephalocele,* and *cranioschisis* (or *anencephaly*). The most severe defect in this category is a completely open neural tube and dorsal midline, termed *craniorachischisis.*

The *second stage* occurs during the fifth and sixth weeks of development and relates to the formation of the telencephalon in conjunction with the cranial, facial, and neck structures derived from the branchial arches. This stage is sometimes called *ventral induction,* because of the relationship of the prechordal mesoderm to the cephalic end of the neural tube. Defects that occur during this stage can cause severe abnormalities in the formation of the telencephalon, such as *holoprosencephaly* (failure to form telencephalic vesicles), and craniofacial deformities.

The *third stage* is *proliferative activity* of the ventricular and subventricular zones, most active during the eighth to the sixteenth weeks of gestation. Because of injury (genetic, chemi-

Table 2-3. Examples of Neuroectodermal Dysplasias and Some of Their Common Skin and Nervous System Manifestations

Disease	Skin	Nervous system
Von Recklinghausen disease	Neurofibromas	Schwannomas
	Café-au-lait spots	Gliomas
		Meningeal angioma
Sturge-Weber syndrome	Port-wine nevus of face	Cortical calcification
Tuberous sclerosis	Adenoma sebaceum	Periventricular tumors
	Subungual fibromas	Cortical giant cell tumors
	Depigmented patches	Gliomas

cal, infectious) to the proliferating pool of neuroblasts during this stage, the number of neurons may not be sufficient to form a normal-sized brain, resulting in *microcephaly,* or, in less severe cases, to elaborate the proper number and type of synapses, which may account for some cases of mental retardation in persons with grossly normal brains.

The *fourth stage* is the period of most active *migration* of neurons and spongioblasts from the subventricular zone into the intermediate zone and, in the telencephalon, into the cortical plate. This process is most active from the twelfth to the twentieth week of gestation. Pathologic processes affecting the fetus during this period are likely to cause malformations attributable to disordered or arrested migration. The clearest example of this is *heterotopia,* collections of neurons and other gray matter components in areas where they do not occur normally, such as the subcortical white matter. Other malformations attributable to migratory disorders include formation of abnormal gyri, which may be larger (pachygyria) or smaller (microgyria) than normal. Migratory disorders may be either localized or generalized, depending on the nature of the pathologic process; they often occur in concert with disorders of proliferation, because the third and fourth stages overlap in time.

The process that dominates the *fifth stage* of development, which extends from the sixth gestational month to maturity, is *differentiation* of neurons and glia. This maturational process includes not only physical growth but also development of functional connections (synapses) and associated neurochemical mediators. Widespread disturbances of these processes do not usually lead to obvious gross

malformations of the nervous system but rather to subtle functional disturbances, such as *learning disabilities* and *mental retardation.*

The *sixth stage* of development is associated with *myelination* of the nervous system. This process extends from the last half of gestation up to age 18 and is most evident from birth to age 2. Although myelination is defective in areas of the central nervous system affected by the processes mentioned above, damage that primarily affects this process does not produce obvious structural malformations, such as mentioned above. Instead, genetic or extrinsic damage to the process of myelination results in myelin either failing to form or, once formed, to degenerate due to faulty structure. Genetic disorders in this category are called *leukodystrophies,* which usually occur in the first 2 years of life.

Because the skin and the nervous system are both derived from ectoderm, it is not surprising that genetically determined disorders may affect them together. A group of disorders known as *neurocutaneous syndromes,* or *neuroectodermal dysplasias,* is characterized by specific abnormalities in both the skin and the nervous system. Common manifestations of the three most commonly seen disorders of this type are outlined in Table 2-3.

The retina of the eye is also a derivative of the central nervous system. As with the skin, the retina may be affected by disorders that involve the nervous system, and observation of the retina with an ophthalmoscope may provide information about the disorder. An example of this association is *Tay-Sachs disease,* the lipid-storage disease in which neurons of the central nervous system accumulate large amounts of gangliosides. This accumulation is reflected in the retina by a "cherry red spot" in the macula, due to the storage of lipids and the relative opacification of retinal ganglion cells surrounding the macula. Retinal tumors also may be seen in the neuroectodermal dysplasias, and malformations of the eye sometimes accompany anomalies of the nervous system.

Objectives

1. Describe the formation of the primitive streak, notochord, neural plate, neural folds, neural tube, and neural crest.
2. On a transverse section of the neural tube, identify the ventricular, subventricular, intermediate, and mantle zones and the alar and basal plates.
3. Name the major functional systems of the brain and spinal cord, and describe their origin in terms of their relationship to the components of the wall of the neural tube mentioned above.
4. List the five major subdivisions of the cephalic portion of the neural tube, their associated central cavities, and major adult structures derived from them.
5. Name the major immature cytologic elements in the ventricular and subventricular zones and their derivatives in the mature central nervous system.
6. Describe the major processes involved in forming the mature pattern of synaptic connections between distant neuronal groups.
7. Describe the formation of the peripheral nervous system and how its connections with the central nervous system are formed.
8. List two major types of developmental abnormalities of the nervous system, and give examples of each.

Clinical Problems

1. A newborn girl has a large bulging mass over the lower portion of the spinal column. There is no skin overlying this mass, and ill-defined neural structures can be seen through the glistening membranes of the fluid-filled mass. The infant does not move her legs.
   a. What embryologic process was not completed in this child?
   b. What primitive structure was involved and at what stage in the development?
   c. Which types of functions are probably absent in this child?
   d. What is the origin of the structures involved in this defect?
   e. What primitive layers of the spinal cord might be involved?
   f. Name the disorder.
2. A 4-year-old boy has white spots (phakomas) in the retina of his eyes, as seen with an ophthalmoscope, and red lesions over his face. He also has convulsions and mental retardation.
   a. What is the congenital basis for all these findings?
   b. From what primitive structures do the eyes develop?
   c. What are the two primitive neural cell types from which tumors might arise?
   d. What is the functional embryologic classification of the nerve fibers from the eye?
   e. Name the disorder.

Additional Reading

The Boulder Committee. Embryonic vertebrate central nervous system: Revised terminology. *Anat. Rec.* 166:257, 1970.

Brody, B. A., et al. Sequence of central nervous system myelination in human infancy: I. An autopsy study of myelination. *J. Neuropath. Exp. Neurol.* 46:283, 1987.

Cowan, W. M. The development of the brain. *Sci. Am.* 241(3):112, 1979.

Crelin, E. S., Netter, F. H., and Shapter, R. K. Development of the nervous system: A logical approach to neuroanatomy. *Clin. Symp.* 26(2):1, 1974.

Goodman, H. M. *Basic Medical Endocrinology.* New York: Raven, 1988.

Langman, J. *Langman's Medical Embryology* (6th ed.). Baltimore: Williams & Wilkins, 1990.

Moore, K. L. *The Developing Human: Clinically Oriented Embryology* (4th ed.). Philadelphia: Saunders, 1988.

Shatz, C. J. The developing brain. *Sci. Am.* 267(3):61, 1992

— 3 —

Diagnosis of Neurologic Disorders: Anatomical Localization

The diagnosis of neurologic disorders is a skill that requires the application of basic scientific information to a clinical problem. As knowledge of the nervous system grows, more complicated neurologic problems can be solved in more sophisticated ways; however, the basic approach to the solution of all neurologic problems remains unchanged. In arriving at a solution, three questions must be answered: (1) Is there a lesion involving the nervous system? (2) Where is the lesion located? (3) What is the (histopathologic) nature of the lesion?

Answering the first question is undeniably the most difficult, since it requires a familiarity not only with clinical neurology but also with other disciplines of medicine. In time, as the manifestations of neurologic disorders become better known, the neurologic origin of certain symptoms will be identified with increasing confidence.

To answer the question "Where is the location of the lesion that has caused the signs and symptoms?" requires an understanding of the organization of the nervous system and an ability to relate the patient's description and the physician's observations of dysfunction to a particular area or areas in the nervous system.

In addition to localizing a lesion in an area in the nervous system, the physician must determine the nature of the lesion. An infarct (stroke), tumor, or abscess may lead to similar signs and symptoms. The manner in which these symptoms evolve, the temporal profile, provides the clues to distinguish these disorders and to predict the histopathologic changes responsible for the observed abnormality.

A physician highly skilled in neurologic-anatomical diagnosis is capable of localizing a lesion in the nervous system to within millimeters of its actual site. Although this type of skill is laudable, it is often more than is required of even the practicing neurologist. In most clinical situations, for proper patient management it is sufficient to decide whether the responsible lesion is producing dysfunction in one or more longitudinal systems, to relate those abnormalities to one (or more) of several gross anatomical levels, and to determine whether the presumed lesion is on the right side, on the left side, or in the midline or is diffuse and involves homologous areas bilaterally. Neurologic disorders may affect one or more of the following systems:

1. Cerebrospinal fluid system
2. Sensory system
3. Motor system
4. Internal regulation system
5. Consciousness system
6. Vascular system

and may occur at one or more of the following levels:

1. Supratentorial level
2. Posterior fossa level
3. Spinal level
4. Peripheral level

Familiarity with these major systems and levels will aid in the diagnosis of neurologic disorders. Each system and level will be discussed in further detail in subsequent chapters; this chapter emphasizes the anatomy of the levels.

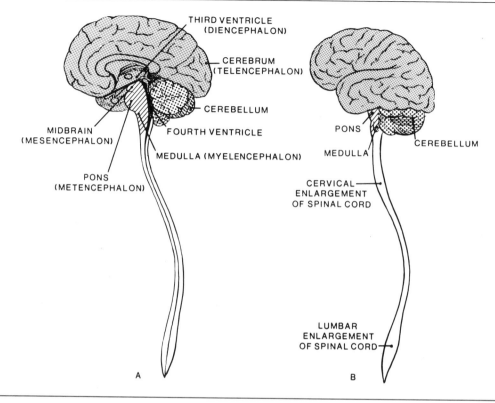

Fig. 3-1. Medial (A) and lateral (B) views of sections through brain and spinal cord illustrating major levels: supratentorial (*dark shading*), posterior fossa with brain stem (*lines*) and cerebellum (*dots*), and spinal (*clear area*). Peripheral level is not shown.

Overview

The major structures of the central nervous system — the brain and the spinal cord — are surrounded by three fibrous connective tissue linings called *meninges* and are encased in a protective bony skeleton. The brain, consisting of derivatives of the primitive telencephalon, diencephalon, mesencephalon, metencephalon, and myelencephalon (Fig. 3-1), is enclosed in the *skull;* the spinal cord is situated in the spinal column. Cranial and peripheral nerves must pass through these surrounding investments to reach more peripheral structures.

The major anatomical levels to be discussed are defined by the meninges and bony structures to which they are related. The divisions between the anatomical levels used in this book are not exact, and there will be some divergence from strict anatomical definitions found in other textbooks. However, as defined, the levels have boundaries that are clinically useful in understanding neurologic disorders.

Supratentorial Level

The floor of the human skull (Fig. 3-2) is divided into three distinct compartments (*fossae*) on each side: anterior, middle, and posterior. A rigid membrane, the *tentorium cerebelli,* separates the anterior and middle fossae from the posterior fossa (Fig. 3-3). The tentorium lies in a nearly horizontal plane and attaches laterally to the petrous ridges and posteriorly to the occipital bone. The portion of the nervous system located above the tentorium cerebelli constitutes the *supratentorial level.* The major anatomical structures of this level are derivatives of the telencephalon and diencephalon and consist primarily of the cerebral hemispheres, basal ganglia, thalamus, hypothalamus, and cranial nerves I (olfactory) and II (optic).

FORAMINA	STRUCTURES
CRIBRIFORM PLATE OF ETHMOID	OLFACTORY NERVES
OPTIC FORAMEN	OPTIC NERVE, OPHTHALMIC ARTERY
SUPERIOR ORBITAL FISSURE	OCULOMOTOR, TROCHLEAR, ABDUCENS AND OPHTHALMIC DIVISIONS OF TRIGEMINAL NERVE
FORAMEN ROTUNDUM	MAXILLARY DIVISION OF TRIGEMINAL NERVE
FORAMEN OVALE	MANDIBULAR DIVISION OF TRIGEMINAL NERVE
FORAMEN LACERUM	INTERNAL CAROTID ARTERY, SYMPATHETIC NERVE
FORAMEN SPINOSUM	MIDDLE MENINGEAL ARTERY AND VEIN
INTERNAL ACOUSTIC MEATUS	FACIAL AND AUDITORY NERVES INTERNAL AUDITORY ARTERY
JUGULAR FORAMEN	GLOSSOPHARYNGEAL, VAGUS, AND SPINAL ACCESSORY NERVES, JUGULAR VEIN
HYPOGLOSSAL CANAL	HYPOGLOSSAL NERVE
FORAMEN MAGNUM	MEDULLA, MENINGES, SPINAL ACCESSORY NERVE, VERTEBRAL ARTERIES, ANTERIOR AND POSTERIOR SPINAL ARTERIES

Bones/labels on diagram: SELLA TURCICA, FRONTAL BONE (ORBITAL PLATE), ANTERIOR FOSSA, ETHMOID BONE, SPHENOID BONE, MIDDLE FOSSA, DORSUM SELLAE, TEMPORAL BONE (SQUAMOUS PORTION), TEMPORAL BONE (PETROUS PORTION), POSTERIOR FOSSA, OCCIPITAL BONE

Fig. 3-2. Base of cranial cavity, viewed from above, illustrating major cranial fossae, bones of base of skull, foramina, and their associated structures.

Posterior Fossa Level

Structures located within the skull, below the tentorium cerebelli but above the *foramen magnum* (the opening of the skull to the spinal canal), constitute the *posterior fossa level.* These structures — the midbrain, pons, medulla, and cerebellum — are the derivatives of the mesencephalon, metencephalon, and myelencephalon. Cranial nerves III through XII are located in the posterior fossa. Anatomically and physiologically, these nerves are analogous to other peripheral nerves; however, functionally they are intimately related to the mesencephalon, metencephalon, and myelencephalon and therefore are studied along with the structures of the posterior fossa. Those segments of cranial nerves contained in the bony skull are considered part of the posterior fossa level. After these nerves emerge from the skull, they are part of the peripheral level.

Spinal Level

The portion of the central nervous system located below the foramen magnum of the skull but contained in the vertebral column constitutes the *spinal level* (Fig. 3-4). This level has a considerable longitudinal extent, reaching from the skull to the sacrum. However, the spinal cord itself (the major structure at the spinal level) does not extend that entire length. A series of spinal nerves arise in the spinal canal and exit through the intervertebral foramina. Nerves contained in the bony vertebral column and in the intervertebral foramina are part of the spinal level. After these nerves leave the vertebral column, they become part of the peripheral level. The vertebral column itself is part of the spinal level.

Peripheral Level

The *peripheral level* includes all neuromuscular structures located outside the skull and vertebral column, including the cranial and peripheral nerves, their peripheral branches, and the structures (including muscle) that are innervated by these nerves. The autonomic ganglia and nerves are also part of the peripheral level.

Gross Neuroanatomy — Introduction to Anatomical Levels

The major anatomical features of each of the major levels of the nervous system will be reviewed. Before doing so, however, it is useful

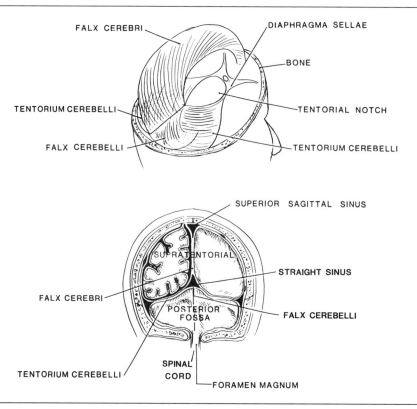

Fig. 3-3. Reflections of dura mater forming falx cerebri and tentorium cerebelli (*top*). Structures located above tentorium are part of supratentorial level; those below tentorium but above foramen magnum are part of posterior fossa level (*bottom*). (Redrawn from B. Pansky, and E. L. House. *Review of Gross Anatomy* [3rd ed.]. New York: Macmillan, 1975.)

to discuss individually certain structures that may be related to more than one of the major levels previously defined.

The Skull

The skull (Fig. 3-5) is formed by the union of a number of bones and can be grossly subdivided into (1) the facial bones and orbits, (2) the sinus cavities within the bones that form the anterior aspect of the skull, and (3) the cranial bones. The cranial bones surround the brain in the cranial cavity and provide a nonyielding protective covering for the brain. In contrast to other protective structures in the body, the cranial bones severely limit the expansion of the brain, even when expansion becomes necessary in response to specific pathologic processes. The cranial cavity is formed by the *frontal, parietal, sphenoid, temporal,* and *occipital* bones. The bones forming

the base of the cavity are shown in Figure 3-2. A roentgenogram of the skull shows the bones as lighter areas, and structures on the opposite sides of the skull are overlapped (Fig. 3-6).

When the base of the cranial cavity is viewed from above, three distinct areas are noted: the *anterior, middle,* and *posterior* fossae. In addition there are symmetrically placed holes (foramina) located in the base of the skull, through which the cranial nerves emerge to innervate peripheral structures.

Meningeal Coverings

The meninges are an important supporting element of the central nervous system and include the dura mater, arachnoid, and pia mater (Fig. 3-7). The outermost fibrous membrane, the *dura mater,* consists of two layers of connective tissue that are fused, except in certain regions where they separate to form the

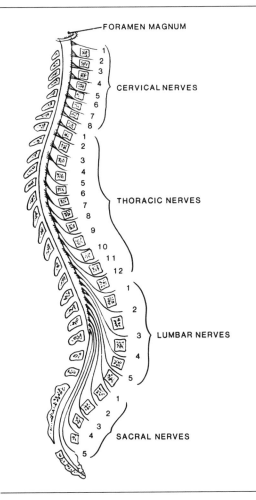

FORAMEN MAGNUM

CERVICAL NERVES

THORACIC NERVES

LUMBAR NERVES

SACRAL NERVES

Fig. 3-4. Structures at spinal level include spinal cord, nerve roots contained in vertebral column, and vertebral column itself.

intracranial venous sinuses. The dura mater is folded into the cranial cavity in two areas to form distinct fibrous barriers: the *falx cerebri,* which is located between the two cerebral hemispheres, and the *tentorium cerebelli,* which demarcates the superior limit of the posterior fossa. The delicate, filamentous *arachnoid* lies beneath the dura mater and appears to be loosely applied to the surface of the brain. *Pacchionian granulations* (arachnoid villi) are small tufts of arachnoid invaginated into dural venous sinuses, especially along the dorsal convexity of the cerebral hemispheres, superior to the longitudinal (interhemispheric) fissure. Many of the major arterial channels can be seen on the surface of the

brain beneath the arachnoid. The innermost layer, the *pia mater,* is composed of a very thin layer of mesoderm that is so closely attached to the brain surface that it cannot be seen in gross specimens.

Several important potential and actual spaces are found in association with these meningeal coverings (see Fig. 3-7). Between the bone and the dura mater is the *epidural space,* and beneath the dura mater is the *subdural space.* The bone, dura, and arachnoid are normally closely applied to one another so that the epidural and subdural spaces are potential spaces in which blood or pus may accumulate. Beneath the arachnoid is the *subarachnoid space,* which surrounds the entire brain and spinal cord and which is filled with cerebrospinal fluid. The subarachnoid space communicates with the interior of the brain via the ventricular system (Fig. 3-8).

The Ventricular System

Located within the depth of the brain is the ventricular system (Fig. 3-9), a derivative of the primitive embryonic neural canal. *Cerebrospinal fluid* is formed within the ventricles by the *choroid plexus* (located in each ventricle) and is circulated throughout the ventricles and subarachnoid space.

The cavity contained within each cerebral hemisphere is the *lateral ventricle,* which communicates with the cavity of the diencephalon, the *third ventricle,* via the *foramen of Monro.* The caudal end of the third ventricle narrows into the cavity of the mesencephalon, the *aqueduct of Sylvius,* which leads into the *fourth ventricle.* Communication with the subarachnoid spaces is via the two lateral *foramina of Luschka* and the central *foramen of Magendie* (all located in the walls of the fourth ventricle). The portion of the primitive central canal of the spinal cord becomes obliterated in the mature human nervous system and is usually identified only as a cluster of ependymal and glial cells in the central regions of the spinal cord.

Blood Vessels

Blood enters the skull via two arterial systems (Fig. 3-10). The brain is supplied by the posteriorly located *vertebrobasilar system* and the

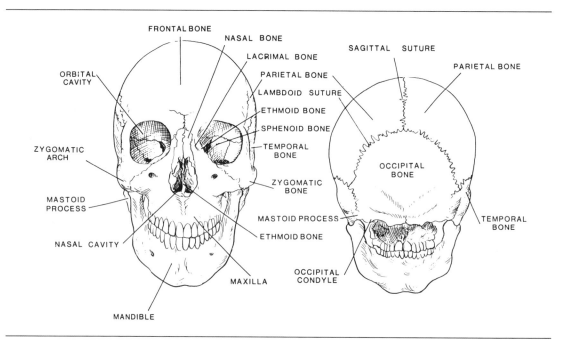

Fig. 3-5. Anterior (*left*) and posterior (*right*) views illustrating major bones of skull. Hollow sinus cavities are located within frontal, ethmoid, sphenoid, and maxillary bones.

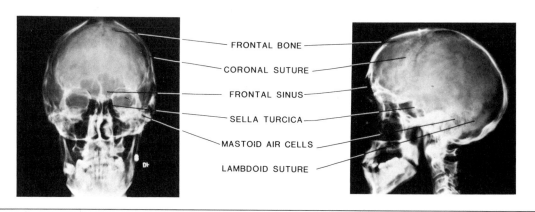

Fig. 3-6. Anterior (*left*) and lateral (*right*) views illustrating major bones of skull. Air-filled sinuses and nasal cavities appear darker. Compare with Figure 3-5.

anteriorly located *carotid system.* A series of anastomotic channels lying at the base of the brain, known as the *circle of Willis,* permits communication between these two systems.

The *internal carotid artery* and its major branches, the *anterior cerebral* and *middle cerebral* arteries, can be seen at the base of the brain (see Fig. 3-10). The anterior cere-

bral arteries are connected to each other by the small *anterior communicating artery* and continue in the midline between the two hemispheres to supply blood to their medial surfaces. The middle cerebral artery courses laterally between the temporal and the frontal lobes and emerges from the *insula* between the frontal and temporal lobes, where

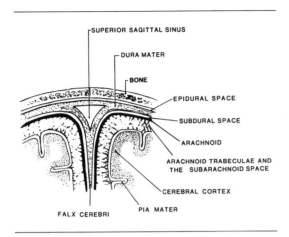

Fig. 3-7. Meninges and meningeal spaces. Coronal section through paramedian region of cerebral hemispheres.

its branches spread over and supply blood to the lateral surface of the hemisphere (Fig. 3-11).

Additional blood is carried to the brain by the two *vertebral arteries,* which enter the skull via the foramen magnum and join at the caudal border of the pons to form the *basilar artery* (see Fig. 3-10). Branches from these arteries normally provide the sole arterial supply to the occipital lobe, undersurface of the temporal lobe, thalamus, midbrain, pons, cerebellum, medulla, and portions of the cervical spinal cord. The *posterior inferior cerebellar arteries* are branches of the vertebral arteries, whereas the *anterior inferior cerebellar arteries* and *superior cerebellar arteries* are branches of the basilar artery.

The basilar artery continues cephalad until it divides into the *posterior cerebral arteries.* The *posterior communicating arteries* usually arise as branches of the posterior cerebral arteries and join those vessels with the internal carotid arteries to complete the circle of Willis.

Blood leaves the head by way of veins (Fig. 3-12) that course over the cerebral hemispheres to converge into large channels, the *venous sinuses,* contained within the layers of the dura mater. The most prominent of these sinuses are the *superior sagittal sinus* and *inferior sagittal sinus,* which run longitudinally from front to back in the falx cerebri between the hemispheres. The major venous channels merge in the occipital region and form the *transverse* and *sigmoid sinuses,* which exit through the skull via the jugular foramen as the *internal jugular veins.*

Fig. 3-8. Cranial subarachnoid space and its communication with both spinal subarachnoid space and ventricular system.

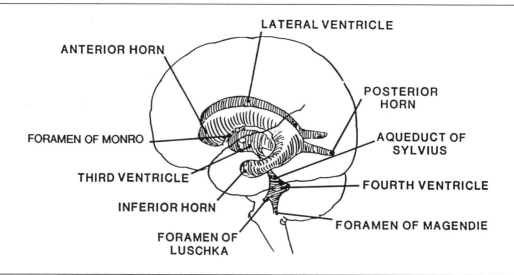

Fig. 3-9. Ventricular system. Cerebrospinal fluid is formed by choroid plexus in the ventricles. This fluid circulates and communicates with subarachnoid space via foramina of Luschka and Magendie.

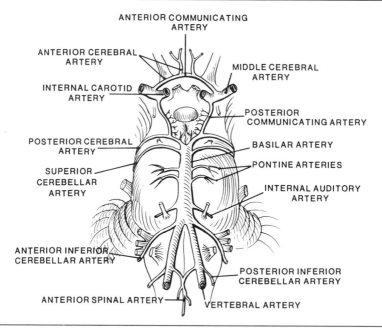

Fig. 3-10. Arterial supply to brain as viewed from base. Major arterial supply is via internal carotid and vertebrobasilar systems, which communicate with each other via series of anastomotic channels known as the circle of Willis.

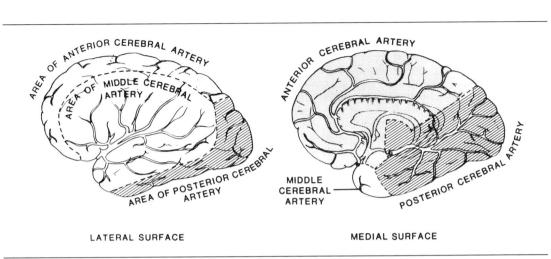

LATERAL SURFACE   MEDIAL SURFACE

Fig. 3-11. Lateral and medial surfaces of cerebral hemisphere illustrating distribution of blood supply of major arteries. Anterior and middle cerebral arteries are branches of internal carotid arteries; posterior cerebral arteries are branches of basilar artery. (Redrawn from B. Pansky and E. L. House. *Review of Gross Anatomy* [3rd ed.]. New York: Macmillan, 1975.)

Fig. 3-12. Venous drainage of cerebral hemispheres. Blood circulating over cortex collects in superior sagittal sinus (*left*); blood from deeper structures enters other venous sinuses (*right*). Direction of flow is toward confluence of sinuses in occipital region and then toward internal jugular veins by way of transverse and sigmoid sinuses. (*S* = sinus; *V* = vein.) (Redrawn from B. Pansky and E. L. House. *Review of Gross Anatomy* [3rd ed.]. New York: Macmillan, 1975.)

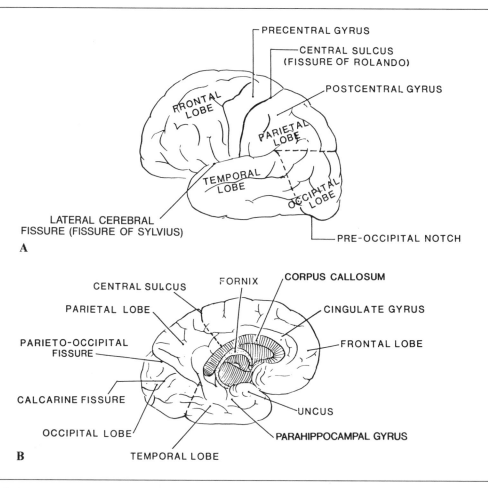

Fig. 3-13. Lateral (A) and medial (B) surfaces of cerebral hemispheres illustrating major gyri and sulci and division of hemispheres into five major lobes: frontal, parietal, temporal, occipital, and limbic.

The Supratentorial Level

The major structures at the supratentorial level are the telencephalic derivatives (the cerebral hemispheres), the diencephalon, and cranial nerves I and II.

Cerebral Hemispheres

Through a process of growth and proliferation, the telencephalic structures differentiate into the cerebral hemispheres. The *longitudinal (interhemispheric) fissure* separates the cerebrum into two cerebral hemispheres. The surface of each hemisphere is convoluted: the folds are known as *gyri* and are separated from one another by grooves, or *sulci*. Certain grooves are more prominent, deeper, and

more constant and are known as *fissures*. The fissures must be identified in order to locate the four major lobes into which each hemisphere is divided: *frontal, parietal, temporal,* and *occipital.* As shown in Fig. 3-13, the following serve as important landmarks in defining the limits of each lobe: *lateral fissure (fissure of Sylvius), central sulcus (fissure of Rolando), parietooccipital fissure,* and *preoccipital notch.* The *calcarine fissure* divides the occipital lobe. Within the fissure of Sylvius is buried a portion of the cortex known as the *insula.* The central sulcus separates the *precentral gyrus* of the frontal lobe from the *postcentral gyrus* of the parietal lobe. A line drawn from the end of the fissure of Sylvius to the preoccipital notch serves to demarcate the

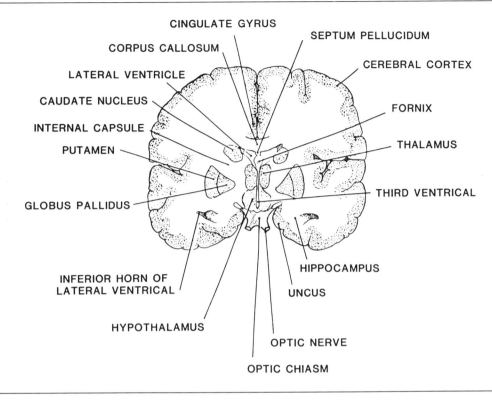

Fig. 3-14. Coronal section through cerebral hemispheres. The gray matter is shown as stippled area.

limits of the temporal lobe, whereas a similar line from the preoccipital notch to the parietooccipital fissure delineates the occipital lobe.

Certain structures, best seen on the mesial surface of the hemispheres, are not included in the traditional division of the brain into four lobes. The *corpus callosum* represents a prominent fiber tract for transfer of information from one hemisphere to another. A number of the remaining prominent structures seen on the mesial surface are related functionally and anatomically to the processing of memory and emotion. These structures have been grouped into a functional unit of the brain called the *limbic lobe* (see Fig. 3-13). Some of the major structures visible on the medial surface of the brain are the *uncus* (located on the medial aspect of the temporal lobe), the *parahippocampal gyrus* (also on the medial temporal lobe), the *fornix* (a fiber bundle connecting the hypothalamus with the hippocampus), and

the *cingulate gyrus* (located above the corpus callosum).

A coronal (Fig. 3-14) and a horizontal (Fig. 3-15) section through the cerebrum reveal several important structures within the substance of the brain. Computerized tomographic (CT) scans usually show the brain in horizontal sections (see Fig. 6-18). The two lateral ventricles and the third ventricle occupy a central position. The *gray matter* (mainly nuclear areas and cerebral cortex) and *white matter* (regions where fiber tracts are traveling) can be differentiated. Several distinct, large gray nuclear masses can be seen. The *thalamus* (an important relay area for the motor and sensory systems) is located lateral to the third ventricle. The *basal ganglia*, composed of the *caudate nucleus, putamen,* and *globus pallidus,* are all part of the motor system. A large and important area of white matter, the *internal capsule,* passes between these central nuclear masses and trans-

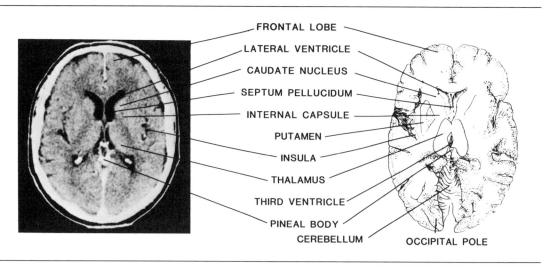

FRONTAL LOBE
LATERAL VENTRICLE
CAUDATE NUCLEUS
SEPTUM PELLUCIDUM
INTERNAL CAPSULE
PUTAMEN
INSULA
THALAMUS
THIRD VENTRICLE
PINEAL BODY
CEREBELLUM
OCCIPITAL POLE

Fig. 3-15. Horizontal section through cerebral hemispheres at the level of the thalamus (*right*); areas of gray matter are stippled. The cerebellum beneath the occipital lobes can be seen in the midline. Computerized tomographic scan (*left*) is through the hemispheres at a slightly different angle. Bone, falx, and choroid calcification are white on the scan.

fers information between the *cerebral cortex* and the lower structures.

Diencephalon

The diencephalon represents a zone of transition between the cerebrum at the supratentorial level and the structures in the posterior fossa. The diencephalon consists of the *third ventricle* and those structures related to it, including the *thalamus, hypothalamus, optic pathways,* and *pineal body* (Fig. 3-16). At the base of the hypothalamus is an important neuroendocrine structure, the *hypophysis* or *pituitary gland.* It is located in the middle of the skull in the bony sella turcica. All these structures are at the supratentorial level.

Cranial Nerves I and II

The *olfactory bulb* and *tract* (I) are located at the base of each frontal lobe. The olfactory nerves are axons passing from the nasal cavity through the cribriform plate to connect to the olfactory bulb. The *optic nerves* (II) develop as an outgrowth from the primitive diencephalon. The optic pathway from the orbit consists of the *optic nerve, optic chiasm,* and *optic tract.* The intracranial portions of these nerves are at the supratentorial level.

The Posterior Fossa Level

The major structures contained in this level are the *brain stem,* the cerebellum, and the origins of cranial nerves III through XII.

Brain Stem

The term *brain stem* is not a precise anatomical term and therefore has been defined in different ways. However, the term is so commonly used in neurologic discussions that one must be familiar with it. As defined herein, the *brain stem* consists of the portion of the brain that remains after removal of the cerebral and cerebellar hemispheres (see Fig. 3-1). Cephalad from the spinal cord, the brain stem includes the *medulla oblongata* (myelencephalon), *pons* (metencephalon), and *midbrain* (mesencephalon). Only the pontine portion of the metencephalon is part of the brain stem; the cerebellum is excluded. The upper portion of the brain stem is continuous with the diencephalon, where overlapping structures make precise definition difficult. In this text, the diencephalon is not included as a part of the brain stem; the *superior colliculus* is used to demarcate the upper border of the brain stem. The *red nucleus* and the *substantia nigra* are both present in the upper mesencephalon and

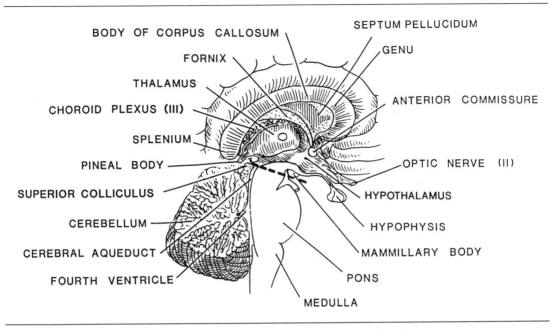

Fig. 3-16. Median sagittal section through diencephalon, brain stem, and cerebellum. Dotted line above level of superior colliculus separates supratentorial and posterior fossa levels.

extend into the posterior diencephalon, thereby overlapping the supratentorial and posterior fossa levels.

The longitudinal separation of the brain stem into midbrain, pons, and medulla is made primarily by a large bundle of prominent crossing fibers on the ventral and lateral surfaces of the brain stem that connect the brain stem to the cerebellum (Fig. 3-17). These fibers demarcate the extent of the pons. The medulla is immediately caudal, and the midbrain is cephalad to these fibers. The brain stem at the midbrain and pons is divided dorsoventrally into three regions. The area dorsal to the aqueduct of Sylvius is the *tectum,* whose major structures are the superior and inferior colliculi (corpora quadrigemina). The area of multiple nuclei and intermingled pathways ventral to the aqueduct and fourth ventricle is the *tegmentum.* The large distinct cerebral and cerebellar white matter pathways in the most ventral regions below the tegmentum make up the *base* or *basal region* of the midbrain and pons.

Cerebellum

The cerebellum consists of two *hemispheres* and a midline *vermis* (Fig. 3-18). The cerebel-

lar surface is much more highly convoluted than is the surface of the cerebrum, with folds known as *folia.* The cerebellum is metencephalic in derivation and therefore is associated structurally with the pons. The cerebellum lies dorsal to the fourth ventricle, the pons, and the medulla.

Cranial Nerves III through XII

Emerging from the brain stem are 10 pairs of nerves, which can be identified in Figure 3-17. (Cranial nerves I and II are *not* contained in the posterior fossa.) The names, location, and general function of all the cranial nerves are summarized in Table 3-1.

The Spinal Level

The major structures contained in this level are the spinal cord, the origins of the spinal nerves within the vertebral column, and the vertebral column itself.

The *spinal cord* is surrounded by meninges similar to those that surround the brain (Fig. 3-19). Outside the dura mater is the *epidural space,* an actual space that contains fat and venous plexuses. The *arachnoid* adjacent to

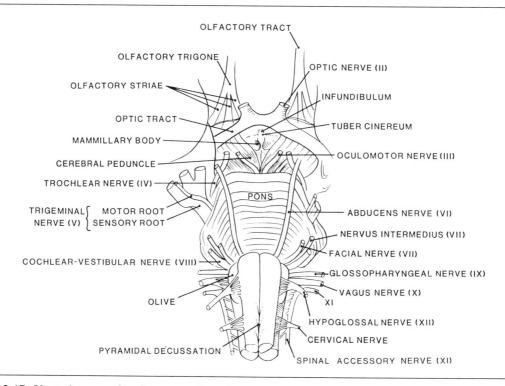

Fig. 3-17. Ventral aspect of brain stem and cranial nerves. Cranial nerve I is not shown. It ends at the olfactory bulb, from which the olfactory tract arises. Cranial nerves I and II arise at the supratentorial level; cranial nerves III through XII arise in the posterior fossa. (Redrawn from B. Pansky and E. L. House. *Review of Gross Anatomy* [3rd ed.]. New York: Macmillan, 1975.)

Table 3-1. Location and General Function of the Cranial Nerves

Nerve	Anatomical relationship	Function
I Olfactory	Cerebral hemispheres	Smell
II Optic	Diencephalon, cerebral hemispheres	Vision
III Oculomotor	Midbrain	Eye movement
IV Trochlear	Midbrain	Eye movement
V Trigeminal	Pons	Facial sensation, jaw movement
VI Abducens	Pons	Eye movement
VII Facial	Pons	Facial movement
VIII Cochlear-vestibular	Pons, medulla	Hearing and balance
IX Glossopharyngeal	Medulla	Throat movement
X Vagus	Medulla	Throat and larynx movement, and control of visceral organs
XI Spinal accessory	Medulla, spinal cord	Shoulder and neck movement
XII Hypoglossal	Medulla	Tongue movement

the inner surface of the dura mater forms the subarachnoid space, which contains the cerebrospinal fluid. The spinal *pia mater* is closely applied to the surface of the spinal cord but is visible as the *dentate ligaments* extending on either side between the origins of the spinal nerve roots. These ligaments join the arachnoid at intervals and are inserted into the dura mater. The dural sac and *subarachnoid space* end at the level of the second sacral vertebra

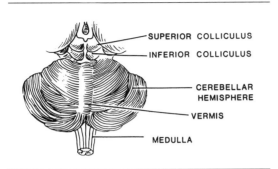

Fig. 3-18. Cerebellum as viewed from its dorsal surface.

(Fig. 3-20). The pia mater continues caudally as a filamentous membrane (the *filum terminale*) from the end of the spinal cord (the *conus medullaris*). It fuses with the dural sac at the second sacral vertebral level and is attached to the dorsal surface of the coccyx as the *sacrococcygeal ligament.*

The adult spinal cord begins rostrally from the caudal margin of the medulla at the level of the foramen magnum and terminates opposite the caudal margin of the first lumbar vertebra. The spinal cord, therefore, does *not* extend the entire length of the spinal canal. Throughout much of the length of the cord a spinal segment is *not* adjacent to its corresponding vertebral segment.

The spinal cord exhibits *cervical* and *lumbosacral enlargements.* Cross sections show a relative increase in gray matter in these two re-gions, to account for the relative enlargement in these areas. Thirty-one pairs of *spinal nerves* are attached to the spinal cord via *dorsal* (posterior) and *ventral* (anterior) *nerve roots.* Segmentally there are 8 cervical, 12 thoracic, 5 lumbar, 5 sacral, and 1 coccygeal spinal nerve on each side. At their origins, the nerve roots consist of multiple filaments, which, on the posterior (dorsal) surface of the cord, exit from a relatively constant groove, the *posterior lateral sulcus.* The dorsal and ventral roots of each spinal nerve join as they enter the intervertebral foramen of the spine. After leaving the spinal cord, the roots of the lumbar and sacral spinal nerves run caudally a number of segments toward their exit. The collection of spinal nerve roots contained in the lumbosacral spinal canal is known as the *cauda equina* (see Fig. 3-19). Although most of the spinal nerves have both a ventral (motor) and a dorsal (sensory) root, often the first cervical nerve has only a motor root, while the first coccygeal nerve and the fifth sacral nerve have only a sensory root. Surrounding the spinal cord is the *vertebral column,* consisting of 7 cervical, 12 thoracic, and 5 lumbar vertebrae, the fused sacrum, and the coccyx (see Fig. 3-20).

The Peripheral Level

The major structures of the peripheral level are the somatic nerves, the autonomic nerves and ganglia, the neuromuscular junction, the muscles of the skeleton, and the peripheral

Fig. 3-19. Cross sections of vertebral column at cervical and lumbar vertebral levels. (Redrawn from B. Pansky and E. L. House. *Review of Gross Anatomy* [3rd ed.]. New York: Macmillan, 1975.)

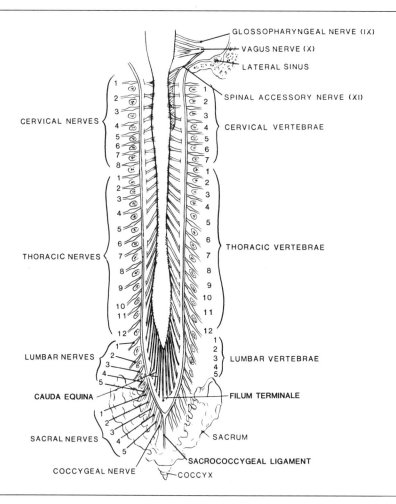

Fig. 3-20. Dorsal view of spinal level. Note spinal cord itself terminates between the L-1 and L-2 vertebrae. Caudal end of spinal cord is conus medullaris, and collection of nerve roots in lumbar region is cauda equina. (Redrawn from B. Pansky and E. L. House. *Review of Gross Anatomy* [3rd ed.]. New York: Macmillan, 1975.)

sensory receptors. The spinal nerves, as they emerge from the vertebral column, enter the peripheral level. These spinal nerves, which were formed by the joining of dorsal and ventral roots, contain somatic and autonomic motor and sensory nerve fibers and branch into posterior and anterior divisions as they enter the peripheral level. Fibers of the anterior divisions en route to the limbs come together and are rearranged in plexuses. The *brachial plexus,* located in the axillary region, redistributes the fibers to the major nerves of the upper extremities: median, ulnar, radial, axillary, and musculocutaneous. The *lumbosacral plexus,* located in the lower abdominal

cavity and pelvis, redistributes the fibers to the major nerves in the lower extremities: femoral, obturator, and sciatic, which divides into the tibial and peroneal nerves.

Gross Neuroanatomy — Introduction to the Longitudinal Systems

The gross anatomical features of each of the major levels have been reviewed. At this point, some of these same structures should be related to the major longitudinal systems, which will be studied in further detail in subsequent chapters.

The Cerebrospinal Fluid System

Structures included in the cerebrospinal fluid system are the meninges (dura, pia, and arachnoid), the meningeal spaces (epidural, subdural, and subarachnoid), the ventricular system, and the cerebrospinal fluid. This system, present at the supratentorial, posterior fossa, and spinal levels, provides both cushioning and buffering for the central nervous system and helps maintain a stable environment for neural function.

The Sensory System

This system receives somatosensory information from the external environment and transmits it to the central nervous system (afferent), where it can be processed and used for adaptive behavior. Elements of the somatosensory system are found at all major levels and include the peripheral receptor organs; afferent fibers traveling in cranial, peripheral, and spinal nerves; dorsal root ganglia; ascending pathways in the spinal cord and brain stem; portions of the thalamus; and the thalamocortical radiations that terminate primarily in the sensory cortex of the parietal lobe. In addition, structures related to the special sensory systems (vision, taste, smell, hearing, and balance) are located at the supratentorial, posterior fossa, and peripheral levels.

The Motor System

The motor system initiates and controls activity in the somatic muscles via efferent connections of the motor cortex and other areas of the frontal lobes; descending pathways that traverse the internal capsule, cerebral peduncles, medullary pyramids, and other areas of the brain stem; portions of the spinal cord, including the ventral horns; ventral roots; efferent fibers traveling in both peripheral and cranial nerves; and muscle, the major effector organ of the motor system. Also included in this system are the cerebellum and basal ganglia and related pathways. The motor system is thus present at all major levels and is directly involved in the performance of all motor activity mediated by striated musculature.

The Internal Regulation System

The internal regulation system is composed of the structures in the nervous system that monitor and control the function of visceral glands and organs. It contains both afferent and efferent components, which interact to maintain the internal environment (homeostasis). The system has major representation at all levels of the nervous system. Important structures include areas of the limbic lobe and hypothalamus (supratentorial); the reticular formation and fibers traveling in cranial nerves (posterior fossa); longitudinal pathways in the spinal cord and brain stem; and numerous ganglia, receptors, and effectors found at the peripheral level.

The Consciousness System

Functioning as an additional afferent system, the consciousness system allows a person selectively to attend to and perceive isolated stimuli and maintains various levels of wakefulness, awareness, and consciousness. Structures contained within this system are found only at the posterior fossa and supratentorial levels and include portions of the central core of the brain stem and diencephalon (reticular formation and ascending projectional pathways), portions of the thalamus, basal forebrain, and pathways that project diffusely to widespread areas of cerebral cortex. All lobes of the brain are part of this system.

The Vascular System

Each organ in the body must have blood vessels to provide a relatively constant supply of oxygen and other nutrients as well as a means for removal of metabolic wastes. The vascular system is therefore found at all major levels of the nervous system and includes the arteries, arterioles, capillaries, veins, and dural sinuses. These supply supratentorial, posterior fossa, spinal, and peripheral nervous system structures.

As noted in Chapter 2 (Developmental Organization of the Nervous System), a transverse organization is imposed on the neural tube. Structures located near the core, or inner tube, represent phylogenetically older pathways with indirect, diffuse, and nonspecific relay functions related largely to the consciousness and internal regulation systems. Structures located near the outer surface represent newer pathways that have more direct, relatively specific relay functions related to the sensory and motor systems.

At this point in the study of gross neuroanatomy, a precise distinction is not made between the structures of the inner and outer core. However, as the student progresses through the study of the longitudinal systems, further reference will be made to these areas. Further details about the anatomical structures associated with these areas are given in Chapter 12 (The Neurochemical Systems).

Clinical Correlations

Neurologic diagnosis includes identification of the anatomical location and pathology of the disorder. Through the use of problem-solving skills that are already familiar and the assignment of some functional significance to the anatomical structures discussed in this chapter, the reader can begin to solve clinical neurologic problems by identifying the anatomical location.

In certain respects, an analogy may be drawn between the nervous system and an electrical circuit. The nervous system can be considered as a series of electrical cables laid out in a specific plan (Fig. 3-21). Leading to and from the cerebral hemispheres are two parallel cables (representing a longitudinal system) that conduct impulses from one segment to another. Scattered along these *intersegmental* cables are several smaller branching *segmental* wires. As in basic electricity, damage (a lesion) anywhere along the course of the main intersegmental cables causes malfunction in all areas beyond that point, whereas damage to the segmental wires causes malfunction only within that specific segment. In applying this analogy to humans, we note that the higher centers exert control or receive information from the body segments through long *intersegmental pathways* and that one side of the brain is associated with function on the *opposite* side of the body.

Anatomical diagnosis first requires the ability to relate the patient's signs and symp-

Fig. 3-21. Major nervous system connections. (A = cranial nerves; B = peripheral nerves.) Note long intersegmental pathways leading to and from higher centers and multiple, short segmental pathways (cranial and peripheral nerves) to the peripheral level.

toms to specific longitudinal systems within the nervous system. Neurologic diagnosis relies mainly on the symptoms of dysfunction in the sensory, motor, and consciousness systems, whose organization is similar to the schematic pathways seen in Figure 3-21. Symptoms of dysfunction in the sensory system consist of altered sensation, described by the patient as pain, numbness, tingling, or loss of sensation. Symptoms of dysfunction in the motor system consist primarily of weakness, paralysis, incoordination, shaking, or jerking. Lesions of the consciousness system, which is located only at the supratentorial and posterior fossa levels, are expressed as altered states of consciousness and coma. The presence of any of these or related symptoms identifies the longitudinal system involved in a disease.

Localization is determined by the level of the nervous system in which the pathway function is interrupted. To aid in localization, the functions of each of the major anatomical levels are described in the following sections and are schematically represented in Figure 3-22.

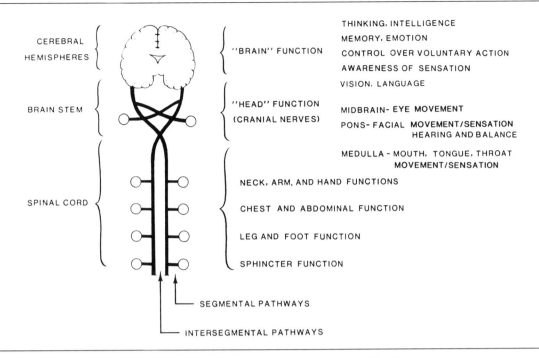

Fig. 3-22. Summary of functions associated with the major anatomical levels.

Peripheral Level

The spinal and cranial nerves, after they emerge from the vertebral column and skull, and the structures they innervate, constitute the major components of the peripheral level. Each emerging nerve defines a specific *segment*. A lesion in one of these pathways alters all function within that segment but has no effect on functions carried to and from other segments. Thus, in the presence of a peripheral lesion, *loss of sensation and muscle weakness* in a focal area are common. Often, peripheral nerve damage is not complete and the sensation of *pain* is produced. Therefore, in addition to sensory loss and weakness, pain in a segmental distribution is an important clue to a lesion at the peripheral level.

Spinal Level

The spinal cord has two functions. It is the structure from which individual segments of the limbs and trunk originate, and it transmits information to and from higher centers. Therefore, lesions at the spinal level may alter *segmental* functions in the region of the ab-

normality and alter *intersegmental* function below the lesion. Except in complete transections of the spinal cord, all functions are not altered equally; however, even under those circumstances, the characteristic combination of segmental loss of function at the site of the lesion and intersegmental loss below it usually can be identified.

The spinal cord is a narrow structure that contains the major intersegmental pathways for both sides of the neuraxis (nervous system). Therefore, in spinal lesions, bilateral involvement from a single focal lesion is not uncommon. Furthermore, because of the length of the spinal column, specific segmental functions can be assigned to certain areas of it. The upper portion (cervical) is related primarily to arm function, the midportion (thoracic) to the trunk, the lower portion (lumbar) to the legs, and the lowermost area (sacral) to anal-genital-urinary functions.

Posterior Fossa Level

The cranial nerves mediate segmental function for the head and arise in the posterior fossa. Lesions at the posterior fossa level therefore produce segmental and intersegmental disturbances, just as occur at the spinal level. The *segmental* nerves of the brain stem are the cranial nerves, which control movement and sensation in the head (see Table 3-1). Brain-stem lesions often alter these segmental functions. In addition, since the brain stem is also an area where intersegmental pathways cross, or have crossed, to the opposite side of the brain, a characteristic pattern is often seen with focal lesions. Lesions of the posterior fossa cause loss of segmental head function *ipsilateral* (same side) to the lesion; if the lesion also involves intersegmental pathways, it causes loss of intersegmental function on the side of the body *contralateral* (opposite) to the lesion (see Fig. 3-22). Extensive lesions in the brain stem may affect the consciousness system and produce coma.

Supratentorial Level

Each cerebral hemisphere exerts its control over the opposite side of the body. Therefore, supratentorial lesions are associated with loss of intersegmental sensory or motor function on the opposite side of the body. In addition, some functions are associated almost exclusively with the supratentorial level and may be considered segmental functions of this level. These functions are language (almost always localized to the left side of the brain), memory, intelligence, cognition, olfaction, and vision. When abnormal, they serve to further localize the disorder to the supratentorial level (see Fig. 3-22). Extensive lesions involving the structures of the supratentorial level may alter consciousness and produce coma.

Precise localization is possible when an area can be identified where both segmental and intersegmental functions are altered in one or more systems.

The major features to be determined in the anatomical diagnosis of neurologic disorders are whether:

1. The responsible lesion is *focal,* strictly confined to a single well-circumscribed area. If the lesion is focal, the *anatomical level* and whether the abnormality is located on the right or left or in the midline of the nervous system must be defined.

2. The responsible lesion is *diffuse* and nonfocal. A diffuse lesion may involve only a single level or may involve multiple levels. In general, a lesion is considered to be diffuse if it involves bilateral regions in the nervous system without extending across the midline as a single, circumscribed lesion.

Objectives

1. Define the boundaries of the major anatomical levels (supratentorial, posterior fossa, spinal, and peripheral), and identify on gross specimen, photograph, or other reproduction the major anatomical structures contained in each level.
2. Given a cross-section specimen, drawing, or reproduction, identify the approximate area of the neuraxis to which the specimen belongs (that is, cerebral hemisphere; mesencephalon; pons; medulla; cerebellum; cervical, thoracic, lumbar, or sacral spinal cord).
3. Given a clinical problem, answer the following two questions:
   a. The signs and symptoms contained in the protocol are most likely the manifestation of disease at which of the following *levels* of the nervous system?
      (1) Supratentorial level
      (2) Posterior fossa level
      (3) Spinal level
      (4) Peripheral level
      (5) More than one level
   b. Within the level you have selected, the responsible lesion is most likely:
      (1) Focal, on the *right* side of the nervous system
      (2) Focal, on the *left* side of the nervous system
      (3) Focal, but involving the *midline* and *contiguous* structures on both sides of the nervous system
      (4) Nonfocal and diffusely located

Clinical Problems

The following is a series of case histories of neurologic disorders. The problems were selected to illustrate examples of involvement in different regions of the nervous system. Read each history carefully. On the basis of the information presented, try to localize the lesion in accordance with the objectives above. When you have arrived at a conclusion for each case, review the pertinent anatomical structures in that area.

1. A 19-year-old man was involved in an automobile accident 4 months earlier. He sustained only minor bruises about the head and face. When he returned to school in the fall, he seemed to be uninterested in his schoolwork and began to complain of headaches. He dragged his right foot when he walked and used his right hand clumsily. He had a slight droop to the right side of his face. (Answers refer to items under a and b of objective 3.)

2. A 68-year-old man awakened one morning and noted that he was unable to speak clearly. He wanted to ask for help but could utter only the words "go now." His wife noted some weakness of the right side of his face and right arm and leg. He seemed unable to answer the questions that his wife posed to him.

3. A 26-year-old man awoke and noted that all the muscles on the left side of his face seemed to be paralyzed. Sensation was normal, although he was aware of an inability to taste on the left side of his tongue. He had no other difficulties. Six weeks later, he noted gradual and continued improvement.

4. A 42-year-old man noted, over a period of several years, the onset of ringing in his right ear and loss of hearing in that ear. In addition, he experienced right facial weakness and decreased sensation. In the weeks before his examination, he noted stiffness and weakness of his left arm and leg.

5. A 24-year-old woman was involved in an automobile accident. When examined, she had complete loss of sensation from the arms downward. She could not move her hands or legs and had no sensation below the armpits. She was incontinent.

6. For no apparent reason, a 64-year-old woman began to experience pain beginning in her back and encircling the right side of her chest about the level of her breast. A rash later appeared in the same distribution. She continued to have pain in that region, and sensation in that region was greatly diminished.

7. The patient, a 46-year-old woman, described a pain that was similar to the one noted in problem 6. The pain involved the left side of her chest. (No rash was present.) Her symptoms increased over several months but remained localized in a rather circumscribed region of her chest. She was concerned about "heart trouble." In addition, she complained of difficulty in walking. Her left leg seemed to be weak and stiff, and at times the left leg felt "numb."

Additional Reading

Brodal, P. *The Central Nervous System: Structure & Function.* New York: Oxford University Press, 1992.

Carpenter, M. B. *Core Text of Neuroanatomy* (4th ed.). Baltimore: Williams & Wilkins, 1991.

Gilman, S., and Winans Newman, S. (eds.). *Manter and Gatz's Essentials of Clinical Neuroanatomy and Neurophysiology* (8th ed.). Philadelphia: Davis, 1992.

Haines, D. E. *Neuroanatomy: An Atlas of Structures, Sections, and Systems* (3rd ed.). Baltimore: Urban & Schwarzenberg, 1991.

Netter, F. H. *The Ciba Collection of Medical Illustrations.* Vol. 1: *Nervous System.* Part I: Anatomy and Physiology. West Caldwell, N. J.: CIBA Pharmaceutical Company, 1983.

Watson, C. *Basic Human Neuroanatomy: An Introductory Atlas* (4th ed.). Boston: Little, Brown, 1991.

— 4 —

Diagnosis of Neurologic Disorders: Neurocytology and the Pathologic Reactions of the Nervous System

The principles of anatomical localization have been introduced in Chapter 3. Anatomical localization, however, is but one part of the diagnosis of neurologic disorders; it is also necessary to determine the pathologic features of the lesion involved. Identification of the pathologic condition requires knowledge of the cellular elements of the nervous system (neurocytology) and the ways in which these cells react to noxious stimuli (pathologic reactions).

Two major factors must be considered in describing lesions of the nervous system:

1. The topography of the lesion. The anatomical location of the pathologic process and a judgment as to whether the abnormality is
   a. *Focal.* Strictly confined to a single circumscribed anatomical area.
   b. *Diffuse.* Distributed over wide areas of the nervous system. A diffuse lesion may involve only a single level (for example, supratentorial or spinal level), or it may be distributed over multiple levels. A diffuse lesion involves bilaterally symmetrical areas in the nervous system, without extending across the midline as a single, circumscribed lesion.
2. The morphology of the lesion. The gross and histologic appearance of the abnormal area and a judgment as to whether the pathologic process is
   a. *Nonmass.* One that is altering cellular function in the area of the lesion but is not significantly interfering with neighboring cell performance. In this type of lesion, the pathologic process is not, by

virtue of its size or volume, compressing, destroying, or damaging nearby structures.
   b. *Mass.* One that not only alters cellular function in the area of the lesion but also is of sufficient size and volume to interfere with neighboring cell functions by compressing, destroying, or altering nearby cells.

Integration of the *topographic* and *morphologic* descriptions provides a precise pathologic diagnosis. When patients are examined clinically, tissue is not available for study, yet on the basis of the signs and symptoms and their evolution, the nature of the responsible pathologic lesion can be deduced. This chapter provides the information necessary to accomplish that task.

Overview

The nervous system is composed of neurons, supporting cells of neuroectodermal origin, and supporting cells of mesodermal origin. *Neurons* are derived solely from ectoderm and are the functional units of the nervous system, capable of generating and conducting the electrical activity that underlies nervous system performance. Mature neurons do not undergo proliferation; therefore, most disease processes that affect neurons produce only neuronal degeneration and loss.

The *supporting cells of neuroectodermal origin* are the oligodendroglia, Schwann cells, astrocytes, and ependymal cells. *Oligodendroglial cells* are responsible for the formation of the myelin sheaths that invest and surround axons in the central nervous system, while *Schwann cells* serve a similar function in the peripheral nervous system. Disease processes affecting these cells are associated with myelin breakdown and loss (demyelination). *Astrocytes* are widely distributed throughout the central nervous system, lie near both the neurons and the blood vessels, and thus help to provide much of the metabolic support of neural elements. Disease processes are often associated with astrocytic proliferation, which results in gliosis, the scar tissue of the central nervous system. Astrocytes also may react to metabolic disturbances in more specific ways. *Ependymal cells* line the entire ventricular system and provide a selective barrier between the ventricular fluid and the brain substance. Noxious stimuli may produce a loss of ependymal cells. Epithelium of the choroid plexus is a derivative of ependyma and has an important role in the formation of cerebrospinal fluid.

The *supporting cells of mesodermal origin* are microglia and connective tissue cells. *Microglia* migrate into the central nervous system, and although normally present in small numbers, they can proliferate rapidly to become scavenger cells, or *macrophages*, which remove damaged tissue. With the exception of vascular structures, the parenchyma of the brain is almost devoid of elements of *connective tissue*; however, the nervous system is surrounded by the meninges, which are of mesodermal, connective tissue origin.

Disease processes may affect one or more of these cytologic elements, and differences in their histologic features form the morphologic basis for the various clinical features of neurologic diseases. The signs and symptoms produced by these disorders reflect the anatomical location and histologic evolution (temporal profile) of the underlying pathologic lesion. *Degenerative disorders* are characterized by gradual neuronal damage in widespread areas of the nervous system and therefore are seen clinically as chronic, progressive, and diffuse diseases. *Neoplastic disorders* present clinically as chronic, focal, progressive disorders. Any cell type in the nervous system can undergo neoplastic change to form a gradually enlarging, localized mass of proliferating cells (a neoplasm).

Vascular diseases may be of several pathologic types, but they are all associated with sudden alteration in structure and function. Therefore, disorders of this etiologic category are always acute in onset, but they may be either focal (infarct, intracerebral hemorrhage) or diffuse (subarachnoid hemorrhage, anoxic encephalopathy) in distribution. Because foreign pathogens invading the nervous system generally produce a rapid but not immediate cellular response, *inflammatory disease*, which may be either focal (abscess) or diffuse (meningitis, encephalitis), commonly presents as a progressive, subacute disorder. The temporal profile of *immunologic diseases* is variable, but it generally takes the form of a multifocal or diffuse disorder, with subacute or chronic progression.

Toxic or metabolic diseases alter neural function over widespread areas and therefore present with diffuse signs and symptoms. However, depending on the responsible agent, the resultant symptoms may make their appearance as acute, subacute, or chronic disorders. *Traumatic lesions* of the nervous system usually are focal and of acute onset, reflecting the effects of the immediate damage of tissue produced by the offending agent. At times, however, delayed effects of a traumatic lesion may produce clinical symptoms and present a pattern of a chronic, progressive lesion.

Structural Elements of the Nervous System

The nervous system is composed of three basic categories of cells: (1) nerve cells, called *neurons*, which are the major functional units of the nervous system; (2) supporting cells of neuroectodermal origin (oligodendroglia, Schwann cells, astrocytes, and ependymal cells); and (3) supporting cells of mesodermal origin (microglia and connective tissue elements).

The first two categories of cells, the neurons and the supporting cells of neuroectodermal origin, are derived from the primitive neuroepithelium that lines the neural tube and from the cells of the neural crest. The processes of differentiation and migration followed by these cells are outlined in Chapter 2 (Develop-

Table 4-1. Stains in Neuropathology

Use	Stain	Comment
Routine	Hematoxylin and eosin (H & E)	General tissue stain; nuclei stain blue, cytoplasm stains red
Nissl bodies	Nissl (for example, cresyl violet)	Stains nuclei and Nissl bodies blue; faint or no staining of cytoplasm
Neurofibrils (axons)	Silver impregnations (for example, Bodian or Bielschowsky)	Stain intracellular neurofibrils and axis cylinders black
Myelin sheaths	Luxol-fast blue; Weigert	Stains normal but not degenerating myelin
Myelin (degenerating)	Marchi (osmium tetroxide)	Intense staining of degenerating myelin; faint staining of normal myelin
Astrocytes	Cajal (gold sublimate)	Astrocytes stain black
Glial fibers	Mallory's phosphotungstic acid-hematoxylin; Holzer (crystal violet)	Stains astrocytic fibers and is useful for demarcating reactive astrocytes
Microglia and oligodendroglia	Variations of Hortega's silver-impregnation methods	Stain microglia or oligodendroglia black depending on method

mental Organization of the Nervous System: Neuroembryology). The third category, mesodermal supporting tissue, is derived from the mesoderm that surrounds the neural tube during development.

The structure of all these cell types and their interrelationships have been studied extensively at the light microscopic and electron microscopic levels. Any description of their microscopic appearance, therefore, must include a statement of the method on which the description is based. Nerve tissue is routinely studied at the light microscopic level by using thin sections of tissue to which stains are applied. Stains have been developed that emphasize certain features of cells while obscuring others. Some of these stains are dyes that react with and bind to certain chemical groups in the tissue, rendering them colored. Other stains are salts of heavy metals, especially silver salts, which undergo a physicochemical reaction with and "impregnate" certain structural elements in the tissue. Table 4-1 outlines the uses of some of the stains commonly employed in the study of nerve tissue.

Neurons

The neuron is the most important structural element of the nervous system because it generates and conducts the electrical activity that is associated with the function of the nervous system.

Unlike most other cells of the body, normal nerve cells in the fully developed human do not undergo division and replication. Neurons vary greatly in their size and shape from one region of the nervous system to another (Fig. 4-1).

However, they possess certain common features that are most readily demonstrated in the largest neurons, for example, the large motor neurons of the anterior horns of the spinal cord (Figs. 4-2, 4-3). In routine preparations, the cell bodies of these neurons, which may be 100 μm in diameter, are irregular in outline because of the numerous processes that extend outward from the cell body at irregular intervals. Neurons possess a large nucleus within which a conspicuous nucleolus can be found. Otherwise the nucleus appears to be relatively clear, or vesicular, because of the dispersion of the nuclear chromatin. The cytoplasm surrounding the nucleus constitutes the main cell body, or *perikaryon*, and contains the same types of organelles for metabolism as do other cells in the body, for example, mitochondria, Golgi apparatus, lysosomes, and endoplasmic reticulum. However, two types of organelles are unusually conspicuous in neurons and distinguish them from other cells in the body.

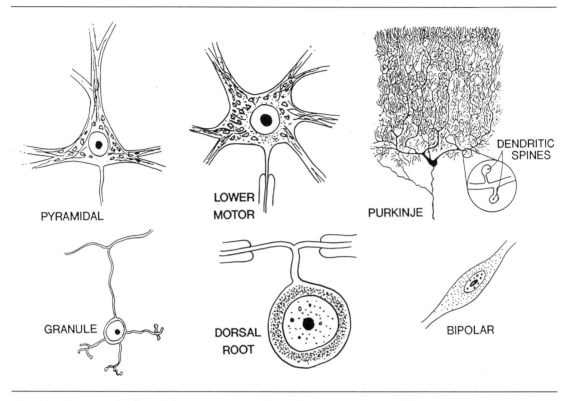

PYRAMIDAL

LOWER
MOTOR

PURKINJE

DENDRITIC
SPINES

GRANULE

DORSAL
ROOT

BIPOLAR

Fig. 4-1. Neurons of different sizes and configurations from various areas of the nervous system.

The endoplasmic reticulum is heavily laden with ribonucleoprotein granules (rough endoplasmic reticulum). Concentrations of these rough endoplasmic reticulum membranes produce the appearance, at the light microscopic level, of dense basophilic bodies (see Fig. 4-3). These structures are called *Nissl granules* (named after the German pathologist, Franz Nissl, who first described them). Various basic blue dyes, which stain Nissl granules as the most conspicuous element in brain tissue, are called Nissl stains; the Nissl granules also are well seen in routine preparations with hematoxylin and eosin.

The second type of organelle that is conspicuous in neurons is the fibrillar component of the cytoplasm. With the light microscope, neurofibrils can be demonstrated only with silver impregnation stains (Fig. 4-4). The fibrils demonstrated in this way correspond to three ultrastructural components of the cell:

1. Neurofilaments, which are 10-nm-diameter intermediate cytoskeletal filaments and are immunologically unique to nerve cells. They are distributed throughout the cell body and all the processes of the neuron.
2. Neurotubules, which are 20 to 30 nm in diameter and indistinguishable from the microtubes of other cells. They are more numerous in dendrites than axons and probably function in cytoplasmic transport mechanisms.
3. Microfilaments, which are 5 nm in diameter and identical to those found in all animal cells.

Processes of nerve cells extend outward from the cell body into the surrounding tissue. These processes are called either *dendrites* or *axons*, and the number, length, and branching of these processes vary markedly from one type of neuron to another. Neurons possess only one axon; the remaining processes are dendrites. The region of the cell body that forms the root of the axon, the *axon hillock*, does not have Nissl granules and appears to be relatively pale on Nissl and hematoxylin and

Fig. 4-2. Spinal motor neuron.

eosin staining (see Fig. 4-3). From this region, the axon extends outward for distances that vary from a few millimeters to several feet. In general, the diameter of an axon varies with its length. Functionally, the axon is the portion of the neuron that conducts electrical activity away from the cell body, toward an effector organ (muscle, glands) or toward the next neuron in a chain or circuit.

Axons are unable to synthesize proteins. Axonal survival depends on transport of substances from the cell bodies. This is called *axonal transport*. There are three types of axonal transport: (1) fast anterograde transport, which transports proteins for synaptic function; (2) slow anterograde transport, which transports proteins of the cytoskeleton; and (3) retrograde transport, which transports growth factors and other substances from the periphery to the cell body. Axonal transport

requires adenosine triphosphate (ATP) and is impaired during energy failure.

Neurons of the central nervous system have one or, usually, many dendrites. Nissl granules in at least the proximal portions of the dendrites make them visible in routine preparations. The dendrites extend a relatively short distance from the cell body and usually branch repeatedly. Dendrites are, in a sense, the antennae of the nerve cell, and they transmit incoming signals toward the cell body.

Communication between neurons is accomplished at specialized regions of these cells called *synapses* (see Fig. 4-2). Synapses are the anatomical basis for the transfer of a signal from one neuron to another. The axon of a nerve cell usually terminates on and forms a synapse with the dendrites or cell body of another. At the region of the synapse, the axon terminal may be enlarged (*terminal bouton*).

Fig. 4-3. Spinal motor neuron showing (A) nucleus, (B) nucleolus, (C) cytoplasm filled with Nissl granules, (D) axon hillock, and (E) dendrite. (Nissl stain; ×400.)

Fig. 4-4. Spinal motor neuron showing numerous fibrils streaming through cytoplasm of cell body and processes. Background contains processes of other neurons. (Bodian stain; ×400.)

At some synapses, the dendrite presents a small projection, the dendritic spine, on which the axon terminates. Synapses do not always occur at the terminal end of an axon but may form in places where an axon passes by a dendrite or cell body. These are called *en passant synapses*. Electron micrographs show that the axonal (presynaptic) and dendritic (postsynaptic) membranes are thickened. They do not actually touch but are separated by a space, the *synaptic cleft*, which is 200 to 300 Å wide. Rare synapses in the human brain have bridges across the synaptic cleft, providing the opportunity for direct electrical contact. In the axon terminal are tiny vesicles (synaptic vesicles) that contain the chemical neurotransmitters responsible for the transfer of the signal from the presynaptic to the postsynaptic cell. The dendritic tree and cell body of the neuron may be covered by hundreds of synapses from multiple sources. Its axon may branch repeatedly and form synapses on many other neurons. This is partly the basis for the complexity and the flexibility of the function of the nervous system. In the periphery, axons may terminate not only on other nerve cells but also on gland or muscle cells where synapse-like structures are also found.

Certain neurons have characteristic appearances that bear the names of the neuroanatomists who originally described them. Examples include the Betz cells of the inner pyramidal layer of the cerebral cortex and the Purkinje cells in the middle layer of the cerebellar cortex. In addition, Golgi recognized two distinct types of neurons. Axons of type I neurons project well outside the dendritic field of the cells and travel some distance away from the cell body of origin. These cells can conduct information for long distances within the central nervous system. Type II neurons have very short axons that terminate on cells near (and often within) the dendritic field of the cell body of origin. These cells are probably more involved in data processing than in data conduction.

Supporting Cells of Neuroectodermal Origin

Oligodendroglia and Schwann Cells

These two cell types are discussed together because they share a very important function: They form the insulating sheaths (called myelin) that surround the axons in the central and peripheral nervous systems (see Fig. 4-2).

Myelin formation around peripheral axons is performed by the Schwann cells. In routine histologic sections of the axons in peripheral nerves, nuclei of Schwann cells are recognized as elongated structures oriented in the direction of the axis cylinders (Fig. 4-5). In transverse sections of peripheral nerves, most of the axons are surrounded by a myelin sheath (Fig. 4-6), but the relationship among the myelin sheath, Schwann cell, and axon is not ob-

Fig. 4-5. Longitudinal section of peripheral nerve showing Schwann cell nuclei oriented in long axis of nerve fibers. (H & E; ×250.)

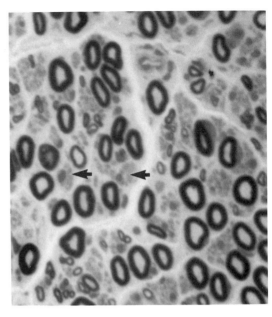

Fig. 4-6. Light micrograph of a transverse 1-μ-thick section of a normal human sensory (sural) nerve showing the spectrum of myelinated fiber diameters and less distinct profiles of Schwann cells (*arrows*) containing unmyelinated fibers. (Original magnification ×400.)

vious with the light microscope. In transverse sections of a peripheral myelinated axon viewed in the electron microscope, the relationship becomes more apparent (Fig. 4-7). The plasma membrane of the Schwann cell invests the axon and is wound around it (Fig. 4-8). The cytoplasm is squeezed out, and the internal surfaces of the membranes are fused. In each successive turn, the outer surfaces of adjacent turns also fuse. Thus, a spiral of fused-Schwann-cell cytoplasmic membrane is formed. The resulting multilayered protein-lipid substance is called *myelin.* The number of spirals that the Schwann cell process makes around the axon determines the thickness of the myelin sheath. In very small axons, the Schwann cell membrane may simply invest them once and make no turns at all. These axons are considered unmyelinated fibers. A single Schwann cell may invest a segment of several unmyelinated fibers in this way (Fig. 4-9). However, in myelinated fibers, a Schwann cell is related to a segment of only one axon. The physiologic significance of the thickness of the myelin sheath and of unmyelinated fibers is discussed in later chapters.

If myelinated axons of a peripheral nerve are "teased" apart so that a single fiber may be studied, there are numerous Schwann cells along its length, each forming the myelin sheath over a short segment of the axon (Fig. 4-10). Each segment of myelin belongs to a single Schwann cell along a given axon. There

is a minute gap between each myelin segment, where the fiber appears to be constricted. These gaps are the *nodes of Ranvier.* Therefore, the myelin segment is often referred to as an internode, and the distance between the nodes of Ranvier as the internodal length. The internodal length varies directly with the thickness of the myelin sheath along any given fiber, approaching 1 mm in length in the largest fibers.

In routine preparations of the central nervous system, oligodendroglial cells are recognized as small, round nuclei with a dense chromatin network (Fig. 4-11). With no cytoplasm being stained, the nuclei seem to be surrounded by a clear halo. Oligodendroglial cells lie in both gray and white matter. In gray matter, they lie near neurons (perineuronal satellites) and their function is unknown. In white matter, the oligodendroglia lie among the myelinated fibers, but their precise relationship to myelin is not apparent at the light microscopic level. With the electron microscope, the same relationship of oligodendroglial cell

Fig. 4-7. A. Electron micrograph (×3600) of a human sural nerve showing mixture of large myelinated (L), small myelinated (S), and unmyelinated (U) fibers. B. Higher power view of unmyelinated fibers. (×10,000.) (*ScC* = Schwann cell cytoplasm; *Ax* = axon; *ScN* = Schwann cell nucleus.)

to myelin that is present between Schwann cell and peripheral myelin can be demonstrated. The oligodendroglial cell sends out cytoplasmic extensions that wrap themselves around an axon and fuse (see Figs. 4-2, 4-8).

A major difference between the central and the peripheral nervous system is that a single oligodendroglial cell may myelinate a segment of several axons in its vicinity, whereas a Schwann cell myelinates a segment of only one axon. A second major difference is that each nerve fiber in a peripheral nerve is invested by a *basement membrane* that is continuous over each Schwann cell that contributes a myelin segment to that fiber. No basement membranes occur around oligodendroglial cells or central axons. These two differences are among the more significant factors in the different abilities of central and peripheral axons to regenerate after axonal injury.

Astrocytes

Astrocytes are easily recognized in sections of central nervous system tissue stained with hematoxylin and eosin; they have oval nuclei, slightly larger and less densely stained than oligodendroglial nuclei (see Fig. 4-11). Cytoplasm and processes of normal astrocytes are not seen with these methods. However, with metallic impregnation stains, notably the gold sublimate stains of Cajal, astrocytes show an elaborate radiating system of processes from which their name is derived (Fig. 4-12). There are minor anatomical variations by which astrocytes may be separated into different types, for example, protoplasmic astrocytes, which predominate in gray matter, and fibrous astrocytes, which predominate in white matter. These minor morphologic differences have no known functional significance.

Astrocytes traditionally have been assigned

SCHWANN CELL

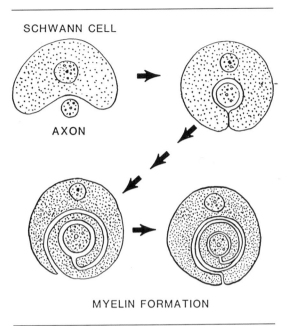

AXON

MYELIN FORMATION

Fig. 4-8. Progressive steps in myelination of axon by Schwann cell.

UNMYELINATED AXONS

Fig. 4-9. Relationship between Schwann cell and unmyelinated axons. Many unmyelinated axons may be invested by a single Schwann cell.

a largely passive function in the central nervous system because of the historical concept of glial cells as the "glue" and as cells that form the framework on which neurons and their processes are organized and held together. This function is most evident during embryogenesis, in which the migration of neurons from the ventricular layer to the outer layers of the neural tube is directed and guided by

Fig. 4-10. Schwann cell-myelin-axon relationship in longitudinal section. Portions of three myelin segments (internodes) separated by two nodes of Ranvier are represented.

Fig. 4-11. Section of brain tissue in which nuclei belonging to various types of glial cells are seen, including oligodendroglia (*o*), astrocytes (*a*), and microglia (*m*). A portion of neuron (*N*) is seen at the lower right. (H & E; ×250.)

the radiating processes of astrocytes. There is, however, substantial evidence that astrocytes have a more active role in the physiology of the central nervous system. One or more expanded processes of each astrocyte abuts on the wall of a capillary, forming part of the nearly continuous sheath of astrocytic foot processes that surround the capillary network in the brain and spinal cord (see Fig. 4-12). The remaining processes terminate in relationship to the nonsynaptic regions of neurons and of other glial cells. This arrangement suggests that astrocytes function as a conduit for the transport of ions and molecules between the extracellular environment of these cells and the capillary wall. The relationship of this

Fig. 4-12. Astrocytes as seen with a gold sublimate stain. Note many processes ending on walls of capillaries (*C*). (Cajal stain; ×400.)

Fig. 4-14. Choroid plexus. Each tuft consists of a core containing a dilated capillary surrounded by small amount of connective tissue and covered by choroidal epithelial cells. (H & E; ×100.)

Fig. 4-13. Ependyma lining the ventricle of an infant. Note continuous layer of columnar cells with cilia on their free (ventricular) border. (H & E; ×100.)

function to the phenomenon called the *blood-brain barrier* is described below. Finally, astrocytes play a critical role in almost all pathologic reactions of the nervous system, as described in the following section.

Ependymal Cells

When the epithelium of the neural tube has proliferated in the ventricular zone, and the major portion of its cells have differentiated and migrated, a single layer of ciliated columnar epithelial cells (the *ependyma*) is left lining the cavity of the neural tube (Fig. 4-13).

In the cerebrum and brain stem of the ma-ture brain, the ependyma lines the entire ventricular system. The central canal of the spinal cord is usually obliterated as an open cavity when development is complete, and the central region of the adult cord is represented by a nest of ependymal cells with a disorganized appearance. The ependymal lining of the ventricular system forms a selective barrier between the ventricular fluid and the brain substance, since tight junctions between the plasma membranes of adjacent ependymal cells serve to inhibit the passage of certain substances.

The choroid plexus is formed when the thinned roof plate, consisting of a layer of ependymal cells, invaginates the ventricular cavity ahead of a vascular-connective-tissue component derived from the pia mater. Enormous elaboration of these evaginations leads to the formation of many small tufts, each of which has essentially the same structure (Fig. 4-14). The ventricular surface of a choroidal tuft is lined by cuboidal epithelial cells, which are modified ependymal cells. The free surface of a choroidal cell displays numerous microvilli on electron microscopic examination. Beneath the surface epithelium is a core of richly vascular connective tissue.

The function of the choroid plexus is to form the cerebrospinal fluid. It does this by filtering water and selected molecules out of the blood that passes through its capillaries

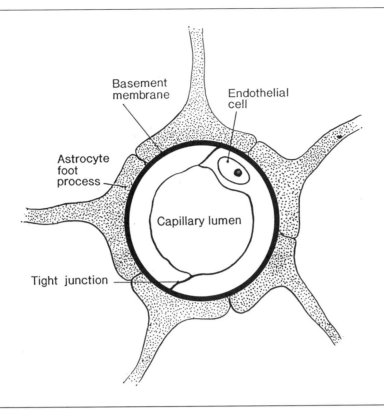

Fig. 4-15. Nonfenestrated capillary in the central nervous system. Endothelial cells are joined by tight junctions and surrounded by a basement membrane and sheath of astrocytic foot processes.

and by passing this solution through its epithelial cells into the ventricular system.

Supporting Cells of Mesodermal Origin

Capillaries and the Blood-Brain Barrier

The anatomy and physiology of the arterial supply and venous drainage of the central nervous system are described in Chapter 11 (The Vascular System). Cerebral arteries, arterioles, venules, and veins do not differ structurally from vessels of similar size and function in other organs. Capillaries of the nervous system, however, are unique in their ultrastructure and physiology. Capillaries are composed of a single layer of endothelial cells surrounded by a basement membrane. In the central nervous system, the capillaries are invested by a nearly continuous layer of *astrocytic extensions* called *foot processes* (Fig. 4-15). Only the capillary basement membrane intervenes between the plasma membrane of

the astrocyte and the endothelial cell plasma membrane. In the capillaries of all other organs, there are pores and channels between individual endothelial cells through which water and solutes can pass from the blood to the extracellular space. In most of the central nervous system, on the other hand, adjacent endothelial cells are joined by continuous tight junctions formed by the fusion of the external layers of the plasma membranes. Thus, for substances to enter the extracellular space of the brain, they must pass through rather than between endothelial cells. This is the anatomical basis of the *blood-brain barrier.*

The barrier is not absolute, and its efficiency in preventing the entry of substances into the central nervous system varies widely with different classes of molecules. Small, highly lipid-soluble molecules such as volatile anesthetics and alcohol pass through the blood-brain barrier easily because of their solubility in the lipid bilayer of the endothelial cell membrane.

Large, complex molecules, including most proteins and many drugs, are completely excluded from the brain under normal circumstances. Between the two extremes of uninhibited access and total exclusion are many other substances such as electrolytes, glucose, and amino acids that enter the brain by highly selective transport mechanisms. Specific transport proteins move these molecules across the luminal cytoplasmic membrane of the endothelial cell, through the cytoplasm, and out of the endothelial cell across the antiluminal cell membrane. The layer of astrocytic foot processes that ensheaths the capillaries of the central nervous system was once thought to contribute to blood-brain barrier function. However, it appears that it does not exclude substances from entering the extracellular space of the brain, but rather that its main function is the rapid transfer of ions such as potassium from the extracellular environment of neurons, where they might be harmful, to the region of the capillary wall where they can be transported out of the central nervous system. The barrier function is usually absent from a few small regions of the central nervous system such as the anterior third ventricle, tuber cinereum of the hypothalamus, the pineal gland, and the area postrema of the caudal fourth ventricle. Through these selected areas, the brain is able to monitor the composition of the blood, which is important for certain critical homeostatic functions.

The tight junctions that join the capillary endothelial cells in the central nervous system are quite fragile. Also, the active transport mechanisms that are critical to the function of the blood-brain barrier are highly energy-dependent and require a constant supply of ATP generated by oxidative metabolism. It is not surprising, then, that breakdown of the barrier is a common and early pathologic response to almost any form of injury to the central nervous system, including trauma, ischemia, inflammation, and pressure from mass lesions. The most conspicuous result of this breakdown is the influx of excessive water into the extracellular space of the brain, which produces cerebral edema (see Fig. 6-12).

In the later subacute and chronic stages of cerebral injury, endothelial cells participate in the reparative process by proliferation and formation of new capillaries, which again acquire the barrier mechanism. The mechanism of this process is not fully understood, but it clearly requires contact between endothelial cells and neural tissue.

The capillaries of peripheral nerves (endoneural capillaries) are also nonfenestrated and joined by tight junctions, providing the *blood-nerve barrier*, which is similar in function to the blood-brain barrier. Ganglia, on the other hand, have fenestrated capillaries, theoretically making them more susceptible to blood-borne disorders.

Microglia

These cells are not derived from the neuroepithelium; they are mesodermal cells that migrate into the central nervous system, along with blood vessels from the mesoderm that surround the neural tube. They are seen as small, elongated, darkly staining nuclei in hematoxylin and eosin-stained sections (see Fig. 4-11). Normally they are present only in small numbers and are widely scattered in the nervous system. Their major function becomes manifest only when a destructive process affects the central nervous system, at which time the cells proliferate rapidly and become scavenger cells, or macrophages, ingesting and removing damaged tissue.

Connective Tissue

The brain and spinal cord are permeated by a rich network of blood vessels, which, except at the capillary level, have a thin collagenous investment making up the adventitia. Other than the vascular structures, the parenchyma of the central nervous system is almost devoid of fibrous connective tissue elements, which accounts for its extremely soft consistency. Thus, fibroblasts rarely participate in reactive or reparative processes (scar formation) in diseases of the central nervous system.

The central nervous system is surrounded by three connective tissue membranes called *meninges*. The two inner membranes, the pia mater and arachnoid, are the *leptomeninges* and are very thin and delicate. The outer membrane, the *dura mater* or the pachymeninx, is thick and tough.

The peripheral nerves are rich in fibrous connective tissue. Each myelinated nerve fiber in a peripheral nerve is invested by a thin layer of collagen, the *endoneurium*. Groups of nerve fibers are bound together in fascicles by a *perineurium*. Finally, the fascicles that comprise a nerve trunk are surrounded by a thick sheath, the *epineurium*. The three connective tissue sheaths of a peripheral nerve are analogous to the three layers of the meninges (pia mater, arachnoid, and dura mater) and are continuous with them at the spinal nerve level.

Pathologic Reactions of the Structural Elements

Each of the cellular elements of the nervous system may undergo physical change in response to disease states. In some disorders, the pathologic alteration may be primarily functional (physiologic) — there may be little change in the physical appearance of the cell, yet the cell cannot function normally. In many diseases of the nervous system, however, the physical appearance of the cell is altered. When the nervous system is affected by disease, the cells undergo changes that reflect either the damage done to them by the pathologic process or their reaction to it. Some of these morphologic changes are "nonspecific" and may be seen in many entirely different types of diseases. Other changes may be "specific" and indicate a particular type of disease or even a specific disease entity. In this section, we review some of the more common and important pathologic changes seen in the individual cell types studied above. In most pathologic conditions, the various cell types react in concert, and the pathologic diagnosis is derived from analysis of the total tissue reaction.

The pathologic appearance of cells revealed under the light microscope or electron microscope, as described in the following paragraphs, ultimately reflects changes in the structure and arrangement of molecules in the cell. The molecular species that are most affected and the manner in which they are affected depend on the mechanism of the injury. In some diseases, the mechanism of cell injury or death is programmed into the genetic material of the cell. The defective DNA template results in faulty structure and function of the gene product, often an enzyme or an important structural protein. Defects of this type may be compatible with normal cell function for long periods of time, but ultimately they cause damage to the metabolic machinery or structural integrity of the cell, with eventual loss of function. In most disease processes, damage to cells results from extrinsic factors, such as loss of availability of essential nutrients, entry of toxic substances into the cell, or attachment of antibodies to the cell membrane. Any of these mechanisms can initiate a cascade of events that finally produces cell damage and death. Some of these mechanisms are discussed in more detail in the following paragraphs dealing with specific pathologic changes.

Pathologic Reactions of Neurons

Nonspecific Reactions
Almost any disease leading to the death of a patient is associated with changes in body chemistry and physiology that may affect the appearance of neurons. In addition, catabolic processes that proceed after death (autolysis) and the mechanical procedures involved in obtaining and processing tissue can distort the appearance of neurons. It is not surprising, then, that almost any histologic section of brain tissue contains some neurons that deviate from "normal" in size, shape, and affinity for stains. Shrunken, dark-staining neurons, as well as swollen, pale-staining cells, are often encountered. Although these neurons are not normal in the strict sense, the factors responsible for their nonspecific change are usually not identifiable. Neuronal loss is another nonspecific change that may result from any form of severe damage to a neuron. Under pathologic circumstances, neuronal loss is usually accompanied by a reaction of other tissue elements (astrocytes, microglia), which marks the site of damage. Neuronal changes of a more specific type can accompany certain pathologic processes and, when present, can help to define the pathophysiologic basis for those disorders.

Specific Pathologic Reactions
Ischemic cell change (Fig. 4-16) takes place in response to deprivation of oxygen and cessation of oxidative metabolism; the neurons undergo a readily recognized morphologic

Fig. 4-16. Ischemic cell change. Neuron is shrunken, nucleus is pyknotic, and cytoplasm is diffusely eosinophilic. (H & E; ×400.)

change. Eight to twelve hours after the insult, the neuron becomes smaller and its outline becomes more sharply angular. The cytoplasm becomes distinctly eosinophilic. The nucleus shrinks and becomes homogeneously darkly stained. This is an irreversible change, and the end result is complete dissolution of the cell. Ischemic cell change may be brought about by any condition that deprives the neuron of oxygen, including loss of blood flow, lack of oxygen in the blood, lack of substrates necessary for oxidative metabolism, or the presence of a poison such as cyanide, which blocks oxidative metabolism. The typical morphologic change of ischemic damage may be preceded briefly by certain nonspecific changes, such as acute swelling of the neuron.

The biochemical and molecular events that result in ischemic damage to neurons are complex. The exact point at which they become irreversible and produce necrosis is uncertain. It is generally accepted that several (2–5) minutes of complete oxygen deprivation results in irreversible neuronal damage, although under certain circumstances such as extreme hypothermia, this period of time may be significantly increased. Without oxygen, the respiratory chain process on the inner mitochondrial membrane—the most important source of ATP for energy-dependent cell functions—comes to a rapid halt. ATP stores are quickly depleted, and these functions, including maintenance of transmembrane ion channels, be-

come impaired. With the mitochondrial respiratory chain impaired, glycolysis of the remaining stores of glucose is anaerobic and proceeds only to pyruvate, which is then reduced to lactate. The accumulation of lactic acid and free fatty acids (resulting from impaired ATP-dependent lipid metabolism) produces *intracellular acidosis*, which further inhibits mitochondrial function.

There are at least three other processes that occur more or less in concert and ultimately lead to cell death and destruction. These are excitotoxicity, accumulation of intracellular calcium, and generation of free radicals.

A great deal of attention has been focused in recent years on the role of *excitatory neurotransmitters*, especially glutamate, in both acute and chronic nerve cell damage. Hypoxia affects the presynaptic membranes at excitatory synapses in a manner that impairs reuptake of glutamate and perhaps enhances its release. The excess extracellular glutamate has several damaging effects due to the opening of ion channels associated with glutamate receptors ("excitotoxicity"). The opening of sodium and chloride channels leads to the influx of these ions along with water. In extreme situations, this can lead to acute swelling and lysis of the cell. The opening of voltage-dependent calcium channels, allowing influx of calcium into the cytosol, as discussed below, is an additional harmful effect of excitotoxicity.

Intracellular calcium ion concentration is normally maintained at a low level by its relative impermeability at resting membrane potential as well as by active transport mechanisms that favor the extrusion of calcium from the cell. In addition, calcium concentration in the cytosol is particularly low, because normally it is sequestered by active transport mechanisms in the endoplasmic reticulum and mitochondria. In hypoxic conditions, all the processes cited above (loss of energy-dependent transport mechanisms, excitotoxic membrane depolarization) and other processes combine to increase cytosolic calcium concentration, producing several adverse effects on the cell. The most important is the activation of calcium-dependent degradative enzymes (proteases, phospholipases, and endonucleases) that attack the cytoskeleton, cell membranes, and nuclear DNA. Also, high calcium concentration further inhibits mitochondrial function.

The generation of free radicals, especially oxygen free radicals such as superoxide and hydroxyl ions, is another mechanism of hypoxic cell injury that has been extensively investigated in recent years. Like excitatory transmitter release and intracellular calcium accumulation, it can be the result of tissue hypoxia as well as the mediator of further tissue damage. Free radical generation seems to occur primarily during reperfusion after a period of ischemia. Among the direct effects of free radicals are the peroxidation of fatty acids, which leads to the ultimate destruction of lipid molecules, and further disruption of calcium homeostasis, which leads to aggravation of the sequence of events described above.

Although the above mechanisms of cell injury and death have been described in the context of acute hypoxic injury, it should be emphasized that one or several of them, evolving much more slowly, may be the ultimate mechanism of cell death in chronic neurologic diseases. As examples, one could cite the proposed excitotoxic damage to motor neurons in amyotrophic lateral sclerosis and the oxygen free-radical-mediated damage to the substantia nigra in Parkinson's disease.

Central chromatolysis (Fig. 4-17) is a change in neuron cell bodies after severe injury to their axons. Thus, it is sometimes called the *axonal reaction*. In human pathology, this change is usually recognized only in large motor cells, such as the spinal ventral horn cells and motor nuclei of cranial nerves when their axons are injured close to the central nervous system. The reaction consists of swelling of the cell body and dissolution of the Nissl granules, beginning close to the nucleus and spreading to the periphery of the cell, where a rim of Nissl granules may be found intact. The nucleus migrates to the periphery of the cell body. These changes usually begin 2 to 3 days after injury and reach a maximum in 2 to 3 weeks. Unlike ischemic cell change, central chromatolysis is reversible, and the neuron may revert to a normal appearance in a few months.

Wallerian degeneration occurs in the distal part of an axon, when its parent cell body is destroyed or separated from the axon by disease or injury along its course. In both the

Fig. 4-17. Central chromatolysis. Cell is swollen, nucleus (*N*) is eccentric, and Nissl granules have disappeared except at periphery. (H & E; ×400.)

central and peripheral nervous systems, an axon cannot survive when it is separated from its cell body. The process of degeneration of the axon and its myelin sheath is called *wallerian degeneration* (after Waller, who in 1850 first described it in peripheral nerves).

The changes seen in the degenerating axon are impairment of axonal transport and the rapid disappearance of the neurofibrils, followed by the breaking up of the axon into short fragments that eventually disappear completely (Fig. 4-18). As axonal fragmentation proceeds, the myelin sheath begins to fragment in a similar manner into oval segments (ovoids). Each oval segment of myelin, containing a fragment of axon, is called a *digestive chamber* because the axon seems to be digested within it. At the same time, the myelin fragment is undergoing biochemical changes including breakdown into its component lipids. These lipids are eventually removed by phagocytosis.

Some notable differences exist between this process in the central and peripheral nervous systems. Wallerian degeneration proceeds more rapidly in peripheral nerves, where degenerative changes are completed in a few weeks, whereas in the central nervous system the degeneration proceeds over several months. More importantly, in the peripheral nervous system, regeneration of the nerve is possible if the parent cell body survives; this regeneration does not occur in the central ner-

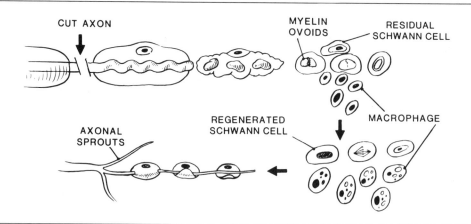

Fig. 4-18. Sequence of events in wallerian degeneration and early peripheral nerve regeneration. After degeneration and removal of myelin and axonal debris, sprouts from severed end of axon may find their way into tube of regenerated Schwann cell.

vous system. Each axon and myelin sheath in a peripheral nerve is surrounded by a basement membrane, which belongs to the Schwann cell, and by a delicate connective tissue sheath, the *endoneurium*. These structures maintain their integrity even as the axon and myelin degenerate. In addition, the Schwann cells, with the potential of forming new myelin, proliferate along the length of the degenerating fiber. Thus, the distal portion of a damaged nerve provides a superstructure that is ready to receive and myelinate new axonal sprouts growing from the proximal portion. If these axonal sprouts can find their way into one of these "tubes," they will continue to grow at a rate of about 3 mm per day, and function may be restored eventually. In the central nervous system, there are no basement membranes or collagen sheaths surrounding nerve fibers, and oligodendroglia are incapable of proliferation. Thus, new axonal growth, even if it should begin, has no path to follow, and functionally significant regeneration of tracts does not occur after damage to the central nervous system.

Injury of an axon generally results in no change in the postsynaptic cell. There are exceptions: for example, when the motor innervation of a muscle is destroyed, the muscle becomes atrophic. A similar phenomenon, *transneuronal degeneration*, has been observed in certain pathways in the central ner-

vous system. The process apparently depends on the removal of some "trophic" influence by which the axon maintains the condition of the postsynaptic element. The nature of such trophic influences is unknown.

The processes of chromatolysis and wallerian degeneration were used in the past to trace neuroanatomical pathways. When the axons of a functional group of neurons are sectioned or otherwise damaged, the cell bodies of the neurons from which the axons originate can be located by finding which neurons undergo chromatolysis. Conversely, the neuroanatomist may destroy a group of neuronal cell bodies within a particular nucleus of the central nervous system and may then trace the route taken by the axons by staining the degenerating fibers with techniques designed to demonstrate either degenerating myelin or degenerating axons.

Neurofibrillary degeneration is the formation of clumped masses of neurofibrils within the cytoplasm (Fig. 4-19) and is a common, readily recognized change in neurons of the central nervous system. This change, *Alzheimer's neurofibrillary degeneration*, is best seen with silver-impregnation stains. It is a neuronal degeneration that is most closely associated with clinical dementia. The change is seen to some extent in hippocampal neurons of many "normal" aged people and is found throughout the cerebral cortex and in other parts of the brain in a severe dementing process known as Alzheimer's dis-

Fig. 4-19. Neuron showing neurofibrillary degeneration (*NF*). Note tangle of thickened neurofibrils in cell body and axon. Senile plaque (*SP*) is seen on right. (Bodian stain; ×400.)

Fig. 4-21. Neuron in Tay-Sachs disease (lipid-storage disease). Note ballooning of cytoplasm with stored material, forcing nucleus and Nissl granules to one corner of cell. (H & E; ×400.)

Fig. 4-20. A. Lewy body (*arrow*) in cytoplasm of pigmented neuron in Parkinson's disease. B. Cowdry type A intranuclear inclusion (*arrow*) in subacute sclerosing panencephalitis. (H & E; ×400.)

ease. Alzheimer's degeneration is also a prominent change found in a few other conditions classed as "degenerative" diseases. The senile plaque is a closely associated pathologic change noted primarily in senile dementia and Alzheimer's disease. Typical senile plaques consist of a central deposit of amyloid (the core) surrounded by a halo of degenerated nerve processes and reactive elements, such as astrocytic fibers and microglia.

Inclusion body formation refers to abnormal, discrete deposits in nerve cells (Fig. 4-20) and, when present, often identifies the type of disease and sometimes the specific disease. Inclusion bodies can be divided into intranuclear and intracytoplasmic types. The appearance and significance of the most important types of neuronal inclusions are outlined in Table 4-2.

Storage cells refer to the accumulation of metabolic products within nerve cells. A number of metabolic diseases of the nervous system are associated with this accumulation. Most of these disorders involve the storage of lipids. As these lipid products accumulate, the cell body swells so much that it is referred to as a "balloon" cell (Fig. 4-21). Identification of the specific disease requires biochemical identification of the stored material.

Pathologic Reactions of Oligodendroglia

The oligodendroglial cells, as identified in routine preparations, undergo few reactions of

Table 4-2. Inclusion Bodies

Location	Name	Staining characteristics	Disease association
Cytoplasm	Lewy body	Eosinophilic with concentric lamination	Parkinson's disease
Cytoplasm	Pick body	Metallophilic (silver, gold)	Pick's disease
Cytoplasm	Lafora body	Basophilic	Myoclonus epilepsy
Cytoplasm	Negri body	Eosinophilic	Rabies
Nucleus	Cowdry type A inclusion	Eosinophilic	Viral infections: herpes simplex, subacute sclerosing panencephalitis, cytomegalic inclusion disease

Fig. 4-22. Transverse section of pons of patient with multiple sclerosis. A. Myelin stain showing plaques of demyelination (*light areas*). (Luxol-fast blue; ×4.) B. Glial fiber stain showing gliosis of demyelinated areas (*dark areas*). (Holzer stain; ×4.)

pathognomonic importance. They seem to be extremely sensitive to injury and, when affected by a pathologic process, oligodendroglial nuclei simply shrink or break up and vanish. The myelin that they form, however, is an extremely important indicator of disease of the central nervous system. Just as the oligodendroglial cell is readily damaged by most pathologic processes, the myelin sheaths are also extremely sensitive to injury. Partial or complete loss of myelin in an area of injury is easily seen in myelin stains such as the Luxol-fast blue stain (see Fig. 4-22A). Sections stained in this way provide the most reliable method of studying the topography of most disease processes.

In addition to the nonspecific injury to myelin associated with most kinds of disease, there are two groups of diseases that specific-

ally affect myelin sheaths. The first group is called the *demyelinating* or *myelinoclastic* diseases. In these disorders, normal myelin is attacked by some exogenous agent, usually unknown, and broken down into its component lipids (as in wallerian degeneration) and absorbed. The axons that the myelin surrounds are left relatively intact. The most common and important disease in this group is multiple sclerosis.

The process of demyelination in multiple sclerosis and some other diseases of the central and peripheral nervous system, such as postvaccinal encephalomyelitis and the Guillain-Barré syndrome, involves immunologic mechanisms. While details of the pathogenesis of these disorders remain to be clarified, humoral- and cell-mediated immunologic reactions involving myelin components set in motion the cytotoxic and inflammatory processes that lead to demyelination.

The second group of diseases are the *leukodystrophies* or *dysmyelinating* diseases. In these disorders, myelin is abnormally formed owing to a genetically determined error in metabolism. Because the myelin is abnormally constituted, it is unstable and breaks down. The type of metabolic defect often can be determined by histochemical staining reactions and biochemical analysis of the tissue.

Pathologic Reactions of Schwann Cells

Disease processes affecting the Schwann cells that surround peripheral axons produce segmental loss of myelin (segmental demyelination). If the disease is severe, there also may be associated secondary axonal destruction and wallerian degeneration. In certain genetic disorders affecting peripheral nerve (hypertrophic neuropathies), there is repeated demyelination and remyelination of nerve fibers. Each episode leaves a layer of Schwann cells and collagen, forming concentric layers around the axon. Such nerves become large and firm; the axons may finally be lost, leaving only the stroma of the connective tissue.

Pathologic Reactions of Astrocytes

Almost any injury to central nervous system tissue can produce a reaction of astrocytes. The terms *astrocytosis, astrogliosis,* and *gliosis* refer to this nonspecific response whereby astrocytes form "scars" in injured neural tissue. Strictly speaking, astrocytosis refers to the early stages of the reaction in which astrocytes proliferate and increase greatly in number. As this occurs, their cytoplasm becomes visible with hematoxylin and eosin stains as an eosinophilic apron of cytoplasm with somewhat irregular margins. At this stage, they are known as "plump" or *gemistocytic* (from the German *gemaste* = stuffed) astrocytes (Fig. 4-23). These plump astrocytes then form progressively longer and thicker processes, which form a dense network in the damaged tissue. This network of tissue is the equivalent of a scar formed by fibroblasts in other body tissues. The fibers of reactive astrocytes, while readily visible in hematoxylin and eosin stains, are seen even more clearly with special

Fig. 4-23. Reactive astrocytes at border of infarct. Note expansion of cytoplasm, producing plump appearance and dense tangle of fibers in background. (H & E; ×250.)

stains like Mallory's phosphotungstic acid-hematoxylin or Holzer stain. With the latter techniques, an area of gliosis can be seen in a section even without the aid of a microscope, which is of advantage in mapping the topography of a large lesion (see Fig. 4-22B).

Astrocytes also may react in more specific ways to certain injuries, especially metabolic disturbances. The most notable example is the presence of acutely swollen astrocytic nuclei, called Alzheimer's type 2 astrocytes, in hepatic failure. Astrocytes may also form intranuclear inclusion bodies in certain viral infections.

Pathologic Reactions of Microglia

Microglial cells react in a stereotyped way to most diseases that affect the central nervous system. Injury to other cellular constituents of the central nervous system usually leads to multiplication of nearby microglial cells (Fig. 4-24). The nuclei of these microglial cells become elongated and form *rod* cells. If actual tissue necrosis does not occur, the reaction may progress no further. The presence of many rod cells then usually indicates the presence of low-grade chronic irritation of the tissue. An example of such a condition is the chronic encephalitis associated with syphilis (general paresis).

If tissue necrosis occurs, the microglial cells continue to proliferate and their nuclei be-

Fig. 4-24. Margin of recent infarct showing proliferating microglial cells. (H & E; ×100.)

Fig. 4-26. Damaged neuron undergoing neuronophagia by cluster of microglial cells. (H & E; ×250.)

Fig. 4-25. Lipid-laden macrophages (gitter cells) in area of necrosis. Note small eccentric nuclei and foamy cytoplasm. (H & E; ×250.)

come rounded. Their cytoplasm becomes evident as it begins to engulf the debris of the necrotic tissue. Because of the high fat content of central nervous system tissue, most of the engulfed material is lipid, and the cytoplasm assumes a foamy appearance. At this stage, the cells are referred to as *lipid-laden macrophages* or gitter cells (Fig. 4-25). In large lesions, many, perhaps even most, of the gitter cells probably were not microglial cells originally but rather were blood-borne macrophages that migrated into the lesion. Eventually, most of the macrophages in a destructive lesion of the central nervous system are reabsorbed back into the bloodstream. At times,

microglia attack isolated, damaged neurons. This process is called *neuronophagia* (Fig. 4-26). When the neuron has been engulfed, the cluster of microglia remaining in its place is a *microglial nodule*.

Cerebral Edema

In the discussion of the blood-brain barrier, it was noted that almost any pathologic process that affects the brain can result in cerebral edema by virtue of its effect on cerebral capillaries. The loss of integrity of the blood-brain barrier allows excessive water accompanied by solutes (such as serum proteins) that are normally excluded from the extracellular space of the brain to enter this compartment. This is the most common variety of cerebral edema, called *vasogenic edema*. The fluid collects in the extracellular space, predominantly in the white matter. The resulting mass effect can produce a clinically significant increase in intracranial pressure as described in Chapter 6 (The Cerebrospinal Fluid System; see Fig. 6-12).

Another commonly recognized form of cerebral edema is referred to as *cytotoxic edema*. It results from pathologic processes, usually toxic or metabolic, that affect the cell membranes of neurons and glial cells so they are unable to maintain normal pump mechanisms. The loss of membrane integrity results in the intracellular accumulation of water. This type of edema is more likely to affect gray matter. Although it may cause severe functional abnormalities, it is rarely sufficient to produce a clinically significant mass effect. The two types of cerebral edema are not mutually exclusive and often occur together in pathologic processes such as infarction, which affects both the blood-brain barrier and neuronal and glial cell membranes.

Other Pathologic Reactions

Ependymal cells react in a very limited way to noxious stimuli (which most often are infectious). There is often loss of ependymal cells; however, the proliferation of subependymal astrocytes that is frequently associated with this loss forms *ependymal granulations* that may be seen along certain areas of the ventricular system.

In response to injury, blood vessels may respond by capillary proliferation, and when inflammation is present, infiltration of leukocytes occurs, as it does in other tissues.

Uncontrolled cellular proliferation of any of the cellular elements results in a *neoplasm* (a localized accumulation of abnormal tissue, a mass lesion). The type of neoplasm is named after the predominant cell type (such as astrocytoma, oligodendroglioma, or schwannoma).

Clinicopathologic Correlations

Clinical diagnosis in neurology requires the analysis of two types of data. The first type is obtained from both the history and the neurologic examination and enables localization of the disease process within the nervous system. On this basis, neurologic disease may be classified as *focal*, involving a single circumscribed area or group of contiguous structures in the nervous system; *multifocal*, involving more than one circumscribed area or several noncontiguous structures; and *diffuse*, involving portions of the nervous system in a bilateral, symmetrical fashion.

The localization of the pathologic process depends partly on a knowledge of the functional anatomy of the nervous system, outlined in Chapter 3 (Diagnosis of Neurologic Disorders: Anatomical Localization). Vastly different types of pathologic processes located in the same anatomic structure may produce similar symptoms and signs. Since the mani-

festations of disease are dependent on where a lesion is located and not on its pathologic nature, the pathologic diagnosis must utilize a second type of data — information obtained from the patient's history that relates to the onset and evolution (temporal profile) of the disease. The development of symptoms can be classified in the following terms: *acute*, within minutes; *subacute*, within days; and *chronic*, within weeks or months. The evolution (course of symptoms after the onset) may be categorized as *transient*, when symptoms have resolved completely after onset; *improving*, when symptoms have decreased from their maximum but have not completely resolved; *progressive*, when symptoms continue to increase in severity or when new symptoms make their appearance; and *stationary*, when symptoms remain unchanged after reaching maximum severity and show no significant change during a period of observation.

Combining the above terms allows clinical differentiation between mass and nonmass lesions. Although other clues for differentiation are discussed in later chapters, the presence of a *mass lesion* should be considered when the signs and symptoms, whether acute, subacute, or chronic in onset, suggest progression of a focal lesion. A *nonmass* lesion should be considered when the lesion is diffuse in location or when the symptoms and signs suggest a nonprogressive focal abnormality.

As the text proceeds, qualification of these definitions will be required; an attempt to explain exceptions to these general statements will be made at appropriate times.

Interpretation of the temporal profile of disease depends on an understanding of the way in which pathologic processes affect nerve tissue and the rates at which various destructive and reparative processes proceed. Knowledge of the basic types of cellular and tissue reactions is a prerequisite to making this type of analysis. For the purposes of recognizing and understanding clinical neurologic disease, it is sufficient to become familiar with six types of pathologic changes that occur within the nervous system: (1) degenerative disease, (2) neoplastic disease, (3) vascular disease, (4) inflammatory disease, (5) toxic-metabolic disease, and (6) traumatic disease. In the following paragraphs, the temporal and spatial characteristics of these major disease categories are outlined.

Degenerative Disease

The term *degenerative* is applied to a large group of neurologic diseases for which no cause is apparent. As causes of these diseases are found (viral infection, metabolic error), they will be moved to the appropriate disease category; many conditions in this group are familial biochemical disorders. These disorders are characterized by a gradual decrease in neuronal function. Sometimes the pathologically altered neurons show specific changes, such as neurofibrillary tangles or inclusion body formations; more often, the neurons simply atrophy and disappear. The neuronal degeneration is accompanied by astrocytic proliferation in the central nervous system. Topographically, degenerative diseases affect the nervous system in a diffuse manner in that they are usually bilateral and symmetric and may affect multiple levels of the nervous system. The clinical correlation of degenerative diseases, therefore, can be summarized by the terms *chronic, progressive*, and *diffuse*.

Neoplastic Disease

Any cell type in the nervous system can undergo neoplastic change and proliferate in an unrestrained manner. Generally, the causes of neoplasia are obscure although certain genetic, infectious, and chemical factors have been implicated in some neoplasms. Tumors are named by adding the suffix *-oma* to the name of the constituent cell type. Cells of the nervous system vary greatly in their apparent potential to undergo neoplasia.

There is a general correlation between the normal capacity of a cell to undergo cell division and its tendency to undergo neoplasia. Nerve cells are normally incapable of cell division after differentiation is complete, and neoplasms of nerve cells (neurocytomas) are extremely rare. Astrocytes are the most reactive cells of the central nervous system, and the astrocytomas are the most common primary tumors of the central nervous system. Oligodendrogliomas, ependymomas, and microgliomas occur less frequently. The cells of the leptomeninges and the Schwann cells of nerve roots and peripheral nerves give rise to meningiomas and schwannomas, respectively.

All these tumor types are believed to arise from relatively mature cell types that are normally present in the nervous system. In each cell type, however, tumors vary in the rapidity of growth, the likelihood of recurrence after surgery, and the length of patient survival. These factors correspond fairly well to the histologic malignancy of the tumor. Tumors of the central nervous system, except in extremely rare instances, do not metastasize outside the central nervous system; thus, one of the major criteria of malignancy in other forms of neoplasia does not apply to tumors of the central nervous system. The degree of malignancy of these tumors may be graded by considering the degree of pleomorphism (lack of uniformity of appearance and nuclear-cytoplasmic ratio) of tumor cells, frequency of mitotic figures, proliferation of tumor vessels, and necrosis of tumor tissue. Especially in infants and children, tumors of immature cellular elements or tumors of cells not normally present in the nervous system (teratomas) are often seen. In children, the medulloblastoma of the cerebellum is especially common and is probably derived from immature cerebellar stem cells, with both neuroblastic and spongioblastic potential. In addition, systemic cancer can spread as secondary growth (metastasize) to the central nervous system.

A neoplastic mass progressively increases in size and alters the function of the region in which it lies. It may also alter the function of adjacent structures by compression or by the formation of edema around the primary mass. The cardinal topographic feature of a neoplasm, therefore, is its *focal* character. The clinical correlate of neoplastic disease may be summarized by the terms *chronic, progressive*, and *focal*. It must be mentioned at this point that not all progressively expanding (mass) lesions in the nervous system are composed of neoplastic cells. Blood clots (hematomas) and edema may be produced by different basic disease processes, and they represent common examples of nonneoplastic mass lesions.

Vascular Disease

Neurons deprived of metabolic support from the blood in the form of oxygen and glucose cease functioning in seconds and undergo pathologic change in minutes. Therefore the hallmark of a vascular disease process is its *sudden onset*. Neurologic function is altered abruptly and usually maximally at the time of the initial insult. Vascular disease, however, is of several types, and although this is dealt with more fully in the section on the vascular system, certain general distinctions must be drawn here. The most common type of vascular disease is the *infarct*. The chronologic, microscopic events that occur in a region of an infarct may be listed as follows:

6 to 12 hours	Nerve cells may show acute swelling with staining pallor; as the process progresses, the neurons show the typical ischemic change described earlier in this chapter.
24 to 48 hours	Leukocytes appear from the blood vessels and begin migrating into the brain substance.
48 to 72 hours	Microglia proliferate and macrophages begin to appear and steadily increase in number up to the third week, after which they gradually diminish in number; the early stage corresponds only to the gross softening of the lesion (encephalomalacia) and then later to cyst formation.
4 to 5 days	In the region of astrocyte survival, the astrocytes begin to proliferate and show the changes described on page 67; this process goes on, reaching a peak at about 6 weeks, and a glial scar is formed.
2 weeks	During the second week, surviving capillaries also proliferate and take part in the attempted repair process.

The characteristic ischemic cell change is the hallmark of infarction. Although diffuse anoxic insults may occur, infarcts usually result from the cessation of the blood supply to a specific area of the nervous system and are generally *well localized*. The histologic events are primarily attempts at repair and, therefore, the course of a patient's symptoms is generally one of stabilization or improvement. Clinical progression of symptoms, when it occurs, usually indicates cerebral edema or, more rarely, continuing infarction of adjacent tissue after the initial event (progressing stroke).

The second type of vascular disorder is the *cerebral hemorrhage*. Instead of an interruption of vascular supply to an area, a blood vessel may rupture within the brain tissue, with localized accumulation of a blood clot within the neural tissues (an intraparenchymal hemorrhage). In this situation, both the symptoms and pathologic changes would be expected to appear abruptly and be focal, but because of the continuing pathologic changes that occur in response to a localized hemorrhage compressing neighboring tissue, progression might be seen.

A third type of vascular change occurs when a blood vessel, usually on the surface of the brain, suddenly ruptures and blood is spread over the surface of the brain and throughout the subarachnoid space (a subarachnoid hemorrhage). In this situation, the symptoms and pathologic changes are of abrupt onset but are diffusely distributed in the nervous system.

Although seemingly complex, the clinical correlates of vascular disease can be summarized as follows: (1) vascular disease is always acute in onset; (2) vascular disease may be focal or diffuse in distribution; (3) if diffuse in distribution, a condition like a subarachnoid hemorrhage or a diffuse anoxic process is considered; and (4) if distribution is focal, the lesion is likely to be an infarct or a hemorrhage, and if it shows features of progression, it is likely to be a hemorrhage.

Inflammatory Disease

In response to microorganisms, immunologic reactions, and toxic chemicals, a complex series of events called the *inflammatory re-*

sponse occurs in any system or organ of the body, including the nervous system. This response usually occurs rapidly but not suddenly and may therefore be termed *subacute* in its temporal profile. The pathologic hallmark of the inflammatory response is the outpouring of white blood cells. In certain types of infections, especially bacterial, the major component of the exudate is polymorphonuclear leukocytes. In immunologic reactions and indolent infections, the predominant cells are mononuclear cells, especially lymphocytes.

Most inflammatory diseases of the central nervous system, particularly infections, are diffusely distributed either in the leptomeninges and cerebrospinal fluid (meningitis) or in the parenchyma of the brain (encephalitis). Other inflammatory diseases in the central nervous system are more likely to be focal, such as inflammation in the spinal cord, which occurs in multiple sclerosis. Inflammation also may occur in the peripheral nervous system, either in single nerves (mononeuritis) or in multiple nerves (polyneuritis). Infections sometimes localize in a specific area of the brain. In response to this localized area of inflammation, astrocytes proliferate in the surrounding tissue, and a wall of glial fibers is formed that limits the spread of the infection. The inflamed brain becomes softened and liquefied, and eventually there may be a cavity. This process is called *abscess formation*. A brain abscess can exert a mass effect and progressively expand and compress neighboring structures.

The clinical correlates of inflammatory disease may be summarized as follows: (1) the course is usually subacute and progressive and (2) it may be diffuse in distribution, as in meningitis or encephalitis, or focal, as in an abscess, myelitis, or mononeuritis.

Immunologic Disease

The body may defend itself against various pathogens by developing an immunologic response to targeted proteins. These are usually agents foreign to the body, such as microorganisms; however, because of faulty recognition mechanisms, they may be a normal constituent of the body. The response may be mediated by humoral or cellular mechanisms or by both. The humoral mechanism involves the activation of B lymphocytes and the production of antibodies. Antibodies may affect neuronal function by binding to neurotransmitter receptor sites or to ion channels in the cell membrane of neurons. Cellular mechanisms involve the activation of T lymphocytes, which feature a variety of the functional classes including cytotoxic T cells that may bind to the antigen-presenting target cell and destroy it. T lymphocytes also produce a group of soluble substances called *cytokines*, which include interleukins, interferons, and tumor necrosis factors. Cytokines may have a direct toxic effect on neurons, oligodendroglial cells, and astrocytes and cause altered function in the nervous system.

The demyelination that occurs in multiple sclerosis and the failure of neuromuscular transmission that occurs in myasthenia gravis are examples of immunologic processes that result in neurologic disease. In acquired immunodeficiency syndrome (AIDS), nervous system macrophages are infected with the human immunodeficiency virus. These cells respond by releasing cytokines that indirectly attack neurons, producing some of the neurologic symptoms observed in patients with AIDS.

The scope of immunologic disease is undefined, but it is quite broad. Therefore, the clinical correlates of immunologic disease are variable. The symptoms produced are usually diffuse, but their pathophysiology may involve only selected cells or portions of cells in the nervous system or elsewhere in the body. Suppression or failure of normal immunologic mechanisms also predisposes the body to clinical infection by organisms ordinarily not pathogenic under conditions in which there is an intact immunologic system. The course of immunologic disease is usually one of subacute or chronic progression.

Toxic-Metabolic Disease

Various chemical agents, both endogenous and exogenous, may alter neuronal function. Vitamin deficiencies, genetic biochemical disorders, and the encephalopathies of kidney and liver disease are examples. When function

Table 4-3. Summary of the Most Important Temporal and Spatial Features
of the Major Disease Categories[a,b,c,d]

	Acute	Subacute	Chronic
Focal	Vascular (infarct or intraparenchymal hemorrhage)	Inflammatory (abscess, myelitis)	Neoplasm
Diffuse	Vascular (subarachnoid hemorrhage, anoxia)	Inflammatory (meningitis, encephalitis)	Degenerative

[a]Metabolic and toxic disorders are usually diffuse and may follow any temporal profile, depending on the toxin or metabolite involved.
[b]Traumatic disorders are usually acute in onset, but their localization and course depend on the site of trauma, severity of trauma, and delayed complications.
[c]Immunologic disorders are usually diffuse but may involve selected cells or portions of cells. They are usually subacute or chronic and progressive.
[d]Almost all focal, progressive disorders are *mass lesions*; in general, the type of mass determines the course. For example, hemorrhages are acute, abscesses subacute, and neoplasms chronic. The basic distinction between *mass* and *nonmass* lesions carries extremely important therapeutic as well as diagnostic implications.

is altered, the manifestations are almost always diffusely distributed throughout the nervous system. Depending on the nature of the specific toxin or metabolic abnormality, the effect may be exerted on the nervous system *acutely*, *subacutely*, or *chronically*. Pathologic changes vary with the noxious agent but may include such reactions as ischemia, edema, demyelination, and cell death.

Traumatic Disease

Trauma to the nervous system is almost always acute in onset, with a clearly identifiable precipitating event (automobile accident, fall, missile wound). Injuries to the peripheral nervous system are focal. Injuries to the central nervous system are frequently diffuse in their initial manifestations, presenting as the syndrome of concussion, which reflects widespread physiologic damage to the central nervous system. Traumatic damage is usually maximum at onset, and the natural course is one of resolution or improvement. This type of disturbance usually improves, until only the areas of severe anatomical damage (contusions, lacerations, hematomas) become clinically manifest, and the symptoms therefore become focal.

An important exception to the rule of trauma being maximal at onset and improving thereafter is that of delayed intracranial hemorrhage. The two most common forms are the epidural and the subdural hemorrhage. The epidural hematoma usually results from fracture of the temporal bone and a tear in the middle meningeal artery, which runs in a groove in the inner

table of the skull. Bleeding then occurs between the temporal bone and the dura mater. The bleeding is arterial and therefore brisk, and a significant hematoma accumulates within minutes to hours after the injury. Symptoms progress rapidly. Subdural hematomas result from tears in the veins that cross the subdural space in passing from the brain surface to the dural sinuses. The bleeding is venous and therefore under low pressure. The slow accumulation of blood with progression of symptoms may not manifest itself for days, weeks, or even months after the trauma.

The clinical correlates of traumatic disease may be summarized as follows: (1) in the peripheral nervous system, the symptoms are focal; in the central nervous system, they may be focal, but are often diffuse at onset and later become focal; (2) the onset is usually acute; and (3) the usual course is one of improvement or stabilization, but the symptoms may be subacutely or chronically progressive.

The most important temporal and spatial features of the major disease categories are summarized in Table 4-3.

Objectives

1. Define the general functional role and embryonic origin of neuron, astrocyte, oligodendroglia, microglial cell, ependymal cell, and Schwann cell.
2. Describe ischemic cell change, neurofibrillary degeneration, inclusion body formation, central chromatolysis, wallerian de-

generation, astrocytosis, demyelination, and cerebral edema.

3. Describe the clinical and pathologic features of degenerative disease, neoplastic disease, vascular disease, inflammatory disease, toxic-metabolic disease, and traumatic disease.

4. On a photograph, be able to recognize neuron, astrocyte, oligodendroglia, microglial cell, ependymal cell, ischemia and infarction, neoplasia, diffuse inflammation, abscess formation, and degenerative disease.

5. In a clinical situation, be able to answer the following four questions:
   a. The signs and symptoms contained in the protocol are most likely the manifestation of disease at which of the following *levels* of the nervous system?
      (1) Supratentorial level
      (2) Posterior fossa level
      (3) Spinal level
      (4) Peripheral level
      (5) More than one level
   b. Within the level you have selected, the responsible lesion is most likely:
      (1) Focal, on the *right* side of the nervous system
      (2) Focal, on the *left* side of the nervous system
      (3) Focal, but involving *midline* and *contiguous structures* on both sides of the nervous system
      (4) Nonfocal and diffusely located
   c. The principal pathologic lesion responsible for the symptoms is most likely:
      (1) Some form of *mass* lesion
      (2) Some form of *nonmass* lesion
   d. The cause of the responsible lesion is most likely:
      (1) Vascular
      (2) Degenerative
      (3) Inflammatory
      (4) Immunologic
      (5) Neoplastic
      (6) Toxic-metabolic
      (7) Traumatic

Clinical Problems

For each of the following problems, identify the level, lateralization, presence of mass, and cause as outlined in objective 5.

1. A 68-year-old, right-handed man noted heaviness in his left arm while reading a newspaper. He tried to stand up but could not support his weight on his left leg. He was able to call for help. When his wife came to the room, she noted that the left side of his face was sagging.

2. A 6-year-old, right-handed girl with known congenital heart disease began to complain of headaches. Several days later, the severity of the headaches increased, and she was noted to have a left hemiparesis and a left homonymous hemianopia.

3. A 54-year-old, right-handed woman noted some difficulty in expressing her thoughts. This difficulty was mild, and she paid little attention to it. Weeks later, she complained of clumsiness and weakness in her right arm and leg, but the results of an examination by her physician were considered to be normal. Headaches appeared several months later, along with increasing right-sided weakness. She was also aware of an inability to see the right half of the visual field with either eye.

4. A 46-year-old, left-handed woman suddenly noted the onset of a severe bitemporal-occipital headache. On lying down, she became violently ill, with nausea and vomiting. She complained of a stiff neck. She was taken immediately to the hospital, where she was noted to be somnolent but to respond appropriately when stimulated. She could move all four extremities with equal facility. Her level of consciousness deteriorated, and she became deeply comatose.

5. A 4-year-old, right-handed boy complained of a sore throat, chills, and fever. He was put to bed and given aspirin and fluids. The next morning, he noted headache and an increasingly stiff neck. His temperature was 105°F (40.5°C). When seen at a physician's office later that afternoon, he was difficult to arouse. He was confused and delirious when stimulated. He held his neck rigid, but moved his extremities on command.

6. A 50-year-old, right-handed woman, formerly an executive secretary for a local banker, underwent neurologic evaluation

because she had had a marked personality change during the past several months. Her memory was poor. She could no longer do even simple calculations, and she had difficulty in following commands. She seemed ill informed about current events and no longer seemed interested in her personal appearance. Results of the remainder of the examination were unremarkable.

7. A 54-year-old, right-handed woman suddenly became dizzy, with nausea and vomiting. Examination revealed dysarthria, difficulty in swallowing (with weakness of the left palate), loss of pinprick sensation over the left side of the face and the right side of the body, and marked ataxia on using the left extremities.

8. A 62-year-old, right-handed man began to note generalized muscle cramps, which he attributed to a charley horse. In the ensuing months, he became aware of weakness in his arms and legs as well as some difficulty in speaking and in swallowing. Examination revealed weakness and atrophy and fasciculations of nearly all muscle groups, with no sensory changes. The sign of Babinski was present bilaterally.

9. A 68-year-old, right-handed man noted the sudden onset of severe pain in the chest and abdomen. Almost immediately after the pain he became weak and was unable to support any weight on his right leg. Examination revealed marked weakness of the right lower extremity, with a decrease in the perception of pinprick in the left leg to about the level of the umbilicus.

10. A 46-year-old, right-handed woman noted (in the absence of back pain) gradually increasing pain and numbness extending down her right leg. After these symptoms had been present for 12 months, she consulted her physician, who found slight weakness of the plantar-flexor muscles, absent ankle reflex, and decreased sensation in the posterior aspect of the calf—all on the right side.

Additional Reading

Adams, J. H., and Duchen, L. W. (eds.). *Greenfield's Neuropathology* (5th ed.). New York: Oxford University Press, 1992.

Goldstein, G. W., and Betz, A. L. The blood-brain barrier. *Sci. Am.* 255:74, Sept. 1986.

Haymaker, W., and Adams, R. D. *Histology and Histopathology of the Nervous System.* Springfield, Ill.: Thomas, 1982.

Hirano, A. (ed.). *Color Atlas of Pathology of the Nervous System* (2nd ed.). New York: Igaku-Shoin, 1988.

Hirano, A. *A Guide to Neuropathology.* New York: Igaku-Shoin, 1981.

Okazaki, H. *Fundamentals of Neuropathology: Morphologic Basis of Neurologic Disorders* (2nd ed.). New York: Igaku-Shoin, 1989.

Poirier, J., Gray, F., and Escourolle, R. *Manual of Basic Neuropathology* (3rd ed.). Philadelphia: Saunders, 1990.

— 5 —

Diagnosis of Neurologic Disorders: Transient Disorders and Neurophysiology

Knowing the location and function of the structural components of the nervous system presented in Chapter 3 permits localization of the site of a lesion. The temporal profile of the major types of disease, as presented in Chapter 4, assists in identifying the cause of the disorder. However, one temporal profile has not yet been considered, that of the *transient* or rapidly reversible abnormality. Many diseases that produce signs or symptoms of brief duration may not produce destructive changes in cells and may occur without demonstrable histologic abnormality of the involved structures. To understand transient manifestations of disease, it is necessary to understand the mechanism by which the cells of the nervous system process information and to understand their physiology. Transient alterations in the physiology of the cells cause transient symptoms and signs. This chapter provides an introduction to the physiology of neurons, axons, and muscle fibers, which is the basis for information transmission in the central and peripheral neural structures and for the transient symptoms and signs that accompany disease states.

The major function of the nervous system is the transmission, storage, and processing of information. This function is accomplished by the generation, conduction, and integration of electrical activity and by the synthesis and release of chemical agents.

Information is conducted from one region to another as electrical activity, commonly known as nerve impulses, which are *generated* by neuronal cell bodies or axons and *conducted* by axons. Information is *transmitted* between cells by *neurotransmitters* and *neuromodulators,* the chemical agents that convey the signals from one cell to the next. Information is *integrated* by the interaction of electrical activity in single cells and in groups of cells. Although this chapter will discuss only the physiology of single cells, it must be remembered that the activity of the central and peripheral nervous systems never depends on the activity of a single neuron or axon but is always mediated by a group of cells or nerve fibers. Information is represented in the nervous system by a change in activity in a group of cells or fibers, as they respond to some change in their input. The interactions of neurons in large groups are considered in later sections.

Overview

Normal function in a single neuron as it participates in the processing of information is manifested as electrical potentials. These potentials are called membrane potentials and are present in the cell bodies and axons of all neurons and in muscle fibers. They include the following types of membrane potentials: resting potentials; action potentials; and such local potentials as synaptic potentials, generator potentials, and electrotonic potentials. All membrane potentials result from ion flow through channels in the membrane.

Cell membranes separate ions into different concentrations on the exterior and interior of the cell. Membrane potentials change in response to flow of these ions through pores, the channels in the membrane. Ionic flow in channels is controlled by channel opening through action by chemical agents or electrical current (chemical-gated or voltage-gated).

Neural tissue has several mechanisms for the transfer, storage, and processing of information. These differ among the areas and cells in the nervous system. The newer, lateral, direct relay systems located in the outer tube of the central nervous system use more rapidly acting, localized agents called *neurotransmitters.* The older, diffuse systems located in the core, or inner tube, generally use slower and more widely acting chemical agents called *neuromodulators* in addition to neurotransmitters. Neurotransmitters act rapidly in localized areas by opening channels for sodium, potassium, or chloride ions. Neuromodulators act slowly, modulating neural excitability through changes in the potassium or calcium channels. Neuromodulators are more characteristic of diffuse systems, whereas neurotransmitters are preponderant in direct relay systems. The configuration of membrane channels makes them specific for particular ions.

The *membrane potential* is the difference in electrical potential between the inside and the outside of a cell. All neurons, axons, and muscle fibers have a membrane potential. The *resting potential* is the baseline level of the membrane potential when the cell is at rest and not processing information. This potential depends primarily on the potassium channel. When a cell is active in the processing of information, the membrane potential varies. These variations are either local potentials or action potentials.

Action potentials are the electrical signals or nerve impulses by which information is conducted from one area to another within a single cell. The action potential is an all-or-none change in membrane potential in the body or axon of a neuron or within a muscle fiber. It either occurs fully or not at all and depends on the sodium channel. When this potential occurs, it spreads to all other parts of the cell in which it arises. The function of action potentials is thereby to conduct bits of information from one place to another. The action potential is initiated by one form of local potential, the electrotonic potential.

Local potentials are localized changes in a number of ion channels that change the mem-

brane potential in response to stimuli. They are graded signals whose size varies in proportion to the size of the stimulus. They remain localized in the area of the cell in which they are generated; that is, they do not spread to involve the entire cell. Local potentials can be summated and integrated by single cells and are thereby an integral part of the processing of information by the nervous system. Changes in ion channels are generated by (1) a neurotransmitter or neuromodulator, (2) synaptic potentials and generator potentials, or (3) by the flow of electrical current, the electrotonic potentials.

Synaptic potentials are variations in the membrane potential that occur at *synapses,* the specialized areas of cells where adjacent cells are in intimate contact. Synaptic potentials are local potentials arising from postsynaptic ion channel opening in response to the action of a neurotransmitter or neuromodulator released by presynaptic cells. Neurotransmitters and neuromodulators transmit information from one cell to another by converting the electrical signal (action potential) into a chemical signal (neurotransmitter or neuromodulator release) and then back into an electrical signal (synaptic potential or membrane potential change). In turn, synaptic potentials produce electrotonic potentials, which can then initiate another action potential.

Generator potentials are the variations in membrane potentials that occur in receptors — those neural structures in the body, such as the touch receptors in the skin or the light receptors in the eye, that respond to specific stimuli. Generator potentials are also local potentials caused by opening of ion channels and are localized and graded. They can generate electrotonic potentials and thereby initiate action potentials (Fig. 5-1).

A localized change in membrane potential results in current flow to surrounding areas of membrane. This current flow produces a small change in the membrane potential of adjacent areas. This change is called an *electrotonic potential.* The main features of these potentials are summarized in Table 5-1.

Transient alterations in function may be due to a disruption of the ion channels, neurotransmitters or neuromodulators underlying

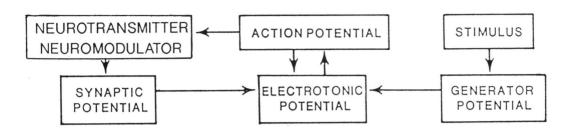

Fig. 5-1. Initiation of electrical potentials in the nervous system. Arrows indicate potentials that may be initiated by each element.

Table 5-1. Characteristics of Different Membrane Potential Variations

Characteristic	Action potential	Local Potentials		
		Electrotonic	Synaptic	Generator
Graded and localized	−	+	+	+
All-or-none spread	+	−	−	−
Active membrane channel	Na^+, K^+	None	Na^+, K^+, Ca^{2+} or Cl^-	Na^+, K^+
Initiated by	Electrotonic potential	Action, synaptic, or generator potentials	Chemical neurotransmitter	Stimulus

the normal generation of the resting potential, the synaptic potential, the generator potential, or the action potential.

Resting Potential

The resting potential is the *absolute difference* in electrical potential between the inside and outside of an inactive neuron, axon, or muscle fiber. If an electrical connection is made between the inside and the outside of a neuron, the cell acts as a battery, and an electrical current will flow. The potential is generally near 80 mV, with the inside of the cell *negative* with respect to the outside. The resting potential can be measured directly by using a microelectrode. The tip of such an electrode must be less than 1 μm in diameter to be inserted into a nerve or muscle cell. By connecting the microelectrode to an appropriate amplifier, the membrane potential can be recorded and displayed on an oscilloscope (Fig. 5-2).

The oscilloscope registers the potential difference between the two electrical inputs and is displayed as a vertical deflection of a spot of light that moves continuously from left to right across the cathode ray tube of the oscilloscope. A negative membrane potential is registered as a downward deflection, and thus when a microelectrode enters a neuron or muscle fiber, the oscilloscope beam moves down to a new position.

Because the resting potential is the absolute difference in potential between the inside and the outside of the cell, a negative sign need not be included in describing the value of a resting potential. In addition, a "fall" or "reduction" in resting potential will mean *less negativity* inside, and the oscilloscope beam will move up toward the baseline.

The resting potential in nerve and muscle cells depends on two factors: (1) the cell membrane contains *ion channels,* pores that can selectively pass specific ions based on their physical properties, thus making it a *semipermeable membrane* with different permeabilities for different ions and (2) the cell membrane contains an *energy-dependent mechanism that moves ions* from one side of the membrane to the other, producing different concentrations of ions on the inside and outside of the cell. An understanding of the manner in which these two characteristics of

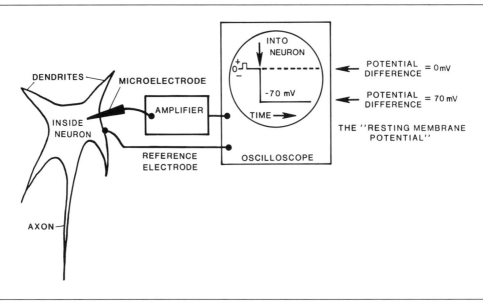

Fig. 5-2. Oscilloscopic recording of membrane potential from neuron.

cell membranes result in the generation of the resting potential requires some knowledge of semipermeable membranes and the biophysics of ionic solutions.

Biophysical Considerations

When a material is dissolved in water, its molecular motion results in the material spreading from a region of higher concentration to a region of lower concentration, until it is equally distributed throughout the solution. The molecular motion is thus a source of energy that does work on the molecules and is referred to as the *diffusion pressure*. Diffusion pressure is a function of the molecular motion and the relative concentration of the material in different areas. (Molecular motion increases with temperature.)

Body fluids contain charged ions of different sizes in solution. Sodium (Na^+), potassium (K^+), chloride (Cl^-), and calcium (Ca^{2+}) are of particular importance in nerve and muscle cells. Ions with a positive charge such as Na^+ and K^+ are *cations;* those with a negative charge are *anions.* In addition to these simple ions, there are many large intracellular ions, primarily proteins, that are negatively charged and referred to as anions (A^{2-}). Because ions have an electrical charge, they are acted on by differences in electrical potential. Anions move toward the positive pole (the anode), and cations move toward the negative pole (the cathode) of an applied voltage. Thus, a voltage produces an *electrical pressure,* which also can act as a source of energy that does work on ions in solution.

A *semipermeable membrane* permits the passage of some substances but not others. The ease with which a molecule can move through a membrane is called the *membrane permeability.* The ease with which a charged molecule (ion) can move through a membrane is its *conductance.* The conductance of an ion is the reciprocal of the electrical resistance to movement of that ion through the membrane. The permeability and conductance are generally similar for any given ion.

If a salt is dissolved into two ions of opposite charge on one side of a semipermeable membrane, the membrane may be permeable to neither of the ions, to one of the ions, or to both of the ions. If it is permeable to neither, water moves across the membrane and reduces the concentration (osmotic pressure). If the membrane is permeable to both of the ions, they both move across the membrane by diffusion pressure until each is equally distributed on the two sides of the membrane. If the salt dissolves into two ions of different sizes, one with a high conductance and the other with a low conductance, an interesting phenomenon occurs. The diffusion pressure moves the diffusible ion across the membrane into the area of lower concentration. As this occurs, a separation of charges develops because the nondiffusible ions all remain on one side of the membrane and have a charge opposite that of the diffusible ions, which move through the membrane.

Two regions that accumulate different charges have an electrical potential difference. Therefore, as the diffusible ions move across the membrane, an electrical potential develops that resists the movement of the diffusible ions across the membrane. The net ionic movement continues until *the diffusion pressure equals the electrical pressure.* At this time, the system is in equilibrium. At equilibrium, there continues to be random ionic movements, but no net movement of ions occurs. The electrical potential developed across the membrane at equilibrium is called the *equilibrium potential.* An algebraic representation of the equilibrium potential can be derived because the physical determinants of the diffusion pressure and electrical pressure are known. The final equation is the Nernst equation.

Electrical pressure is defined by:

$$W_e = E_m \cdot Z_i \cdot F$$

in which W_e = electrical pressure (work required to move an ion against a voltage)
E_m = absolute membrane potential
Z_i = valence (number of charges on the ion)
F = faraday (number of coulombs per mol of ion)

Diffusion pressure is defined by:

$$W_d = R \cdot T \cdot (\ln[C]_{hi} - \ln[C]_{lo})$$

in which W_d = diffusion pressure (work required to move an ion against a concentration gradient)
R = universal gas constant

T = absolute temperature
$\ln$ = natural logarithm
$[C]_{hi}$ = ion concentration on the more concentrated side of the membrane
$[C]_{lo}$ = ion concentration on the less concentrated side

At equilibrium:

$$W_e = W_d \text{ and therefore}$$
$$E_m \cdot Z_i \cdot F = R \cdot T \cdot (\ln[C]_{hi} - \ln[C]_{lo})$$

By rearrangement, the equilibrium potential is:

$$E_m = \frac{R \cdot T}{F \cdot Z_i} \cdot \ln\left(\frac{[C]_{hi}}{[C]_{lo}}\right)$$

The *Nernst equation* is an important relationship that defines the equilibrium potential, E_m, inside the cell for any ion in terms of its concentration on the two sides of a membrane. From the Nernst equation, the polarity of the potential depends on whether the ion is an anion or a cation: E_m for a cation will be (+) on the low concentration side, and E_m for an anion will be (−) on the low concentration side. By substituting for the constants at room temperature, converting to a base 10 logarithm, and converting to millivolts, we get a useful form of the equation:

$$E_m = 58 \log_{10} \frac{[C]_{lo}}{[C]_{hi}} \text{ for cations}$$

For example:

$$E_{Na} = 58 \log_{10} \frac{[140]}{[25]} = 43.3$$

$$E_m = 58 \log_{10} \frac{[C]_{hi}}{[C]_{lo}} \text{ for anions}$$

We may use these equations to calculate the equilibrium potential for any ion if we know the concentrations of that ion on the two sides of the membrane. This potential only develops if the membrane is permeable to the ion. A more precise representation of the actual voltage developed across a membrane with unequal concentrations of an ion on the two sides of the membrane also must include the permeability (P) since the membrane potential (E_K) depends on the ease with which the ion can diffuse across the membrane. Algebraically, for potassium in which P_K = potassium conductance:

$$E_K = \frac{R \cdot T}{F \cdot Z_i} \cdot \ln \frac{P_K \cdot [K^+]_o}{P_K \cdot [K^+]_i}$$

If a membrane is permeable to multiple ions that are present in differing concentrations on either side of the membrane, the resultant membrane potential is a function of the concentrations of each of the ions and of their relative permeabilities. The *Goldman equation* combines these factors for the major ions that influence the membrane potential in nerve and muscle cells:

$$E_m = \frac{R \cdot T}{F \cdot Z_i} \cdot \ln \frac{P_K \cdot [K^+]_o + P_{Na} \cdot [Na^+]_o + P_{Cl} \cdot [Cl^-]_i}{P_K \cdot [K^+]_i + P_{Na} \cdot [Na^+]_i + P_{Cl} \cdot [Cl^-]_o}$$

The Goldman equation permits the calculation of the membrane potential for various neurons or muscle fibers. Such calculations, on the basis of the actual ionic concentrations and ionic permeabilities, agree with measurements of these values in living cells. Since the potassium permeability in most living cells is much greater than the sodium permeability, the resting potential is near the equilibrium potential of potassium. The approximate neuronal equilibrium potentials of the major ions are $K^+ = -100$ mV, $Na^+ = +40$ mV, $Cl^- = -75$ mV, $Ca^{2+} = +250$ mV.

These equations also show that a change in either ionic permeability or ionic concentrations can alter membrane potential. If the *concentration gradient* of an ion is reduced, there will be a lower equilibrium potential for that ion. If the resting membrane potential is determined by the equilibrium potential of that ion, the resting potential will decrease. In contrast, if the *permeability* for an ion is increased by opening of channels for that ion, the membrane potential will approach the equilibrium potential of that ion, and it may increase or decrease, depending on whether the membrane potential is above or below the equilibrium potential. The movements of ions that occur with normal cellular activity are not sufficient to produce significant concentration changes; therefore, membrane potential fluctuations are normally due to permeability changes caused by channel opening and closing.

The Cell Membrane

The membranes of excitable cells contain separate pores, or channels, for individual ions. The pores differ in permeability to different ions. The ion channels are protein macromolecules embedded in the bilayer lipid membrane (Fig. 5-3) and are of various sizes and shapes. They are hydrophilic pores lined with electrical charges that repel or attract the ions. Voltage-sensitive gates or gating potentials at the entrance of the channels regulate the movement of the ions into them, effectively opening or closing them. When there is a strong gating potential, the ions are repelled; when the gating potential is weak, ions can pass into the channels. In the resting state, the gates of the sodium channels are almost completely closed, whereas those of the potassium channels are partially open, making the membrane approximately 50 to 100 times more permeable to potassium than to sodium ions. The gating potential can be altered by a neurotransmitter, a physical stimulus, or a change in the membrane potential that can cause the gates to open or close and thereby allow or prevent more ions from entering the channels. For example, a decrease in the membrane potential can cause an opening of the sodium gates, with an increase in the permeability of the membrane to sodium ions.

In addition to sodium, chloride, and potassium channels, there are calcium channels that allow the movement of calcium ions across the nerve membrane. These are most abundant at axon terminals, where the influx of calcium ions is necessary for the release of neurotransmitter substances. Calcium ions also help regulate the sodium gates by producing an electrical field or gating potential that blocks the entry of sodium ions into the membrane. When calcium ions are decreased in the extracellular fluid, the

Fig. 5-3. Diagram of cell membrane with ion channels formed by protein structures embedded in the lipid membrane.

sodium gates fail to close and sodium ions continue to leak in.

The movement of ions through the membrane is also dependent on the hydration charge. Most ions are bound to water molecules, which must be removed before the ions can pass through the channel. The amount of energy necessary to remove the water molecules is referred to as the *hydration energy.* This energy is less for potassium ions than for other ions, thus allowing for an easier transfer of potassium ions through the membrane.

Ion channels differ in several ways from one another. The density of ion channels differs along a cell membrane in some cells, which adds differences in permeability. The threshold for change of an ion channel, the rate of change, and the duration of change in response to a neurotransmitter or to voltage can also differ, adding further complexity to the system. Other factors affecting the movement of ions across the membrane are the potential difference and the concentration gradients across the membrane.

Active Transport

Nerve and muscle cells obtain energy from glucose and oxygen via the glycolytic pathways, the Krebs cycle, and the electron trans-

port system. These pathways provide the energy for normal cell function in the form of adenosine triphosphate (ATP). ATP is partly consumed in generating the resting potential by a mechanism in the membrane, which moves potassium in and sodium out of the cell, with slightly more sodium being moved than potassium. This movement is referred to as *active transport,* and the system through which it occurs is the *sodium pump.* The sodium pump moves sodium out of the cell and potassium into the cell against their concentration gradients. Chloride moves out of the cell passively with sodium. The large internal anions are nondiffusible and remain intracellular. A defect in the energy-producing system due to anoxia or to an enzyme block results in cessation of active transport and in an inability to generate and maintain a resting potential.

The Resting Potential

Active transport across the cell membrane results in unequal concentrations of the ions on opposite sides of the membrane and in a diffusion pressure to move the ions back down their concentration gradients. *Potassium* diffuses through the membrane most readily because potassium channels are more open and potassium conductance is much higher than that of other ions. Therefore, potassium is the largest source of separation of positive and negative charges (voltage) as it diffuses out and leaves the large anions behind. This is illustrated schematically in Figure 5-4. In Figure 5-4, the ionic concentrations have been established with a high external and a low internal concentration of sodium, and a high internal and a low external concentration of potassium initially (A), with large, nondiffusible anions shown inside. The conductance of potassium is much greater than that of sodium, and potassium diffuses out of the cell to produce the separation of positive and negative charges that establishes a membrane potential (B). However, the potential difference resists this redistribution of ions, and a balance between A and B occurs (C), with a resultant resting potential at equilibrium.

In the living cell, there is a continuous small influx of sodium and an efflux (outward flow) of potassium ions, which are transferred back across the membrane by the sodium pump.

Because the net diffusion of ions is continuous across the membrane, and the ions are returned by the sodium pump, a true equilibrium does not occur. However, as long as the pump keeps up with the inward leak of sodium and an outward leak of potassium, a steady membrane potential is established, which is referred to as the *steady state*. Therefore, the resting potential in living cells is a steady state and not an equilibrium potential. The normal ionic concentrations in mammalian neurons are shown in Table 5-2.

The opening of an ion channel moves the membrane potential toward the equilibrium potential of that ion. Opening sodium or calcium channels produces movement of positive charges into the cell and makes the inside less negative and thus reduces the membrane potential. The opening of more potassium channels causes movement of the positive potassium ions from the inside to the outside of the neuron, thus making the inside more negative and increasing the resting membrane potential. The opening of more chloride channels stabilizes the membrane potential near the resting potential.

Similar mechanisms are at work in all nerve and muscle cells, although the actual concentrations of the ions vary widely in different cells. Some examples of the determination of the resting potential from ionic concentrations by the Nernst equation are shown in Table 5-3, which also illustrates that, despite different ionic concentrations, the similar extracellular-intracellular ratios result in similar resting potentials. Some glial cells that are

Table 5-2. Relative Ionic Conditions in Mammalian Neurons

Condition	Sodium	Potassium	Chloride
Internal concentration	Low	High	Low
External concentration	High	Low	High
Resting permeability	Low	High	Moderate

Table 5-3. Ionic Concentration in Neurons of Various Species

Cell	Ion	Extracellular concentration (mm/L)	Intracellular concentration (mm/L)	Extracellular-intracellular ratio	Equilibrium potential inside
Squid axon (RP 70 mV)*	Na^+	450.0	50	9:1	+55
	K^+	20.0	400	1:20	−76
	Cl^-	560.0	40	14:1	−104
Cat motor neuron (RP 65 mV)	Na^+	150.0	15	10:1	+58
	K^+	5.5	150	1:27	−83
	Cl^-	125.0	9	14:1	−107
Human skeletal muscle (RP 80 mV)	Na^+	150.0	26	6:1	+53
	K^+	4.0	150	1:38	−95
	Cl^-	105.0	4	26:1	−85

*RP = resting potential.

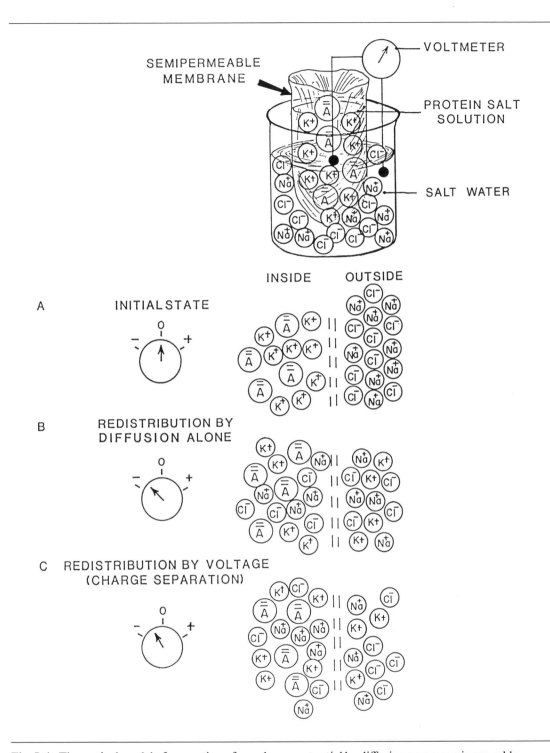

Fig. 5-4. Theoretical model of generation of membrane potential by diffusion across semipermeable membrane. A. Equal amounts of anions and cations dissolved on each side of membrane — no voltage gradient. Membrane is permeable to all ions except large anions ($\overline{A}$). B. K^+, Na^+, and Cl^- redistribute themselves solely by diffusion; this results in a charge separation, with greater negativity inside. C. Electrical pressure due to charge separation and diffusion pressure due to concentration differences are balanced at resting membrane potential.

Table 5-4. Examples of Ion Channels

Ion channel	Equilibrium potential	Location	Function
Voltage-gated			
Na$^+$	+35	Node of Ranvier Axon hillock	Initiation and conduction of action potential
K$^+$	−90	Diffuse along internode	Repolarization of action potential
		Diffuse in neurons	Decrease neuronal excitability and discharge
Ca^{2+}	+200	Dendrite	Slow depolarization
		Soma	Burst firing
		Terminal	Oscillatory firing Neurotransmitter release
Chemical-gated			
Cl$^-$ (GABA)	−75	Dendrite Soma	Synaptic inhibition
Cation channel (L-glutamate, acetylcholine)	0	Dendrite Soma	Synaptic excitation

potassium-dependent also have resting potentials of 70 to 90 mV.

The concentration gradient of calcium is similar to that of sodium, with an even higher positive (inside) equilibrium potential. However, calcium has such a low conductance that it does not contribute directly to the resting potential. It is, however, adsorbed on the external surface of the membrane, where it is involved in membrane changes occurring during the activity of cells. In general, calcium tends to reduce or limit changes in the sodium or potassium conductances. It acts, thereby, as a membrane "stabilizer." A calcium current mediates the conduction of some spikes in dendrites and in cardiac muscle and participates in the release of neurotransmitter.

The alternation in ionic conductance that occurs with changes in the configuration of membrane proteins varies with the specific channel. An ion channel may be opened or closed by action of a chemical agent on the channel or by a voltage applied to the channel (Table 5-4). For example, the sodium current has two forms, a transient, rapidly inactivated current that occurs with action potentials and a more persistent current that contributes to steady-state firing of a neuron. A number of types of potassium and calcium currents with distinct effects have also been described.

Local Potentials

In the normal nerve cell or muscle cell with adequate sources of oxygen and glucose, the resting potential is maintained at a stable, relatively unchanging level. However, the resting potential readily changes in response to various stimuli. The membrane potential can change from the resting state in only two ways. It can either become more negative inside, *hyperpolarization,* or less negative inside, *depolarization.* Even if the membrane potential reverses, so that the inside becomes positive with respect to the outside, it is still referred to as depolarization, because the potential is less negative than the resting potential.

The changes in the membrane potential that occur with anoxia or a change in the concentration of the ions on either side of the membrane are relatively long lasting (minutes to hours). In contrast, rapid changes (seconds or less) can occur in response to electrical, mechanical, or chemical stimuli. These changes occur as a result of current flow through the membrane. *Transient currents* in living tissues are due to the movement of charged ions and can flow through the membrane as a result of an applied voltage or of a change in membrane conductance.

A *local potential* is a transient shift of the membrane potential in a localized area of the cell. This may occur in response to various stimuli and may have either a hyperpolarizing or a depolarizing effect. Local potentials result from the current flow due to localized change in ion channels that alter permeability to one or more ions. Ion channel opening or closing may result from (1) a chemical agent (neurotransmitter or neuromodulator) acting on the channel, a *synaptic potential,* (2) deformation of the membrane and channel by a mechanical stimulus, a *generator potential,* or (3) a current from an externally applied voltage, an *electrotonic potential.*

Synaptic potentials are the response to information carried by a neurotransmitter or neuromodulator released by an adjacent cell. Generator potentials are the response to external stimuli. Electrotonic potentials participate in the transfer of information throughout a cell by action potentials.

Ionic Basis of Local Potentials

Local potentials result from the flow of current through the membrane with a change in channels that are open or closed in response to a chemical agent, mechanical deformation, or an applied voltage.

Neurotransmitters and neuromodulators produce synaptic potentials by one of six mechanisms:

1. Opening of potassium channels increases potassium conductance, resulting in hyperpolarization, a relatively slow process.
2. Opening of sodium channels increases sodium conductance, resulting in depolarization, a relatively fast process.
3. Opening of both potassium and sodium channels increases the conductance of both ions, resulting in a depolarization but to a lesser degree than in 2 above.
4. Opening of chloride channels increases chloride conductance, resulting in rapid stabilization or hyperpolarization of the membrane voltage.
5. Closing of potassium channels, resulting in a *slow* depolarization.
6. Opening of calcium channels, resulting in a *slow* depolarization.

Generator potentials occur primarily by opening of both sodium and potassium channels and increasing conductance of both ions. This produces depolarization. They also occur in response to specific molecules that activate olfactory receptors and to photic stimuli that activate photoreceptors in the retina of the eye.

Electrotonic potentials occur in one of two ways:

1. Opening of sodium channels by a current arising from a voltage in an adjacent area of membrane. This produces depolarization.
2. Opening or closing of several different ion channels by an externally applied voltage. Application of a negative voltage to the outside of the membrane causes outward current flow and depolarization of the membrane. Application of a positive potential to the outside of the membrane causes inward current flow and hyperpolarization of the membrane.

When a voltage is applied to the outside of the axonal membrane, the negative pole is commonly referred to as the *cathode;* the positive pole is the *anode.* The current flow at the cathode depolarizes, whereas that at the anode hyperpolarizes a membrane.

Characteristics of Local Potentials

All local potentials have certain common characteristics. Most importantly, the local potential is a *graded* potential; that is, its amplitude is proportional to the size of the stimulus (Fig. 5-5). Measurement of a local potential uses the resting potential as its baseline so that, if the membrane's resting potential is depolarized from 80 to 70 mV during the local potential, the local potential has an amplitude of 10 mV. This potential change is one of decreasing negativity or of depolarization, but it could also be one of increasing negativity or of hyperpolarization.

Because the local potential is a graded response, proportional to the size of the stimulus, the occurrence of a second stimulus, before the first subsides, results in a larger local potential. Therefore, local potentials can be *summated.* They are summated algebraically, so that similar potentials are additive,

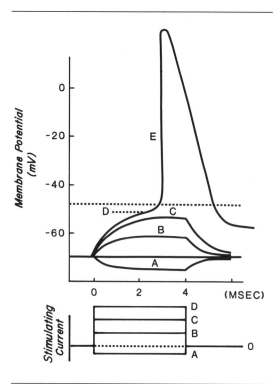

Fig. 5-5. Local potentials. These potentials are shown as upward deflection if they are a depolarization and as downward deflection if they are a hyperpolarization. Resting potential is 70 mV. At time zero, electrical currents of varied polarities and voltage are applied to the membrane (*lower diagram*). A is an anodal current; B, C, and D are cathodal currents. A produces a transient hyperpolarization; B, C, and D produce a transient depolarization that is graded and proportional to size of stimulus. All of these are local potential. D produces an action potential, E.

whereas hyperpolarizing and depolarizing potentials tend to cancel out each other. Summated potentials may reach threshold and produce an action potential when single potentials individually are subthreshold.

When a stimulus is applied in a localized area of the membrane, the change in membrane potential has both a temporal and a spatial distribution. A study of the temporal course of the local potential (see Fig. 5-5) shows that the increase in the potential is not instantaneous but that it develops over a few milliseconds. After the stimulus ends, the potential subsides over a few milliseconds as well. Local potentials therefore have a temporal course that outlasts the stimulus. The oc-

currence of a second stimulus at the same site shortly after the first produces another local potential, which summates with any residual of the earlier one that has not yet subsided. This summation of local potentials occurring near each other in time is called *temporal summation* (Fig. 5-6B).

Different synaptic potentials have different time courses. Most synaptic potentials range from 10 to 15 msec in duration; however, some are very brief, lasting less than 1 msec, but others may last several seconds or several minutes. The longer the duration of the synaptic potential, the more chance there is for temporal summation to occur. By means of temporal summation, the cell can integrate signals that arrive at different times.

Study of the spatial distribution of local potentials reveals another of their characteristics. As their name implies, they remain *localized* in the region where the stimulus is applied; they do not spread throughout the entire cell. However, the locally applied stimulus, because of local current flow, has an effect on the nearby membrane. The potential change is not sharply confined to the area of the stimulus but falls off over a finite distance along the membrane, usually a few millimeters. The application of a simultaneous second stimulus near the first (but not at the same site) results in summation of the potentials in the border zones, *spatial summation* (see Fig. 5-6). Thus, the membrane of the cell can act as an integrator of stimuli that arrive from different sources and that impinge on areas of membrane near one another. Spatial and temporal summation are important mechanisms in the processing of information by single neurons; when summated local potentials reach threshold, they initiate an action potential.

If a current or voltage is applied to a membrane for more than a few milliseconds, the ion channels revert to their resting state, changing ionic conductances of the membrane in a direction to restore the resting potential to baseline value. This phenomenon is known as *accommodation* (Fig. 5-7). Therefore, if an electrical stimulus is increased slowly, accommodation can occur and no change in the membrane potential will be seen. The changes in conductance during ac-

Fig. 5-6. Summation of local potentials in neuron. A. Spatial summation occurs when increasing numbers of nerve terminals release more neurotransmitter to produce larger excitatory postsynaptic potentials (*EPSPs*). B. Temporal summation occurs when a single terminal discharges repetitively more rapidly to produce larger EPSPs.

Fig. 5-7. Accommodation of membrane potential to applied stimulus of constant strength. Note response to a sudden cessation of stimulus.

commodation require several milliseconds, both to develop and to subside. As a result, if an electrical stimulus is gradually applied so that accommodation prevents a change in resting potential, then when the stimulus is suddenly turned off, the residual change in conductance will produce a transient change in resting potential. Thus accommodation can result in a cell responding to the cessation of a stimulus.

Action Potentials

Action potentials have several advantages for the rapid transfer of information in the nervous system. Because action potentials are all-or-none — they either occur or do not occur — they can transfer information without loss over relatively long distances. Their all-or-none feature also allows coding of information as frequency rather than the less stable measure of amplitude. Also, their threshold eliminates the effects of small, random changes in membrane potential.

Threshold

The membranes of neurons, axons, and muscle cells have another characteristic that is basic to their ability to transmit information from one area to another, their *excitability*. If a membrane is depolarized by a stimulus, there is a point at which suddenly many sodium channels open. This point is known as

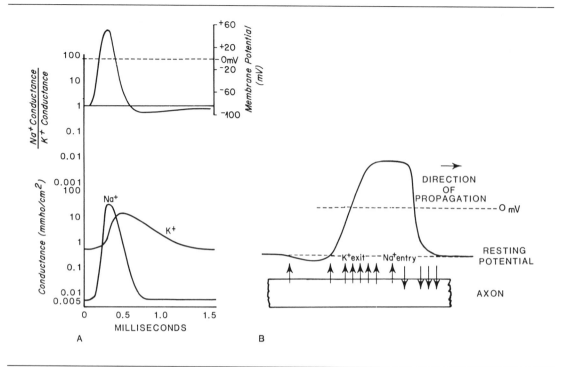

Fig. 5-8. Conductance changes during action potential. A. Temporal sequence at single site along axon is shown. Changes in conductances (permeabilities) of sodium and potassium are plotted against time as they change with associated changes in membrane potential. Note that sodium conductance changes several thousandfold early in the process, whereas potassium conductance changes only about thirtyfold during later stages and persists longer than sodium conductance changes. B. Spatial distribution of action potential over a length of axon at a single instant.

the *threshold* for excitation (see Fig. 5-5). If the depolarization does not reach threshold, the evoked activity is a local potential.

Threshold may be reached by a single local potential or by summated local potentials. When threshold is reached, there is a sudden increase in the membrane's permeability to sodium. This change in conductance results in the action potential.

Ionic Basis of Action Potential

In the resting state, many more potassium channels are open, the conductance of sodium is much less than that of potassium, and the resting potential is near the equilibrium potential of potassium. At threshold, many sodium channels open so that the conductance of sodium suddenly becomes greater than that of potassium, and the membrane potential

shifts toward the equilibrium potential of sodium, which is approximately +60 mV. This depolarization reverses the polarity of the membrane, the inside becoming positive with respect to the outside. With the opening of the sodium channels and increased sodium conductance, there is a flow of current with the inward movement of sodium ions. The change in sodium conductance is usually transient, lasting only a few milliseconds, and is followed by opening of potassium channels, an increase in the potassium conductance, and an outward movement of potassium ions. These three changes overlap, and the potential of the membrane during these changes is a function of the ratios of the conductances (Fig. 5-8). Sodium conductance increases several thousandfold early in the process, whereas potassium conductance increases less, does so later, and persists longer. The conductance

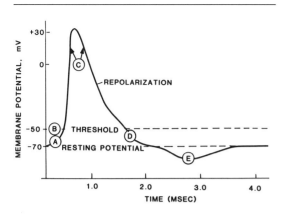

Fig. 5-9. Components of action potential with resting potential of 70 mV: A, local, electronic potential; B, threshold level; C, spike; D, negative (depolarizing) afterpotential; and E, positive (hyperpolarizing) afterpotential.

changes for these two ions result in ionic shifts and current flows that are associated with a membrane potential change, the *action potential* (see Fig. 5-8).

The action potential is a sudden, short-duration, all-or-none change in the membrane potential that occurs if the membrane potential reaches threshold. Its component parts are shown in Figure 5-9. The initial portion of the membrane potential change is the local potential. At threshold, the rising phase of the action potential suddenly changes because of the influx of positive ions. In most nerve cells and skeletal muscle cells, the inward current during the rising phase of the action potential is carried by sodium ions, because sodium conductance is markedly increased. The action potential also could be carried by calcium ions if the calcium conductance increased sufficiently, as occurs in some dendrites. Repolarization begins as sodium conductance decreases and/or potassium conductance increases. The decreased flow of sodium ions is followed by an efflux of potassium ions. The rate of return of the membrane potential to the baseline slows after the sodium conductance has returned to baseline, producing a small residual on the negative component of the action potential, which is called the *negative afterpotential.* In some myelinated axons, repolarization occurs by a decrease in sodium conductance with no change in potassium conductance.

The afterpotential is positive when the membrane potential is recorded with a microelectrode within the cell, but it is called negative because it is negative when recorded with an extracellular electrode. The increase in potassium conductance persists and results in a hyperpolarization after the spike component of the action potential, the *afterhyperpolarization.* The afterhyperpolarization is due to continued efflux of potassium ions, with a greater than resting difference in potential between the inside and outside of the cell. The afterhyperpolarization is positive when measured with extracellular electrodes and therefore is called a *positive afterpotential.* During the positive afterpotential, the membrane potential is near the potassium equilibrium potential, and oxygen consumption is increased with increased activity of the sodium pump.

The amounts of sodium and potassium that move across the membrane during the action potential are small, buffered by surrounding astrocytes, and do not change the concentration enough to result in a change in the resting potential. In addition, the sodium that moves in during the action potential is continually removed by the sodium pump during the relatively long intervals between action potentials.

Excitability

The excitability of a membrane is the ease with which an action potential can be generated and is usually measured in terms of the voltage required to initiate an action potential. During increased sodium conductance, the membrane cannot be stimulated to discharge again. A second stimulus at this time is without effect; therefore, action potentials, unlike local potentials, cannot summate. This period of unresponsiveness is the *absolute refractory period* (Fig. 5-10). As sodium conductance returns to normal, the membrane again becomes excitable, but for a short period, the *relative refractory period,* it requires a larger stimulus to produce a smaller action potential. After the relative refractory period, while the negative afterpotential is subsiding, the membrane is partially depolarized, is closer to threshold, and has an increased excitability. This period is the *supernormal period.* Finally,

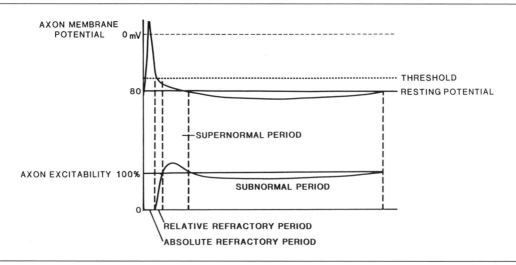

Fig. 5-10. Excitability changes during action potential. Lower portion of illustration shows ease with which another action potential can be elicited (change in threshold). During absolute and relative refractory periods, amplitude of action potential evoked is low. Subsequently, it is normal.

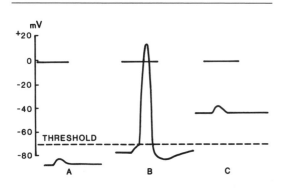

Fig. 5-11. Effect of stimulation of neuron at different resting potentials as recorded with microelectrode. A. Membrane is hyperpolarized, and stimulus produces subthreshold local potential. B. Membrane is normally polarized at −65 mV, and stimulus produces local potential that reaches threshold and results in action potential. C. Membrane is depolarized beyond threshold, and stimulus again produces only small local potential.

during the positive afterpotential, the membrane is hyperpolarized away from threshold, and larger stimuli are required. This period is the *subnormal period.*

Up to now, the term *threshold* has been used to refer to the membrane potential at which sodium channels open and an action potential is generated. The threshold of a membrane remains relatively constant. If the membrane potential becomes hyperpolarized, the membrane potential moves away from threshold, and the membrane is less excitable. If the membrane potential moves closer to threshold, the membrane becomes more excitable and will generate an action potential with a smaller stimulus. If the membrane potential is very near threshold, the cell may fire spontaneously. If the membrane potential remains more *depolarized* than threshold, however, the membrane cannot be stimulated to fire another action potential (Fig. 5-11).

The term *threshold* is also used to describe the voltage required to excite an action potential with an externally applied stimulus. When threshold is used in this sense, an axon with an increased excitability due to partial depolarization may be said to have a lower "threshold" for stimulation, even though the actual threshold is unchanged. The first meaning of threshold is used when intracellular recordings are considered, and the second is used in reference to extracellular stimulation and recording.

The threshold of the nerve membrane differs in different parts of the neuron: it is high in the dendrite and soma and lowest at the axon hillock. Thus, an action potential is usually generated in the area of the axon hillock.

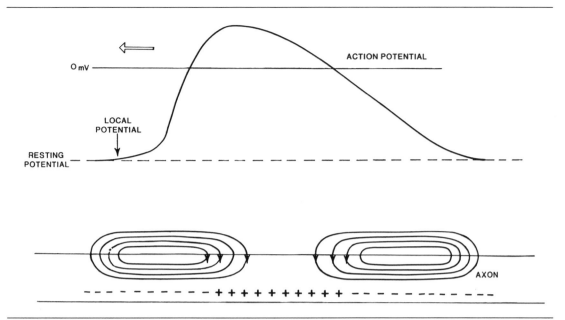

Fig. 5-12. Current flow and voltage changes in axon in region of action potential. The voltage changes along the membrane are shown in the upper part of the figure and the spatial distribution of current flow is shown in the lower part as arrows through the axon membrane.

Propagation

Another important characteristic of action potentials is their propagation. An action potential initiated in any part of a neuron or muscle cell spreads to all other regions of that cell. For instance, if an action potential is initiated in an axon in the tip of the finger, the potential spreads along the entire length of that axon to its cell body in the dorsal root ganglion, and then along the central axon, ascending in the spinal cord to the brain stem. This characteristic permits the nervous system to transmit information from one area to another.

When an area of membrane is depolarized during an action potential, ionic currents flow (Fig. 5-12). In the area of depolarization, sodium ions carry positive charges inward. There is also a longitudinal flow of current both inside and outside the membrane. This flow of positive charges (current) toward nondepolarized regions internally and toward depolarized regions externally tends to depolarize the membrane in the areas that surround the region of action potential. This depolarization is an electro-

tonic potential. In normal tissue, this depolarization is sufficient to shift the membrane potential to threshold and thereby to generate an action potential in the immediately adjacent membrane. The action potential thus will spread away from its site of initiation along an axon or muscle fiber. Because of the refractory period, the potential cannot reverse and spread back into an area just depolarized.

The rate of conduction of the action potential along the membrane depends on the amount of longitudinal current flow and on the amount of current needed to produce depolarization in the adjacent membrane. The longitudinal current flow can be increased by increasing the diameter of an axon or muscle fiber, since this increase reduces the internal resistance, just as a larger electrical wire has a lower electrical resistance. However, many axons in the central and peripheral nervous systems obtain an increased conduction velocity because they are insulated with a myelin sheath. A myelinated axon has its membrane bared only at the nodes of Ranvier, so that transmembrane current flow occurs almost exclusively at the nodal area. When cur-

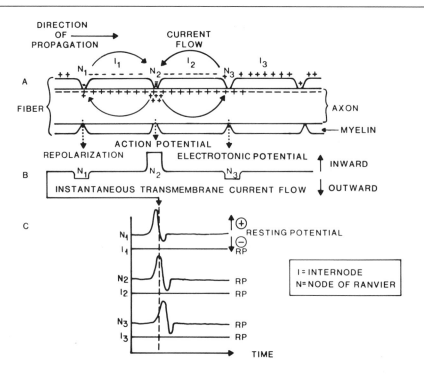

Fig. 5-13. Saltatory conduction along axon from left to right. A. Charge distribution along axon is shown with action potential (depolarization) at second node of Ranvier (N_2). Current flow spreads to next node (N_3). B. Membrane current flow along axon is shown. C. Portion of action potential found at each node is indicated by dotted lines.

rent flow opens enough sodium channels to reach threshold in the nodal area, it results in many more sodium channels opening and an influx of sodium ions with a generation of an action potential. The nodal area in the mammalian nervous system is unique in that it consists almost exclusively of sodium channels, with an almost complete absence of potassium channels. The potassium channels are located at the paranodal regions (adjacent to the node), which are covered by myelin. The action potential generated at the node consists predominantly of inward sodium currents with little outward potassium currents, and repolarization is achieved by means of sodium inactivation and leakage currents. An action potential at one node of Ranvier produces sufficient longitudinal current flow to depolarize adjacent nodes to threshold, thereby propagating the action potential along the nerve in a skipping manner called *saltatory conduction* (Fig. 5-13).

Patterns of Activity

Information in the nervous system is coded by the number and type of axons that are active and by the firing pattern of action potentials in the axons. This activity is initiated in peripheral receptors or in neurons. Neuronal firing of action potentials may occur spontaneously or only in response to external stimulation. *Beating,* or *pacing, neurons* fire repetitively at a constant frequency; their intrinsic firing rate may be increased or decreased by external stimulation. *Bursting neurons* generate regular bursts of action potentials separated by hyperpolarization of the membrane. Such neurons are important for rhythmic behavior such as breathing, walking, and chewing. Neurons that fire in response to external stimulation may do so in one of three ways. A *sustained response neuron* shows repeated action potentials with a constant firing frequency that reflects the strength of the stimulus. A *delayed response neuron* fires action potentials only after stimulation of sufficient intensity. An *accommodation response neuron* fires only a single potential at the onset of stimulation and remains silent thereafter.

Synaptic Transmission

The exchange of information between cells occurs by synaptic transmission that is usually chemically mediated. The two broad categories of synaptic agents, *neuromodulators* and *neurotransmitters,* coexist in many neurons; however, they evolved separately and have generally different distributions. Neuromodulators modify the activity of cells for longer periods by indirect action on ion channels through intermediate proteins. Neurotransmitters have rapid, brief effects on ion channels through direct effects on the channels. Neuromodulators are primarily associated with the older, diffuse systems, such as the internal regulation system, located in the inner tube of the neuraxis. Neurotransmitters are associated with the more recently developed, specific projection pathways located in the outer tube of the neuraxis, such as specific sensory and direct motor pathways.

Neurotransmitters and neuromodulators are produced in neurons, transported to their sites of release, released into synaptic clefts, diffuse across the cleft, and interact with receptors on the receiving neuron. These processes are described below specifically for the major agents. "Neuromodulators" are often referred to as "neurotransmitters." In this text, when the term "neurotransmitter" is used to include neuromodulators, it is in quotation marks. Therefore, it must be remembered that "neurotransmitters" refers to two quite distinct synaptic agents. In addition, synaptic transmission is electrically mediated in a small proportion of neurons, which are described below. "Neurotransmission" may include three types of processes: electrical transmission, fast chemical transmission by neurotransmitters, and slow chemical transmission by neuromodulators.

Neurotransmission may be divergent, with single agents acting in widespread areas, or it may be convergent, with multiple "neuro-transmitters" acting on localized targets. Most often, individual axon terminals release multiple agents, some of which are divergent and some of which act locally.

The terminations of the axons of most neurons are specialized to release neurotransmitters or neuromodulators (or both), chemical agents that act on other cells. Neurotransmitters, including acetylcholine, gamma-aminobutyric acid (GABA), and glutamate, act rapidly to open sodium, potassium, or chloride channels in localized areas of postsynaptic membrane of neurons. Neuromodulators, such as monoamines and neuropeptides acting via G-protein receptors, have longer lasting effects on potassium and calcium channels. A single axon terminal may contain more than one of these neuroactive substances, which may act on nearby presynaptic or postsynaptic receptors. Neuropeptides are synthesized in the cell body, and other agents are synthesized in the terminal by enzymes manufactured in the cell body and transferred down the axon by an active, oxygen-dependent axoplasmic transport system.

"Neurotransmitters" are stored in vesicles, membranous structures in the nerve terminal. The vesicles are of two types: large, dense-core vesicles store neuropeptides, and small, clear vesicles store the other "neurotransmitters." "Neurotransmitters" are released from the vesicles in discrete amounts, or *quanta,* by exocytosis. Release is initiated by depolarization of the nerve terminal but can be modified by presynaptic inhibition, inhibitory feedback, transmitters from neighboring terminals, and local substances such as adenosine.

Nerve terminal depolarization triggers localized, fast entry of a large amount of calcium ions, resulting in fusion of the vesicles with the presynaptic membrane through the action of calmodulin and several membrane proteins. The preferential release of monoamines and neuropeptides with different rates of axon terminal depolarization — monoamines are released at low rates and neuropeptides at high rates — allows frequency-dependent chemical coding (Fig. 5-14). Release of quanta is a function of nerve impulse amplitude. An axon terminal (presynaptic terminal) that synapses on another terminal (postsynaptic terminal)

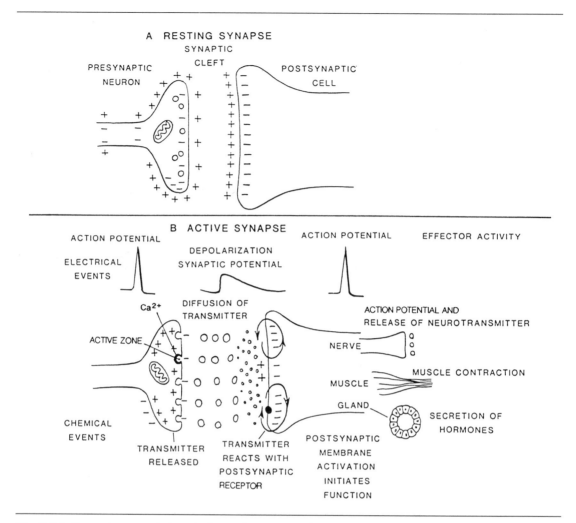

Fig. 5-14. Synaptic transmission. A. In resting synapse, both presynaptic nerve terminal and postsynaptic membrane are normally polarized. B. In active synapse, action potential invades nerve terminal (from left in the diagram) and depolarizes it. Depolarization of nerve terminal of presynaptic neuron results in release of neurotransmitter from nerve terminal. Neurotransmitter diffuses across synaptic cleft and produces local current flow and synaptic potential in the postsynaptic membrane, which initiates the effector activity (neuronal transmission, neurotransmitter release, hormonal secretion, or muscle contraction).

can partially depolarize the postsynaptic terminal, thus decreasing the amplitude of its nerve impulses. Consequently, the postsynaptic terminal releases fewer quanta of "neurotransmitter." This process is called *presynaptic inhibition* (Fig. 5-15).

"Neurotransmitters" diffuse across the synaptic cleft, the narrow space between the axon terminal and the membrane of the postsynaptic cell. The subsynaptic portion of the postsyn-

aptic membrane is a specialized portion of the cell that contains receptors that respond to the "neurotransmitters" with a change in ion channel permeability. The change in permeability results in current flow; the associated localized potential change in the postsynaptic membrane is the *synaptic potential*. The synaptic potential, like other local potentials, is a graded response that is proportional to the amount of "neurotransmitter" released. The potential re-

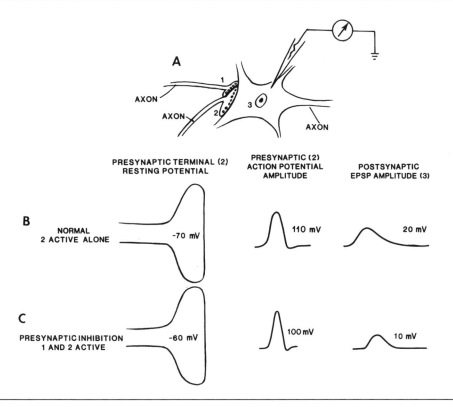

Fig. 5-15. A. Presynaptic inhibition of neuron 3 when axon 1 partially depolarizes axon 2. B. Response to axon 2 acting alone. C. Response to axon 2 after depolarization of axon 1. In the latter case, there is less neurotransmitter and a smaller excitatory postsynaptic potential (*EPSP*).

mains localized to the area of the synapse, unless enough sodium channels open to depolarize the membrane to threshold and initiate an action potential. "Neurotransmitter" actions are terminated by (1) reuptake by nerve terminals (amino acid, catecholamines, and serotonin), (2) enzymatic degradation (acetylcholine, histamine, and neuropeptides), or (3) diffusion out of the synaptic cleft. Individual "neurotransmitters" can produce different effects on different receptors (Table 5-5).

Specific receptors in the postsynaptic membrane bind the neurotransmitter or neuromodulator and initiate an effect called *transduction*. Two main classes of receptor molecules activate distinct pharmacologic effects. *Ligand-gated receptors* have the ion channel as an integral part of the receptor molecule and respond directly to neurotransmitters. Neurotransmitter binding produces a confor-

mational change that opens the channel directly, produces fast postsynaptic potentials, and results in rapid action, such as excitation by acetylcholine and excitatory amino acids (for example, L-glutamate), or inhibition by GABA. *G-protein-coupled receptors* activate the ion channel indirectly through guanine-nucleotide-regulated protein to produce the slow postsynaptic potentials of catecholamines, serotonin, histamine, neuropeptides, adenosine, and some amino acids (see Table 5-5).

"Neurotransmitters" are excitatory if they produce depolarization through a transient increase in conductance of sodium or calcium or decrease in conductance of potassium (see Table 5-4). Inhibitory effects occur through hyperpolarization by an increase in chloride or potassium current (Fig. 5-16). An increase in chloride conductance in effect clamps the membrane at the chloride equilibrium poten-

Table 5-5. Comparison of Classic Neurotransmitters and Neuromodulators

	Classic neurotransmitter	Neuromodulator
Function	Rapid synaptic excitation or inhibition	Modulation of neural excitability
Receptor mechanism	Ion channel receptors	G-protein-coupled receptors
Ionic mechanism	Opening of either cation channel (fast EPSP) or Cl^- channel (fast IPSP)	Opening or closing of voltage-gated K^+ or Ca^{2+} channels (slow IPSP and slow EPSP)
Example	L-Glutamate	L-Glutamate (metabotropic)
	GABA (GABA$_A$)	GABA (GABA$_B$)
	Acetylcholine (nicotinic)	Acetylcholine (muscarinic)
		Monoamines
		Neuropeptides
		Adenosine
Systems	Relay systems, direct	Diffuse systems, indirect
	Sensory	Internal regulation
	Motor	Consciousness

EPSP = excitatory postsynaptic potential; IPSP = inhibitory postsynaptic potential.

tial and prevents action potentials from occurring. Neurotransmitters affecting chloride conductance thereby inhibit activity. Fast *excitatory postsynaptic potentials (EPSPs)* are mediated by nicotinic receptors for acetylcholine and amino acids. Fast *inhibitory postsynaptic potentials (IPSPs)* are mediated by GABA receptors and glycine receptors. Slow excitatory and inhibitory postsynaptic potentials triggered by activation of G-protein-coupled receptors regulate neuronal excitability by opening or closing potassium or calcium channels.

Neuromodulators acting on G-protein receptors modulate activity through second messengers either by activating enzymes that regulate phosphorylation of cellular proteins or by inducing transcription of *early genes.* The latter can modify synaptic proteins to produce the enduring structural changes underlying the plasticity of the nervous system. These are manifested as memory in the brain.

Another action of neuromodulators (monoamines and neuropeptides) on membrane is *volume transmission.* This involves diffusion of the neurochemical through the extracellular space of the brain to act on receptors located at a distance. These substances affect not only neurons but also glial cells and blood vessels.

Many agents have been identified as "neurotransmitters." These include acetyl-

choline, biogenic monoamines (norepinephrine, histamine, dopamine, and serotonin), and amino acids (GABA, glutamic acid, and glycine). "Neurotransmitters" released into synaptic clefts to act on adjacent cells should be contrasted with hormones such as insulin, which is a large peptide molecule synthesized in neurons or endocrine glands and secreted into the circulation. Hormones act widely on large numbers of cells but with a slower time course than "neurotransmitters." Some peptides may act as hormones when released from some cells or as neuromodulators when released from other cells. Many small neuroactive peptides have been identified, including substance P, enkephalins, endorphin, somatostatin, vasopressin, bradykinin, angiotensin, insulin, glucagon, corticotropin, oxytocin, and thyroid-releasing hormone.

The neurotransmitters at some synapses are well defined. Acetylcholine, for instance, is released at the neuromuscular junction, in autonomic pathways, and in the basal ganglia; norepinephrine is released at other autonomic nerve terminals and in the locus ceruleus, a brain stem nucleus. Dopamine is released in the basal ganglia and hypothalamus and GABA in the cerebellum and by spinal cord inhibitory neurons. Substance P is the neurotransmitter for dorsal root ganglion cells. Because synapses are specialized to respond to

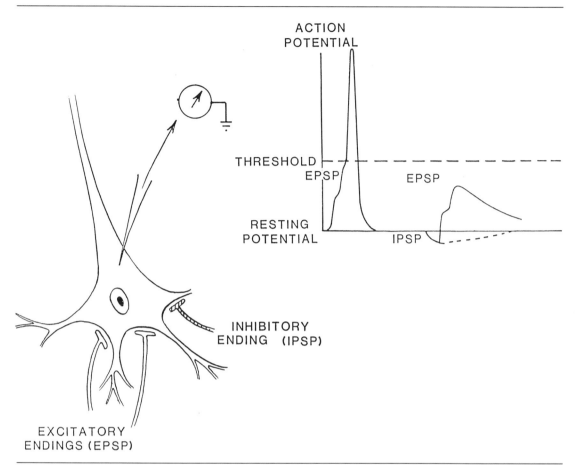

Fig. 5-16. Postsynaptic inhibition in the neuron on the left occurs when the inhibitory and excitatory endings are active simultaneously. On the right, a microelectrode recording shows two excitatory postsynaptic potentials (*EPSP*) summating to initiate action potential. When there is a simultaneous occurrence of an inhibitory postsynaptic potential (*IPSP*), depolarization is too low to reach threshold, and no action potential occurs.

neurotransmitters, they are also very susceptible to the action of other chemical agents or drugs. Many of the drugs used in clinical medicine have their pharmacologic site of action at the synapse.

The mechanism underlying chemical synaptic transmission should make it apparent that synaptic transmission has three unique characteristics. First, conduction at a synapse is delayed because of the brief interval of time required for the chemical events to occur. Second, because the two sides of the synapse are specialized to perform only one function, transmission can occur in only one direction across the synapse. The cells of the nervous system are thereby polarized in the direction of impulse transmission. Third, because nerve impulses from many sources impinge on single cells in the central and the peripheral nervous systems, synaptic potentials summate both temporally and spatially. The membrane of a cell is continually bombarded with neuromodulators and neurotransmitters, which produce either EPSPs or IPSPs of varying duration. When the membrane potential reaches threshold, an action potential is generated. A single neuron thereby can integrate activity from many sources. A summary of the electrical events in a single cell underlying the transmission, integration, and conduction of information is shown in Figure 5-17.

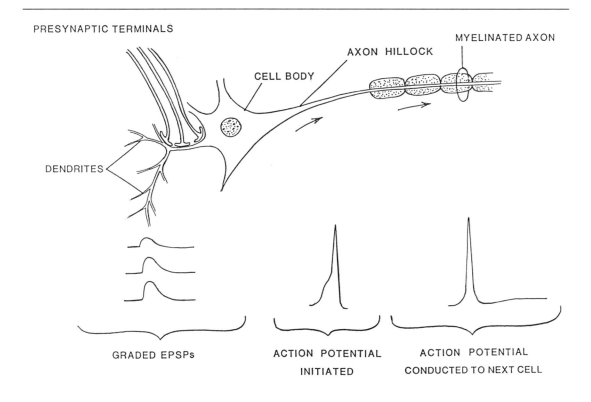

PRESYNAPTIC TERMINALS

MYELINATED AXON

AXON HILLOCK

CELL BODY

DENDRITES

GRADED EPSPs

ACTION POTENTIAL INITIATED

ACTION POTENTIAL CONDUCTED TO NEXT CELL

Fig. 5-17. Neuronal electrical activity from its initiation by excitatory postsynaptic potentials (*EPSPs*) to its transmission as action potential to another area.

Electrical Synapses

Although most synapses in the nervous system use chemical transmitters, neurons with junctions that contain channels extending from the cytoplasm of the presynaptic neuron to that of the postsynaptic neuron interact electrically. In these electrical synapses, the bridging channels mediate ionic current flow from one cell to the other. The transmission across the electrical synapse is very rapid, without the synaptic delay of chemical synapses. Electrical synapses are also bidirectional, in contrast to chemical synapses, which transmit signals in only one direction.

Clinical Correlations

The mechanisms of information transfer and processing in the neuromuscular system may be altered transiently and produce a clinical deficit of relatively short duration (seconds to hours).

Such an alteration of function may be due either to a loss of activity or to an overactivity of neurons. A few examples of such changes are described below. In each of these examples, there need be no permanent or histologic damage to the cells, as is typical of drug effects. Drugs produce cellular excitation or inhibition by increasing or decreasing ionic channel flow.

The resting potential depends primarily on potassium concentration. An alteration in extracellular potassium, therefore, will have its effects mainly on the resting potential. A *reduction in extracellular potassium* will increase the concentration gradient and equilibrium potential of potassium and thereby will increase the resting potential (hyperpolarize). Such hyperpolarized cells are less excitable because the membrane potential is farther from threshold, and fewer or no action potentials can be elicited. The function in those cells will be lost, as may occur in the case of those patients who have lost potassium because of disease or medication.

An *increase in extracellular potassium* will reduce the concentration gradient and result in a lower resting potential. Small increases in extracellular potassium will produce a resting potential closer to threshold (partially depolarized), and the cell will be more excitable and will fire action potentials in response to smaller stimuli. If the resting potential is very near threshold, the cell may fire spontaneously. However, a greater increase in extracellular potassium with a very low concentration gradient will give a persistently low resting potential at a level above threshold, resulting in a depolarization block. The cell will be unable to fire, and function will be lost. Therefore, increased extracellular potassium may produce either excessive activity or a loss of activity in neurons, axons, or muscle fibers. Excessive cell discharge due to mild depolarization may cause a convulsion.

A change in potassium conductance also can occur in disease states, although the change is not associated with any specific disorders. The increase in potassium conductance during normal action potentials is associated with movement of potassium across the membrane, but the amount is not sufficient to change the potassium concentration or to alter the equilibrium potential. After prolonged excessive activity, there may be sufficient loss of potassium from the cell to partially depolarize the cell, but this is usually not sufficient to be associated with clinically recognizable abnormalities other than muscle cramps.

Extracellular potassium concentration may be elevated in a number of disorders. In particular, this elevation is considered to be one of the major mechanisms by which *anoxia* or *hypoxia* produces transient symptoms and signs, as in fainting. Without oxygen, the normal concentration gradients cannot be maintained, and the resting potential decreases as potassium accumulates in the extracellular space. This may be associated with spontaneous firing of the cell, if mild, or with loss of function, if severe. Loss of function is seen first as the inability to generate action potentials, and when very severe, as the loss of local potentials. Anoxia also blocks the metabolic processes that maintain other cellular activity (such as movement of materials down axons) and protein synthesis. Therefore, anoxia may produce abnormalities in axons, neurons, synapses, and muscle fibers. However, the effects on the mechanisms underlying the electrical activity at the synapse (transmission of signals between cells) and the cell body (integration of signals) are altered earliest and most severely. All these changes also may be seen in severe kidney disease and in hyperkalemic periodic paralysis, both of which have altered serum levels of potassium.

The sodium ions are of primary importance in the generation of an action potential, and anything that interferes with the flow of sodium ions can block the generation of action potentials. Interference can occur either by an alteration in sodium conductance or by a change in sodium ion concentration. If sodium conductance cannot be increased or if the conductance is increased continuously, the membrane cannot generate action potentials and conduction of the action potential will be blocked. Tetrodotoxin, a fish toxin that blocks the sodium channel, inhibits conduction in axons and has been used to study axon physiology.

Structural changes in the membrane may result in an *increased sodium conductance* (leaky membrane), and the membrane potential will be closer to the sodium equilibrium potential (partially depolarized). The cell then will have increased excitability if the "leak" is mild or a block of conduction if the leak is severe.

An elevation of extracellular sodium increases the sodium equilibrium potential, the size of the action potential, and the rate of rise of the action potential. Such increases do not have significant clinical effects. A reduction in the extracellular sodium has the reverse effect; that is, it may lower the spike potential amplitude and slow its rate of increase. If the spike potential is low enough, it may not generate sufficient local current to discharge adjacent membrane, and action potential conduction may be blocked.

Calcium acts primarily as a membrane stabilizer, and its absence results in a reduced concentration gradient for sodium and potassium. Thus, hypocalcemia reduces the resting potential, increases excitability, and may produce spontaneous activity. In addition, because the entry of calcium into the membrane is necessary for a release of neurotransmitter, a low calcium level may block synaptic trans-

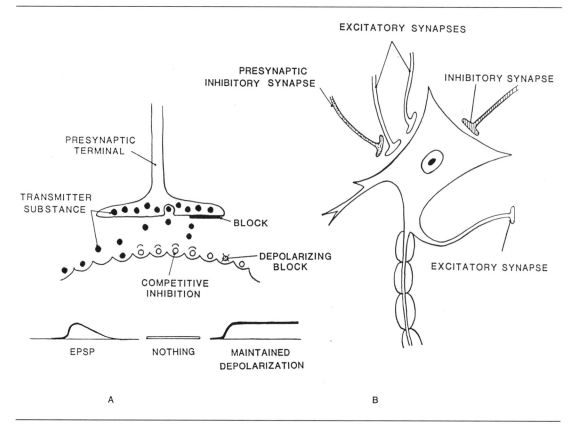

Fig. 5-18. Abnormalities of synaptic transmission may occur as shown in A. Types of transmission block include block of transmitter release (*block*), block of transmitter binding to postsynaptic membrane (*competitive inhibition*), or binding of another depolarizing agent to membrane (*depolarizing block*). B. These types of abnormalities may occur at each neuronal synapse shown.

mission. Hypocalcemia therefore may have opposite effects; that is, it may impair synaptic transmission but produce spontaneous firing of a neuron or axon. An excess of calcium tends to block action potentials and to enhance synaptic transmission. Hypercalcemia does not produce demonstrable changes, except at very high calcium concentrations, whereas even moderate hypocalcemia may produce muscle twitching or tingling.

The electrical activity of neuronal membranes is altered not only by ionic changes but also by the action of drugs. Synaptic transmission is particularly susceptible to a number of drugs that may act on the presynaptic or postsynaptic membranes. Examples of types of transmission block are illustrated in Figure 5-18. There may be a presynaptic block of transmitter release or a postsynaptic block by competitive inhibition of the postsynaptic re-

ceptors, by inactivating agents, or by depolarizing substances. Drugs also may act on the axonal membrane. Local anesthetics, for example, prevent changes in sodium conductance, thereby blocking the conduction of action potentials. A therapeutic agent that blocks potassium channels and thus slows repolarization of action potentials is 3, 4-diaminopyridine (3,4-DAP). Longer duration action potentials are able to increase function in certain abnormal axons. Lambert-Eaton myasthenic syndrome is a paraneoplastic disorder due to antibodies formed by lung carcinoma cells. The antibodies block the calcium binding at nerve terminals that is necessary for release of acetylcholine in neuromuscular and autonomic transmission. Thus, patients typically have muscle weakness, dry mouth, and other autonomic symptoms that are relieved by 3,4-DAP. Patients with multiple sclerosis have an autoimmune disorder, with weakness and sensory loss due to demyelination of axons. Transmission of action potentials through partially demyelinated segments can be enhanced with 3,4-DAP. This can provide symptomatic relief. As might be expected, side effects associated with 3,4-DAP are tingling sensation and seizures.

The membrane of a cell also is altered when it loses its synaptic input. Normal function of many neurons and muscle fibers depends on the release of a trophic factor from the presynaptic nerve terminal. Loss of all or most of the input to a cell may result in cell atrophy and in other structural changes in the appearance of the cell. An autonomic neuron that has also lost its innervation becomes much more sensitive to neurotransmitters, a phenomenon called *denervation hypersensitivity,* in which the cellular response to a constant stimulus increases after a cell has lost some of its normal input. This phenomenon is considered further in subsequent chapters.

Each of these types of alteration in neuronal or muscle cell physiology can produce symptoms or signs of short duration — transient disorders. The particular findings in a patient depend on which cells are altered. If the changes are in neurons that subserve sensation, there may be a loss of sensation or an abnormal sensation such as tingling, loss of vision, or "seeing stars." In other systems, there might be loss of strength, twitching in muscles, loss of intellect, or abnormal behavior.

In all these cases, the physiologic alterations are not specific and may be the concomitant of any one of a number of diseases. Transient disorders do not permit a pathologic or etiologic diagnosis. Any of the types of disease (vascular, neoplastic, inflammatory) may be associated with a physiologic alteration of the type described. Therefore, the pathology of a disorder cannot be deduced when its temporal profile is solely that of transient episodes.

Summary

The transmission of information in the neuromuscular system depends on the generation of a resting potential that acts as a reserve of energy poised for release when the valve is turned on. Ionic channels act as the *"valve,"* and the *"energy"* is the ionic concentration gradient. The release of energy is seen either as local, graded potentials or as propagated, action potentials that arise when the local potentials reach threshold. Information is moved from one area to another as action potentials conducted by single cells. The information is integrated by the interaction of local potentials generated in response to the neurotransmitters released from depolarized nerve terminals.

In this system, information can be coded either as the rate of discharge in individual cells or axons, or as the number and combination of active cells. Both of these are important mechanisms, for although the activity of the nervous system can be conveniently described in terms of the electrical activity of single cells, the combined activity of large numbers of cells and axons determines the behavior of the organism.

Objectives

1. Describe cell membrane and ion channel structure.
2. Describe and distinguish between neurotransmitters and neuromodulators in their interactions with ion channels.
3. Describe the mechanism by which the resting potential is generated and maintained.
4. List the characteristics of a local potential, and name three examples.
5. Describe the features of an action potential and the associated ionic changes.
6. Describe the events in synaptic transmission.
7. Define the following terms: depolarization, steady state, equilibrium potential, sodium pump, threshold, afterpotential, accommodation, refractory period, saltatory conduction, excitatory postsynaptic potential, endplate potential, conductance, active transport, spatial summation, presynaptic inhibition, and denervation hypersensitivity.
8. Describe the effect of anoxia and of an alteration in extracellular sodium, potassium, or calcium on the resting and action potentials. List which of these conditions could result in excessive electrical discharges.

Clinical Problems

1. A 64-year-old man had a sudden occlusion of a blood vessel in an area of the brain that controls speech and was unable to speak for 10 minutes. His speech then gradually returned to normal over a 15-minute period. By what mechanism could this recovery occur?

2. A 55-year-old teacher had a brain tumor, with severe right-sided paralysis and signs of brain swelling. When he was given a drug that reduced cerebral edema, his paralysis improved.
   a. If the edema resulted in extracellular sodium dilution, what would be the effect on the action potential amplitude and electrotonic potential amplitudes?
   b. If the osmotic pressure changes produced efflux of potassium from the cell and influx of water into the cell, what would be the effect of the edema on the resting potential?

3. A 36-year-old woman with multiple sclerosis with focal areas of loss of myelin in the central nervous system had a 2-week loss of vision in one eye. How could loss of myelin in the optic nerve have affected her vision?

4. After sitting in a biochemistry lecture for 1½ hours and sleeping with your arm over a chair for 10 minutes, you awaken with a numb hand. As you rub it, it tingles. Which of the following could account for the tingling?
   a. The resting membrane potential moves closer to threshold.
   b. Hyperpolarization of the nerve membrane.
   c. Increased extracellular potassium concentration.
   d. Prolonged positive afterpotential.

5. Some poisons block the action of neurotransmitter at the postsynaptic membrane. What effect could this have on: (a) end-plate potential, (b) generator potential, (c) excitatory postsynaptic potential, (d) accommodation?

6. A 22-year-old woman undergoing spine surgery for idiopathic scoliosis was given succinylcholine, an agent that opens the sodium and chloride channels in muscle for 20 to 30 minutes to induce paralysis during tracheal intubation. If this agent were to act on comparable channels in the central nervous system, what effect would be expected on the neuromodulators of the internal regulation system?

7. A man named Nernst has a wooden boat with a hole in the bottom that he uses on Lake Sodium. When he wants to sit and fish, he lets the boat fill with water until no more comes in, and he keeps his feet up. This condition is one of (a)_____. If he wants to go elsewhere, he must lower the water level in the boat, so he turns on his Lake Sodium pump, which pumps water out. He then achieves a condition in which inflow equals outflow, with little water in the boat. This he calls (b)_____. It requires energy, so the pumping process is called (c)_____.

Additional Reading

Black, J. A., Kocsis, J. D., and Waxman, S. G. Ion channel organization of the myelinated fiber. *Trends Neurosci.* 13:48, 1990.

Koester, J. Membrane Potential. In E. R. Kandel, J. H. Schwartz, and T. M. Jessell (eds.), *Principles of Neural Science* (3rd ed.). New York: Elsevier, 1991. Pp. 81–94.

Koester, J. Passive Membrane Properties of the Neuron. In E. R. Kandel, J. H. Schwartz, and T. M. Jessell (eds.), *Principles of Neural Science* (3rd ed.). New York: Elsevier, 1991. Pp. 95–103.

Koester, J. Voltage-gated Ion Channels and the Generation of the Action Potential. In E. R. Kandel, J. H. Schwartz, and T. M. Jessell (eds.), *Principles of Neural Science* (3rd ed.). New York: Elsevier, 1991. Pp. 104–118.

Levitan, I. B., and Kaczmarek, L. K. *The Neuron: Cell and Molecular Biology.* New York: Oxford University Press, 1991.

Lewis, D. L., et al. Intracellular regulation of ion channels in cell membranes. *Mayo Clin. Proc.* 65:1127, 1990.

Llinás, R. R. The intrinsic electrophysiological properties of mammalian neurons: Insights into central nervous system function. *Science* 242:1654, 1988.

McCormick, D. A. Membrane Properties and Neurotransmitter Actions. In G. M. Shepherd (ed.), *The Synaptic Organization of the Brain* (3rd ed.). New York: Oxford University Press, 1990. Pp. 32–66.

Siegelbaum, S. A., and Koester, J. Ion Channels. In E. R. Kandel, J. H. Schwartz, and T. M. Jessell (eds.), *Principles of Neural Science* (3rd ed.). New York: Elsevier, 1991. Pp. 66–79.

— II —

Longitudinal Systems

— 6 —

The Cerebrospinal Fluid System

The meninges, ventricular system, subarachnoid spaces, and cerebrospinal fluid (CSF) constitute a functionally unique system that has an important role in maintaining a stable environment within which the nervous system can function. The series of membranes that constitute the meninges serve as supportive and protective structures for nerve tissue. The CSF itself provides a cushioning effect during rapid movements of the head and a mechanical buoyancy to the brain. The density of brain tissue is only slightly greater than that of CSF, and the average weight of the brain is 1,500 g. However, the CSF exerts a considerable buoyant effect on the brain. In addition, it provides a pathway for the removal of brain metabolites and functions as a chemical reservoir, protecting the local environment of the brain from some of the changes that may occur in the blood, thus ensuring the brain's continued undisturbed performance. The CSF system is found at the supratentorial, posterior fossa, and spinal levels. Because of the extensive anatomical distribution and function of the CSF system, pathologic alterations to it can occur in a wide variety of neurologic disorders.

Overview

Structures included in the CSF system are the meninges and meningeal spaces formed between the meningeal linings and the brain, the ventricular system, and the CSF itself.

The *meninges* consist of three mesodermally derived membranes: the dura mater (outermost), the arachnoid, and the thin pia mater (innermost), which adheres closely to the structures of the central nervous system. The epidural space lies external to the dura mater, between it and bone. The subdural space lies between the dura mater and the arachnoid, and the subarachnoid space lies between the arachnoid and the pia mater and contains CSF. Cerebrospinal fluid is also contained in the cavities in the brain: the two lateral ventricles, the aqueduct of Sylvius, and the third and fourth ventricles.

The composition of CSF is similar but not identical to that of plasma. Cerebrospinal fluid is formed by a combination of processes, including passive diffusion, facilitated diffusion, and active transport, and is produced primarily but not exclusively by the choroid plexus of the ventricular system. There is a slow circulation of the CSF through the ventricular system into the subarachnoid space and over the surface of the brain and spinal cord. Most of the CSF passes from the arachnoid villi into the venous sinuses.

Because of the close relationship between the CSF system and the neural tissue, pathologic processes that primarily alter the function of the CSF system may secondarily alter nervous system function. Furthermore, because the central nervous system is bathed and surrounded by CSF, disease processes that primarily affect the nervous system may be secondarily reflected by changes in the anatomy and physiology of this system. Examination of the composition of the CSF and of the structure of this system therefore becomes an important and useful neurodiagnostic tool.

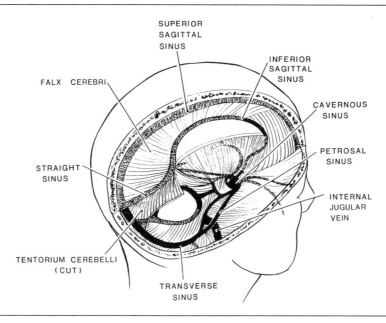

SUPERIOR
SAGITTAL
SINUS

INFERIOR
SAGITTAL
SINUS

FALX CEREBRI

CAVERNOUS
SINUS

PETROSAL
SINUS

STRAIGHT
SINUS

INTERNAL
JUGULAR
VEIN

TENTORIUM CEREBELLI
(CUT)

TRANSVERSE
SINUS

Fig. 6-1. Dura mater and its major sinuses. Dorsolateral view illustrating falx cerebri, tentorium cerebelli, and dura lining base of skull. The dural venous sinuses are stippled or black.

Anatomy of the CSF System

Dura Mater and Its Major Folds

The *dura mater* is a tough, fibrous membrane. In the cranial cavity, it consists of two almost inseparable layers. The outer (periosteal) dura is firmly attached to the periosteum of the cranial bones. Therefore the *epidural space* between the dura mater and bone is normally not present. It is a potential space that becomes of pathologic importance if the dura mater is separated from bone by blood (epidural hematoma) or by pus (epidural abscess). The inner (meningeal) layer of the dura mater remains attached to the outer layer except where they are separated to form venous channels, the *dural venous sinuses.*

The *falx cerebri* is a sickle-shaped reflection of meningeal dura that extends into the interhemispheric fissure to separate the two cerebral hemispheres. It extends from the base of the anterior fossa to the internal occipital protuberance. Its upper margin contains the *superior sagittal sinus,* and its lower free edge, which arches over the corpus callosum, contains the *inferior sagittal sinus* (Fig. 6-1).

At the level of the internal occipital protuberance, the dura forming the falx cerebri extends laterally to form a winglike structure, the *tentorium cerebelli.* The outer border of the tentorium is attached to the occipital bone and along the upper edges of the petrous bones. Thus, it separates the ventral surface of the cerebral hemispheres from the dorsal surface of the cerebellum and divides the cranial cavity into the supratentorial compartment (anterior and middle cranial fossae and their contents) and the infratentorial, or posterior fossa, compartment (see Fig. 3-3). The cerebellar hemispheres contained in the posterior fossa are partially separated by a downward extension of dura, the *falx cerebelli.* The wings of the tentorium converge and attach to the posterior clinoid process of the sella turcica. The free border of the tentorium thus forms an opening, the *tentorial notch,* which surrounds the midbrain at the transition between the posterior fossa and the middle fossa.

The two layers of the dura mater remain tightly attached as they pass through the foramen magnum into the spinal canal. At the

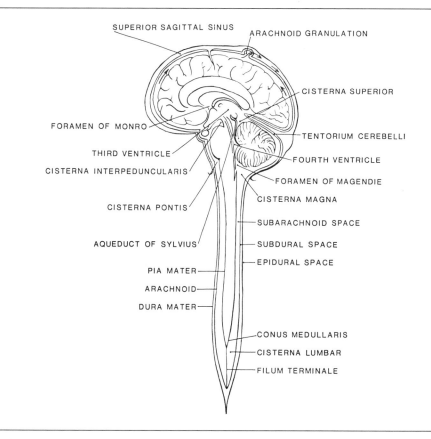

SUPERIOR SAGITTAL SINUS

ARACHNOID GRANULATION

CISTERNA SUPERIOR

FORAMEN OF MONRO

TENTORIUM CEREBELLI

THIRD VENTRICLE

FOURTH VENTRICLE

CISTERNA INTERPEDUNCULARIS

FORAMEN OF MAGENDIE

CISTERNA PONTIS

CISTERNA MAGNA

SUBARACHNOID SPACE

AQUEDUCT OF SYLVIUS

SUBDURAL SPACE

EPIDURAL SPACE

PIA MATER

ARACHNOID

DURA MATER

CONUS MEDULLARIS

CISTERNA LUMBAR

FILUM TERMINALE

Fig. 6-2. The CSF system illustrating meningeal layers, ventricles, and subarachnoid cisterns. (Redrawn from C. R. Noback and R. J. Demarest. *The Nervous System: Introduction and Review.* New York: McGraw-Hill, 1977.)

level of the second or third cervical vertebra, the meningeal dura separates widely from the inner periosteum of bone and forms a narrow sac extending to the level of the second sacral vertebra. The spinal epidural space thus formed between the dura and the periosteum contains fat and vascular structures (principally veins). The conus medullaris, the lower end of the spinal cord (Fig. 6-2), terminates at the level of the second lumbar vertebra. A thin remnant of central nervous system tissue, the *filum terminale,* extends caudally from the conus medullaris to the termination of the dural sac at the second sacral level. The filum terminale is composed of glial cells, ependyma, and astrocytes, covered by pia mater. The dura is pierced by the roots of the spinal and cranial nerves along the length of the brain stem and spinal cord.

Leptomeninges (Arachnoid and Pia Mater)

Embryologically, the leptomeninges, the arachnoid and pia mater, begin as a single membrane, which becomes separated by numerous confluent subarachnoid spaces containing CSF. The arachnoid, however, remains attached to the pia mater by numerous weblike trabeculae (Fig. 6-3). Although the pia mater adheres tightly to the surfaces of the brain and spinal cord, the arachnoid is closely applied to the inner surface of the meningeal dura mater throughout the neuraxis. The potential space between the dura mater and the arachnoid is termed the *subdural space* and normally contains a thin layer of fluid. In pathologic states, blood may accumulate in this location and produce a *subdural hematoma.*

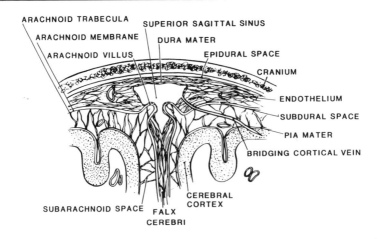

Fig. 6-3. Meninges and meningeal spaces. Diagrammatic coronal section through paramedian region of cerebral hemispheres. Note bridging vein extending from cortex to superior sagittal sinus. Tear of this type of vein is a common cause of subarachnoid and subdural bleeding.

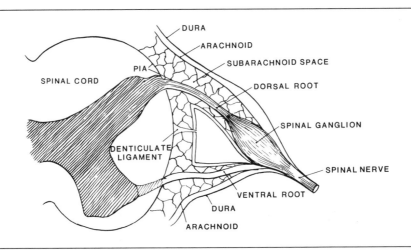

Fig. 6-4. Meningeal relationships at spinal level. Note investments of spinal nerve root by dura mater as it leaves spinal canal. The denticulate ligaments attach spinal cord to dura laterally.

As a result of the relationship of the arachnoid to the dura mater, and the pia mater to neural tissue, the *subarachnoid space* varies greatly in size and shape, particularly over the surfaces of the brain and in the lumbar region of the spinal canal (see Fig. 6-2). In the cranial cavity, these enlargements of the subarachnoid space are called *cisterns,* and they are usually named for their anatomical location (for example, the interpeduncular cistern is located between the cerebral peduncles; the cisterna magna is a large space below the cerebellum). In the spinal canal, where the spinal cord ends at the level of the second lumbar vertebra and the arachnoid remains closely applied to the dura mater to the level of the second sacral vertebra, a large lumbar subarachnoid space is formed

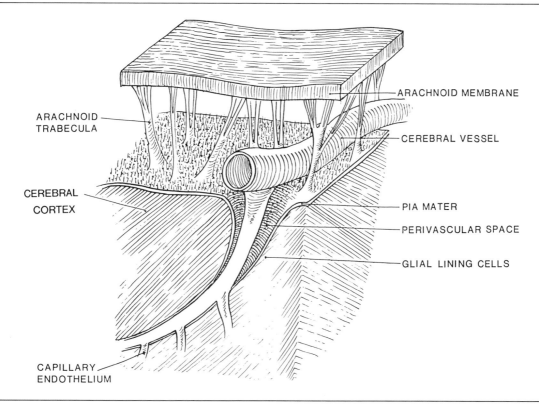

ARACHNOID MEMBRANE

ARACHNOID TRABECULA

CEREBRAL VESSEL

CEREBRAL CORTEX

PIA MATER

PERIVASCULAR SPACE

GLIAL LINING CELLS

CAPILLARY ENDOTHELIUM

Fig. 6-5. Detailed relationships of meninges and structures in subarachnoid space. An arteriole carries pia mater into the cerebral cortex.

that contains a reservoir of CSF, the filum terminale, and the nerve roots of the cauda equina as they pass to their intervertebral foramina. The major arterial channels of the brain are located in the subarachnoid space. Bleeding from these vessels results in *subarachnoid hemorrhage.*

On gross inspection, the pia mater cannot be seen except at intervals in the spinal canal, where it extends laterally to attach to the dura mater as the *denticulate ligaments* (Fig. 6-4). Throughout the rest of its distribution, the pia mater closely invests the central nervous system, its few cell layers being separated from the outermost neural tissue, the *astrocytic glia limitans,* by a thin layer of collagen. In the trabeculae, the cells of the pia and arachnoid are contiguous and are called *leptomeninges* (see Fig. 6-2). Arterioles, as they dip into the parenchyma of the brain, are invested with a sheath of leptomeninges that disappears at the capillary level to leave only the endothelium of the blood vessel and its basement membrane in direct contact with the astrocytic glia limitans (Fig. 6-5). This forms the so-called blood-brain barrier.

Blood-brain barrier is a descriptive term first used many years ago when it was observed that certain dyes injected intravenously would stain all body organs except the brain; yet the same dyes injected into the CSF would produce staining of brain tissue. It was therefore postulated that a "barrier" for the passage of the dye was located between the blood and the brain. The tight junctions of the unfenestrated endothelial cells are of major importance in maintaining the integrity of the blood-brain barrier. These junctions are not, however, the only blood-brain barrier, but merely part of a system of barriers (some anatomical, others physiologic) that serve to produce differences in the chemical composition of the brain, CSF, and blood.

Arachnoid villi (or granulations) (see Fig. 6-2) are invaginations of the arachnoid into the dural venous sinuses. Fluid circulating

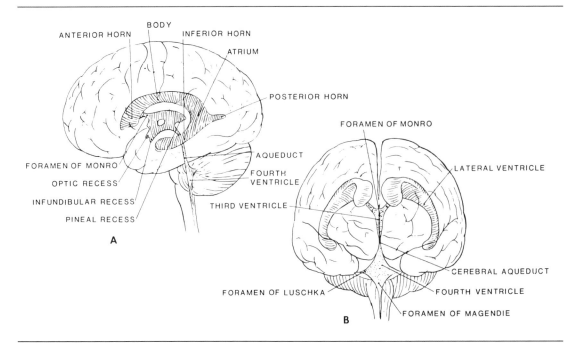

Fig. 6-6. Ventricular system. A. Lateral view. B. Anterior view. The pons has been removed from the illustration to display the anatomy of the fourth ventricle. (Redrawn from C. R. Noback and R. J. Demarest. *The Nervous System: Introduction and Review.* New York: McGraw-Hill, 1977.)

through these villi passes into the venous blood and systemic circulation.

Ventricular System of the Brain

The ventricular system (Fig. 6-6) is lined with ciliated cuboidal epithelium (derived from ectoderm) called *ependyma. Tanycytes* are specialized ependymal cells that lack cilia and are located in the lining of the floor of the third ventricle. They may be involved in the release of hypophysiotropic hormones from the hypothalamus into the portal circulation. *Choroid plexuses* are found in the lateral, third, and fourth ventricles. They are multitufted vascular organs that arise embryologically when ependyma, leptomeninges, and blood vessels fold into the ventricles. These structures, rich in the enzymes that are found in other secretory organs, are the main (but not the only) source for the production of the CSF. *Pinocytosis* is the movement of substances across the cell membrane in the form of tiny vesicles formed by pinching off a section of the surface membrane. The pro-

cess of pinocytotic transport has been identified in the choroid plexus.

A *lateral ventricle* (Fig. 6-7) is located in each of the cerebral hemispheres and is divided into an anterior horn located in the frontal lobe, body and atrium (or trigone) in the parietal lobe, posterior horn in the occipital lobe, and inferior horn in the temporal lobe. The lateral ventricles communicate with each other and the *third ventricle* of the diencephalon via the *interventricular foramina of Monro.* The *aqueduct of Sylvius* traverses the mesencephalon and leads from the third ventricle to the *fourth ventricle,* located dorsal to the pons and medulla. Communication of the ventricular system with the subarachnoid space is in the fourth ventricle via two *foramina of Luschka* and the *foramen of Magendie.* A small and discontinuous *central canal* extends for a short distance from the caudal aspect of the fourth ventricle. At the spinal level, this canal is usually obliterated, and therefore, in the normal adult, only a few ependymal cells remain as remnants of the once prominent central canal of the embryo.

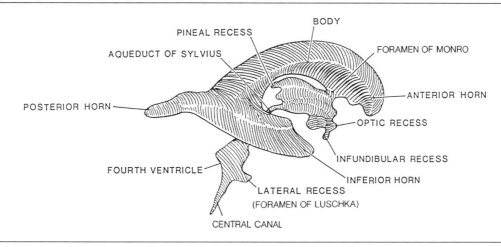

Fig. 6-7. Detailed anatomy of ventricular system. (Redrawn from M. W. Woerdeman. *Atlas of Human Anatomy: Descriptive and Regional.* Baltimore: Williams & Wilkins, 1948.)

The Cerebrospinal Fluid

Formation and Circulation of CSF

The rate of CSF formation remains relatively constant at approximately 0.35 ml per minute (500 ml/day). Because the total volume of CSF in the adult is 90 to 150 ml, the processes of CSF formation and resorption must remain in delicate balance in order to prevent alteration in structure and function of the brain.

The production of CSF is an active process, mediated partly by the enzyme carbonic anhydrase. CSF production is relatively independent of hydrostatic forces; however, a decrease in choroid plexus perfusion pressure to 50 mm Hg causes a decrease in CSF production. In contrast, the rate of CSF absorption is proportional to the hydrostatic pressure, with greater absorption occurring in the presence of increasing CSF pressure.

Nerve terminals have been identified on plexus arterioles and on the cells of the secretory epithelium. Thus, alterations in CSF production may occur in response to both intrinsic and extrinsic neurotransmitter systems, including norepinephrine and vasopressin.

Most of the CSF is actively secreted into the ventricular system by the choroid plexuses; however, these are not the only source of CSF. Some is derived directly from the interstitial fluid of the brain and crosses the ependyma to enter the ventricles. Additional exchange may take place between the neural tissue and the subarachnoid space across the pia mater.

Circulation of the CSF is pulsatile and promoted by the beating of the cilia of the ependymal cells and the pulsatile changes in the volume of intracranial blood that occurs with cardiac systole and with respiratory movements. The to and fro movement of CSF results in a directional flow that is from the lateral, third, and fourth ventricles to the subarachnoid space, where it then circulates in two major directions. The more important pathway is rostrally through the tentorial notch and then dorsally toward the intracranial venous system, where CSF exits through arachnoid villi that project into the dural venous sinuses, particularly the superior sagittal sinus. While the exact mechanism of transfer of CSF to venous blood through the arachnoid villi is incompletely understood, transcellular transport via giant vacuoles seems most likely. The villi act as one-way valves, preventing entrance of blood into the CSF. A hydrostatic pressure of 70 mm H_2O or greater forces the CSF into the sinuses. The second pathway, a quantitatively less important and slower route taken by the CSF after its exit from the ventricular system, is downward through the foramen magnum into the spinal subarachnoid space, where it is partially resorbed through the leptomeninges.

CSF Pressure

The craniovertebral cavity and its dural lining are a closed space. Any increase in the size or volume of one of the three "compartments" (blood, CSF, brain) in the cavity can occur only in conjunction with an equal reduction in the size or volume of the others, or with a consequent increase in pressure. Normally, however, the contents of the three compartments are relatively constant, producing a CSF pressure of 50 to 200 mm H_2O when recorded in the lumbar subarachnoid sac with the patient lying in a lateral recumbent position.

Minor oscillations occur in CSF pressure recorded in this manner in response to respiration and arterial pulsation, as varied amounts of blood enter and leave the craniovertebral cavity. Certain additional maneuvers cause wider oscillations in CSF pressure. Compression of the jugular veins, for example, impedes the outflow of blood from the brain, expands the venous vascular bed, and causes a rapid increase in intracranial pressure. Because the lumbar subarachnoid sac is directly continuous with the intracranial subarachnoid space, this increase in pressure is transmitted throughout the ventriculosubarachnoid system (as long as there is no obstruction to the flow of CSF). The spinal epidural venous plexuses normally contribute to the CSF pressure by continuous tamponade of the spinal dural sac. Increased intrathoracic or intraabdominal pressure (coughing, sneezing, straining at the stool, or abdominal compression) can thereby increase CSF pressure.

In certain pathologic conditions, the increase in the volume of some of the components of the cranial cavity cannot be compensated for by readjustments in the volume of the other constituents. In this situation, intracranial pressure increases to abnormal levels. In addition, *plateau waves,* a pathologic increase in intracranial pressure, are occasionally noted. These acute elevations in pressure may be as high as 600 to 1,300 mm H_2O and may be 5 to 20 minutes in duration. The cause of these pressure increases, which are accompanied by a reduction in cerebral blood flow, is not known.

Monitoring of CSF pressure has been used in various clinical situations (most notably in cases of head trauma) to help guide the management of patients with known or suspected increased intracranial pressure. The symptoms and consequences of increased intracranial pressure will be discussed later.

The Blood-Brain–CSF Barrier System

The central nervous system contains two basic fluid compartments: extracellular (CSF and interstitial fluid) and intracellular (primarily fluid within the cytoplasm of neurons and glial cells). The chemical compositions of these two fluid compartments are dissimilar, and the composition of each fluid differs significantly from that of blood. The chemical composition of the central nervous system fluid compartments is maintained within relatively narrow limits despite large fluctuations in the composition of extracellular fluid elsewhere in the body. Therefore, factors other than simple diffusion must be responsible for the passage of chemicals from one compartment to another.

Historically, reference has been made to a blood-brain barrier, implying an anatomical structure that would explain the variable distribution of substances in each compartment. Although not the sole explanation for the blood-brain barrier, anatomical considerations do have an important role. Morphologically, the choroidal epithelium, arachnoid membrane, and capillary endothelial cells have *tight junctions* that obliterate the intercellular clefts normally between cells. This anatomical feature impedes the diffusion of larger molecules. Some areas of the brain, however, are excluded from this blood-brain barrier system (perhaps as a means of allowing neuronal receptors to "sample" plasma directly). In these regions, the capillary endothelium contains fenestrations that allow proteins and small molecules to pass from the blood to adjacent tissue. Areas that lack tight junctions in the capillary endothelium and have some homeostatic function are the area postrema (in the brain stem, near the "vomiting center"), a region of the hypothalamus, the neurohypophysis, the pineal gland, and other small areas of glial-ependymal specialization located along the surface of the ventricles. These regions are termed *circumventricular organs.* They have fenestrated capillaries rather than tight junctions, abundant capillary loops, and large perivascular spaces. Because of their unique structure and connections (neural and humoral sampling), circumventricular organs are important for homeostasis.

There are also other physicochemical factors, such as lipid solubility, protein binding, and state of ionization, that alter the passage of substances from one fluid compartment to another. In addition, certain substances are transported across membranes by carrier-mediated, facilitated diffusion systems, whereas others are transported by energy-requiring, active transport systems. Therefore, although one commonly refers to a blood-brain barrier, one is in effect referring to a wide variety of barrier systems, some anatomical and physicochemical, which act together to maintain homeostasis.

With the breakdown of this barrier in various pathologic conditions, several changes occur that are reflected as alterations in the composition of CSF. Four major mechanisms are believed to be involved in the increased vascular permeability noted in disease states: (1) interendothelial passage across tight junctions, (2) transendothelial flow, (3) vesicular transport, and (4) neovascularization.

Composition of CSF

One additional function of the CSF is to provide a pathway for the removal of the products of cerebral metabolism. In this regard, the CSF has been referred to as a large metabolic "sink," a reservoir that allows metabolites of the brain to "drain" into it and then to enter the systemic circulation. The composition of the CSF thus is a reflection of the processes previously described as well as of the metabolic activity of the central nervous system.

Appearance
The CSF is normally clear and colorless; turbidity or discoloration is always abnormal. Turbidity is most commonly due to increased numbers of red or white blood cells. The most important cause of discoloration of the CSF is bleeding in the subarachnoid space. With subarachnoid hemorrhage (usually due to trauma or rupture of an intracranial vessel), the fluid

is initially pink to red, depending on the severity of the bleeding. During the 2 to 10 hours after such an event, the red blood cells undergo lysis, and the liberated hemoglobin is broken down to form bilirubin, which imparts a yellow color (xanthochromia) to the CSF. A yellow discoloration also may be due to a markedly elevated level of CSF protein or be secondary to an elevation in the level of plasma bilirubin.

Cellular Elements
Normal CSF contains no more than 5 lymphocytes per microliter. A cell count of 5 to 10 cells is very suspicious, and a count greater than 10 is definitely abnormal and suggests the presence of disease in the central nervous system or in the meninges. The presence of polymorphonuclear leukocytes is always indicative of disease.

Microbiologic Features
Cerebrospinal fluid is normally sterile. Therefore, results of microbiologic studies (Gram's stains, cultures) should be negative.

Protein
The normal total CSF protein concentration is no greater than 45 mg per deciliter. The capillary endothelial membrane is highly effective in limiting the concentration of protein in the CSF, and elevation in the CSF protein concentration is a frequent (but nonspecific) pathologic finding, suggestive of disease involving the central nervous system or meninges.

The amount of protein normally present in CSF is much less than that in plasma, although the relative proportions of the protein fractions are similar. Most of the CSF protein is probably derived from the plasma. One protein of clinical significance is the gamma globulin fraction. Normally, gamma globulin is synthesized outside the central nervous system. The normal concentration of gamma globulin in lumbar fluid is less than 13 percent of the total CSF protein concentration. In conditions such as multiple sclerosis, neurosyphilis, and some other subacute or chronic infections of the central nervous system, the gamma globulin level increases in association with a normal or slightly elevated total protein level. (For this observation to be valid, there must be no change in the level of serum gamma globulin.) Such an increase in the gamma globulin in the CSF suggests an abnormal formation of gamma globulin by chronic inflammatory cells within the nervous system, with diffusion of the protein from brain to CSF.

Measurement of immunoglobulin G (IgG), which accounts for almost all of the gamma globulin in normal CSF and in most disease states, is a more sensitive indicator of central nervous system inflammation and immunoglobulin production than is total gamma globulin in disorders such as multiple sclerosis. Agar gel electrophoresis of concentrated CSF allows identification of qualitative changes in the IgG fraction. In normal CSF and in most noninflammatory neurologic diseases, the IgG fraction forms a diffuse, homogeneous zone of migration. Normal CSF IgG is less than 8.4 mg per deciliter. In multiple sclerosis and some other subacute and chronic inflammatory diseases, two or more discrete subfractions, which represent specific antibody populations called *oligoclonal bands,* are identified within the IgG migration zone. Another protein fraction derived from the central nervous system, myelin basic protein, can be identified by radioimmunoassay. It is not present in normal CSF and is an indicator of active demyelination.

Glucose
The glucose in CSF is normally about 60 to 70 percent of that in plasma. The normal range in patients with blood levels of 80 to 120 mg per deciliter, therefore, is between 45 and 80 mg per deciliter. Values less than 35 to 40 mg per deciliter are abnormal.

Glucose enters the CSF from plasma by both simple and facilitated diffusion, and similar mechanisms are responsible for its removal. In addition, glucose is metabolized by arachnoidal, ependymal, neuronal, and glial cells, or it may leave the CSF with water (bulk flow).

Changes in levels of CSF glucose reflect similar changes in the blood, but a variable time is required before the CSF glucose equilibrates with the blood glucose. Thus, the CSF concentration does not reach a maximum for about 2 hours after the rapid intravenous injections of hypertonic glucose, and there is a similar delay in the lowering of the CSF glucose level after insulin-induced hypoglycemia. Therefore, when the CSF glucose determination is of diagnostic importance, CSF and blood levels should be obtained simultaneously, with the patient in a fasting state.

An increased CSF glucose level is of little diagnostic importance and likely reflects an increase in the serum glucose level. A low CSF glucose level (in the presence of a normal blood concentration) is, however, very important. The CSF glucose level is characteristically low in acute bacterial and chronic fungal infections of the central nervous system. (It is frequently normal in viral infections.) Low CSF glucose values in the presence of bacterial infection are believed to be due to increased glycolysis by polymorphonuclear leukocytes, glucose utilization by bacteria, increased glycolysis by neural elements, or a breakdown of facilitated diffusion of glucose, which effectively slows the rate of entry of glucose into the central nervous system.

Clinical Correlations I: Disorders of the CSF System

Syndrome of Increased Intracranial Pressure

An uncompensated increase in the volume of any of the constituents of the cranial vault results in an increase in intracranial pressure. Such an increase can occur from an increase in the total volume of brain tissue (as with diffuse cerebral edema), a focal increase in brain volume (as with an intracerebral hemorrhage, neoplasm, or other mass lesion), an increase in CSF volume without an associated loss of brain tissue (as in hydrocephalus), or diffuse vasodilatation or venous obstruction (from any of several causes). While many clinical symptoms may be associated with increased intracranial pressure, none is individually diagnostic of this condition; yet together they form a characteristic clinical pattern consisting of the following:

1. *Headache* is believed to be due to traction on the pain-sensitive structures within the cranium. Factors that tend to increase this

Fig. 6-8. Optic fundus and optic nerve head. A. Normal optic disk. B. Papilledema. Disk margins are elevated and blurred; venous congestion and hemorrhages are seen surrounding disk.

traction, such as coughing, straining, or position change, tend to precipitate or aggravate the headache.

2. *Nausea* and *vomiting* are associated with the vagal motor centers, which are located in the floor of the fourth ventricle and which mediate the motility of the gastrointestinal tract. Increased ventricular pressure transmitted to these centers may account for these symptoms.

3. *Bradycardia* is presumed to be due to pressure on a vagal control mechanism similar to that proposed for nausea and vomiting.

4. *Elevated blood pressure* is related to intracranial pressure; as intracranial pressure increases, the arterial blood pressure also must increase if brain blood flow is to continue. This reflex is mediated by structures located in the ventrolateral medulla.

5. *Papilledema* is characterized by elevation and blurring of the optic disk margin, as viewed with an ophthalmoscope (Fig. 6-8). The subdural and subarachnoid spaces of the brain extend along the course of the optic nerve (Fig. 6-9). Increased pressure within the skull and subarachnoid space thus can be transmitted to the nerve, causing impairment of axonal transport. This results in edema of the nerve head.

6. *Alterations in consciousness* occur if the pressure increase is large, and as further

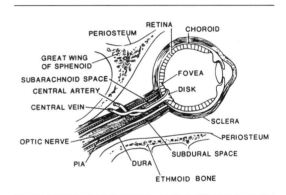

Fig. 6-9. Relationships of meninges and meningeal spaces to optic nerve. Increased intracranial pressure may result in edema of optic nerve head.

pathologic change develops, consciousness may be lost because of diffuse hypoperfusion and secondary brain stem compression (see Chapter 10, The Consciousness System).

7. *Changes in the skull* occur in children and adults. In children, in whom the bones of the cranial vault have not yet permanently fused, chronic increases in pressure may be partially compensated for by a modest separation of the bones at the suture lines. In infants, in whom a "soft spot" (fontanelle) is not yet ossified, this membranous structure located at the vertex of the head may

is impaired. The rate of CSF formation by the choroid plexus remains relatively constant, and because the relative amount of CSF increases, there is a corresponding increase in ventricular pressure, and progressive dilatation of the ventricles (hydrocephalus) occurs in regions proximal to the blockage (Fig. 6-10). Signs and symptoms of increased intracranial pressure also may develop.

Before adequate techniques for visualization of the ventricular system were available, clinicians devised a method for determining the site of blockage in hydrocephalus. Histologic studies of the pathology had shown that the obstruction was most commonly either (1) within the ventricular system itself, that is, proximal to the outlets of the fourth ventricle as in, for example, aqueductal stenosis; or (2) outside the ventricular system where inadequate circulation over the convexities of the brain prevents adequate resorption, for example, after meningitis or subarachnoid hemorrhage (Fig. 6-11). To differentiate these two conditions, a cannula was inserted through the skull into the ventricular system and a second cannula was inserted into the lumbar subarachnoid space. If dye that was injected into the ventricles could later be recovered in the lumbar sac, then a *communicating hydrocephalus* indicating an extraventricular blockage was present; if no dye was recovered, then a *noncommunicating hydrocephalus* indicating a blockage within the ventricular system was present. Although clinicians no longer use this method of diagnosis, the responsible lesions are still often referred to as producing either a communicating or a noncommunicating hydrocephalus.

The term *hydrocephalus* also describes the situation that occurs in brain atrophy. Coincident with the reduction in volume of brain tissue, there is enlargement of the ventricles and subarachnoid spaces, with an increase in the amount of CSF. The total volume of the intracranial contents remains unchanged, however, and there is no increase in intracranial pressure. This type of process is referred to as *hydrocephalus ex vacuo*.

Fig. 6-10. Coronal sections of cerebral hemispheres showing hydrocephalus. Note marked dilatation of lateral ventricles, with thinning of cerebral walls at expense of white matter. In lower (more posterior) section, the thin septum has been artificially torn.

become tense and bulge outward. In adults, in whom bony fusion is complete and the skull is incapable of further expansion, some demineralization of bone, especially around the sella turcica, is occasionally seen.

This clinical syndrome may occur in isolation, but more commonly, it is superimposed on the signs and symptoms of the underlying pathologic lesion. If the syndrome of increased intracranial pressure occurs with signs of a focal lesion, whether acute, subacute, or chronic in their evolution, the diagnosis of a mass lesion becomes highly likely.

Hydrocephalus

In certain pathologic conditions, the pathway for CSF circulation is blocked and absorption

Cerebral Edema

Brain swelling, or *edema,* is an increase in brain volume due to an increase in the water

Fig. 6-11. Communicating hydrocephalus as shown by magnetic resonance imaging. A. Horizontal view. B. Sagittal view.

content of the brain. It is a nonspecific condition that can be associated with a wide variety of cerebral disorders, including hypoxia, meningitis, neoplasm, abscess, and infarction. Three major types of brain edema have been described:

1. *Vasogenic edema* results from an increase in permeability of brain capillary endothelial cells and produces an increase in extracellular fluid volume.
2. *Cytotoxic edema* is an increase in the intracellular fluid volume of the brain. This form of edema is presumably caused by a failure of the ATP-dependent sodium pump mechanism, with the result that sodium efflux is altered and water enters the cell in order to maintain osmotic equilibrium.
3. *Interstitial edema* is a periventricular transudate seen in cases of communicating hydrocephalus with increased CSF pressure and passive movement of CSF from the ventricles to the surrounding periventricular regions.

Although the first type of edema is most often seen surrounding focal brain lesions and the second is seen in association with hypoxia, either type may be relatively well localized or diffuse and widespread. Both types result in an increase in intracranial volume and pressure, causing symptoms of increased intracranial pressure that may be superimposed on the underlying pathologic process (Fig. 6-12). Clinical monitoring of intracranial pressure can be accomplished with a transducer surgically placed through the skull. The constant assessment of pressure-related changes provides a physiologic basis for therapeutic intervention.

Syndrome of Acute Meningeal Irritation

A number of noxious agents produce meningeal irritation, but, regardless of the cause, the clinical manifestations are similar and consist of the following:

1. *Headache* is usually prominent and severe and is due to vasodilatation or to chemical irritation or inflammation (or both) of the major pain-sensitive structures.
2. *Stiff neck* is caused by irritation of the meninges in the posterior fossa and upper cervical spinal canal, which stimulates spinal nerve roots and results in reflex spasm and contraction of the posterior neck muscles. This increased resistance to neck flexion is termed *nuchal rigidity.*
3. *Alteration in consciousness* results from a pathologic process that is widespread and

Fig. 6-12. Cerebral edema (associated with neighboring meningioma — not shown). Note pallor and swelling of white matter of left hemisphere, with marked shift of midline structures from left to right. (Luxol-fast blue stain; ×1.)

severe, causing diffuse depression of cortical function and change in the level of consciousness.

The most common causes of this syndrome are bacterial meningitis, viral encephalitis, and subarachnoid hemorrhage. Each of these superimposes its own characteristic signature on the general pattern of meningeal irritation.

Bacterial Meningitis
An inflammation of the CSF system can be caused by bacterial invasion and can be accompanied by a characteristic leukocytic exudate in the pia mater and arachnoid, as well as in structures adjacent to the leptomeninges (Fig. 6-13). Bacteria may be found in the CSF and within neutrophilic white blood cells. The type of leukocytic exudate reflects the nature of the invading organism. Most commonly, infections caused by meningococcus, *Haemophilus influenzae,* staphylococcus, and streptococcus organisms are accompanied by a polymorphonuclear exudate, whereas more indolent infections, such as those caused by

the tubercle bacillus, are associated with a predominance of lymphocytes. The pathologic reaction is widely distributed throughout the leptomeninges, but it may be most extensive in the basal subarachnoid cisterns. The clinical-anatomical-temporal profile of this disorder is that of diffuse, subacute, and progressive involvement of the nervous system, with the superimposed features of fever and systemic reaction and the syndrome of meningeal irritation, and with or without evidence of increased intracranial pressure. After treatment or subsiding of the infection, reactive changes may occur within the CSF system, which can impair CSF absorption and result in hydrocephalus.

Viral Encephalitis
Viral infections usually induce remarkably few gross pathologic changes in the brain. Vascular dilatation, congestion, and edema are not uncommon, and occasional petechial hemorrhages may be seen in the cortex. Histopathologically, there are necrosis of nerve cells and neuronophagia, perivascular cuffing by

Fig. 6-13. Acute purulent bacterial meningitis. A. Brain in situ viewed from left side showing marked clouding of subarachnoid space. B. Cortex of brain showing adjacent subarachnoid space filled with acute inflammatory cells. (H & E; ×250.)

Table 6-1. CSF Findings in Syndromes Involving Meningeal Irritation

CSF	Normal	Subarachnoid hemorrhage	Bacterial meningitis	Viral encephalitis
Appearance	Clear	Bloody	Cloudy	Clear to slightly cloudy
Cell count	<5 lymphocytes	Red blood cells present; white blood cells in proportion to red blood cells in the peripheral blood count	Usually >1,000 white blood cells; mostly polymorphonuclear leukocytes	Usually 25–500 white blood cells, mostly lymphocytes
Protein	<45 mg/dl	Normal to slightly elevated	Usually elevated >100 mg/dl	Minimally elevated, usually <100 mg/dl
Glucose	>45 mg/dl	Normal (rarely reduced)	Reduced	Normal
Microbiologic findings	Negative	Negative	Positive Gram's stain; positive cultures	Negative Gram's stain; negative viral cultures usually

lymphocytes and mononuclear leukocytes, and meningeal infiltration by similar cells. The clinical-anatomical-temporal profile of this disorder is virtually identical to that noted for bacterial meningitis (diffuse, subacute, and progressive); however, because of the difference in inflammatory response, the findings on examination of the CSF may differ (Table 6-1).

Subarachnoid Hemorrhage

The acute rupture of an intracranial vessel may produce little pathologic change in the brain itself. As red blood cells intermix with CSF, the signs and symptoms of meningeal irritation are to be expected. Most commonly, subarachnoid hemorrhage occurs as a result of trauma, rupture of an intracranial aneurysm, or leakage from an arteriovenous malformation. Although

Fig. 6-14. Base of brain after acute subarachnoid hemorrhage due to ruptured aneurysm. Note blood throughout subarachnoid space is concentrated in major cisterns.

the source of bleeding is often from a single well-localized source, blood rapidly mixes with CSF and is distributed throughout the neuraxis (Fig. 6-14). A diffuse, acute, and sometimes progressive disorder results. Only rarely does the aneurysm produce focal signs.

Examination of the CSF by lumbar puncture is the usual means of initially differentiating the disorders that produce the syndrome of meningeal irritation (see Table 6-1).

Intracranial Epidural Hematoma

The epidural hemorrhage lies between the dura mater and the inner table of the skull and most commonly occurs from a skull fracture or traumatic laceration of the *middle meningeal artery*. Blood then dissects the dura mater from bone, forming a localized, rapidly expanding intracranial mass. Typically, the patient receives an injury to the head of sufficient degree to produce a period of unconsciousness. Thereafter, depending on the rate of bleeding, the patient becomes increasingly drowsy and then lapses into stupor and finally

into deep coma. The cerebral hemisphere is pushed medially by the enlarging mass, thereby compressing the upper brain stem against the unyielding tentorium cerebelli. The patient will die unless emergency measures are taken to evacuate the blood clot.

The clinical-anatomical-temporal profile of this lesion is that of an acute, focal, and progressive lesion, with evidence of increased intracranial pressure. A history of trauma is often present.

Intracranial Subdural Hematoma

Subdural hematomas are most commonly seen in infants and in adults of middle age and beyond, particularly adults who are likely to suffer head injury (for example, alcoholics). The injury that produces the hematoma may be severe or so mild that it is forgotten.

At the time of injury, a tear usually occurs in a cortical vein at the point where it attaches to the superior longitudinal sinus. As a result, a small amount of bleeding occurs in the subdural space. This initial blood is often not enough to cause noticeable symptoms. Fibroblasts and capillaries proliferate and surround this blood with a fibrous membrane derived from the dura mater. Enlargement of the hematoma results from recurrent bleeding of the neomembrane or from increased osmotic activity of disintegrating red blood cells. With further increase in size, the intracranial volume increases, compressing the underlying brain (Fig. 6-15). The typical clinical-anatomical-temporal profile of this not uncommon and potentially treatable disorder is that of a chronic, focal, progressive lesion with symptoms of increased intracranial pressure.

Clinical Correlations II: Diagnostic Studies Utilizing the CSF System

The anatomy, physiology, and the known pathologic changes that may occur within the CSF system serve as the basis for many neurodiagnostic tests.

Lumbar Puncture

Although lumbar puncture is a procedure with little risk or discomfort to the patient, exami-

Fig. 6-15. Left subdural hematoma. Note accumulation of blood between dura mater and arachnoid, with compression of left cerebral hemisphere.

nation of the CSF via puncture of the lumbar subarachnoid sac is not a routine diagnostic test. Lumbar puncture is indicated only when it is necessary to obtain specific information about the cellular or chemical constituents of the CSF. The procedure is usually contraindicated if there is known or suspected increased intracranial pressure, because in certain instances (especially those of localized mass lesions), sudden alteration in CSF pressure dynamics can lead to herniation of the brain contents through the foramen magnum and clinical decompensation or death. Usually, when increased intracranial pressure is suspected, a brain imaging study (such as computerized tomography or magnetic resonance imaging) is performed to help define the nature of the intracranial pathologic process before deciding whether lumbar puncture is needed.

The examination is usually performed in one of the three lower lumbar interspaces (Fig. 6-16). Puncture above the L-2–L-3 interspace (the region of the conus medullaris) is inadvisable. In infants or children in whom the spinal

cord may be situated at a lower level, the puncture should be performed in the L-4–L-5 or L-5–S-1 interspace.

With the patient in a lateral recumbent position, the use of a simple manometer allows measurement of CSF pressure (normally less than 200 mm H_2O). To ensure that the needle is properly placed in the subarachnoid sac, the pressure response to gentle coughing, straining, or abdominal compression should be observed. Normally, a prompt increase in pressure of at least 40 mm H_2O results from the elevation of central venous pressure that accompanies these maneuvers.

In patients with suspected spinal cord disease, the jugular compression test (Queckenstedt's test) may be performed. Prior to the removal of any fluid, the jugular veins are compressed manually by an assistant. There normally should be an abrupt increase in spinal fluid pressure of between 100 and 300 mm H_2O within 10 seconds after the compression and a prompt decrease upon release. The compression procedure retards venous drainage from the skull and increases

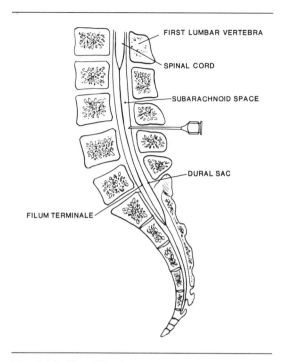

FIRST LUMBAR VERTEBRA

SPINAL CORD

SUBARACHNOID SPACE

DURAL SAC

FILUM TERMINALE

Fig. 6-16. Site of lumbar puncture. Note that in the normal adult, the caudal border of spinal cord lies at the L-1 to L-2 vertebral level.

intracranial pressure. In the absence of a blockage in the spinal subarachnoid pathways, this increase in pressure is transmitted to the lumbar subarachnoid sac. An absent or sluggish increase in pressure, with a delayed or absent decrease upon release, is suggestive of obstruction in the subarachnoid pathways, usually by a spinal mass lesion located cephalad to the needle site. Since this test is a means of determining the presence or absence of a spinal subarachnoid blockage, it is never done routinely and is *contraindicated* for all conditions other than suspected spinal cord disease. Patients with suspected intracranial disease may already have an increase in intracranial pressure, and compression of the jugular veins will further increase this pressure.

After determination of the initial pressure, the appearance of the fluid is noted, and 5 to 15 ml of CSF is removed for cell count, protein analysis, glucose determination, and microbiologic and other studies. A serologic test for syphilis is generally performed on all spinal fluid specimens because that disease, char-

acterized partly by a chronic inflammatory reaction in the central nervous system, may mimic many other disorders.

Even with the most experienced examiners, occasionally one of the veins lying in the spinal epidural space is nicked by the lumbar puncture needle; a "traumatic tap" results, bloody fluid is obtained, and one must then differentiate this from a true subarachnoid hemorrhage. In a traumatic tap, fluid collected in successive test tubes usually shows decreasing amounts of red blood cells, while in cases of hemorrhagic disease the blood staining of fluid remains uniform. Furthermore, in a hemorrhagic disorder several hours often have elapsed between the onset of symptoms and the performance of a lumbar puncture, and xanthochromic staining of the supernatant fluid is seen in a centrifuged specimen; this staining is not noted in the case of a traumatic puncture.

Myelography

Myelography consists of the introduction of a radiopaque substance, usually via a lumbar puncture, into the subarachnoid space. Myelography can be utilized to study the spinal canal (Fig. 6-17A) and posterior fossa (Fig. 6-17B) and is often combined with computerized tomography for better definition of abnormality at the spinal level.

Computerized Tomographic Imaging

Computerized tomography (CT) is another method of studying the anatomy of the intracranial space in patients. This technique, which is rapid, painless, and almost free of risk, permits visualization of the ventriculosubarachnoid system and parenchymal structures at the spinal, posterior fossa, and supratentorial levels (Fig. 6-18).

All computerized tomographic imaging techniques are based on four general principles. First, they all look at a physical characteristic of small volumes of tissue (voxels) within a "slice" of the body in a particular plane. Second, they have an array of detectors that allow measurement of that characteristic in each voxel from many different directions. Third, they have a computer that allows them to mathematically process the

Fig. 6-17. Myelograms. A. Anteroposterior view showing filling of lumbar sub-arachnoid space. B. By tilting patient downward, contrast medium can be used to visualize entire spinal canal and structures contained in posterior fossa (lateral view).

data collected in the detectors in such a way that it localizes each voxel within the slice and assigns it a relative value. Finally, they have a display module that creates a map of the location and relative value of the charac-teristic in each voxel addressed. This pro-duces a picture in which each voxel is repre-sented by a dot (pixel) of relative intensity on a black-white (or sometimes color) scale. The shade is proportional to the magnitude or intensity of the tissue characteristic mea-sured. The resolution of anatomical and pathologic detail of the resulting picture de-pends on the matrix (number of pixels per unit area) and the range of differences in the characteristic under study that can be mea-sured. In x-ray computerized tomographic scanning, the tissue characteristic measured is electron density as manifested by attenua-tion of an x-ray beam. In positron emission tomographic scanning, it is the ability of tis-sue to take up molecules containing positron emitting isotopes. In magnetic resonance imaging, it is the density and physical state of mobile hydrogen nuclei (protons) in the tissue.

X-Ray Computerized Tomography

Computerized tomographic techniques using x-rays to generate the scan were the first to be developed for clinical use. Thin beams of x-ray are passed through the patient's head, and the amount of energy transmitted (not ab-sorbed by structures in its path) is measured by an x-ray detector on the opposite side of the head. This is repeated thousands of times (within a few seconds) from every point around the circumference of the head. The absorption data are processed by a computer, which reconstructs a horizontal section of the head about 1 cm thick. The entire cranial con-tents can be demonstrated by generating a se-ries of adjacent sections. The ventricular sys-tem and any distortions and displacements can be identified. Most hemorrhages, infarcts, and tumors in the substance of the brain can be detected because their density (x-ray ab-sorption) differs from that of normal brain. Intravenously administered contrast media (iodine-containing compounds) aid in visual-izing lesions that are vascular or in which the blood-brain barrier is disturbed.

Fig. 6-18. Computerized tomograms (horizontal sections). A. Level of caudate and thalamus. B. Base of brain at level of midbrain.

Magnetic Resonance Imaging

Magnetic resonance imaging is the most recently developed technique for imaging the internal structures of the body, including the central nervous system (Fig. 6-19). The physics of magnetic resonance imaging are complicated and beyond the scope of this discussion. Briefly, hydrogen nuclei (protons) in tissue, mostly as part of water molecules, normally are aligned randomly. When the body is placed in a strong magnetic field, the protons, which behave as tiny magnets because of their spin, align longitudinally in the direction of the flux lines of the field. When a pulse of energy in the form of radio frequency waves is delivered to the tissue, the aligned protons adsorb energy and tilt away from the longitudinal toward the transverse axis of the magnetic field. When the radio frequency pulse is turned off, the protons begin to realign in the axis of the main magnetic field. It is during this process that they emit radio frequency energy that is picked up by the detectors. Protons spin at a frequency directly proportional to the local magnetic

field. The frequency of this spin is the frequency picked up by the detectors. The different frequencies seen by the detector array allow the voxels to be localized in space.

Signals are only sent from the tissue during the return, or relaxation phase, from transverse magnetization back to longitudinal magnetization. Loss of transverse magnetization occurs from reorientation of protons in the main magnetic field and from magnetic interactions of spinning protons in the tissue, causing them to become out of phase with one another. These two phenomena occur at exponential rates that have time constants referred to as T1 and T2, respectively. In addition to local tissue factors, the intensity of the signal in each voxel is determined by the sequence of radio frequency pulses, the interval between the pulses, the interval between excitation and detection, and the number of times the sequence is repeated. These factors are under operator control and can be manipulated to emphasize signals generated by either T1 or T2 relaxation phenomena. The resulting images are referred to as being *T1-* or *T2-weighted.* They display

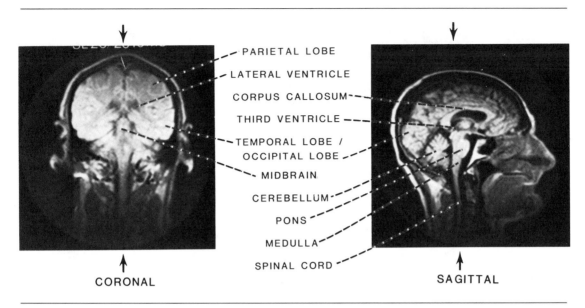

PARIETAL LOBE
LATERAL VENTRICLE
CORPUS CALLOSUM
THIRD VENTRICLE
TEMPORAL LOBE /
OCCIPITAL LOBE
MIDBRAIN
CEREBELLUM
PONS
MEDULLA
SPINAL CORD

CORONAL   SAGITTAL

Fig. 6-19. Magnetic resonance imaging of head in computer-reconstructed coronal and sagittal planes. Arrows indicate level of images of the other plane.

Table 6-2. Advantages of Magnetic Resonance Imaging Compared with X-Ray Computerized Tomography

No exposure to ionizing radiation
No interference by surrounding bone
Superior resolution of soft tissue
Images can be produced in virtually any plane
Able to image flowing blood
Physiologic imaging

somewhat different tissue characteristics and, therefore, different signal intensities in the same tissue.

From a practical clinical standpoint, the major advantage of magnetic resonance imaging over computerized tomography is the greater sensitivity of the technique and greater anatomical detail of the images generated (Fig. 6-20). Other advantages are listed in Table 6-2. Currently, the drawbacks to the use of magnetic resonance imaging are the need for much greater patient cooperation because of the time required to generate images (which are degraded by any motion), the inability to scan patients with pacemakers or other electronic or metallic implants that could be affected by a magnetic field, and the cost.

Air Encephalography

Numerous attempts have been made to define intracranial contents. Pneumoencephalography, a technique that now is seldom used in modern neurologic diagnosis, was important several years ago. In this technique, air or another gas is introduced into the subarachnoid space, usually via lumbar puncture, and the patient is held in an upright position for a brief time. Because air is lighter than CSF, it rises in the subarachnoid space through the foramen magnum and is distributed in the ventricular system and parts of the intracranial subarachnoid space (Fig. 6-21).

Superior demonstration of the ventricular-subarachnoid system by computerized tomography and magnetic resonance imaging has essentially eliminated air encephalography from clinical practice.

Other Techniques

Although *radioisotope brain scan* is another imaging technique that is rapidly being replaced by newer studies, the physiologic basis for the procedure is important. Normally, large molecules are prevented from entering brain tissue by the blood-brain barrier. Many focal injuries to the brain are accompanied by

Fig. 6-20. Magnetic resonance imaging — coronal sections of brain. A. Normal brain. B. Brain with atrophy and enlarged ventricles.

Fig. 6-21. Pneumoencephalograms. A. Anteroposterior view outlining lateral ventricles and third ventricle. Some extraventricular air is seen outlining cerebral cortex. B. Lateral view of ventricular system.

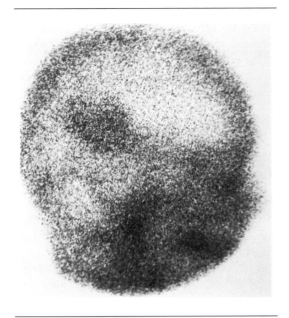

Fig. 6-22. Radioisotope brain scan (right lateral scan; face is to the right). Lesion is indicated by area of abnormal accumulation of indicator noted in right parietal lobe.

a local breakdown in this barrier system, with subsequent diffusion of larger molecules into brain tissue. If a normally nondiffusible molecule is labeled with a radioisotope and is injected intravenously into a normal person and the brain is scanned for evidence of radioactive accumulation, the activity will be concentrated primarily in the regions of normal blood flow (that is, the venous sinuses). If, however, the patient has an area of focal disease, with normal blood flow but breakdown of the barrier system, some of the indicator will leak out from the normal vascular compartment and accumulate in the region of injury. This accumulation results in an abnormal area of increased radioactivity in the brain scan that corresponds to the area of disease (Fig. 6-22).

By injecting a radioisotope into the lumbar subarachnoid space, physiologic observations can be made of the circulation of CSF. Normally, the injected material will rise and accumulate both within the ventricular system and over the convexity of the brain. Localization of the indicator within the ventricles and failure to circulate over the brain surface after 48 hours are suggestive of a blockage in the ex-

traventricular CSF pathways. Both signs are frequently seen in cases of a communicating hydrocephalus. This technique is called *radioisotope cisternography*.

Neurologic Examination of the CSF System

As part of the neurologic examination of patients with suspected disease of the CSF system, it is necessary to search specifically for signs of increased intracranial pressure and meningeal irritation. In addition, assessment of this system occasionally requires the performance of lumbar puncture.

An increase in intracranial pressure is suspected on the basis of the clinical-anatomical-temporal profile of the illness and the constellation of signs and symptoms outlined previously. Not all patients with increased intracranial pressure have papilledema; however, ophthalmoscopic visualization of the optic nerve head in search of papilledema should be carefully performed on all such patients. One must be cautious; although the presence of edema of the nerve head should always raise the possibility of an elevation in intracranial pressure, it may be associated with other conditions.

The presence of meningeal irritation is best determined by examining for *nuchal rigidity*. When there is meningeal irritation, the side-to-side movement of the neck causes little discomfort, and frequently the first 10 to 15 degrees of neck flexion meet with little resistance, but with additional flexion, resistance and discomfort increase rapidly. To reduce the effects of traction on the lumbosacral roots when the neck is flexed, a patient with meningeal irritation may automatically flex the hips and knees. (This type of abnormal response seen with meningeal irritation is referred to as *Brudzinski's sign*.) An additional and related test can be performed with the patient recumbent and the legs flexed at the hips and knees. In this position, the lumbosacral nerve roots are relatively slack, and maneuvers designed to stretch these nerve roots (such as extension of the knee) normally produce no discomfort. In the presence of meningeal irritation, there are pain and increased resistance (Kernig's sign). When

Kernig's sign is encountered in the absence of nuchal rigidity (and especially if it is unilateral), it is indicative of an irritative process involving the lumbosacral nerve roots rather than of diffuse meningeal irritation.

Objectives

1. Define or identify the following: dura mater, arachnoid, pia mater, epidural space, subdural space, subarachnoid space, dural sinuses, falx cerebri, tentorium cerebelli, blood-brain barrier, choroid plexuses, lateral ventricles, foramen of Monro, third ventricle, aqueduct of Sylvius, fourth ventricle, and foramina of Luschka and Magendie.
2. Describe and trace the formation, circulation, and absorption of cerebrospinal fluid.
3. Define communicating hydrocephalus and noncommunicating hydrocephalus. Give an example of each type, describe its location, and state the anatomicopathologic consequences of a lesion in that location.
4. Discuss the relationship between the contents of the cranial cavity and intracranial pressure, and give examples of general pathologic states that may result in increased pressure.
5. Interpret the significance of abnormalities in CSF color, cellular composition, serologic findings, total protein level, gamma globulin concentration, sugar level, and culture, and list the CSF findings in meningitis, encephalitis, subarachnoid hemorrhage, and traumatic puncture.
6. Describe or list the features of the syndrome of meningeal irritation.
7. Describe or list the features that indicate increased intracranial pressure.
8. Describe the neuroanatomical basis for the following neurodiagnostic studies: myelography, pneumoencephalography, ventriculography, computerized tomography, magnetic resonance imaging, and radioisotope cisternography.

Clinical Problems

1. A 10-month-old infant presents with an enlarging head and a delay in reaching devel-

opmental milestones. The neurologic examination confirms the developmental delay and also reveals a tense, bulging, enlarged anterior fontanelle; ophthalmoscopic examination reveals normal fundi; and the head circumference is 50 cm. An opening pressure of 200 mm H_2O is found on lumbar puncture. Based on these findings, answer the following questions:
   a. How do we know the head is abnormally large?
   b. What are the possible causes of a large head?
   c. What tests might be useful in obtaining information about the infant's ventricular system?
   d. Does the lesion found in this patient (see answer to previous question) produce a communicating or noncommunicating type of hydrocephalus?
   e. What changes would you expect to find in the configuration of the ventricular system in a ventriculogram performed on
      (1) This patient
      (2) A patient with chronic obstruction of the foramina of Luschka and Magendie
      (3) A patient with inflammatory obliteration of the intracranial arachnoid villi
      (4) A patient with an acute subarachnoid hemorrhage
2. A 38-year-old man with the same pathologic condition as the infant in problem 1 has a normal head size, papilledema, and an opening pressure of 500 mm H_2O on lumbar puncture. How can you explain the differences in these two cases?
3. A 37-year-old man is seen because of a 6-month history of progressive weakness in his legs and loss of pain and thermal sensation to the level of his nipples. Based on your findings on physical examination and normal roentgenographic findings in the head and in the cervical, thoracic, and lumbar regions of the spinal column, you perform a lumbar puncture with the following results:
   a. Hydrodynamics:
      (1) Opening pressure of 80 mm H_2O
      (2) Spontaneous pulsations

Respiratory: 10 to 20 mm H_2O
Cardiac: None
(3) Abdominal compression gives prompt increase of 70 mm H_2O with rapid decrease to 80 mm H_2O on release of pressure
(4) Jugular compression gives an increase of 50 mm H_2O over 20 seconds, with a return of 100 mm H_2O 50 seconds after release of pressure
b. Spinal fluid examination:
(1) Appearance: Slightly yellow, clear fluid
(2) Cells:
(a) White blood cells = 4 lymphocytes per microliter
(b) Red blood cells = 0
(3) Chemistry:
(a) Protein = 700 mg/dl
(b) Glucose = 65 mg/dl
(c) Blood sugar = 100 mg/dl

Based on these findings, answer the following questions:
a. What is the location of this lesion? (level? lateralization?) Is this a mass lesion? What is the cause?
b. How would you explain each of the hydrodynamic findings on the lumbar puncture?
c. What structures did the lumbar puncture needle penetrate before CSF began to drip from the needle?
d. What radiologic study might help you locate the lesion(s) accurately?

4. You are called to the emergency room to see a semicomatose elderly woman who responds to painful stimuli with movement of all four extremities. She was brought to the hospital by police ambulance after being found in her apartment by neighbors who had not seen her for 3 days. The physical examination reveals blood pressure 120/80 mm Hg, pulse 120 per minute, respiration 124 per minute, and temperature 39.5°C rectally. There is marked resistance to flexion but not to lateral rotation of the neck. Results of the remainder of the examination are normal. A lumbar puncture reveals an opening pressure of 270 mm H_2O. CSF examination reveals the following:
a. Appearance before centrifugation:
Tube #1: 2+ pink; 2+ turbid
Tube #3: slightly pink; 2+ turbid
b. Appearance after centrifugation:
All tubes clear and colorless
c. Cell counts:
Tube #1: 300 white blood cells (90% polymorphonuclear leukocytes), 2,800 red blood cells
Tube #3: 320 white blood cells (90% polymorphonuclear leukocytes), 700 red blood cells
d. Protein:
Tube #1: 180 mg/dl
Tube #3: 176 mg/dl
e. Glucose:
10 mg/dl in all tubes
Based on these findings, answer the following questions:
(1) What is the location of this lesion? (level? lateralization?) Is this a mass lesion? What is the cause?
(2) How do you explain the differences in appearance and cellular count of the CSF between tubes #1 and #3?
(3) What would you expect to find on Gram's stain of the CSF? On culture of the CSF?
(4) How would you explain the CSF glucose result?
(5) Would you have performed jugular compression? Explain.

Additional Reading

Davson, H., Welch, K., and Segal, M. B. *Physiology and Pathophysiology of the Cerebrospinal Fluid.* Edinburgh: Churchill Livingstone, 1987.

Fishman, R. A. *Cerebrospinal Fluid in Diseases of the Nervous System* (2nd ed.). Philadelphia: Saunders, 1992.

Lyons, M. K., and Meyer, F. B. Cerebrospinal fluid physiology and the management of increased intracranial pressure. *Mayo Clin. Proc.* 65:684, 1990.

North, B., and Reilly, P. Comparison among three methods of intracranial pressure recording. *Neurosurgery* 18:730, 1986.

— 7 —

The Sensory System

The function of the sensory system is to provide information to the central nervous system about the *external* world, the *internal* environment, and the *position* of the body in space. Impulses traveling toward the central nervous system are called *afferent impulses.* Afferent information may be transmitted (1) as conscious data that are perceived by the organism and then used to modify behavior, (2) as unconscious data that, although used to modify behavior, remain unperceived by the organism, and (3) as both conscious and unconscious data. *Sensory pathways* are afferent pathways involved in conscious perception. Afferent impulses are functionally subdivided into the following:

1. General somatic afferent (GSA) — sensory information from skin, striated muscles, and joints
2. General visceral afferent (GVA) — sensory information, largely unconscious in nature, from serosal and mucosal surfaces and smooth muscle of the viscera
3. Special somatic afferent (SSA) — sensory information relating to vision, audition, and equilibrium
4. Special visceral afferent (SVA) — sensory information relating to taste and smell

Discriminative general and special somatic sensory pathways are part of the *outer tube systems*, whereas viscerosensory pathways are part of the *inner tube*, or *core, systems*. Although introductory comments are made in relation to each of these subdivisions, this chapter is concerned primarily with the organization and function of the *general somatic afferent system.*

Overview

The translation of information from the environment is the function of the *receptor organs.* The function of these specialized portions of the peripheral nervous system is to convert mechanical, chemical, photic, and other forms of energy into electrical potentials, a form of information that can be used by the nervous system. Action potentials are then transmitted by specific *sensory pathways* to those regions of the central nervous system where they can be integrated and perceived. The peripheral region from which a stimulus affects a central sensory neuron is the *sensory field* of that neuron.

The pathways involved in conscious perception have both a hierarchical and a parallel organization. Hierarchical organization means that sensory information is transmitted sequentially via several orders of neurons located in *relay nuclei* and is processed at each relay station under the control of higher stations in the pathway. Parallel organization implies that different submodalities within tactile, visual, and other sensations are transmitted via separate, parallel channels and that a given sensory modality, such as simple touch, can be transmitted by different ascending pathways.

Somatosensory pathways from the trunk and extremities course in the spinal cord, and those transmitting information from the face form the trigeminal system. The trigeminal

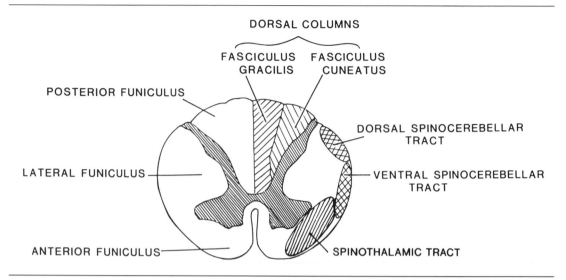

Fig. 7-1. Cross section of upper cervical spinal cord illustrating location of major ascending sensory pathways and their relationship to posterior, lateral, and anterior funiculi.

system is discussed further in Chapter 15 (The Posterior Fossa Level). The somatosensory pathways commonly tested clinically consist of three orders of neurons:

The *first-order neurons* are the receptor neurons; they are derivatives of the neural crest. Their cell bodies lie outside the central nervous system in *dorsal root ganglia*, and their axons bifurcate into a peripheral branch and a central branch. The peripheral branch contributes to a *sensory nerve* and innervates receptor organs. The central branch enters the spinal cord or the brain stem via a *dorsal*, or *sensory*, *root*. The area of the skin innervated by a single dorsal root is called a *dermatome*.

The *second-order neurons* have cell bodies located in regions of the embryonic alar plate, that is, in the gray matter of the dorsal horn of the spinal cord or in relay nuclei of the medulla. The axons of these second-order neurons decussate (cross the midline) and continue cephalad. The axons of first- or second-order neurons, as they ascend in the spinal cord, are grouped into tracts (fasciculi) located primarily in the white matter (funiculi) of the spinal cord (Fig. 7-1). In the brain stem, the axons of second-order neurons continue to ascend in tracts (in this region, some are referred to as *lemnisci*) to reach the *thalamus*, where they terminate in specific sensory nuclei. Along their ascending course, these sensory pathways maintain a *somatotopic organization*, so that the surface of the body is represented in a topographic manner both in the pathways and in the relay stations.

The *third-order neurons* have cell bodies in the sensory relay nuclei of the thalamus. Somatosensory thalamic neurons are located in the *ventral posterior complex* of the thalamus, which includes the *ventral posterolateral* nucleus for sensory inputs from the trunk and extremities and the *ventral posteromedial* nucleus for sensory inputs from the face (via the trigeminal system). Like other relay stations, thalamic relay nuclei have a somatotopic and submodality-specific organization. Axons of somatosensory thalamic neurons pass via the thalamocortical radiation to the *primary somatosensory cortex* of the parietal lobe.

The primary somatosensory cortex is located in the postcentral gyrus of the parietal lobe and is concerned with discriminative aspects of reception and appreciation of somatic sensory impulses. It consists of at least four functionally distinct areas, each containing a complete somatotopic map. Fibers terminate in the postcentral gyrus in an organized fashion, with the lower extremity represented on the medial surface of the hemisphere and the arm and hand represented on the lateral sur-

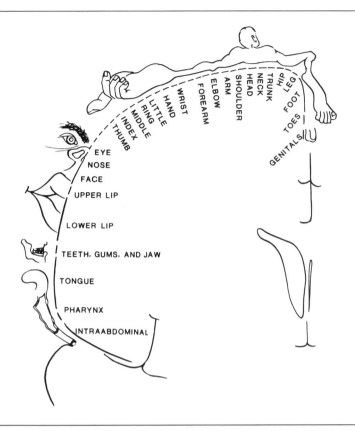

Fig. 7-2. Coronal section of a cerebral hemisphere showing the distribution of sensory fibers in the postcentral gyrus (sensory homunculus). (Redrawn from W. Penfield and T. Rasmussen. *The Cerebral Cortex of Man: A Clinical Study of Localization of Function.* New York: Macmillan, 1950.)

face. The face, mouth, and tongue are represented in the suprasylvian region (Fig. 7-2).

An important feature of the somatosensory and other sensory cortices is that the representation of the body map is dynamic, *use-dependent cortical plasticity.* Thus, the shape and size of the representation of a particular body part may be modified in response to peripheral injury, training, and so forth. Cortical representation of pain occurs not only in the parietal cortex but also in the *cingulate gyrus.*

Somatosensory pathways can be subdivided into three main groups:

The pathways that follow the general scheme described above are referred to as *direct,* or *discriminative,* pathways and are commonly tested clinically because they allow localization of lesions in the nervous system. These pathways are a component of the *outer tube systems* (Table 7-1). They are somatotopi-cally organized, ascend contralaterally in the lemniscal system, terminate in the ventral posterolateral nucleus of thalamus, and rapidly transmit information about location, onset, intensity, and duration of the stimulus to primary somatosensory cortex. The most important direct pathways include the *direct dorsal column pathway,* for transmission of tactile-discriminative and conscious proprioceptive information, and the spinothalamic tract (also referred to as the *direct spinothalamic* or *neospinothalamic tract*), for transmission of discriminative pain and temperature and tactile information (Table 7-2).

A second group of somatosensory pathways, referred to as *indirect pathways,* mediate arousal-affective aspects of somatic sensation (particularly pain) and visceral sensation. These pathways are a component of the *inner tube,* or *core, systems* (see Table 7-1). Unlike

Table 7-1. Functional Classification of Somatosensory Pathways

	Direct (lemniscal)	Indirect (extralemniscal)
Location in the neuraxis	Outer tube	Inner tube (core)
Number of synapses in the central nervous system	2 or 3	Multiple
Receptive fields	Small	Large
Body representation	Contralateral	Bilateral
Somatotopy	Yes	No
Synapse in reticular formation	No	Yes
Subcortical synapse	No	Yes
Thalamic station	Ventral posterior complex	Midline nuclei
Cortical station	Parietal cortex	Cingulate gyrus
Function	Discriminative	Affective-arousal
Pathways	Dorsal column pathway, spinothalamic pathway, dorsolateral quadrant pathways	Spinoreticulothalamic, spinoreticular, propriospinal pathways

Table 7-2. Direct Systems Commonly Tested Clinically

	Direct dorsal column pathway	Spinothalamic tract
Receptors	Proprioceptors	High-threshold mechanoreceptors
	Tactile receptors	Polymodal nociceptors
		Tactile and thermoreceptors
First-order neuron	Dorsal root ganglion	Dorsal root ganglion
Second-order neuron	Medulla (dorsal column nucleus)	Dorsal horn
Third-order neuron	Ventral posterolateral nucleus of thalamus	Ventral posterolateral and posterior nuclei of thalamus
Decussation	Medulla	Spinal cord
Localization	Ipsilateral dorsal column	Contralateral anterolateral quadrant
Function	Spatiotemporal discrimination (e.g., stereognosis)	Discriminative pain and temperature
	Two-point vibration, joint position	Simple touch

direct pathways, indirect pathways are not helpful for localization of lesions in the central nervous system, because they have poor somatotopy, ascend bilaterally, and terminate diffusely in the reticular formation, intralaminar thalamic nuclei, and other subcortical and cortical regions. Indirect pathways are important for mechanisms of pain and analgesia and for visceral and sexual sensation. They include the *paleospinothalamic*, *spinoreticular*, and *spinomesencephalic tracts* and the *propriospinal multisynaptic system.* Propriospinal neurons interconnect several segments of the spinal cord.

A third group of somatosensory pathways, the *dorsal and ventral spinocerebellar tracts,*

transmit information for unconscious control of posture and movement. These are two-neuron pathways that do not relay in the thalamus but terminate in the ipsilateral cerebellum.

The direct somatosensory pathways are of major importance in understanding and interpreting neurologic disease. Lesions at different levels of the neuraxis alter sensory function in different ways; by correlating the patient's signs and symptoms with the anatomical distribution of these pathways, neurologic disorders can be localized. Abnormalities in the peripheral nerves or spinal roots are distributed in a segmental fashion, often involve all sensory modalities, and may be associated with the sensation of pain. Lesions involving the spinal cord may be associated with segmental sensory loss at the level of the lesion and varied sensory loss at all levels below the lesion. Lesions in the posterior fossa produce contralateral sensory loss over the trunk and extremities and may be associated with ipsilateral sensory disturbance in the face. Supratentorial lesions produce entirely contralateral sensory deficits. Because each somatosensory pathway subserves different functions, loss of a particular sensory modality with preservation of others allows anatomical localization of lesions in the nervous system. Lesions of the direct dorsal column pathway affect tactile discrimination, whereas lesions of the spinothalamic system predominantly affect pain and temperature sensation. Because of overlap, or redundancy, of parallel somatosensory pathways, some somatosensory modalities, particularly touch, can still be perceived in cases of interruption of an individual pathway.

Other sensory pathways, such as the visual pathway, are also important for localization in clinical neurology. Similar to the somatosensory pathways, the visual pathway has a topographic organization (called *retinotopy*), a hierarchical organization (with synaptic relays in the thalamus and primary visual cortex), and parallel organization (with submodality-specific channels transmitting information about object movement or shape and color).

Receptors: General Organization and Mechanisms

Sensory receptors are highly specialized structures that respond to environmental changes by producing action potentials for transmission to the central nervous system. This process is called *transduction*. There are many types of receptors subserving different sensory functions.

Sensory Unit and Receptor Field

Somatosensory receptors constitute the distal, specialized part of the first-order neuron, sometimes associated with nonneural cells. Visual, auditory-vestibular, and taste receptors are specialized structures. A single primary afferent fiber and all the receptors innervated by its peripheral branches constitute a *sensory unit*. The number of peripheral receptors per area of body surface is referred to as *receptor density*. The peripheral region from which a stimulus activates a central neuron is referred to as the *sensory field* of that neuron. The sensory field of most central sensory neurons has a *center-surround organization*. The neural response is greater when the stimulus is applied to the center of the excitatory receptive field and weakest at its periphery. There is a superimposed gradient of inhibition in the sensory field, which may extend beyond the excitatory area, giving rise to an *inhibitory surround*. The size of the sensory fields varies in different parts of the body. Areas with great sensory discrimination, such as the fingertips, have a high density of receptors innervated by a large number of afferents with small sensory fields; thus, stimuli in these regions affect a large number of central neurons. Therefore, the area of central representation of the body map is distorted, and it is not proportional to the size of the area innervated but to its receptor density. Also, the sensory field of a cortical sensory neuron is dynamic and may vary in response to peripheral lesions or other factors. This is known as *cortical plasticity*.

Impulse Initiation in Somatic Sensory Receptors

Although the mechanism by which receptor potentials are produced varies with the receptor organ, certain principles of receptor physiology are common to all. The process starts with the application of a *specific stimulus*, that is, the stimulus for which the receptor has the lowest threshold. *Threshold* is the minimal intensity of stimulus necessary to produce excitation in the appropriate class of first-order neuron. Application of the stimulus produces a local change in the cation permeability of the membrane of the nerve terminal. This gives rise to a local potential called a *generator potential*. In most receptors, the generator potential is *depolarizing*, but in photoreceptors it is hyperpolarizing. If the receptor potential is of sufficient magnitude (suprathreshold), it triggers an *action potential*. Receptor stimulation rarely produces a single action potential but

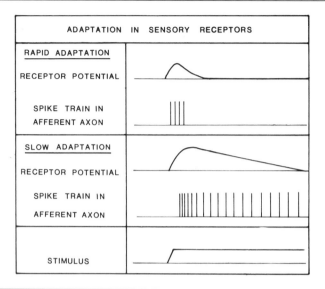

Fig. 7-3. Rate of adaptation in sensory receptors to prolonged stimulus. Adaptation of receptor potentials and spike trains in primary afferent axons in rapid- and slow-adapting receptors is shown.

rather a train of such discharges. The amplitude of the generator potential determines the frequency of the action potentials generated.

Encoding of Somatosensory Information

Because all action potentials have a similar amplitude, the intensity of the stimulus is encoded by (1) the frequency of action potentials in the afferent axons, which is known as *frequency coding*, or *temporal summation*, and (2) increasing the number of sensory units, which is known as *population coding*, or *spatial summation*. The ability to localize a stimulus and to distinguish two closely spaced stimuli is called *spatial discrimination*, which is inversely proportional to the size of the receptive field and directly proportional to the receptor density.

Receptor Adaptation

Receptor adaptation is a function of the intrinsic properties of the receptor. It is the mechanism by which the amplitude of the generator potential, and thus the firing of action potentials, progressively decreases in response to a continuous stimulus (Fig. 7-3). Receptors can be subdivided into *rapidly adapting*, or *phasic*, and *slowly adapting*, or *tonic*, receptors. They

transmit different types of information to the central nervous system. Rapidly adapting receptors detect transient and rapidly changing stimuli. They fire a few impulses on application of a sustained stimulus but are silent during its steady continuation; they may discharge again when the stimulus is removed. The number of action potentials initiated in their axon is related to the rate of change of the stimulus. Rapidly adapting receptors serve to alert the nervous system to any change in the environment and are particularly suitable for spatiotemporal discrimination. Slowly adapting receptors respond to a sustained stimulus with fairly sustained firing. The time course and peak frequency of discharge of rapidly adapting receptors may reflect the final intensity as well as the rate of application of the stimulus. Slowly adapting receptors keep the nervous system constantly appraised of the status of the body and of its relationships with its surroundings.

Receptor fatigue is the transient abolition of the excitability of a sensory receptor in response to repetitive stimulation. Repetitive stimuli produce successively smaller amplitude generator potentials to the point that the receptor no longer responds to either the stimulus or change in the stimulus.

Table 7-3. Classification and Comparison of Receptor Types

Receptor type	Receptor	Modality
Mechanoreceptors		
Somatosensory system	Low-threshold mechanoreceptors	Light touch, vibration
	Muscle spindles	Proprioception
	Tendon organs	Proprioception
	Free nerve endings	Pain, temperature
Vestibular system	Hair cells	Head position and motion
Auditory system	Hair cells	Audition
Internal regulation system	Free nerve endings	Visceral distention, pain
Chemoreceptors		
Taste system	Taste buds	Taste
Olfactory system	Olfactory receptor cells	Olfaction
Internal regulation system	Visceral chemoreceptors	Pain
Photoreceptors	Rods and cones	Vision

Receptor Specificity

Each receptor type is generally specialized so that it is more sensitive (that is, has the lowest threshold) to one particular kind of stimulus. Thus, receptors can be classified according to their sensory modality as *mechanoreceptors, chemoreceptors, thermoreceptors,* and *photoreceptors* (Table 7-3). Receptors also can be classified according to the origin of the stimulus as *exteroceptors* (skin mechanoreceptors for touch and pain, skin thermoreceptors, labyrinthine mechanoreceptors for hearing, retinal photoreceptors, and chemoreceptors for taste and smell), *proprioceptors* (mechanoreceptors in muscles, tendons, and joints and vestibular mechanoreceptors), and *visceral receptors* (mechanoreceptors and chemoreceptors encoding signals related to internal body functions) (see Table 7-3).

Although certain types of receptors respond preferentially to specific stimuli, the somatosensory receptors by themselves are not sufficient for discrimination. Sensory discrimination occurs as a result of a *pattern of activity* in various receptors. The central nervous system integrates the input patterns from multiple receptors to produce the appreciation of specific sensations. Chemoreceptors and receptors for the special senses of vision, taste, audition, and equilibrium are described further in Chapters 15 (The Posterior Fossa Level) and 16 (The Supratentorial Level).

General Organization of the Somatosensory Systems

Somatosensory Receptors

Somatosensory receptors include cutaneous receptors, joint receptors, and muscle receptors. Cutaneous receptors consist of low-threshold mechanoreceptors, which are innervated by large myelinated fibers and transmit touch sensation, and high-threshold mechanoreceptors, chemoreceptors, and thermoreceptors, which are innervated by small myelinated or unmyelinated fibers and mediate pain and temperature sensation. Joint and muscle receptors are mainly innervated by large, rapidly conducting myelinated fibers. Muscle receptors include muscle spindles, which signal muscle length and rate of change in length, Golgi tendon organs, which respond to changes in muscle tension, and free nerve endings, which respond to muscle pressure and pain.

Dorsal Root Ganglion Neurons

Information from somatic receptors is transmitted to the spinal cord by the first-order neurons. The cell bodies of these neurons are located in the dorsal root ganglia (spinal ganglia). Each of these neurons has a single nerve process that divides into two branches. The distal, or peripheral, branch corresponds to the sensory nerve innervating the receptor, and the proximal, or central, branch enters the spinal

Table 7-4. Comparison of Large Neurons and Small Neurons in Dorsal Root Ganglia

	Type	
	Large	Small
Sensory function	Touch	Pain
	Vibration	Temperature
	Joint position	Visceral sensation
	Proprioception	
Axon	Large myelinated	Small myelinated
		Unmyelinated
Receptor	Low-threshold mechanoreceptor	High-threshold mechanoreceptor
	Muscle and joint proprioceptors	Polymodal nociceptors
		Chemoreceptors
		Thermoreceptors
Conduction of stimuli	Orthodromic	Orthodromic and antidromic (axon reflex)
Neurotransmitter	L-Glutamate	L-Glutamate and neuropeptides (e.g., substance P)

cord via the dorsal root. The area of the skin innervated by a single dorsal root is called a *dermatome*. The dermatomes are arranged in a highly ordered way on the body surface. The sensory field of each dorsal root is continuous and tends to form a strip perpendicular to the spinal cord. Each spinal nerve receives afferents from several peripheral nerves; therefore, the area innervated by an individual dorsal root is less well defined than the area innervated by a single peripheral nerve. Furthermore, the areas innervated by different dorsal roots overlap significantly. Whereas damage of a peripheral cutaneous nerve produces a circumscribed area of sensory loss in the skin, damage to the spinal nerve or dorsal root often results in only a moderate sensory deficit.

The two main types of neurons in a dorsal root ganglion are *large neurons*, with large myelinated axons that innervate low-threshold mechanoreceptors (touch) and proprioceptors, and *small neurons*, with small myelinated or unmyelinated axons that innervate nociceptors, thermoreceptors, and visceral receptors (Table 7-4). This subdivision is clinically relevant because diseases that selectively affect large sensory fibers or large dorsal root ganglion neurons produce severe loss of all tactile modalities and proprioception but leave pain and temperature sensation intact. Diseases of small sensory fibers or small dorsal root ganglion neurons affect pain and temperature but spare touch and proprioceptive sensation.

Dorsal Root Entry Zone and Termination in Spinal Cord

Primary afferent fibers from the dorsal root ganglion cells generally enter the spinal cord in the posterolateral sulcus at the *dorsal root entry zone*. In this zone, the larger and most heavily myelinated proprioceptive fibers are located medially (medial division), the medium-sized fibers carrying tactile sensation are intermediate (intermediate division), and the finely myelinated and unmyelinated fibers mediating pain and temperature sensation are located laterally (lateral division) (Fig. 7-4). From this common entry zone, the dorsal root fibers branch to ascend and descend in the white matter and to arborize in the gray matter. The pathways for the different sensory modalities diverge as they ascend in the spinal cord to higher centers.

The medially located large myelinated fibers bifurcate in branches that may (1) ascend directly in the ipsilateral dorsal columns, without synapsing in the spinal cord, as the *direct dorsal column pathway*, (2) synapse on dorsal horn neurons that in turn contribute axons to the dorsal column (the *postsynaptic dorsal column pathway*), dorsolateral funiculus, and spinothalamic tract, (3) synapse in the intermediate gray matter on neurons that give rise to the spinocerebellar tract, (4) synapse on interneurons and motor neurons in the ventral horn for segmental, or myotatic, reflexes, and (5) synapse

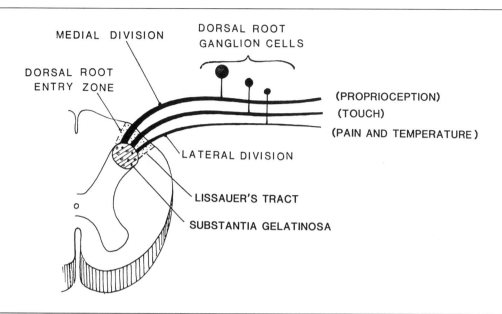

Fig. 7-4. Dorsal root entry zone. Largest, most heavily myelinated fibers mediating proprioception occupy the medial division. Medium-sized myelinated fibers mediating touch are centrally located, and finely myelinated fibers carrying pain and temperature sensation are located in the lateral division.

in the dorsal horn on interneurons that provide segmental modulation of pain transmission.

The laterally located small myelinated and unmyelinated fibers bifurcate into ascending and descending branches that run longitudinally in *Lissauer's tract*, part of the dorsolateral funiculus (see Fig. 7-4). Within several segments, these axons leave Lissauer's tract to enter the dorsal horn and the intermediate gray matter of the spinal cord. In the gray matter they may (1) synapse on different groups of dorsal horn and intermediate gray matter neurons that form the spinothalamic and other tracts ascending in the contralateral ventrolateral quadrant, (2) synapse on dorsal horn interneurons involved in segmental modulation of pain and in intrinsic (propriospinal) intersegmental pathways, and (3) via interneurons, activate somatic and preganglionic autonomic motor neurons to initiate segmental visceral and somatic reflexes.

Spinal Somatosensory Neurons

The second-order spinal somatosensory neurons occupy the dorsal horn and the intermediate gray matter of the spinal cord. These neurons contribute to all somatosensory pathways except the direct dorsal column pathway. Spinal neurons, similar to other central somatosensory neurons, can be subdivided into several types on the basis of their response characteristics, as follows: *nociceptive-specific* neurons, *low-threshold mechanoreceptive* neurons, and *wide dynamic range* neurons (Table 7-5). Wide dynamic range neurons are the most abundant and contribute to all ascending pathways relaying in the spinal cord. One important feature is that an individual type of neuron may change its response characteristics according to segmental and suprasegmental control mechanisms. This is relevant for mechanisms of central pain.

General Organization of Ascending Somatosensory Pathways

From the standpoint of anatomical organization, somatosensory pathways can be subdivided into three groups.

The *direct*, or *lemniscal*, *pathways* are contralateral, somatotopically organized pathways that terminate in the ventral posterior complex of the thalamus and that are inte-

Table 7-5. Functional Classification of Dorsal Horn Neurons

Type of neuron	Primary afferent input	Pathway	Function
Nociceptive-specific	Small myelinated Unmyelinated	Spinothalamic Spinoreticular Spinomesencephalic	Pain
Low-threshold mechanoreceptive	Large myelinated	Postsynaptic dorsal column Spinothalamic Dorsolateral funiculus	Touch Proprioception
Wide-dynamic range	Large myelinated Small myelinated Unmyelinated	Spinothalamic Spinoreticular Spinomesencephalic Postsynaptic dorsal column Dorsolateral funiculus	Pain Temperature Touch Visceral sensation
Thermoceptive	Small myelinated Unmyelinated	Spinothalamic	Temperature

grated in primary sensory cortex. These pathways are involved in sensory discrimination and are useful clinically for localizing central lesions. They run in the outer tube of the neuraxis and include the following: (1) pathways for tactile discrimination and conscious proprioception — the *direct dorsal column–lemniscal pathway* and parallel pathways in the dorsal column and dorsolateral quadrant, and (2) pathways for discriminative aspects of pain and temperature sensation — the *direct spinothalamic*, or *neospinothalamic*, *tract*. Note that simple touch and spatial discrimination are transmitted by the dorsal column, the neospinothalamic tract, and other parallel pathways. Therefore, abnormalities of simple touch are less helpful in localizing lesions in the central nervous system.

The *indirect pathways* have poor somatotopy, ascend bilaterally, have multiple interconnections with the reticular formation and other subcortical regions, relay in midline thalamic nuclei, and affect limbic and paralimbic cortical areas. The indirect pathways are not helpful for localization, but they are important for transmission of affective-arousal components of pain and visceral sensation and for initiation of reflex somatic, autonomic, and hormonal responses to external stimuli. These pathways are part of the inner tube of the neuraxis and include the following: (1) the *paleospinothalamic*, *spinoreticular*, and *spinomesencephalic tracts*, which ascend predominantly in the anterolateral quadrant of

the spinal cord, and (2) the *propriospinal multisynaptic pathway*.

The *spinocerebellar tracts* are two-neuron pathways that transmit unconscious proprioceptive information to the ipsilateral cerebellum.

Specific Somatosensory Pathways

Pathways for Tactile Discrimination and Conscious Proprioception: The Direct Dorsal Column–Lemniscal Pathway and Parallel Lemniscal Pathways

The *direct dorsal column–lemniscal pathway* is important in humans and is critical for highly discriminative tactile sensation, called *stereognosis*, and for fine motor control. The dorsal columns also provide an important pathway for transmission of conscious proprioception (for example, joint position sense), static tactile discrimination (for example, two-point discrimination), and vibration. These last three modalities are also carried in parallel pathways, including the dorsolateral funiculus and the neospinothalamic tract. All these pathways contribute to the *medial lemniscus* located in the brain stem.

Receptors

Tactile discrimination involves an active process with multiple contacts on the skin and integration of low-threshold mechanoreceptive cutaneous and proprioceptive information. There are four main types of low-threshold mechanoreceptors in the skin. Proprioception involves activity of low-threshold mechanoreceptors in the joints, tendons, and muscles. Muscle spindles play a significant role in position sense of the fingers, which is critical for the ability to recognize the form of objects. In humans, the hand, particularly the fingertips, has the highest innervation density and tactile acuity of any body surface and is the most important tactile organ for object identification. This involves the process of *active exploration*.

Dorsal Root Ganglion Neurons

Low-threshold tactile and proprioceptive information is carried by large myelinated, high-conduction velocity axons of large dorsal horn neurons. These primary afferents enter the cord via the medial division of the dorsal root entry zone. Large primary afferents may ascend directly in the ipsilateral dorsal column to synapse on second-order neurons in the medulla (the direct dorsal column pathway) or synapse on second-order neurons in the dorsal horn or intermediate gray matter, which have axons that ascend ipsilaterally in the dorsal columns (postsynaptic dorsal column pathway) and the dorsolateral funiculus. All these pathways relay in the lower medulla and then decussate to ascend with the contralateral medial lemniscus.

Dorsal Column–Lemniscal System

The *direct dorsal column pathway* is the most important component of the lemniscal system and consists of large myelinated, primary dorsal root axons that ascend ipsilaterally to reach the dorsal column nuclei in the medulla (Fig. 7-5). This pathway is critical for spatiotemporal tactile discrimination and fine motor control.

The two major anatomical divisions of the dorsal columns are the *fasciculus gracilis*, which is medial and carries information from the lower extremities and the lower trunk (spinal segment T-7 and lower) and the *fasciculus cuneatus*, which is lateral and carries input from the upper extremities and the upper trunk (spinal segment T-6 and higher). The cutaneous and muscle afferents from the upper and lower limbs are segregated anatomically in the dorsal columns.

Below spinal segment L-1, the *fasciculus gracilis* contains a mixture of rapidly adapting afferents from skin and muscle receptors in the lower extremities. However, above segment L-1, the input from muscle receptors leaves the fasciculus gracilis to terminate in Clarke's nucleus in the thoracic cord, the origin of the dorsal spinocerebellar tract. Thus at cervical levels, the fasciculus gracilis contains almost exclusively rapidly adapting cutaneous afferents, which relay on the *nucleus gracilis* of the medulla.

The *fasciculus cuneatus* is only present at cervical levels and contains a mixture of rapidly adapting afferents from cutaneous and muscle receptors in the upper extremities. Cutaneous and some proprioceptive inputs terminate in the *nucleus cuneatus* of the medulla. However, most input from muscle receptors in the fasciculus cuneatus separates in the medulla to terminate in the external cuneate nucleus (analogous to Clarke's nucleus).

Therefore, the dorsal columns are functionally heterogeneous and carry mostly cutaneous and some proprioceptive inputs to the dorsal column nuclei and proprioceptive input to cerebellar relay nuclei. Therefore, lesions in the dorsal columns at any spinal cord level interfere with input from rapidly adapting cutaneous mechanoreceptors, but lesions above the thoracic cord spare input from muscle receptors in the lower body.

The second-order neurons for the direct dorsal column pathways are located in the dorsal column nuclei of the lower medulla. They are the *nucleus gracilis*, which receives cutaneous inputs from the lower extremity via the fasciculus gracilis, and the *nucleus cuneatus*, which receives cutaneous and some proprioceptive inputs from the upper extremities via the fasciculus cuneatus. The dorsal column nuclei are not simple relay stations but are sites of modulation of sensory transmission critical for sensory discrimination (see below). Second-order axons from the dorsal column nuclei cross to the opposite side in the lower medulla as the *internal arcuate fibers* (the decussation of the medial lemniscus) and then ascend with the medial lemniscus to the thalamus.

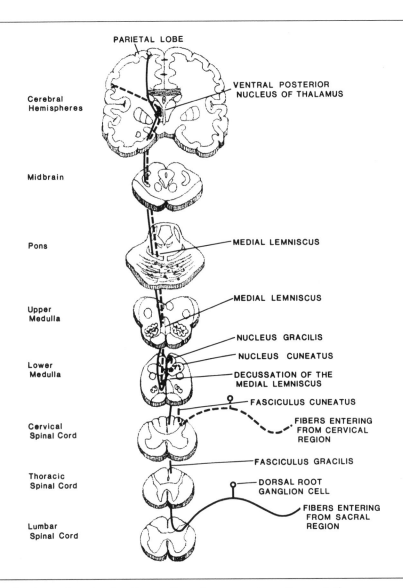

PARIETAL LOBE

VENTRAL POSTERIOR
NUCLEUS OF THALAMUS

Cerebral
Hemispheres

Midbrain

MEDIAL LEMNISCUS

Pons

MEDIAL LEMNISCUS

Upper
Medulla

NUCLEUS GRACILIS

NUCLEUS CUNEATUS

Lower
Medulla

DECUSSATION OF THE
MEDIAL LEMNISCUS

FASCICULUS CUNEATUS

FIBERS ENTERING
FROM CERVICAL
REGION

Cervical
Spinal Cord

FASCICULUS GRACILIS

Thoracic
Spinal Cord

DORSAL ROOT
GANGLION CELL

FIBERS ENTERING
FROM SACRAL
REGION

Lumbar
Spinal Cord

Fig. 7-5. Dorsal column–lemniscal pathway. Conscious proprioception and discriminative sensation.

The medial lemniscus terminates in the *ventral posterolateral nucleus* and other subdivisions of the ventral posterior complex of the thalamus. The ventral posterolateral nucleus receives rapidly adapting cutaneous inputs from the upper and lower extremities and forms a functional unit with the ventral posteromedial nucleus, which receives similar inputs from the face via the trigeminal system. Other subdivisions of the ventral posterior complex receive muscle spindle and slowly adapting mechanoreceptive inputs. Thus, the thalamus contains somatotopically organized,

modality-specific maps of the body surface, with the head represented medially, the hand centrally, and the leg laterally in the ventral posterior complex. Somatosensory thalamic neurons project via the posterior limb of the internal capsule to *primary somatosensory cortex* located in the postcentral gyrus of the parietal lobe.

Primary somatosensory cortex consists of at least four functionally distinct areas; each one contains a separate somatotopic representation of body receptors, with specific representation of cutaneous or proprioceptive inputs.

In each area, the lower extremity is represented on the medial surface of the hemisphere, and the upper extremity and the head are represented on the lateral surface (see Fig. 7-2). Neurons in primary somatosensory cortex have a high degree of submodality specificity and are organized into separate submodality-specific columns. Processing of somatosensory information occurs in the secondary and supplementary sensory cortices and in the somatosensory association cortex in the posterior parietal lobe.

Mechanisms of Sensory Discrimination in the Direct Dorsal Column–Lemniscal System

Features of the dorsal column–lemniscal system crucial for sensory discrimination include small receptive fields, mechanisms of contrast sharpening, and parallel, modality-specific channels.

The fingertips have the smallest receptive fields and the largest cortical representation (larger than the trunk and legs together). The density of innervation of the fingertips is four times that of the palm, and the threshold for discrimination of two points in these areas is 1 millimeter and 10 millimeters, respectively.

The dorsal column nuclei and the ventral posterolateral nucleus of the thalamus are not simple relay stations but are also sites of information processing necessary for spatial and temporal discrimination in the dorsal column–lemniscal system. This involves a process of *contrast sharpening*, which depends on a mechanism known as *lateral inhibition*. Long ascending dorsal column afferents contain the neurotransmitter L-glutamate and excite not only relay cells but also local GABAergic interneurons in the relay nuclei. These inhibitory interneurons also receive excitatory input from somatosensory cortex, and they make presynaptic and postsynaptic inhibitory contacts with both afferent terminals and relay projection cells. Thus, input to a given projection neuron produces, via inhibitory interneurons, lateral inhibition of surrounding projection neurons. Each set of afferent stimuli excites a set of cells that have an inhibitory surround. Summation of the surround inhibition of each field prevents the fusion of the excitatory zones when two stimuli are brought close together. This allows spatial discrimination.

At all relay stations of the dorsal column–lemniscal pathway, there are specific and spatially segregated sensory channels for the various submodalities. In dorsal column nuclei, thalamus, and cerebral cortex, a single nerve cell responds only to one sensory submodality (for example, touch or muscle spindles). All cells responding to one submodality are located together and segregated from cells responding to other submodalities. In the cerebral cortex, each neuron in a vertical column is activated by the same sensory submodality; thus, neurons in a vertical column form the elementary topographic and modality-specific unit of function.

Motor Function of the Direct Dorsal Column Pathway

The dorsal column system has extensive interconnections with the corticospinal motor system. Afferent inputs from the dorsal column–lemniscal system affect firing of corticospinal neurons via thalamocortical and corticocortical connections. Fibers from somatosensory cortex travel in the corticospinal tract to modulate sensory processing in thalamus and dorsal column nuclei. The lemniscal and corticospinal systems are the afferent and efferent components, respectively, of transcortical *long-loop reflexes*, which complement the segmental myotatic reflexes for control of motor neuron activity (see Chapter 8, The Motor System). The dorsal columns also provide rapid sensory feedback for initiation of motor acts (motor programming), guidance of fast (ballistic) movements, and coordination of motor sequences, particularly in the fingers.

Parallel Pathways for Proprioceptive and Tactile Discriminative Function

In addition to the direct dorsal column–lemniscal pathway, other parallel pathways contribute to the lemniscal system and transmit tactile discriminative and proprioceptive information. All these spinal pathways consist of second-order axons from low-threshold mechanoreceptive or wide dynamic range neurons in the dorsal horn. These pathways include (1) the *postsynaptic dorsal column pathway*, which contributes to the ipsilateral gracile and cuneate fasciculi; (2) two pathways that ascend ipsilaterally in the *dorsolateral funiculus* — the *spinocervical tract*, which relays in the lateral cervical nucleus in the upper cervical cord, and the *spinomedullary tract*, which relays in a nucleus of the lower medulla; third-order axons from these two pathways and the postsynaptic dorsal column pathway decussate and join the contralateral medial lemniscus; and (3) the *spinothalamic tract*, which joins the medial lemniscus before reaching the thalamus.

Summary

The lemniscal system consists of several parallel pathways that relay contralateral tactile discriminative and proprioceptive information to the ventral posterior nucleus of the thalamus. Only the direct dorsal column pathway has no spinal station, maintains strict modality specificity, and has mechanisms of contrast sharpening in all its relay stations. Thus, this system is critical for spatiotemporal tactile discrimination and fine motor control. The parallel pathways allow relative sparing of static tactile discrimination and proprioception despite lesions in the dorsal column. Within the dorsal columns, there is a segregation of tactile and proprioceptive inputs arising from the upper and lower extremities. To some degree, the pathways transmitting proprioceptive information to the cortex (medial lemniscus) and to the cerebellum (spinocerebellar tract) overlap anatomically.

Clinical Correlations

The clinical signs of injury to the dorsal column–lemniscal pathway vary according to the site of involvement. Diffuse involvement of large dorsal root ganglion neurons or large myelinated fibers causes loss of tactile discrimination and inability to detect joint position and vibration. These lesions result in inability to manipulate objects without visual guidance and erratic movements of the fingers in the absence of visual clues (pseudoathetosis). These lesions also cause *sensory ataxia*, which is loss of muscle coordination and severe disturbance of gait because of lack of proprioceptive information. Unless the patients can watch the movements of the limbs and correct their errors, they stumble, stagger, and fall.

Central lesions of the dorsal column system produce less severe or partial abnormalities, due to the redundancy of ascending pathways for transmission of tactile and proprioceptive inputs carried by large afferents.

Lesions of the dorsal columns in humans have little effect on many simple tactile abilities but produce major defects in the ability for spatiotemporal discrimination, or stereognosis (the deficit is called *astereognosia*). Stereognosis includes graphesthesia (recognition of numbers drawn on the skin), detection of speed and direction of moving cutaneous stimuli, detection of shapes and patterns, and detection of other stimuli requiring object manipulation and active exploration with the digits (*active touch*). These highly discriminative functions are also affected by lesions in primary somatosensory cortex, thalamus, medial lemniscus, and dorsal column nuclei. In addition to astereognosia, lesions of the fasciculus cuneatus may produce deficits similar to those produced by corticospinal lesions, including loss of dexterity of the fingers and disruption of spatiotemporal motor precision.

Spatial discrimination of static stimuli, such as two-point discrimination, stimulus localization, and joint position sense, is relayed not only by the dorsal column–lemniscal pathways but also by several parallel channels. Thus, this ability may not be permanently impaired after lesions restricted to the dorsal columns. Gross touch-pressure may also travel via parallel pathways, particularly the spinothalamic pathway. Only lesions that involve *both* the dorsal column and the dorsolateral funiculus result in severe deficit of conscious proprioception. Sensory ataxia may require associated involvement of the spinocerebellar pathways.

Pathways for Pain and Temperature: Ventrolateral Quadrant System

The mechanisms and pathways for pain sensation have been more extensively studied than those for temperature sensation. On the basis of clinical data, it is likely that these two pathways travel a similar course through the nervous system; therefore, these two modalities are considered together. The sensation of pain

Table 7-6. Types of Nociceptive Fibers

	High-threshold mechanoreceptive type	Polymodal nociceptive type
Axon	Small myelinated	Unmyelinated
Stimulus	Noxious pressure	Noxious pressure, pinch
		Noxious thermal
		Chemicals (potassium ions, histamine)
Neurotransmitter	L-Glutamate	Substance P
		Calcitonin gene-related peptide
Sensation	First, or fast, pain	Second, or slow, pain
	Well-localized	Diffuse
	Sharp	Dull
	Prickling	Aching
		Burning

has two components: a *sensory-discriminative* component that informs about quality, intensity, and location of the stimulus and an *arousal-affective* component that is involved in the emotional, behavioral, and autonomic responses to pain. These two components are carried in a direct pathway and several indirect pathways, respectively. These pathways are intermingled and ascend mainly in the *spinothalamic tract* in the anterolateral quadrant of the spinal cord.

Receptors

There are specific low-threshold thermoreceptive fibers that are excited by either warming or cooling but not by tactile stimulation. The peripheral receptors for pain are *free nerve endings*, but those for temperature have not been well defined. The two main types of *nociceptive units* are *high-threshold mechanoreceptive units* innervated by small myelinated axons and *polymodal nociceptive units* innervated by unmyelinated axons (Table 7-6). High-threshold mechanoreceptive units respond to noxious mechanical stimuli (pressure) and mediate the so-called *first, or fast, pain*, which is the well-localized, sharp sensation (pricking pain) induced by pinprick or laceration. Polymodal units respond not only to noxious mechanical but also to noxious thermal and chemical (substances released during inflammation) stimuli and mediate the so-called *second*, or *slow, pain*, which is a diffuse, dull-aching or burning discomfort that may outlast the stimulus.

Dorsal Root Ganglion Neurons

The first-order nociceptive neurons include (1) medium-sized dorsal root ganglion neurons with small myelinated fibers that use L-glutamate and that correspond to high-threshold mechanoreceptors, and (2) small dorsal root ganglion neurons with unmyelinated axons that contain various neuropeptides, particularly *substance P*, and that correspond to polymodal nociceptors. Small nociceptive dorsal root neurons may branch extensively to innervate several sensory fields, and some of their proximal projections enter the spinal cord via the ventral roots instead of the dorsal roots (*ventral root afferents*) to reach the dorsal horn.

Small dorsal root ganglion neurons may release neuropeptides antidromically from their peripheral branches at the site of stimulation. Antidromic release of neurotransmitters by peripheral branches is called *axon reflex*. Nociceptive axon reflexes are the basis for the *neurogenic inflammation*, or *flare, response*. Stimulation of nociceptive endings by mechanical damage or local substances released during inflammation (histamine, prostaglandins, potassium ions) not only produces pain but also causes the antidromic release of substance P and other vasoactive neuropeptides, which produce vasodilatation and increase vascular permeability at the site of injury.

Pain fibers, together with fibers involved in temperature and visceral sensation, enter the spinal cord in the lateral division of the dorsal root entry zone and divide into short ascending and descending branches that run longitudinally in the dorsolateral funiculus (Lissauer's tract). Within several segments, they leave the tract to provide excitatory synapses to second-order neurons in the dorsal horn. The excitatory neurotransmitters include L-glutamate and several neuropeptides, particularly substance P.

Dorsal Horn Neurons

The second-order nociceptive neurons include (1) *nociceptive-specific neurons*, which are located superficially in the dorsal horn and receive input solely from small myelinated and unmyelinated fibers, and (2) *wide dynamic range*, or *multiceptive, neurons*, which are located deep in the dorsal horn and in the intermediate gray matter and receive input not only from small myelinated and unmyelinated fibers but also from visceral afferents and large myelinated fibers. Wide dynamic range neurons are functionally important because they contribute most of the axons to the spinothalamic system. Also, these neurons transmit both nociceptive and nonnociceptive information, are the site of viscerosomatic convergence for *referred visceral pain*, and can change their functional properties according to local modulatory influences by central pain modulating mechanisms.

Second-order axons from both nociceptive-specific and wide dynamic range neurons, together with axons from thermoreceptive neurons, cross to the opposite site to continue rostrally in the anterolateral quadrant of the spinal cord, primarily in the spinothalamic pathways.

Organization of Central Nociceptive Pathways

The sensations of pain and temperature are transmitted primarily via the *spinothalamic tract*, which ascends in the contralateral ventrolateral quadrant of the spinal cord (Fig. 7-6). The spinothalamic tract is complex and functionally heterogeneous. It mediates the discriminative and arousal-emotional components of pain sensation as well as thermal, visceral, and simple tactile information. The different components of the spinothalamic tract include (1) a direct pathway, the *neospinothalamic pathway*, which ascends in the outer tube, mediates the discriminative aspect

of pain and temperature, and is important for localization, and (2) several indirect pathways — the *paleospinothalamic, spinoreticular*, and *spinomesencephalic tracts* — for the affective-arousal components of pain; they form part of the core, or inner tube of the neuraxis (Table 7-7).

Direct Pathway: The Neospinothalamic Tract

The *neospinothalamic tract* consists of second-order axons from both nociceptive-specific and wide dynamic range neurons. The axons cross within one or two segments of their origin through the ventral white commissure and ascend strictly contralaterally in the anterolateral quadrant of the spinal cord. The neospinothalamic tract, part of the outer tube systems, has a somatotopic organization in the cord, with the sacral dermatomes represented dorsolaterally and the cervical dermatomes ventromedially. These axons join the medial lemniscus and synapse on third-order neurons located mainly in the *ventral posterolateral nucleus* of the thalamus (see Fig. 7-6). The cortical representation of pain sensation is in the *primary* and *secondary sensory cortices* and in the *cingulate gyrus*.

The neospinothalamic tract is involved in rapid transmission of nociceptive and thermal information for localization and intensity of pain and temperature sensation. Thus, this pathway is important clinically for localization of lesions in the central nervous system. A second important function is to provide a parallel channel for transmission of tactile information, including simple touch and static-discriminative touch modalities.

The spinothalamic pathway transmits information about pain and temperature from the contralateral upper and lower extremities and trunk. Transmissions of pain and temperature sensations from the face and cranium are carried by the trigeminal system. Pain fibers from the face are carried primarily in the trigeminal nerve (cranial nerve V) and have the cell bodies of their primary sensory neurons located in the *gasserian*, or *semilunar, ganglion* (Fig. 7-7). On entering the brain stem in the pontine region, these fibers descend in the ipsilateral *descending*, or *spinal, tract of the trigeminal nerve* to the upper cervical cord. Axons of this tract synapse with second-order neurons in the adjacent *nucleus of the spinal tract of the trigeminal nerve*.

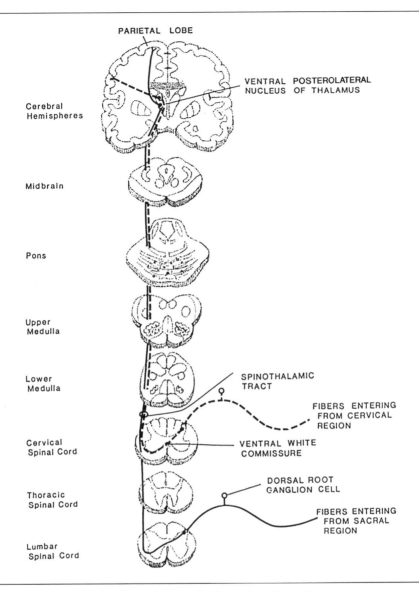

PARIETAL LOBE

VENTRAL POSTEROLATERAL
NUCLEUS OF THALAMUS

Cerebral
Hemispheres

Midbrain

Pons

Upper
Medulla

Lower
Medulla

SPINOTHALAMIC
TRACT

FIBERS ENTERING
FROM CERVICAL
REGION

Cervical
Spinal Cord

VENTRAL WHITE
COMMISSURE

DORSAL ROOT
GANGLION CELL

Thoracic
Spinal Cord

FIBERS ENTERING
FROM SACRAL
REGION

Lumbar
Spinal Cord

Fig. 7-6. Spinothalamic (neospinothalamic) tract. Pathway for pain and temperature sensation.

The axons of the second-order neurons cross to the opposite side of the brain stem and ascend to the ventral posteromedial nucleus of the thalamus. Third-order neurons in this thalamic nucleus project to the parietal lobe via the posterior limb of the internal capsule.

Indirect Pathways for Affective-Arousal Components of Pain

The indirect pathways involved in the affective and arousal aspects of pain sensation originate mainly from wide dynamic range neurons in the deep dorsal horn and intermediate gray matter. Their second-order axons ascend bilaterally in the spinal cord, have poor somatotopy, and make multiple synapses in the reticular formation. These pathways are components of the inner tube systems. Collaterals of these pathways reach the hypothalamus and other areas of the limbic system. Neurons involved in these complex, multisynaptic pathways have large bilateral receptive fields and receive convergent input not only from cutaneous but also from vis-

Table 7-7. Pathways for Pain Transmission

	Direct or lateral (outer tube)	Indirect or medial (inner tube)
Pathway	Neospinothalamic	Paleospinothalamic Spinoreticular Spinomesencephalic Propriospinal
Somatotopy	Yes	No
Body representation	Contralateral	Bilateral
Synapse in reticular formation	No	Yes
Subcortical targets	None	Hypothalamus Limbic system Autonomic centers
Thalamic nucleus	Ventral posterolateral nucleus	Intralaminar nuclei Other midline nuclei
Cortical region	Parietal lobe	Cingulate gyrus
Role	Discriminative pain	Affective-arousal component of pain
Other function	Temperature Touch	

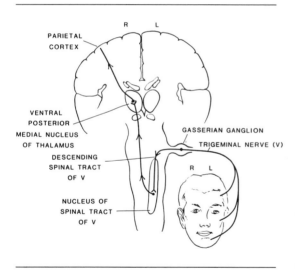

Fig. 7-7. Pathway of pain fibers of the face.

ceral and other receptors. These pathways initiate arousal, autonomic, endocrine, and motor responses to pain stimulation. The two main groups of these pathways are (1) ventrolateral quadrant pathways, which include the *paleospinothalamic, spinoreticular,* and *spinomesencephalic* tracts (Fig. 7-8) and (2) the *propriospinal* multisynaptic ascending system.

In the spinal cord, second-order axons that contribute to these pathways ascend contra-laterally and ipsilaterally in the ventrolateral quadrant (they intermingle with those of the neospinothalamic pathway), the dorsolateral quadrant, and the propriospinal system. The paleospinothalamic tract provides multiple input to the reticular formation and terminates in the *midline and intralaminar thalamic nuclei,* which project diffusely to the cerebral cortex, particularly to the cingulate gyrus. The spinoreticular tract terminates in sensory, motor, autonomic, and endocrine-relay areas of the medullary and pontine reticular formation. The spinomesencephalic tract synapses in the *periaqueductal gray matter.*

The *multisynaptic ascending propriospinal system* originates from neurons in the substantia gelatinosa of the dorsal horn and in the intermediate gray matter. This system forms a functional continuum with the reticular formation of the brain stem.

In addition to transmitting affective-arousal components of pain sensation, all these indirect pathways are important for activation of central antinociceptive (pain inhibition) mechanisms discussed below.

Clinical Correlations

Lesions that involve the peripheral level may cause either the sensation of pain or some loss

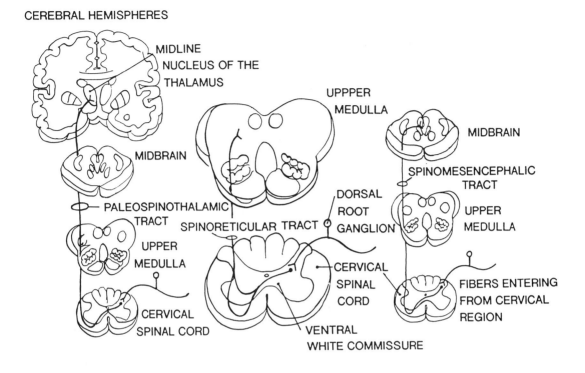

CEREBRAL HEMISPHERES

Fig. 7-8. The three individual pain pathways of the inner tube systems that transmit affective and arousal components of pain. A. Paleospinothalamic tract. B. Spinoreticular tract. C. Spinomesencephalic tract.

of pain and temperature in the distribution of the affected nerves. Lesions of the central nervous system seldom produce pain unless pain-sensitive structures are involved or central pain-controlling pathways are interrupted. A central lesion that interrupts the spinothalamic tract results in inability to perceive painful stimuli and to discriminate between hot and cold in the areas below the lesion. A lesion at the spinal level involving the spinothalamic tract results in contralateral loss of pain and temperature sensation. A lesion at the posterior fossa level produces contralateral loss of pain and temperature in trunk and extremities, but if the same lesion also involves the pain fibers in the descending tract of the trigeminal nerve, there is ipsilateral loss of pain and temperature of the face. The separate pathways for body and limb pain and for facial pain provide the neuroanatomical basis for this clinical observation. Thus, lesions at the level of the medulla produce

crossed anesthesia, whereas those rostral to the medulla produce *complete contralateral hemianesthesia*, which includes the face. Lesions at the supratentorial level produce contralateral loss of pain and temperature. With suprathalamic lesions, crude pain perception may remain intact, but precise localization of painful stimuli is impaired.

Summary
Pain and temperature pathways overlap in the spinal cord. The most important pathway for central transmission of pain and temperature is the spinothalamic system. This system originates predominantly from wide dynamic range neurons of the dorsal horn and intermediate white matter and ascends in the ventrolateral quadrant of the spinal cord. It is a functionally heterogeneous system that includes both a direct spinothalamic, or neospinothalamic, pathway involved in discriminative aspects of pain and temperature (as well

as tactile sensation) and a group of indirect pathways involved in arousal-affective aspects of pain sensation. Pain sensation can be transmitted not only also via the contralateral ventrolateral quadrant system but also via indirect pathways ascending bilaterally in the spinal cord. This may explain the failure of ventrolateral cord lesions to produce permanent relief from pain.

Central Mechanisms of Pain Control

The dorsal horn is not a simple station for pain transmission. It contains various complex, dynamic circuits that support not only transmission of sensory input but also a high degree of sensory processing. One of the most important aspects of this sensory processing is the central modulation of pain transmission.

The transmission of pain is modulated by both *segmental mechanisms* and descending *suprasegmental mechanisms* via complex circuits at the spinal or medullary levels. These regulatory circuits involve primary afferents, descending pathways, and local interneurons.

Interneurons in the Dorsal Horn

Interneurons in the dorsal horn are located primarily in the *substantia gelatinosa*, or lamina II. They may be excitatory or inhibitory. Inhibitory interneurons contain GABA, enkephalins, or other neuropeptides and are important for local processing and modulation of pain transmission. They receive input from segmental large and small primary afferent fibers and from descending supraspinal fibers.

Segmental Mechanisms

There are two important segmental mechanisms for modulation of pain transmission. The first involves inhibition of pain transmission by activation of large-diameter afferents; that is, stimulation of low-threshold, large myelinated mechanoreceptive afferents *inhibits* pain transmission in the dorsal horn, probably by the activation of local inhibitory interneurons. This is the basis for the *gate control theory* of pain modulation. A second mechanism involves exaggeration of pain transmission after repetitive activation of small nociceptive fibers; that is, repetitive firing of nociceptive fibers results in increased activity of dorsal

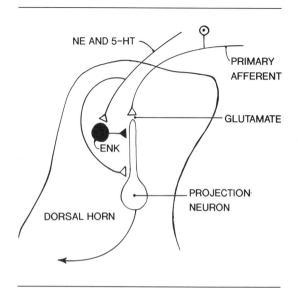

Fig. 7-9. Local circuit in the dorsal horn involved in transmission and modulation of pain sensation at spinal level. Primary afferents release L-glutamate and substance P to excite second-order relay neurons (*projection neuron*) of spinothalamic tract. This transmission is inhibited by local interneurons containing enkephalin (*ENK*) or other transmitters and by descending brain stem pathways containing serotonin (*5-HT*) and norepinephrine (*NE*).

horn nociceptive neurons (Fig. 7-9). This mechanism, known as the *wind-up phenomenon*, may explain the pain present with nerve injury and during nerve regeneration.

Suprasegmental Mechanisms

Several reciprocally connected brain regions form a *central pain-controlling network*. The nuclei and pathways of this *endogenous analgesia system* are part of the internal regulation system of the inner tube and are diffusely distributed. They include the cerebral cortex, thalamus, hypothalamus, brain stem, and dorsal horn. Important components of this system are the *periaqueductal gray matter* of the midbrain, the rostral *ventromedial medulla*, particularly the *raphe nucleus*, which produces serotonin, and the *locus ceruleus* and adjacent medullary neurons that produce norepinephrine (Fig. 7-10). All these central structures have several properties in common: (1) they contain endogenous opioid neurons and receptors; (2) they are stimulated by opioids and

PERIAQUEDUCTAL
GRAY MATTER

RAPHE
NUCLEI

DORSAL
HORN

Fig. 7-10. Brain stem components of the central pain-controlling network (endogenous analgesic system). The periaqueductal gray matter stimulates serotonergic neurons in the raphe nuclei and norepinephrine-synthesizing cell groups of the reticular formation in ventral medulla. Descending serotonergic and noradrenergic pathways inhibit pain transmission in the dorsal horn. The periaqueductal gray matter and ventral medulla are sites for analgesic action of opioids.

mediate the analgesic effects of morphine-like drugs; (3) they receive input from the indirect ascending nociceptive pathways and thus provide *feedback inhibition* of pain transmission; (4) when stimulated, they produce analgesia, and they *selectively affect pain transmission* and do not affect transmission of nonnociceptive information in the dorsal horn.

Opioids disinhibit antinociceptive neurons of the periaqueductal gray matter. These neurons, in turn, activate the serotonergic and noradrenergic bulbospinal neurons that project to the dorsal horn via the dorsolateral fu-

niculus of the spinal cord. Noradrenergic and serotonergic inputs inhibit pain transmission either directly or through inhibitory GABA-containing or opioid-containing interneurons in the dorsal horn.

Clinical Correlations

Organic pain can be divided into *nociceptive pain* and *neurogenic pain. Nociceptive pain* is related to activation of normal pain mechanisms in response to tissue injury. This symptom is most important in calling attention to pathologic processes that occur in many organ systems. Lesions located outside the nervous system frequently stimulate pain-sensitive free nerve endings and produce the subjective sensation of pain. Acute nociceptive pain is initiated by stimulation of nociceptive fibers by several chemical mediators of inflammation (for example, potassium ions, histamine, bradykinin, and prostaglandins) and is potentiated by antidromic release of substance P and other neuropeptides from nociceptive axon terminals (neurogenic inflammation, or flare response). The parenchyma of internal organs, including the brain, is not supplied with pain receptors. However, the wall of arteries, the dura mater, mesothelial surfaces (for example, synovial surfaces, pleura, pericardium, and peritoneum), the wall of hollow viscera, and muscle are subject to inflammation or mechanical traction. Unlike somatic pain, visceral pain is poorly localized and the sensation generally occurs in a surface area of the body remote from the actual source of stimulation. This is the phenomenon known as *referred pain.*

Neurogenic pain includes *neuropathic pain, deafferentation pain,* and *sympathetically maintained pain.*

Neuropathic pain occurs in cases of painful nerve compression or after formation of posttraumatic neuroma following a nerve lesion. This may produce abnormal discharges in the areas of demyelination, selective loss of large-fiber-mediated segmental inhibition, and increased activity of small nociceptive fibers. This is reflected by increased sensitivity to noxious stimulus (*hyperesthesia*), decreased pain threshold after repetitive stimulation (*hyperalgesia*), pain in response to application of innocuous stimulus (*allodynia*), and continuing pain sensation after removal of the stimulus.

Deafferentation pain may complicate any type of injury along the course of the somatosensory pathways. This can occur at the peripheral level (for example, phantom pain after limb amputation), along the ascending pathways (for example, demyelinating spinal cord lesions in multiple sclerosis), or at the level of the thalamus (thalamic syndrome). In these conditions, pain occurs in the area of sensory loss. It is due to perturbation in the central processing of pain information that results from interference with normal pain-controlling mechanisms.

Sympathetically maintained pain is characterized by simultaneous occurrence of pain, local autonomic dysregulation (edema, vasomotor disturbances, and sweat abnormalities) and trophic changes in the skin, soft tissues, and bone. It mainly occurs with lesions of peripheral nerves or roots.

Pathways for Transmission of Simple Touch

Tactile sensation is initiated by stimulation of low-threshold mechanoreceptors in the skin. These receptors vary in degree of adaptation and size of receptive field. The axons of primary, large dorsal root ganglion neurons are in the medial division of the dorsal root entry zone. These large myelinated fibers either ascend directly in the dorsal columns or stimulate low-threshold mechanoreceptive and wide dynamic range neurons in the deep dorsal horn. Thus, simple tactile information is carried rostrally by several parallel pathways, including the direct and postsynaptic dorsal column pathways, the spinocervical tract in the dorsolateral funiculus, and the neospinothalamic tract in the anterolateral quadrant.

All these pathways are part of the outer tube systems. They contribute to the lemniscal system, terminate in the contralateral ventral posterolateral nucleus of thalamus, and activate low-threshold cutaneous mechanoreceptive neurons in the primary somatosensory cortex. These pathways overlap with the ones that mediate discriminative touch and proprioception (dorsal columns) and discriminative

pain and temperature (neospinothalamic tract).

The transmission of simple tactile modalities (detection, localization, and, to some extent, two-point discrimination) via several parallel pathways explains the preservation of sensation of touch despite lesions affecting other sensory modalities. Thus, touch is not very useful clinically for localizing lesions in the central nervous system.

Pathways for Unconscious Proprioception: Spinocerebellar Tracts

Receptors

Inputs from muscle spindles, Golgi tendon organs, joint proprioceptors, and low-threshold mechanoreceptors are not only processed centrally for conscious sensation but are also crucial for unconscious reflex adjustments of posture and muscle tone and for continuous monitoring of motor performance.

Dorsal Root Ganglion Neurons

Joint and muscle receptors are innervated by rapidly conducting, large myelinated peripheral axons of large dorsal root ganglion neurons (first-order neurons). Their proximal axons constitute the primary afferent fibers that enter the spinal cord via the medial division of the dorsal root entry zone. These proprioceptive fibers may (1) course directly through the dorsal gray matter to the ventral gray horn, (2) ascend directly in the dorsal columns or synapse on second-order neurons in the spinal cord to form the lemniscal system, and (3) synapse on second-order neurons in the intermediate gray matter, which contribute to the *spinocerebellar tracts.*

Primary afferent fibers that synapse directly on ventral horn motor neurons initiate a two-neuron muscle stretch reflex that is the anatomical basis for the *muscle-stretch*, or *deep tendon, reflexes* that are commonly tested in clinical neurology. A sudden muscle stretch, as elicited by tapping a tendon with a reflex hammer, stimulates muscle spindle receptors. This in turn produces action potentials in the afferent fibers that enter the spinal cord and synapse on motor neurons in the ventral horn. These ventral horn cells then initiate action potentials that travel back to the muscle of origin and cause it to contract. This is a *local segmental reflex* (see Chapter 14, The Spinal Level). This reflex is lost whenever disease involves the primary proprioceptive axon or other component of the reflex arc at that segment.

More important is the role of primary afferent input to the *interneuronal pool* in the ventral horn. These interneurons integrate primary afferent, supraspinal, and local circuit information to control motor neuron activity for maintenance of muscle tone (degree of stiffness) and execution of coordinated motor acts.

Primary afferent fibers that ascend in the dorsal column–lemniscal system constitute the afferent limb of a *long-loop reflex*; the efferent limb consists of axons in the corticospinal tract.

The *spinocerebellar tracts* transmit information about the activity of the effector muscles or motor neuron pools to the cerebellum, where it is integrated and processed. The cerebellum is capable of modifying the action of different muscle groups so that movements are performed smoothly and accurately. Because the information carried by these pathways does not reach consciousness directly, it is referred to as *unconscious proprioception*.

General Organization of the Spinocerebellar Tracts

The two spinal cord pathways that convey unconscious proprioceptive information to the cerebellum are the *dorsal* and *ventral spinocerebellar tracts*. They are part of the outer tube system and have some features in common, but they also have important anatomical and functional differences. Both tracts (1) originate from neurons in the intermediate gray matter, (2) contain large-diameter, rapidly conducting secondary axons (they are among the highest conducting pathways in the central nervous system), (3) are located in the periphery of the lateral white matter of the spinal cord, (4) transmit information from the *lower extremities*, and (5) provide input predominantly to the *ipsilateral cerebellum*.

Dorsal Spinocerebellar Tract

The *dorsal spinocerebellar tract* originates in neurons of the *nucleus dorsalis of Clarke*

(*Clarke's column*). These neurons are potently excited by first-order proprioceptive fibers from muscle spindles of a single muscle or few agonists and from low-threshold cutaneous mechanoreceptors. Second-order axons from Clarke's column enter the ipsilateral lateral funiculus to form the dorsal spinocerebellar tract. Fibers ascend near the lateral margin of the spinal cord, and at the level of the medulla, they enter the cerebellum through the inferior cerebellar peduncle, or restiform body.

Because Clarke's column is found only between spinal cord segments T-1 and L-1, two modifications of the basic organization of this pathway occur above and below these levels:

(1) Fibers carrying proprioceptive information from the lower extremities and entering *below L-1* course in the dorsal column (fasciculus gracilis) until they reach segment L-1. Thus, there is no dorsal spinocerebellar tract in the lumbosacral spinal cord.

(2) Proprioceptive fibers entering *above T-1* (carrying information from the upper extremities to the cervical cord) do not have access to Clarke's column or to the dorsal spinocerebellar tract. Proprioceptive input from the upper extremities ascends in the dorsal column (fasciculus cuneatus) to synapse in the lower medulla in the *lateral*, or *accessory*, *nucleus cuneatus*, which is analogous to Clarke's column. Second-order neurons from the lateral nucleus cuneatus give rise to axons that form the *cuneocerebellar tract* and that enter the ipsilateral restiform body together with the dorsal spinocerebellar tract.

The dorsal spinocerebellar tract and the cuneocerebellar tract are important in the rapid, efficient transmission of proprioceptive and exteroceptive signals from a single or a few muscles to the cerebellum. This allows *feedback control* of motor performance through cerebellar influences on cortical and subcortical motor nuclei.

Ventral Spinocerebellar Tract

The *ventral spinocerebellar tract* originates in *spinal border cells* in the lateral region of the ventral horn of the lumbar spinal cord. These neurons receive information simultaneously from the same primary proprioceptive and exteroceptive afferents and descending supraspinal pathways affecting ventral horn motor neurons and interneurons. Axons of the spinal border cells cross the midline to form the ventral spinocerebellar tract. This tract is lateral to the ventrolateral quadrant and ascends through the spinal cord, medulla, and pons to enter the cerebellum via a circuitous route through the superior cerebellar peduncle, or brachium conjunctivum. Within the posterior fossa, most of these fibers again cross so that the ventral spinocerebellar tract provides the cerebellum with bilateral but predominantly ipsilateral input about activity in the lower extremities. Input from the upper extremities relays on interneurons at spinal cord level C-7 and C-8. Axons of these interneurons ascend as the *rostral spinocerebellar tract*, reaching predominantly the ipsilateral cerebellum via either the superior or inferior cerebellar peduncle.

The ventral spinocerebellar tract neurons act as comparators between the action of inhibitory and excitatory inputs to spinal motor neurons and interneurons and thus provide the cerebellum with information about the state of excitation of these spinal cord neurons. Therefore, the ventral spinocerebellar tract provides *feed-forward information* to the cerebellum about the activity of motor neuron pools, whereas the dorsal spinocerebellar tract conveys *feedback information* about the resulting movement.

Clinical Correlations

The clinical manifestation of disease involving these pathways is motor incoordination (ataxia) of the extremities. Although these pathways are of great physiologic importance, clinically it is extremely difficult to identify abnormalities from damage of these pathways, which are commonly involved along with the dorsal columns.

Pathways for Other Senses

The pathways discussed above mediate the major general somatic afferent sensations. Sensation from visceral structures (general visceral afferent sensations) is discussed further in Chapter 9 (The Internal Regulation System). The special visceral afferent sensations of taste and smell and the special somatic afferent sensations of hearing and bal-

ance are discussed in association with the posterior fossa (see Chapter 15, The Posterior Fossa Level) and supratentorial (see Chapter 16, The Supratentorial Level) levels. Because of the importance of the special somatic afferent sensation of vision in clinical neurologic diagnosis, this pathway is discussed below.

The visual pathways are located entirely at the supratentorial level (Fig. 7-11). The receptors, first-order, and second-order neurons are located in the retina. Fibers travel in the left optic tract, and the images of the left visual field travel in the right optic tract. The optic tracts project to the thalamus and synapse in the right and left lateral *geniculate body*, where they give rise to fibers that project to the *occipital cortex* as the *optic radiations*. Thus, the visual images of the right half of the visual field project to the left occipital cortex, while the images of the left visual field project to the right occipital cortex.

Lesions located anterior to the optic chiasm in the optic nerves interfere with vision only in the ipsilateral eye (monocular visual loss). Lesions in the center of the optic chiasm interfere only with the nasal crossing fibers, producing a loss of function of the nasal retina and of temporal vision in both eyes (bitemporal hemianopia). Lesions that are located behind the optic chiasm, that is, in the optic tracts, lateral geniculate body, optic radiations, or occipital cortex, produce a loss of vision in the contralateral visual fields of both eyes (homonymous hemianopia).

Clinical Correlations

Disease processes involving the sensory system produce various symptoms, including pain, hypesthesia (reduced sensation), anesthesia (a complete loss of cutaneous sensibility), dysesthesia (an altered or perverted interpretation of sensation, such as a burning, tingling, or painful feeling in response to touch), and paresthesia (spontaneous sensation of prickling or tingling). In some instances, sensory stimuli are more keenly felt than normal (hyperesthesia). It is extremely important in every case of pain or sensory loss to determine its exact distribution.

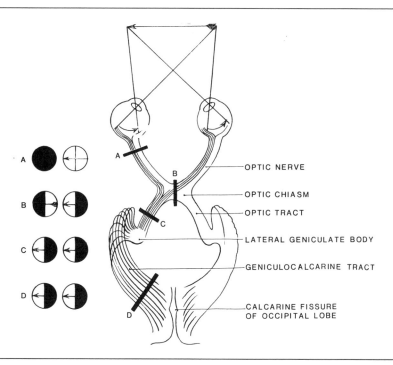

Fig. 7-11. The optic pathways. The visual field defects produced by lesions in these pathways are shown at the left. The visual field of the left eye is shown in the left circle, that of the right eye in the adjacent circle. Lesions anterior to optic chiasm (A) produce monocular visual loss. Lesions at optic chiasm (B) produce bitemporal hemianopia due to involvement of nasal-retinal crossing fibers. Unilateral lesions behind optic chiasm affecting optic tract (C), lateral geniculate body, optic radiations (D), or occipital cortex produce contralateral homonymous hemianopia.

Lesions at the Peripheral Level

The distal axons of the primary sensory neurons mediating all types of afferent input are gathered together, along with motor and autonomic fibers, in peripheral nerves. Thus, a lesion that affects peripheral nerves would be expected to produce a variable sensory loss for all modalities and a loss of muscle-stretch reflexes in the anatomic distribution of that nerve. Some motor or autonomic deficit usually can be found if such fibers are present in the involved nerve. This type of deficit may occur in a focal distribution when only a single peripheral nerve is involved (such as might occur from trauma) and is called *mononeuropathy*. When these symptoms and signs occur in a diffuse distribution, the deficit is called *polyneuropathy*. Pain, paresthesias, or dysesthesias are common accompaniments of peripheral nerve lesions. Figure 7-12 shows the cutaneous distribution of the major peripheral nerves.

Lesions at the Spinal Level

Disease processes located within the spinal canal typically produce (1) a *segmental* neurologic deficit limited to one level of the body and usually caused by involvement of the nerve roots or spinal nerves and (2) an *intersegmental* sensory deficit involving all of the body below a particular level and caused by interruption of the major ascending sensory pathways.

Mechanical compression or local inflammation of a dorsal nerve root or spinal nerve produces pain along the anatomical distribution of the affected root. The area of skin supplied by one dorsal root is known as a *dermatome* (Fig. 7-13); pain due to nerve root involvement in the distribution of one or more dermatomes is known as *radicular pain*. This type

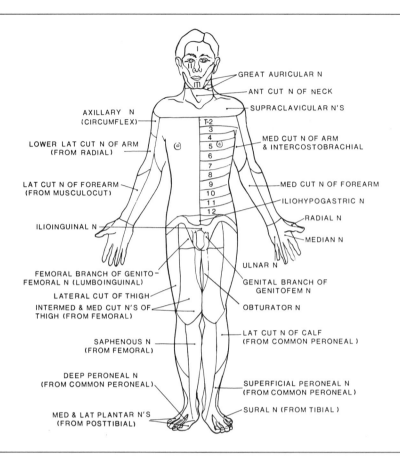

Fig. 7-12. Cutaneous distribution of the major peripheral nerves. (*ANT* = anterior; *CUT* = cutaneous; *INT* = intermediate; *LAT* = lateral; *MED* = medial; *N* = nerve.) (Redrawn from W. Haymaker and B. Woodhall. *Peripheral Nerve Injuries: Principles of Diagnosis* [2nd ed.]. Philadelphia: Saunders, 1953.)

of pain, which may vary in intensity, is often lancinating (a sharp, darting type of pain). Maneuvers that increase intraspinal pressure (and presumably increase the traction on irritated nerve roots), such as coughing, sneezing, and straining, produce a characteristic increase in this type of pain. In addition to producing radicular pain, lesions of the dorsal root or spinal nerve produce areas of paresthesia, hyperesthesia, or loss of cutaneous sensation in a dermatomal distribution. At appropriate levels, segmental loss of muscle-stretch reflexes, weakness, and autonomic disturbances can be seen.

Commissural Syndrome

A special type of segmental deficit can result from a lesion involving the central regions of the spinal cord, usually over several segments. This deficit is characterized by a loss of pain and temperature sensation from interruption of the second-order axons as they are decussating to form the spinothalamic tracts (Fig. 7-14). The sensory loss is bilateral (because fibers from both sides are interrupted by such a lesion), and it involves the crossing fibers of several adjacent segments. Thus, a lesion involving the central regions of segments T-2 through T-5 produces loss of pain and temperature only in those segments. The commissural syndrome can be produced only by a lesion in the substance of the spinal cord. As the lesion enlarges, other adjacent sensory tracts become involved. This type of lesion may result from trauma (hematomyelia), neoplasm, or other conditions including syringomyelia.

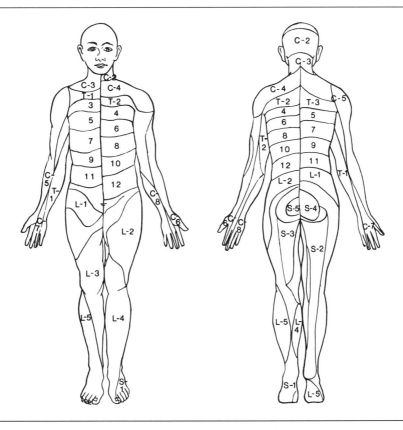

Fig. 7-13. Cutaneous distribution of spinal nerve roots. Note considerable overlap between segments, and note that the distribution differs from that of peripheral nerves. (Redrawn from F. R. Ford. *Diseases of the Nervous System: In Infancy, Childhood and Adolescence* [3rd ed.]. Springfield, Ill.: Thomas, 1952.)

Syringomyelia is a common cause of the commissural syndrome and consists of cavitation occurring within the central area of the spinal cord (Fig. 7-15). Whether the cavity develops as a result of dilatation of the primitive central canal (hydromyelia) or as a result of some other destructive process in the central region of the cord, such as an intramedullary neoplasm, is not always clear. Although initially the cavity is centrally located, expansion of the cavity and surrounding gliosis tends to extend the syrinx irregularly throughout the gray matter and at times into the white matter of the dorsal and lateral columns. The lesion most commonly occurs in the cervical area.

Spinothalamic Tract Syndrome

A lesion involving the spinothalamic tract causes a loss of pain and temperature sensa-

tion on the opposite side of the body, involving all segments below the level of the lesion. Pain and temperature fibers enter through the dorsal root branch and extend rostrally in Lissauer's tract for up to two segments above their entry zone before synapsing with the spinothalamic tract neurons of the dorsal horn. Therefore, the sensory level on the side opposite a spinothalamic tract lesion is usually at least two segments below the level of the actual lesion. Within the spinothalamic tract, the fibers are arranged in a laminar fashion, with the sacral fibers near the periphery and fibers from higher levels toward the center. Hence, lesions arising within the substance of the spinal cord (intramedullary lesions) may involve only the central portions of the tract and spare the peripheral fibers, to produce a loss of pain and temperature in all levels below the lesion except the

A

B

Fig. 7-14. Commissural syndrome. Distribution of loss of pain and temperature sensations, with a lesion in the location shown on the left.

sacral level. This is referred to as *sacral sparing*. When present, sacral sparing is an important clue to an intramedullary spinal cord lesion (Fig. 7-16).

In certain instances of intractable pain involving the lower extremity, pain may be relieved by placing a lesion in the spinothalamic tract (spinothalamic tractotomy). It is usually done by surgically cutting the ventral portion of the lateral funiculus in the cervical area. Although there is probably some damage to the ventral spinocerebellar tract, no permanent symptoms are produced except loss of pain and temperature sensibility on the contralateral side.

Brown-Séquard's Syndrome

This syndrome is seen in pure form with hemisection of the spinal cord. In clinical practice, the syndrome is often partial and incomplete; however, the findings of ipsilateral motor deficit, ipsilateral dorsal column deficit, and contralateral loss of pain and temperature usually are present and are characteristic of a unilateral spinal cord lesion (Fig. 7-17).

Lesions at the Posterior Fossa Level

Disease processes affecting the posterior fossa level are characterized by a contralateral intersegmental loss of sensory function in the trunk

Fig. 7-15. Syringomyelia. A. Magnetic resonance image of syringomyelia at level of cervical spinal cord (*arrow*). B. Transverse section of cervical spinal cord showing central cavity lined by thickened glial membrane and associated with degeneration of surrounding tissue. (H & E; ×4.)

and limbs because of interruption of the major ascending pathways. However, there is frequently also a loss of sensory function (primarily pain and temperature) over the ipsilateral face because of segmental involvement of the trigeminal nerve or its descending tract and nucleus (Fig. 7-18).

Lesions at the Supratentorial Level

At this level, all major sensory pathways have crossed to the contralateral side; therefore, lesions at this level alter sensory function over the entire contralateral side of the body.

Two important variations of sensory loss may be encountered with lesions at this level.

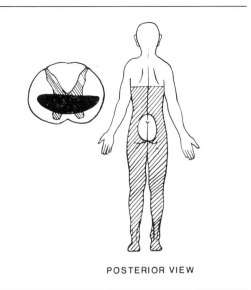

POSTERIOR VIEW

Fig. 7-16. Sensory loss with sacral sparing due to the intramedullary lesion shown on the left, involving lateral spinothalamic tracts bilaterally. (Note that figure in diagram is viewed from behind.)

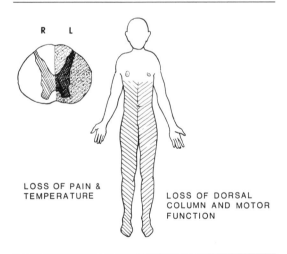

LOSS OF PAIN & TEMPERATURE

LOSS OF DORSAL COLUMN AND MOTOR FUNCTION

Fig. 7-17. Brown-Séquard's syndrome. Sensory loss produced by damage to one-half of the spinal cord by lesion shown on the left. A motor deficit would also be present (see Chapter 8, The Motor System).

Thalamic Syndrome

The thalamus functions as an important integrating and relay station for sensory perception. A lesion affecting the specific sensory nuclei of the thalamus causes a relatively complete loss of all forms of general somatic afferent sensation in the contralateral face, trunk, and limbs (Fig. 7-19). If the portion of

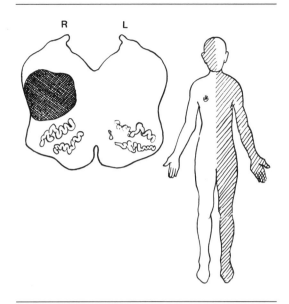

Fig. 7-18. Distribution of pain and temperature sensation loss characteristic of lesions at the posterior fossa level, as shown on the left.

the thalamus related to vision is also involved, a contralateral homonymous hemianopia is produced. After a localized lesion of the thalamus, perhaps due to faulty integration of sensory information, a severe burning (dysesthetic) pain in the area of sensory loss is sometimes produced.

Suprathalamic Syndrome

Lesions that involve sensory pathways from the thalamus to the cortex or in the cortex itself also alter all forms of general somatic afferent sensation on the contralateral side of the body. However, in contrast to the dense loss of sensation found with thalamic lesions, suprathalamic involvement is characterized by only minimal involvement of pain, temperature, touch, and vibratory sensibility and a severe deficit in the discriminative sensations that require cortical participation (Fig. 7-20). These sensations are joint position sense, two-point discrimination, touch localization, and the recognition of objects placed in the hand (stereognosis) and suggest that discriminative sensations require intact thalamocortical pathways for their full appreciation, whereas the primary modalities of superficial sensation are perceived and integrated at the thalamic

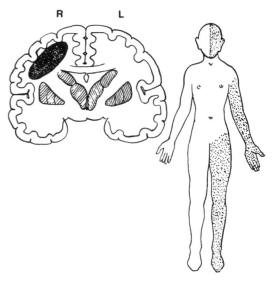

Fig. 7-19. Thalamic syndrome. Loss of all modalities of sensation contralateral to the lesion.

Fig. 7-20. Suprathalamic syndrome. Loss of cortical sensory functions contralateral to the lesion.

level. This type of discriminative sensory loss is often found with lesions of the parietal lobe and is commonly referred to as a *cortical sensory deficit*. If the optic radiations are also involved, a contralateral visual field defect is produced. In the absence of a visual field defect or other signs of supratentorial involvement, this type of sensory deficit may be confused with the findings of dorsal column disease. A severe deficit in conscious proprioception, bilateral involvement, and associated alteration in vibratory sense all favor a lesion of the dorsal columns. When the deficit is unilateral, the distinction between a suprathalamic and a high-cervical spinal cord lesion can be extremely difficult unless other signs and symptoms are present to aid with localization.

Irritative lesions located in the region of the postcentral gyrus may initiate seizures. The clinical manifestations of seizures in this area consist primarily of a feeling of tingling (paresthesias) on the opposite side of the body. As the localized neuronal discharge spreads from its focus of origin, these sensations may be experienced as moving in an orderly fashion dictated by the topographic organization of the gyrus. Further spread to the adjacent precentral gyrus may produce associated motor

activity, and spread to subcortical structures may produce a loss of consciousness.

Somatosensory Evoked Response

The somatosensory evoked response is an electrodiagnostic test that is used to evaluate the sensory system (Fig. 7-21). Evoked responses are electrical potentials that occur with a fixed latency in response to a stimulus. Because these potentials are very small, a number of successive responses need to be averaged and amplified to be seen. The somatosensory evoked responses are potentials occurring in response to stimulation of a peripheral nerve, which can be recorded from the nerve, the plexus, the sensory pathways within the spinal cord and brain stem, the thalamocortical pathways, and the somatosensory cortex. Abnormalities of the somatosensory evoked responses occur with lesions or disease processes involving the sensory pathways at any of these levels and are manifested either by an increase in latency or by a reduced amplitude or an absent response. The somatosensory evoked responses are used to document or to diagnose multiple sclerosis, degenerative processes, traumatic lesions, and other structural lesions affecting the peripheral or central sensory system.

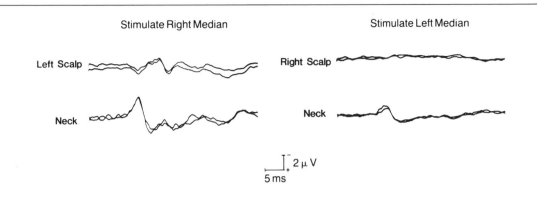

Fig. 7-21. Somatosensory evoked responses recorded from the neck and scalp in a patient with multiple sclerosis. Note decrease in amplitude of potential recorded from left neck and scalp compared with those recorded from right side.

The Differential Diagnosis of Ataxia

Definition

Sensory information is vital to the smooth, harmonious production of motor activity. A failure to produce normally smooth motor acts is referred to as *ataxia*. Ataxia may be manifest in individual limb motions but is more commonly evident during walking. With ataxia, movements become jerky and uncoordinated. The central nervous system must be constantly apprised of the position, tone, and movement of the limbs and trunk. It accomplishes this task by integrating (primarily in the cerebellum) proprioceptive input and information from the receptors for equilibrium, which are located in the labyrinths of the ear, and by relaying these data back to the appropriate motor effectors. Visual input may be used in part to compensate for a defect in this integrating mechanism.

Types of Ataxia

Sensory ataxias include conditions in which motor performance is faulty when the motor pathways and the cerebellum are intact. This occurs because there is a defect in transmitting proprioceptive or equilibratory information to higher centers. Sensory ataxia frequently can be compensated for by using visual input to guide limb position; hence, the ataxia is often worse in the dark or when the eyes are closed. *Motor ataxias* include conditions in which the sensory pathways are intact but motor performance is faulty, and there is a defect

in the integration and processing of proprioceptive information. Motor ataxia is usually due to disease in the cerebellum. This type of ataxia is often poorly compensated for by visual input.

Differentiation

The Romberg test is a quick and convenient method of distinguishing between these two types of ataxias. The patient who shows no unsteadiness when standing with feet together and eyes open but who displays unsteadiness with the eyes closed has a Romberg sign, indicating that the patient has a sensory ataxia. Patients with a motor (cerebellar) ataxia may or may not be unsteady in the Romberg position but show little or no increase in unsteadiness when they close their eyes and thus do not have the Romberg sign.

Patients who have sensory ataxia generally have difficulty with either vestibular function or proprioception, as a result of peripheral nerve or spinal cord disease. Ataxic patients without a Romberg sign often show abnormalities in cerebellar function.

Neurologic Examination: Sensory System

A complete sensory examination includes the evaluation of touch, pain, temperature, joint position, and vibratory senses, as well as various discriminatory modalities. Comparison of one side of the body with the other and with the examiner's own sensory abilities is useful for establishing normal and abnormal. Much of the sensory examination is best performed with the patient's eyes closed to eliminate visual cues. Examination of sensation consists of three portions: (1) qualitative, to determine the elements of sensation that are affected; (2) quantitative, to determine the degree of involvement when sensation is impaired; and (3) anatomical, to map out the areas of sensory impairment.

Sensation is tested in the following manner:

1. *Touch.* Lightly place a piece of cotton on the face, trunk, and extremities, and ask the patient to respond when it is felt.
2. *Pain.* Gently prick the patient with a pin. A more accurate determination can be made by randomly touching the patient with the point or head of a pin and noting whether the patient can appreciate "sharp" and "dull" sensations.
3. *Temperature.* Randomly apply warm and cool objects to the skin, and note the patient's ability to distinguish between them.
4. *Vibration sense.* Place a vibrating tuning fork over bony prominences, and note whether the patient can detect the sensation and can determine when the vibration ceases. (In patients older than 50 years, vibratory sense is often reduced in the feet.)
5. *Joint position sense.* Firmly grasp the sides of the great toe or of a finger, and ask the patient to detect and respond to movements in an upward or downward direction.
6. *Two-point discrimination.* A two-point caliper is used. This sensation is normally examined only on the fingertips by asking the patient to respond to the tactile stimulus of one or two points. The threshold (minimal recognizable separation) is determined and compared on the two sides of the body.
7. *Tactile localization.* Touch the patient, and request that the point of contact be identified.
8. *Graphesthesia.* Ask the patient to identify numbers or letters traced on the palm of his or her hand with a blunt object.
9. *Stereognosis.* Ask the patient to close his or her eyes and identify objects of different sizes, shapes, and textures (such as a coin, key, clip, or safety pin) placed in the hand.

In the absence of any sensory symptoms or the patient's subjective sensation of pain, a brief screening examination consisting of a test of touch, pain, joint position, and vibratory sense in both hands and both feet and of a test of pain and touch perception on the face is all that is required. When a sensory deficit is suspected or identified, the examiner must determine the modality of sensation involved and map its distribution to see if it conforms to that found with lesions of the peripheral nerve, spinal nerve or dorsal root, spinal cord, posterior fossa, or supratentorial region.

Objectives

1. Define receptor, sensory unit, and receptive field.
2. Define receptor potential, frequency and population coding, receptor adaptation, and receptor specificity.
3. Define in physiologic terms the differences between rapidly adapting (phasic) and slowly adapting (tonic) receptors.
4. List the types of somatic receptors.
5. Define hierarchical and parallel organization of somatosensory systems, and list the differences between the direct and indirect somatosensory pathways.
6. Describe the main features of wide dynamic neurons in the dorsal horn.
7. Name the function of the following pathways and trace their paths:
   a. Direct dorsal column–lemniscal tract
   b. Direct spinothalamic (neospinothalamic) tract
   c. Indirect spinothalamic (paleospinothalamic) tract
   d. Dorsal spinocerebellar tract
   e. Ventral spinocerebellar tract
8. Explain the differential effects of lesions involving all large afferents versus lesions restricted to the dorsal columns.
9. Describe the two main types of primary nociceptive units.
10. Explain the concepts of lateral inhibition, gate control, and wind-up phenomenon.
11. Name the main components of the central

pain regulation system. Describe the functions of substance P, opioids, serotonin, and norepinephrine in pain processing.

12. Describe the clinical manifestations of lesions involving the five pathways listed in objective 7, and list the differences that may be encountered when the lesion is located at the peripheral, spinal, posterior fossa, or supratentorial level.

13. Describe sacral sparing, cortical sensory loss, and Brown-Séquard's syndrome, and describe the anatomical basis for these conditions.

14. Describe the mechanisms of sensory dissociation in syringomyelia and selective lesions of large compared with small dorsal root ganglion neurons and fibers.

15. Differentiate between sensory and motor ataxia.

16. Given a patient problem, list the aspects of the history and physical examination that point to a disturbance in the sensory system, localize the area of disturbance to a particular portion of the neuraxis, and state the pathologic nature of the responsible lesion.

Clinical Problems

Each of the following clinical problems illustrates some aspect of dysfunction in the sensory system. For each problem, determine the anatomicopathologic diagnosis (as outlined in the objectives in Chapter 4, Diagnosis of Neurologic Disorders: Neurocytology and Pathologic Reactions of the Nervous System) and answer the related questions.

1. A 48-year-old woman experienced the abrupt onset of pain followed by paresthesia and loss of feeling in a rather circumscribed area along the lateral aspect of her right thigh. Examination revealed a localized area of decreased perception of pinprick, temperature, and touch in this region only. Results of the remainder of the examination were normal.
   a. What is the anatomicopathologic diagnosis?

b. What specific anatomical structure is involved?
   c. How would the distribution of symptoms differ if the lesion involved the median nerve at the wrist?

2. A 40-year-old man had onset of neck pain and paresthesias over the occipital region of the head 6 months ago. These symptoms were aggravated by coughing and sneezing. Three months ago, his symptoms became worse and he noted a tingling sensation up and down his spinal column whenever he bent his neck. One month ago, he noted progressive difficulty in walking in the dark. On examination, he was found to have decreased perception to touch and pinprick over the posterior scalp region, reduced position sense in his arms and legs bilaterally, decreased vibratory sensation in both upper and lower extremities, and decreased ability to perceive discriminative tactile sensation bilaterally.
   a. What is the anatomicopathologic diagnosis?
   b. What segmental structures provide sensory innervation to the posterior scalp region?
   c. What sensory structures are involved by the lesion?
   d. What is the precise level of the responsible lesion?
   e. What most likely are the precise pathologic lesions responsible for this clinical syndrome?
   f. How would the symptoms and signs differ if the lesion were located at the T-6 spinal level?

3. A 41-year-old woman noted a painless, slowly progressive loss of sensation in an area involving the back of her head, neck, shoulders, and both upper extremities. Neurologic examination revealed a sensory loss involving only pain and temperature in this area. Specific testing of all other modalities of sensation in the affected areas and elsewhere revealed no abnormalities, and there were no changes in motor performance, strength, or deep tendon reflexes.
   a. What is the anatomicopathologic diagnosis?

b. What sensory structure(s) is involved by the lesion?

c. What is the most likely pathologic lesion responsible for this clinical syndrome?

4. A 21-year-old soldier returned from the war after receiving a gunshot wound in his spinal column. On examination, you note that he has weakness of the left lower extremity. In addition, he has loss of pain and temperature perception on the right side from about the level of his navel downward. Vibration, joint position sense, and discriminatory function are reduced in the left leg. Touch is normal.

a. What is the anatomicopathologic diagnosis?

b. What is the precise level of the lesion?

c. What is the name given to this type of syndrome?

d. Why was the sensation of touch preserved in this patient?

e. Where in the nervous system would you expect to find evidence of wallerian degeneration?

5. A 68-year-old hypertensive woman awoke one morning noting that she was unable to feel anything over the entire left side of her body. On examination, motor strength and reflexes were normal, as were the visual fields; however, she did not respond to pinprick, temperature, or touch over the left side of her face, trunk, and extremities, and she could not perceive joint motion or vibration in her left arm and leg.

a. What is the anatomicopathologic diagnosis?

b. What specific sensory system structure(s) is most likely involved?

c. Where in the nervous system would you expect to find evidence of wallerian degeneration?

6. A 31-year-old man noticed the gradual onset of headaches. On several occasions during the past month, he experienced spells consisting of a curious tingling, burning sensation that began in the left thumb and the left corner of his mouth. This gradually became more intense and spread to involve his left hand and the left side of his face and then extended up his arm, trunk, and leg. In 5 minutes, the spell would cease, and he would feel tired and sleepy. Examination reveals a striking inability to perceive joint position, motion, and other discriminative testing over the left side. Touch, pain, temperature, and vibratory sense are preserved.

a. What is the anatomicopathologic diagnosis?

b. What is the nature of the spell experienced by the patient?

c. Why were some forms of sensation involved and others not?

Additional Reading

Bonica, J.-J. Anatomic and Physiologic Basis of Nociception and Pain. In J.-J. Bonica (ed.), *The Management of Pain* (2nd ed.). Philadelphia: Lea & Febiger, 1990. Vol. I, pp. 28–94.

Davidoff, R. A. The dorsal columns. *Neurology* 39:1377, 1989.

Fields, H. L., Heinricher, M. M., and Mason, P. Neurotransmitters in nociceptive modulatory circuits. *Annu. Rev. Neurosci.* 14:219, 1991.

Hodge, C. J., Jr., and Apkarian, A. V. The spinothalamic tract. *Crit. Rev. Neurobiol.* 5:363, 1990.

Kaas, J. H. Somatosensory Systems. In G. Paxinos (ed.), *The Human Nervous System*. San Diego: Academic Press, 1990. Pp. 813–844.

Kandel, E. R., and Jessell, T. M. Touch. In E. R. Kandel, J. H. Schwartz, and T. M. Jessell (eds.). *Principles of Neural Science* (3rd ed.). New York: Elsevier, 1991. Pp. 367–384.

Talbot, J. D., et al. Multiple representations of pain in human cerebral cortex. *Science* 251:1355, 1991.

— 8 —

The Motor System

The entire range of human activity — from walking and talking to gymnastics to control of the space shuttle — depends on the motor system coordinating the actions of muscles, bones, and joints with external sensory information and centrally determined goals. These unique capacities of the motor system cannot be duplicated by even the most sophisticated robots, especially the ability to learn new patterns and to adapt to unexpected changes. The inability to duplicate the capabilities of the motor system is a reflection of its complexity and our incomplete understanding of how it works.

All bodily movements, including those of internal organs, are the result of muscle contraction, which is under neural control. The muscles of the limbs, trunk, neck, and head are "general somatic efferent" in embryologic origin and are under control of the somatic motor pathways. The internal organs are part of the internal regulation system and are controlled by limbic motor pathways. The "general visceral efferent" structures that control smooth muscle are described in Chapter 9 (The Internal Regulation System). "Special visceral efferent" structures, such as the phrenic neurons for respiration, are embryologically derived from the branchial arches and receive both limbic and somatic motor input.

The motor system, like the sensory system, includes a complex network of structures and pathways at all levels of the nervous system. This network is organized to mediate many types of motor activity. An understanding of this organization and of the integration of the motor system with the sensory system is necessary for the accurate localization and diagnosis of neurologic disease. Weakness, paralysis, twitching, jerking, staggering, wasting, shaking, stiffness, spasticity, and incoordination involving the arms, legs, eyes, or muscles of speech are all due to impairment of the motor system. This chapter introduces an organization of the motor system that can help in the identification of disorders of the motor system.

Overview

The fundamental organization of the motor system is that of the inner and outer tubes of the neuraxis, as in each of the other longitudinal systems. The older, more diffuse, inner tube portion of the motor system consists of *indirect activation pathways*, which include several tracts that extend from the brain stem to the spinal cord and that predominantly mediate postural and reflex activities. The newer, rapidly acting *direct activation pathway* of the outer tube mediates fine, controlled voluntary movement. The outer tube also gives rise to two *control circuits* that fine tune the activity of the direct activation pathways at the supratentorial level. The descending motor activity in all these pathways ends in interneuron pools that organize the output to the muscles through the ventral horn cells, the *final common pathway neurons* (Fig. 8-1).

Direct Activation Pathway

The largest, best-defined motor pathway is the direct activation (single neuron) pathway that extends from the cerebral cortex to the spinal cord, called the *corticospinal tract*.

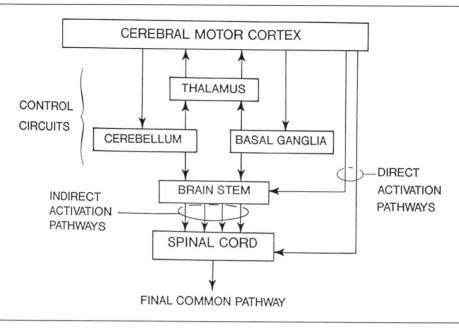

Fig. 8-1. Outline of motor system.

This pathway provides a direct route by which information can travel from the cerebral cortex to the brain stem and spinal cord without an intervening synapse. Its major function is to effect voluntary activity, in particular, skilled movements under conscious control. The direct activation pathway carries signals from three somatotopically organized cortical areas, the primary motor cortex, premotor cortex, and supplementary motor cortex (see Chapter 16, The Supratentorial Level) to the interneuron motor pools in the brain stem and spinal cord.

The direct activation pathway descends from the cerebral cortex through the white matter of the cerebral hemispheres, the brain stem, and the spinal cord to end on interneurons and ventral horn cells. The axons cross the midline at the junction of the brain stem and spinal cord to end on the opposite side. The effectiveness of this pathway depends on an intact final common pathway to carry information to the muscles. The major neurotransmitter in the direct activation pathway is glutamate (excitatory) and gamma-aminobutyric acid (GABA) (inhibitory). Damage to the direct activation pathway results in weakness, with loss of voluntary

movements, especially fine, skilled movements, but preservation of other forms of movements, including segmental reflexes.

Control Circuits

Two parallel pathways, the cerebellar and the basal ganglia pathways, control and modify motor activity. The *cerebellum* and *basal ganglia* both receive input from several motor and sensory cortical areas and project back to the cerebral cortex via the thalamus. They integrate and modulate motor activity primarily through the cerebral cortex and direct activation pathways. However, the cerebellum and basal ganglia also send information to the brain stem and the indirect activation pathways. The basal ganglia are concerned primarily with learned, automatic behavior and with preparing and maintaining the background support, or posture, needed for voluntary motor activity. The major neurotransmitters in the basal ganglia are dopamine and GABA. The cerebellum accomplishes the coordination and correction of movement errors of muscles during active movements. Glutamate and GABA are the major neurotransmitters in the cerebellar circuits. Abnormalities of the control circuits result in disorders of posture and coordination, at times accompanied by *tremor* or other abnormal involuntary movements. Control circuit damage does not produce weakness.

Indirect Activation Pathways

The older, more diffuse, indirect motor pathways are sometimes called *extrapyramidal pathways.* This group of nuclei and tracts is more complex than the direct activation pathway and is composed of a number of short axon cells and intermediate neuronal structures between the brain and spinal cord. These pathways mediate the enormous number of automatic activities involved in normal motor function. For example, the maintenance of erect posture when sitting or standing requires the coordinated contraction of many muscles. This coordination is under subconscious control and is mediated by the indirect activation pathways, which include the reticulospinal, vestibulospinal, and rubrospinal tracts. Disease affecting these pathways is manifested in many ways, depending on the location and structures involved, but the abnormalities are particularly those of abnormal muscle tone and reflexes.

Final Common Pathway

The somatic, or skeletal, muscles that perform the work of moving parts of the body are all under direct control of *lower motor neurons* and contract only in response to activation by these neurons. Each muscle is designed to perform particular movements, but each muscle may be involved in several different motor activities organized by the lower motor neurons and their pools of interneurons. These neurons are located in the ventral horn of the spinal cord and brain stem. A lower motor neuron and the muscle fibers under its control constitute a *motor unit*. The *final common pathway* consists of many motor units through which all activities in the motor system must act.

Each motor unit includes an *alpha motor neuron*, with a cell body in the brain stem or spinal cord and an axon that travels peripherally in a nerve to a specific muscle and divides into a number of terminal axons, and all the muscle fibers on which the terminals synapse.

Acetylcholine is the only neurotransmitter in the final common pathway. Alpha motor neurons and their surrounding interneuronal pool integrate activity from central and peripheral sources and transmit action potentials to the muscles to produce the appropriate level of contraction. Disease processes that impair the function of a motor unit prevent the normal activation of muscle fibers in that motor unit. This is manifested as an inability of the muscle to contract fully (weakness or paralysis).

The final common pathway responds to local input from the sensory system and from descending direct and indirect activation pathways. Local sensory input produces simple reflex responses, such as the knee jerk. This type of activity is involuntary, specific, and localized to limited areas of the body. This input is lost if there is damage to the sensory pathways. Thus, loss of a particular reflex could result from damage to either the final common pathway or the sensory input pathway.

Sensory-Motor Integration

The integration of sensory pathway and motor pathway activity to provide an appropriate response to a particular sensory stimulus is best demonstrated by reflexes. *A reflex is a stereotyped response to a specific sensory stimulus.* In reflexes, action potentials from sensory pathways activate cells in the motor system, which then initiate a specific motor response. One of the most familiar examples of a reflex is the knee jerk, in which the lower leg moves involuntarily in response to tapping of the quadriceps tendon. This is a simple reflex that involves only a primary sensory neuron, a localized portion of the spinal cord, and the final common pathway. Other reflexes are more complex and involve structures at many levels.

Direct Activation Pathway

Anatomy and Physiology

The direct activation pathway is a direct route without synapses from the cerebral cortex in each hemisphere to the ventral horn on the op-

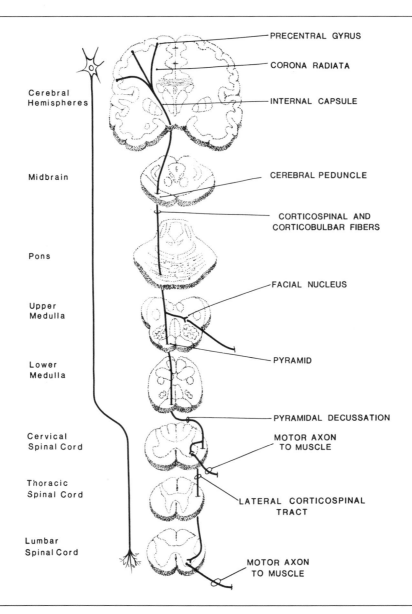

PRECENTRAL GYRUS

CORONA RADIATA

Cerebral
Hemispheres

INTERNAL CAPSULE

Midbrain

CEREBRAL PEDUNCLE

CORTICOSPINAL AND
CORTICOBULBAR FIBERS

Pons

FACIAL NUCLEUS

Upper
Medulla

Lower
Medulla

PYRAMID

PYRAMIDAL DECUSSATION

Cervical
Spinal Cord

MOTOR AXON
TO MUSCLE

Thoracic
Spinal Cord

LATERAL CORTICOSPINAL
TRACT

Lumbar
Spinal Cord

MOTOR AXON
TO MUSCLE

Fig. 8-2. Corticospinal tract. Course of fibers in tract is shown descending through cerebral hemispheres, brain stem, and spinal cord. The tract is composed of axons extending the entire length, as shown schematically for a single neuron on the left.

posite side of the spinal cord and to the motor nuclei in the brain stem. The fibers in the direct activation pathway are corticospinal and corticobulbar. Those traveling to the spinal cord are called the *corticospinal tract*, or the *pyramidal tract*. Those ending on brain-stem nuclei are *corticobulbar fibers*. The neurons from which these tracts arise are known as *upper motor neurons* (Fig. 8-2). The major function of the direct

activation pathway is to initiate and control skilled voluntary activity.

Each corticospinal tract arises primarily from cells in the cortex of the frontal lobe of one hemisphere and descends through the corona radiata into the internal capsule. The tract passes from the internal capsule via the cerebral peduncles to the base of the brain stem, where it forms the medullary pyra-

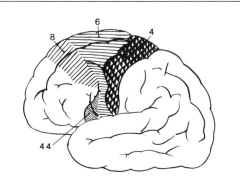

Fig. 8-3. Lateral view of cerebral hemisphere with motor areas (Brodmann's numbering) indicated. Area 4 is motor cortex; area 6 is premotor cortex; area 8 includes the frontal eye fields; area 44 is motor cortex for speech (Broca's area).

mids. At the junction between the medulla and spinal cord, most of the fibers in each pyramid cross the midline (the corticospinal decussation) to lie in the lateral funiculus of the opposite half of the spinal cord. These crossed fibers form the *lateral corticospinal tract* of the cord.

The name "corticospinal tract" is based on its origin and termination. The "pyramidal tract" is so named because of its association with the *medullary pyramids*, the large, paired fiber tracts on the ventral surface of the medulla. Properly speaking, only the corticospinal fibers, in contradistinction to corticobulbar fibers, pass through the pyramids, but it is common to include in the pyramidal tract the upper motor neurons to the spinal cord (corticospinal) and similar (so-called supranuclear) fibers to the brain-stem motor nuclei (corticobulbar). The bulk of the corticospinal fibers arise from cells in the precentral cortex (area 4 and probably area 6 in Brodmann's system) and a few from the postcentral gyrus. About 2 percent of the fibers originate in the giant Betz cells of the fifth layer of the motor cortex in the precentral gyrus (area 4 in Brodmann's numbering system). The remaining fibers are believed to originate in the prefrontal, parietal, and possibly even the occipital and temporal lobes.

Motor Cortex

Motor activity is mediated by three cortical areas, *primary motor cortex, premotor cortex,* and *supplementary motor cortex.* The primary motor cortex occupies the anterior lip of the central sulcus of Rolando and the adjacent precentral gyrus (area 4) (Fig. 8-3). The primary motor cortex integrates input from multiple sources and has a somatotopic organization, with the contralateral body represented upside down just as in sensory cortex (see Fig. 7-2): the head area is located above the fissure of Sylvius, the upper extremity next with the thumb and index finger in proximity to the face, the trunk interposed between the shoulder and hip areas high on the convexity, and the lower limb representation extending onto the paracentral lobule in the longitudinal fissure. The size of the cortical representation varies with the functional importance of the part represented. Thus, the lips, jaw, thumb, and index finger have a large representation; the forehead, trunk, and proximal portions of the limbs have a small one. As in other areas of the central nervous system, there are more neurons in the areas subserving delicate and complex functions. The cortical areas in the frontal lobe anterior to the precentral gyrus (*premotor areas*) are also concerned with motor function. They may be considered areas of cortical programming of voluntary activity, particularly for proximal muscles. Area 6 is an area controlling the performance of background activity in support of the direct activity initiated by the cell columns in area 4. Inferiorly, near the face area is *Broca's area* (area 44) where speech is formulated. Higher, in area 8, voluntary eye movements are controlled. The medial surface of the frontal lobe has a third somatotopically organized area of motor cortex, the *supplementary motor cortex*, just anterior to the foot and leg regions of the primary motor cortex. Supplementary motor cortex transmits signals from other areas of cortex and the basal ganglia to primary motor cortex as part of the planning of voluntary movements. Both premotor cortex and supplementary motor cortex send signals through the direct activation pathway to the final common pathway.

Within the motor cortex, topographic localization is not as strict as in other areas (for example, somatosensory and visual cortices). The motor cortex, however, is functionally subdivided into vertical columns of cells that are concerned with types of movements. These functions, however, can be readily subsumed by other columns. This functional flexibility of the motor cortex is exemplified in several ways. For example, ablation of a small area leads to temporary rather than permanent paralysis, and the result of electrical stimulation varies with the parameters of stimulation. The result of electrical activation also varies with the antecedent set of the area, as determined by previous activity. Thus, repetition of a stimulus after a conditioning shock may elicit a larger (facilitation) or a smaller (inhibition) response, or the opposite response, as when flexion results from a stimulus that previously yielded extension. The activity induced by electrical stimulation of the cortex may continue for some time after cessation of the stimulus. This *afterdischarge* has been attributed to reverberation within cortical circuits, and its peripheral manifestations of tonic (maintained contractions) or clonic (alternating contractions) movements are the experimental equivalent of the corresponding phases of a seizure.

The corticospinal tract controls independent finger movement, in particular, and activates more motor units for increased force. Experimentally, individual muscle contractions have been elicited from cortical stimulation of motor neurons that are organized in columns. Such contractions are fragments of movement, the pieces out of which movement is built by the cortical interconnections. The neurons that give rise to the corticospinal tracts generate action potentials in response to sensory input, and these are relayed to individual muscles. The input to these cells in the motor cortex includes a multitude of excitations and inhibitions. Thus, a given area of cortex may be regarded as a reflex center on which afferents impinge and from which efferents project. Motor cortical areas differ from simpler reflex centers, such as those in the spinal cord, in the complexity of the neuronal circuits and synaptic connections. The synthesis of fragments of movement into useful movements is effected in the motor cortex, but complex behavior, with its sequences of movement, is mediated through wider areas of cortex than the motor strip alone. The voluntary initiation and control of motor activity

includes much of the convexity of the frontal lobe.

Internal Capsule

Axons from the motor cortex converge in the corona radiata toward the internal capsule, where they are compactly gathered. Here, too, there is a topographic localization. The corticobulbar fibers occupy a more anterior location in the posterior limb of the internal capsule than the corticospinal fibers. Thus, the projection fibers are located from anterior to posterior in the following order: face, arm, leg, bladder, and rectum. Anterior to the pyramidal tract fibers are frontopontine fibers and fibers reciprocally connecting the frontal lobe and the thalamus; posterior to the pyramidal fibers are the ascending sensory tracts from the thalamus to the parietal lobe (Fig. 8-4).

Brain Stem

The pyramidal fibers remain grouped together as they pass from the internal capsule to the cerebral peduncle in the midbrain. In the midbrain, the corticospinal and corticobulbar fibers occupy the middle two-thirds of the cerebral peduncle, with the corticobulbar fibers being more medial. During their course in the brain stem, the corticobulbar fibers leave the pyramidal pathway at several levels, some crossing the midline and some remaining uncrossed. These connect with the motor centers and nuclei of the cranial nerves — trigeminal, facial, vagus, spinal accessory, and hypoglossal.

In the pons, the pyramidal fibers are split into small bundles by the interspersed pontine nuclei. The topographic localization persists, with the face medially, leg laterally, and the upper limb in the intermediate position. The fibers reunite in the medulla to form the medullary pyramids. At the lower border of the medulla, the main pyramidal decussation occurs, and about 80 percent of the fibers cross to the opposite side of the spinal cord.

Spinal Cord

In the spinal cord, the crossed pyramidal fibers occupy the lateral column (the *lateral corticospinal tract*) (Fig. 8-5), and the much smaller number of uncrossed pyramidal fibers descend

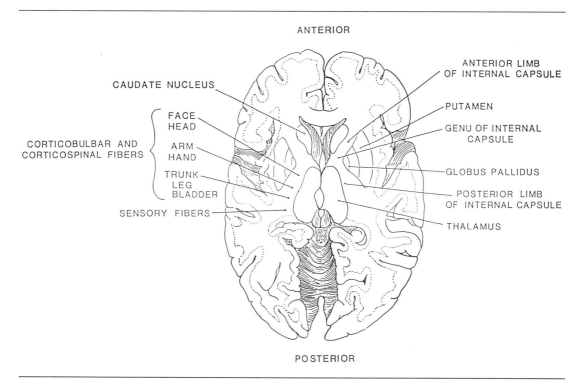

ANTERIOR

CAUDATE NUCLEUS

FACE
HEAD

CORTICOBULBAR AND
CORTICOSPINAL FIBERS

ARM
HAND

TRUNK
LEG
BLADDER

SENSORY FIBERS

ANTERIOR LIMB
OF INTERNAL CAPSULE

PUTAMEN

GENU OF INTERNAL
CAPSULE

GLOBUS PALLIDUS

POSTERIOR LIMB
OF INTERNAL CAPSULE

THALAMUS

POSTERIOR

Fig. 8-4. Horizontal section of cerebral hemisphere showing somatotopic representations of motor function in internal capsule.

in the ventral column (the *ventral corticospinal tract*) to the cervical and thoracic levels. There is doubt whether the ventral corticospinal fibers ultimately cross or remain uncrossed; it is likely that some of them remain uncrossed and are responsible for the ipsilateral innervation of certain muscle groups.

Crossed Innervation

Because of the decussation of most of the fibers of the pyramidal tracts, the voluntary movements of one side of the body are under the control of the opposite cerebral hemisphere. However, there are some exceptions to this rule that are of importance in clinical diagnosis. In general, muscle groups of the two sides of the body that habitually act in unison tend to have a bilateral cortical innervation, whereas muscle groups that act alone in isolated, delicate, and especially in learned movements tend to have a unilateral innervation from the opposite hemisphere. Thus, paraspinal muscles are innervated by both hemispheres, as are the muscles in the upper

half of the face (Fig. 8-6). Because of this arrangement, a massive lesion of one hemisphere causes severe weakness of the opposite side of the body but not of upper facial or paraspinal muscles. These principles do not apply in all cases. Even in muscles such as those of the tongue and the palate, which might be expected to work in unison, there is a greater innervation from the contralateral hemisphere.

Effect on Final Common Pathway

The action potentials descending in the corticospinal tracts travel to the ventral horn of the spinal cord, where they may synapse directly on motor neurons or, more commonly, act on them through interneurons. The corticospinal fibers act on all motor neuron pools but particularly on distal muscles of the arm and hand. They have relatively little tonic effect, although there is some tonic excitation of arm extensors and leg flexors. Corticospinal and corticobulbar fibers act on ventral horn cells primarily via the transmitter glutamate.

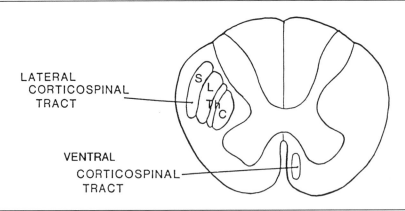

Fig. 8-5. Somatotopic representation of motor function in lateral corticospinal tract. (*C* = cervical; *Th* = thoracic; *L* = lumbar; *S* = sacral.)

Clinical Correlations

Knowledge of the clinical manifestations of disease of the direct activation pathway comes equally from experimental studies and from observation of clinical disorders. For example, the pattern of clinical seizures and results of cortical stimulation have done much to reveal the functional anatomy of the brain. Similarly, planned, discrete ablations in experimental animals and therapeutic ablations by surgeons have filled out the knowledge gained from the study of random lesions of disease.

Disturbances of the corticospinal system may be irritative or paralytic (positive or negative). These two types of disturbance are clinically exemplified by seizures and paralysis and experimentally exemplified by the results of stimulation and ablation. John Hughlings Jackson, from his study of the attacks that now bear his name (jacksonian seizures), surmised that there must be somatotopic representation of motor function in the brain. Focal motor seizures are likely to start in the cortical areas governing the thumb and index finger, the corner of the mouth, or the great toe, because of the relatively large extent of those areas. The spread (march) of the attack is determined by the pattern of cortical localization. Thus, a seizure starting in the thumb and index finger may spread to involve the wrist, elbow, shoulder, trunk, and lower limb, spreading from hip to foot. Seizures arising from premotor cortex or supplementary motor

cortex can cause complex motor actions, such as raising the contralateral hand and turning the head and eyes toward the hand.

Although the terminations of the corticospinal pathways act on all the cells of the ventral horn, they seem to have their major influence on the motor neurons in the lateral portions of the ventral horns, that is, on those controlling the distal movements of the extremities. Therefore, lesions limited to the corticospinal pathways result in a characteristic clinical pattern. There is weakness or paralysis of muscles, especially the distal muscles of the extremities. The impairment is greatest for fine movements, skilled movements, and movements under voluntary control. The paralysis is not associated with atrophy, and reflexes may be preserved, although they are often mildly decreased. The muscles are flaccid, with decreased tone, because of loss of excitatory input to the gamma motor neurons.

The distribution of the weakness is a function of the site of the lesion. If the lesion is localized in a limited area of cortex, then a single limb or one side of the face only may be involved. If the lesion involves only the pyramidal tract fibers in the pyramids of the medulla, then one side of the body below the level of the lesion will be affected. The distribution also depends on whether innervation is unilateral or bilateral. For example, the upper part of the face is spared when corticobulbar lesions involve facial fibers. If the lesion involves the frontal eye fields, there will be pa-

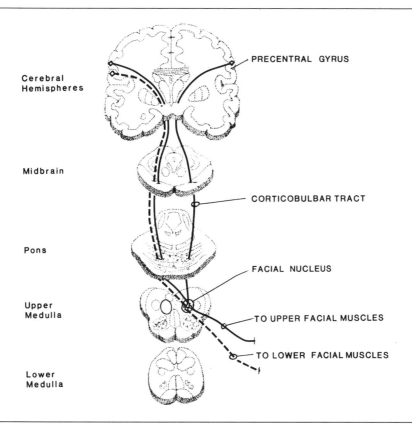

Cerebral
Hemispheres

Midbrain

Pons

Upper
Medulla

Lower
Medulla

PRECENTRAL GYRUS

CORTICOBULBAR TRACT

FACIAL NUCLEUS

TO UPPER FACIAL MUSCLES

TO LOWER FACIAL MUSCLES

Fig. 8-6. Crossed cortical innervation of motor neurons to the facial muscles on one side. The upper facial muscles have bilateral control; lower facial muscles have unilateral control from contralateral hemisphere.

ralysis of conjugate eye movements to the opposite side.

In addition to the weakness, hypotonia, and reduction in reflexes, certain specific signs occur with lesions of the corticospinal pathway. The abdominal and cremasteric reflexes are segmental reflexes that depend on an intact pyramidal tract. With a corticospinal tract lesion, these reflexes are lost on one side. Some abnormal reflexes become manifest after a corticospinal tract lesion. The response to uncomfortable stimulation of the sole of the foot when the corticospinal pathway is damaged is dorsiflexion of the great toe and spreading of the other toes. This is *Babinski's sign* and is a fractionated withdrawal reflex mediated by local spinal cord mechanisms akin to a nociceptive withdrawal reflex. In the normal adult, the corticospinal pathway suppresses this withdrawal response, and the toes are immobile or curl down. With damage to the cortico-

spinal tract, this suppression is lost and Babinski's sign appears. In a similar fashion, gentle stroking of the palm elicits an abnormal grasping response, the *grasp reflex*, when there is motor cortex damage.

The occurrence of this pattern of a distal flaccid paralysis with Babinski's sign is unusual and occurs *only* with small lesions in the medullary pyramids or in the primary motor cortex. In other areas, such as the internal capsule and the spinal cord, the corticospinal pathways (direct activation pathways) are intermingled with fibers of the indirect activation pathways (the extrapyramidal system). The results of combined damage to these systems are significantly different from the flaccid hemiplegia described above. Damage to indirect pathways adds increased tone and spasticity to the list of clinical findings.

Lesions involving anterior portions of the

frontal lobe may spare the primary motor cortex and produce no weakness. However, such lesions can result in impairment of the voluntary activation of the motor system. The loss of the ability to perform skilled motor acts by will when they can still be elicited automatically or reflexly is called *apraxia*. Apraxia may be considered the highest level abnormality of motor function in which the initiation of complex movements is lost. Apraxia may involve any of the motor activities, including speech and movements of the arms, legs, or eyes. Apraxia of *speech* is characterized by an inability to say a word at will, although still being able to think of it and to utter it correctly automatically or reflexly. Motor apraxia of speech is sometimes referred to as a type of aphasia (loss of speech).

The localization of lesions along the pyramidal pathways is relatively straightforward. Widespread cortical lesions may involve all of one side of the body, but a facial, arm, or leg monoplegia is more likely with a lesion of the cerebral cortex. Occasionally, the arm and face are involved together because of their proximity (often with apraxia of speech if the lesion is in the dominant hemisphere). More anterior lesions of the frontal cortex may result in impaired voluntary eye movements or apraxia of motor activity. Lesions in the internal capsule or cerebral peduncles typically produce weakness of the opposite arm and leg and opposite side of the face.

Cortical lesions also may have positive manifestations such as focal seizures. However, seizures do not occur with a lesion of the direct activation pathway at lower levels, for example in the internal capsule or below, where the findings are those of a loss of function such as weakness.

The level of lesions along the pathway sometimes can be identified by the associated segmental involvement of other structures, such as one of the cranial nerves in the case of a brain stem lesion or one of the spinal nerves in cases of cord lesions.

Motor Neuron Disease

Some diseases seem to selectively affect the motor system. One of these is *amyotrophic lateral sclerosis*, or *motor neuron disease*. It is a progressive, degenerative disease of un-

known cause. Pathologically, this condition is characterized by degeneration of the motor cells in the spinal cord, brain stem, and cerebral cortex, associated with secondary axonal degeneration in the peripheral nerves and in the lateral funiculus of the spinal cord (corticospinal tract).

Motor neuron disease expresses itself with varying degrees of involvement in the final common pathway and the direct and indirect activation pathways. Damage to the final common pathway results in diseased ventral horn cells, which are initially irritable, producing frequent, widespread fasciculations. After death and degeneration of the lower motor neurons, there is a combination of flaccid weakness and atrophy of muscle. The denervated muscle fibrillates, although this is not seen clinically. Involvement of the descending pathways may produce Babinski's sign and hyperactive reflexes as well.

Control Circuits

As the demands on the motor pathways have increased with the increase in complexity of motor activity, two separate new components of the motor system, the *basal ganglia* and the *cerebellum*, have developed. The basal ganglia and cerebellum act by helping to control different aspects of motor activity and are considered together as *control circuits*. Both control circuits receive extensive input from several cortical areas and send information back to the cortex through distinct areas of the thalamus. Both control circuits consist of several million neurons more than the direct activation pathways and use different neurotransmitters.

However, the functions and the connections of the two control circuits are different. The basal ganglia are concerned with motor programs, the maintenance of background activity for posture, and the performance of automatic motor actions. The cerebellum coordinates muscle activity during movement for smooth directed movements and participates in initiating movement. The cerebellum has more direct input from the brain stem and spinal cord.

The Basal Ganglia Control Circuit

Anatomy and Physiology

The basal ganglia include the caudate nucleus, putamen, globus pallidus, substantia nigra, and subthalamic nucleus. They contain multiple internal circuit loops, only some of which are described herein. In humans, heterogeneous neuronal populations in the basal ganglia form four distinct, parallel, and chemically specific subsystems: motor, oculomotor, prefrontal, and limbic circuits. This chapter focuses on the motor components.

The term *striatum* refers to the combination of the caudate nucleus and the putamen, the largest subcortical masses of gray matter. (The caudate nucleus and putamen are incompletely separated by the fibers of the internal capsule.) The striatum receives the afferent input to the basal ganglia and, through axonal projections containing GABA, inhibits the globus pallidus. The substantia nigra and the subthalamic nucleus are part of the clinically significant basal ganglia internal circuit loops.

The basal ganglia are derived embryologically from the telencephalon, and anatomically, they are closely related to the cerebral cortex. Yet, despite their large size and knowledge about their location and anatomical connections, the specific functions of the individual components of the basal ganglia still cannot be described. Much of our knowledge comes from a consideration of how the brain functions when these nuclei are not working normally. Specific motor dysfunctions are known to accompany histopathologic or chemical changes in the basal ganglia. Lesions in certain structures closely related to the basal ganglia, such as the substantia nigra and the subthalamic nucleus, also produce pathologic motor symptoms. In general, the basal ganglia control the background tone and posture for movements initiated in the cerebral cortex and participate in automatic movements, such as walking, and in learning new motor behavior by reinforcing active patterns of movement and suppressing other patterns.

Pathways

The striatum receives input primarily from the cerebral cortex. This input is topographically organized, with the primary motor and sensory cortices projecting to the putamen and other areas to the caudate. The striatum receives input also from the intralaminar thalamic nuclei and the substantia nigra and sends efferents to the substantia nigra and globus pallidus. The major efferent pathways from the basal ganglia originate in the globus pallidus (Fig. 8-7). Its major input comes from the striatum, although some input arises from other sources. It sends fibers to a number of areas: to the thalamus for relay back to the cerebral cortex, to the subthalamic nucleus and neighboring areas, including the region of the red nucleus, and to the reticular formation of the brain stem. Of these pallidal efferents, only those to the reticular formation and perhaps those to the area of the red nucleus reach descending pathways to the spinal cord. The bulk of the pallidal efferents project to the ventral anterior *and* ventral lateral oral nuclei of the thalamus via the ansa lenticularis and fasciculus lenticularis. Basal ganglia pathways thus are made up of a number of loops, in particular: (1) striatum to globus pallidus to thalamus to cortex to striatum, (2) striatum to substantia nigra to striatum, and (3) globus pallidus to subthalamus to globus pallidus.

Cortical input to the basal ganglia uses predominantly glutamate as a neurotransmitter. The striatum is the structure in the brain richest in two important central nervous system neurotransmitters, acetylcholine and dopamine, and in enzymes associated with their metabolism. Most of the axons of cells in the striatum are short and terminate within the nuclei in which they lie. Acetylcholine is the synaptic transmitter for most of these neurons. The dopamine in the striatum is manufactured in the substantia nigra and is transmitted to the striatum along the nigrostriatal axons to act as a neurotransmitter in the striatum. Destruction of neurons in the substantia nigra decreases the dopamine content in the striatum. Subthalamic neurons act on the globus pallidus with glutamate. Most efferents from the striatum to the globus pallidus and from the globus pallidus to the substantia nigra release GABA, an inhibitory neurotransmitter.

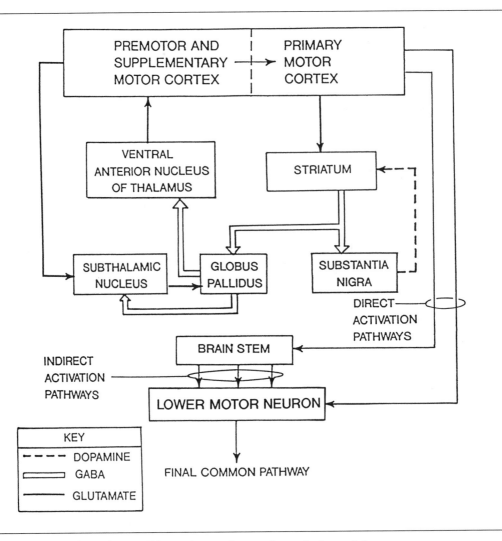

Fig. 8-7. Basal ganglia pathways. The major outflow pathway is from globus pallidus to cortex via nucleus ventralis anterior in the thalamus.

Separate direct (inhibitory) and indirect (excitatory) pathways between the striatum and globus pallidus (not described herein) produce a balance between the inhibitory and excitatory influences of the striatum on the globus pallidus. This balance determines whether the globus pallidus inhibits or disinhibits the thalamocortical motor pathways.

Clinical Correlations

The basal ganglia control system is a damping or modulating system. Excess discharge in the basal ganglia produces slowing; a lack of discharge produces hyperactivity. Lesions in the striatum produce deficits in the ability to per-

form complex motor responses. Pathologic symptoms and signs with disease of the basal ganglia may be classified into two types: abnormal movements and changes in tone. The abnormal movements may be a reduction in mobility (hypokinesia) or involuntary movements (hyperkinesia).

With hypokinesia, there is usually an increase in tone. This increased resistance to passive movements occurs through direct effects on the alpha motor neuron and is known as *rigidity*. Movements are slow, stiff, and initiated or stopped with great difficulty. Abnormal postures are often assumed, which may involve the entire body, one-half of the body, or single limbs. Hypokinesia is often due to disease in the substantia nigra.

Involuntary movements may arise with excessive activity in the dopaminergic fibers. These may be slow and writhing (athetosis) or may involve abnormal posturing of the trunk or an extremity (dystonia). Rapid involuntary movements also can occur. These may be gross, rapid, flinging movements in the presence of lesions of the subthalamic nucleus (hemiballismus), brief rapid jerks in striatal disease (chorea), or regular alternating tremor in substantia nigra disease (parkinsonism). The tremor seen with parkinsonism, the most common form of basal ganglia disease, is characteristic in its 3 to 4 per second, regular alternation *at rest*. It is diminished with voluntary activity.

Speech in basal ganglia disease has various manifestations but can be classified as a *hypokinetic dysarthria* or a *hyperkinetic dysarthria*. The former is more common and is characterized by a quiet, weak, monotonous voice with poor articulation, short rushes of words, and a breathy quality. A hyperkinetic dysarthria is recognizable as sudden changes in speech, such as bursts of loudness, elevation of pitch, voice stoppages, distortion of vowels, and disintegration of articulation.

Examples of hypokinetic and hyperkinetic basal ganglia disorders, with paucity of movement and excessive movement, are parkinsonism and Huntington's disease, respectively. Patients with *Parkinson's disease* have lesions of the substantia nigra and decreased striatal dopamine levels. The dopamine of the substantia nigra acts to inhibit the firing of striatal cells. In its absence, the cells fire action potentials more rapidly. This disordered striatal output results in loss of the normal modifying influence of the basal ganglia on the motor activities of the pyramidal and extrapyramidal pathways. Patients with Parkinson's disease typically have gradually progressive rigidity, akinesia (slow movement), and tremor. Parkinsonism may occur after encephalitis, carbon monoxide poisoning, manganese poisoning, or toxicity from some psychoactive drugs. An illicit "designer drug," MPTP, destroys substantia nigra neurons and causes characteristic parkinsonism. In most patients with this relatively common disorder, there is no apparent cause, and the disease is said to be idiopathic. The pathologic changes in the brain include cellular degeneration in the substantia nigra, whose cells may have hyaline inclusion bodies (Lewy bodies).

Huntington's disease is a chronic, progressive, dominantly inherited disease with onset in adult life. It is a diffuse degenerative disease, with widespread loss of cholinergic and GABAergic neurons and secondary cerebral atrophy. This is most marked in the basal ganglia, especially in the caudate nucleus, which is severely shrunken, producing a characteristic dilatation of the lateral ventricle. There is also atrophy of the cerebral cortex. These degenerative changes underlie the generalized mental deterioration, chorea, and decreased muscle tone. *Chorea* is the random, continuous occurrence of brief, abrupt, jerky movements of any part of the body due to overactivity of dopaminergic neurons. Reflexes and sensation are generally normal. Both parkinsonism and Huntington's disease may be the result of excitotoxic damage to vulnerable neurons.

Another form of chorea, *Sydenham's chorea*, has a subacute onset in children with rheumatic fever. Sydenham's chorea is an immunologic disorder in which the body produces antibodies to the streptococcal bacteria. The protein structure of the streptococcal antigen is similar to that of proteins in the membrane of striatal neurons, so that the antibodies to these antigens also attack basal ganglia neurons and produce chorea. The disorder is usually a transient one with full recovery.

Therapy for several major disorders of the nervous system depends on our understanding of the pathophysiology of the basal ganglia. Examples are the effectiveness of drugs such as dopamine agonists in the treatment of parkinsonism, the use of adrenal or fetal tissue transplants to provide a source of missing neurotransmitters or to supply new innervation to denervated tissue, and the use of stereotaxic lesions in the ventral lateral nucleus of the thalamus to stop severe tremor.

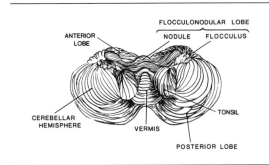

Fig. 8-8. Gross anatomical subdivisions of the cerebellum.

The Cerebellar Control Circuit

Anatomy and Physiology

The cerebellum and its connections comprise the second major control circuit. It is concerned with the coordination of muscle groups during phasic motor activity. The cerebellum initiates and regulates movements, especially skilled movements. This regulation, carried out in conjunction with the motor regulation by the basal ganglia, depends on cerebellar inputs from proprioceptive, somatic, vestibular, visual, and auditory sense organs and from motor and nonmotor portions of the cerebral cortex. The cerebellum acts as comparator between motor plans and motor performance, thereby acting as an error detection system. In turn, the cerebellum sends correction signal outputs to brain stem neurons and to motor cortex. The pathway to the latter involves a relay in the ventral lateral nucleus of the thalamus.

Gross Structure

The cerebellum may be divided from anterior to posterior or from side to side (Fig. 8-8). From anterior to posterior, the cerebellum is made up of the *anterior lobe*, the *posterior lobe*, and the *flocculonodular lobe*. From side to side, it is divided into midline structures and lateral structures. The midline of the anterior and posterior lobes is called the *vermis*, and the lateral portions are the *cerebellar hemispheres*. The midline of the flocculonodular lobe is the nodulus; the lateral portion is the *flocculus*. The flocculonodular lobe is the primary connection with the vestibular apparatus for coordination of location in space and movements. The anterior lobe, a more recent

phylogenetic development, is found in reptiles and amphibians. It receives spinocerebellar proprioceptive information important in regulating primitive motor acts such as postural reflexes. The posterior lobe, the most recent phylogenetic development, is primarily concerned with coordination of voluntary muscle activity and muscle tone.

Nerve fibers enter or leave the cerebellum in three structures: the inferior, middle, and superior cerebellar peduncles. These are also known as the *restiform body*, the *brachium pontis*, and the *brachium conjunctivum*, respectively. Most of the output of the cerebellum originates in the deep cerebellar nuclei: the dentate, the globose, the emboliform, and the fastigial nuclei (Fig. 8-9). Axons of Purkinje cells carrying efferent activity from the cerebellar cortex synapse in these nuclei, which then send axons out via the superior or inferior cerebellar peduncles.

Functional Subdivisions

The cerebellum and its connecting pathways are organized into three functional subdivisions, each with distinct anatomical connections and specific functions. The three functional divisions are the *vestibulocerebellum*, *spinocerebellum*, and *cerebrocerebellum*. These terms indicate the major connections of each segment (Fig. 8-10).

The *vestibulocerebellum* is made up of the flocculonodular lobe and is reciprocally connected with the vestibular nuclei through the inferior cerebellar peduncle. The vestibulocerebellum controls and coordinates axial musculature and movements of the head and eyes.

The *spinocerebellum* is made up of the vermis and paravermis. Its primary input is from the dorsal spinocerebellar tract (via the inferior cerebellar peduncle) and the ventral spinocerebellar tract (via the superior cerebellar peduncle), which provide information about motor performance and motor neuron excitability, respectively. The output of the spinocerebellum arises in the globose and emboliform nuclei, which project to nuclei in the brain stem reticular formation, vestibular nuclei, and red nucleus and through the thalamus to the motor cortex to regulate posture

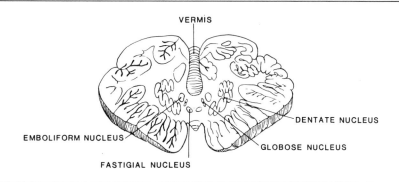

Fig. 8-9. Cerebellar nuclei in horizontal section through cerebellum.

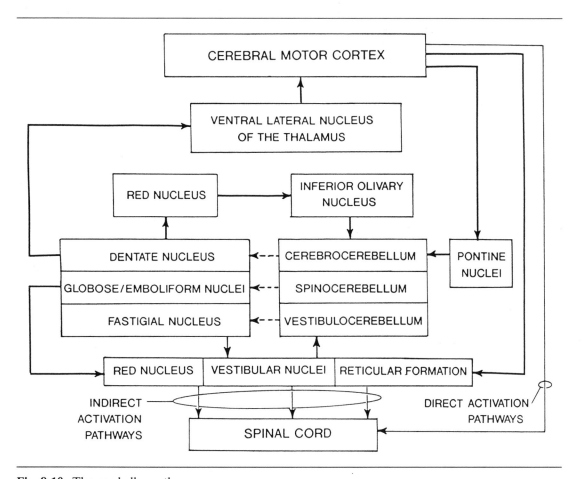

Fig. 8-10. The cerebellar pathways.

and equilibrium. These pathways act to update motor programs as they progress.

The *cerebrocerebellum* is made up of the lateral portions of the cerebellar hemispheres and receives input from pontine nuclei via the middle cerebellar peduncle. The output is from the dentate nucleus through the superior cerebellar peduncle. The axons synapse in the ventral lateral nucleus of the thalamus, which projects to primary motor cortex. The cerebrocerebellum is important in initiation of movement and in coordination of muscles (specifying direction, pattern, and intensity of movement). The cerebrocerebellar projection to the red nucleus is part of a loop that includes the inferior olivary nucleus, which is the origin of the climbing fibers in the cerebellar cortex. This loop is important in the cerebellar error detection system.

The cerebellar pathways thus form three loops. The first is via the dentate nucleus to the opposite thalamus to the cerebral cortex. The loop is completed by axons from the frontal lobe through the internal capsule and cerebral peduncles to the pontine nuclei (frontopontine fibers). Pontine nuclei send axons across the midline via the middle cerebellar peduncle back into the cerebellum. This loop — the longest — modulates voluntary activity. The second loop is also from the dentate nucleus to the opposite red nucleus. It is completed via connections with the inferior olive, which projects back across the midline into the cerebellum via the inferior cerebellar peduncle. This loop corrects motor pattern errors. The third loop interconnects the cerebellum with the ipsilateral vestibular nuclei.

The following generalizations about the cerebellar inputs and outputs are important:

1. The middle cerebellar peduncle is an afferent pathway. Its inflow decussates in the pons.
2. The superior cerebellar peduncle is mostly an efferent pathway, with the exception of the ventral spinocerebellar tract. The superior cerebellar peduncle outflow decussates in the decussation of the brachium conjunctivum.
3. The inferior cerebellar peduncle is mostly afferent, with a strong vestibular and reticular efferent path.
4. Each cerebellar hemisphere is connected to the opposite thalamus and cerebral cortex and controls the ipsilateral extremities.

The major connections of the cerebellum are listed in Table 8-1.

Histology

The cerebellar cortex has three layers: an outer molecular layer, the layer of Purkinje cells, and an inner granular layer. The most prominent neurons of the cerebellum are the *Purkinje cells* (see Fig. 4-1). These are large flask-shaped neurons with extensive dendritic arborizations in the molecular layer of the cerebellar cortex. Axons of Purkinje neurons are the sole output neurons of the cerebellar cortex. These axons contain GABA and synapse on cells of the deep cerebellar nuclei, thus inhibiting them.

The cerebellar cortex has two types of afferent fibers, *mossy fibers* and *climbing fibers*. Both types of afferents use glutamate as a neurotransmitter. All the climbing fibers originate from neurons in the inferior olivary nucleus and form powerful excitatory synapses with Purkinje cell dendrites. All other inputs to the cerebellar cortex form the mossy fibers. They synapse on the granule cells, whose axons synapse on Purkinje cells and continuously activate them. Climbing fibers provide error signals that modify the background firing of Purkinje cells to mediate adaptation and learning. This combination of cells and synapses constitutes an intrinsic circuit that is found throughout the cerebellum and that acts to produce excitatory burst firing in the deep cerebellar nuclei. The major neurotransmitter in this intrinsic circuit is GABA. The cerebellum has a P-form of the calcium channel and a widely acting neuroactive agent, nitric oxide.

The physiology of the cerebellar cortex has certain distinguishing features: the Purkinje cells and other cerebellar neurons spontaneously fire at high rates and are generally inhibitory in their action; that is, the axonal outputs of Purkinje and other neurons depress activity in the cells of the deep cerebellar nuclei. Most of the neurons in the cerebellar nuclei have excitatory effects on their synaptic targets.

Activity in proprioceptive, exteroceptive, visual, auditory, and vestibular systems produces responses in the cerebellum. There is a somatotopic representation of these sensations in the cerebellar cortex. In addition, the cerebral cortex projects in a similar topographic pattern to the deep cerebellar nuclei. This topographic patterning of inputs to the cerebellar cortex is similar to, although less detailed than, the motor and sensory representation in the cerebral cortex.

The cellular organization and pathway connections of the cerebellum are designed to modulate motor activities, including equili-

Table 8-1. Cerebellar Afferents and Efferents

From	Via	To
Input (afferent)		
Vestibular nerve and nuclei	Inferior cerebellar peduncle	Flocculonodular lobe
Spinal cord (dorsal spinocerebellar tract)	Inferior cerebellar peduncle	Anterior lobe and vermis
Basal ganglia (rubroreticulo-olivocerebellar pathway)	Inferior cerebellar peduncle	Posterior lobe
Cerebral cortex (pontine nuclei)	Middle cerebellar peduncle	Posterior lobe
Spinal cord (ventral spinocerebellar tract)	Superior cerebellar peduncle	Anterior lobe
Output (efferent)		
Flocculonodular lobe	Fastigial nucleus and inferior cerebellar peduncle	Vestibular nuclei and reticular formation
Anterior lobe and vermis	Emboliform and globose nuclei and superior cerebellar peduncle	Red nucleus and reticular formation
Posterior lobe	Dentate nucleus and superior cerebellar peduncle	Red nucleus, thalamus, and cerebral cortex

bration, posture and gait, and voluntary movements.

Equilibrium. The flocculonodular lobe modulates equilibrium and the orientation of the head and eyes. This lobe has connections with the vestibular nuclei. Lesions in the flocculonodular lobe produce inability to stand or sit without swaying or falling (truncal ataxia) and abnormalities of head and eye movements (nystagmus).

Posture and Gait. The anterior lobe is concerned mainly with posture, gait, and truncal tone. Lesions produce unsteady walking, staggering (gait ataxia), and hypotonia.

Voluntary Movements. The posterior lobe, in particular the large lateral hemispheres, provides a servomechanism for coordination of skilled action. Lesions in the posterior lobe produce irregular movements of the limbs (limb ataxia), loss of muscle coordination (dyssynergia), loss of ability to measure range of motion (dysmetria), delay in movement initiation, hypotonia, areflexia, and tremor with voluntary activity (intention tremor). The inferior olivary nucleus is active in generating cerebellar tremor. In general, movements become clumsy and uncoordinated.

Clinical Correlations

Three major patterns of cerebellar pathophysiology can be distinguished.

Flocculonodular syndrome occurs especially with midline tumors in children and produces truncal ataxia, with unsteadiness and falling and disturbances with gait and standing. This syndrome is usually associated with nystagmus of the eyes.

Anterior lobe syndrome is commonly due to degenerative disease in adults and is manifested as a severe gait ataxia, without ataxia of the upper limbs and mild ataxia of the legs when they are tested individually.

Cerebellar hemisphere disease produces symptoms of limb ataxia with hypotonia, intention tremor, dyssynergia, and dysmetria ipsilateral to the side of the lesion.

Disorders of speech also occur in cerebellar disease, particularly when it involves the vermis. These disorders are manifested as irregularities of pitch, loudness, and rhythm and are known as *ataxic dysarthria*. Speech is slowed, with excess stress on some words or syllables and random breakdown of articulation.

Many cerebellar disorders can be reversed if they are identified early and treated appropriately. Cerebellar degeneration produced by vitamin E deficiency is an example. Small cell lung carcinoma and ovarian cancers produce antibodies to Purkinje cells that cause cerebellar degeneration. Detection of Purkinje cell antibodies has become an important diagnostic tool in recognizing these cancers early enough to allow curative therapy and to treat the cerebellar disorder. The measurement of ceruloplasm in the diagnosis of Wilson's disease is another example of an important advance in therapy for neurologic diseases.

Certain diseases affect the nervous system widely and have effects on all the components of the motor system. One of these was originally considered to be a degenerative disorder and is now known to be metabolic in origin. *Wilson's disease*, or hepatolenticular degeneration, is a disorder of copper metabolism in which there is excessive deposition of copper in many areas. This results in a typical brown stain at the edge of the cornea (Kayser-Fleischer ring) and damage to the liver. The deposition of copper in the cortex, cerebellum, and basal ganglia produces a combination of motor manifestations from one or more of these structures. The involved areas show loss of neurons, gliosis, atrophy, and, if severe, cavitation. This is most prominent in the putamen and globus pallidus. Because of the widespread involvement, the clinical findings can vary widely and may include tremor, rigidity, bizarre movements, dystonia, spasticity, and Babinski's sign.

Indirect Activation Pathways

Anatomy and Physiology

The motor system derivatives of the inner tube of the neuraxis are the indirect activation pathways, which parallel the direct activation pathways (Fig. 8-11). The major components of the indirect activation pathways are the descending brain stem pathways described below. Each of these pathways receives input from the cerebral cortex, particularly premotor cortex, that is less well-defined than input to the direct activation pathway. Although the control circuits predominantly affect the direct activation pathways, they also influence the indirect activation pathways.

Fig. 8-11. Indirect activation pathways to the spinal cord.

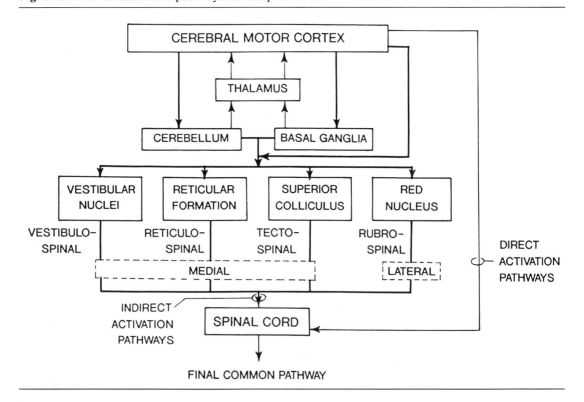

Table 8-2. Descending Motor Pathways

	Medial pathways	Lateral pathways
Fiber tracts	Medullary reticulospinal	Rubrospinal
	Vestibulospinal	Pontine reticulospinal
	Tectospinal	
Termination on	Medial interneurons	Lateral interneurons
	Medial motor neuron pool	Lateral motor neuron pools
	Large motor units	Small motor units
Muscles acted on	Proximal much more than distal muscles	Distal much more than proximal
	Extensors more than flexors	Flexors more than extensors
	Posture and balance	Fractionated movements
Function	Control posture and whole-limb movements	Independent flexor (especially arm) movements

Examples are the globus pallidus projection to the reticular formation and the cerebellar connections with the vestibular nuclei.

The descending brain stem pathways have been divided into two major groups on the basis of their functional and terminal distribution (Table 8-2). The *medial pathways* control posture, synergistic (particularly extensor) whole-limb movements, and orienting movements of the head and body. The *lateral pathways* provide capacity for independent flexor movements, especially of the arm. Another group of pathways with descending fibers is the propriospinal pathways, which interconnect different levels of the spinal cord.

The greatest amount of supraspinal reinforcement of the motor neurons that control posture comes from projection systems originating in the reticular formation and vestibular nuclei. These systems facilitate extensor muscle contraction and inhibit flexor muscle contraction, particularly in axial and proximal muscles. Normally, the activity in these systems is balanced by activity in projections from the cerebral cortex and other forebrain structures that inhibits contraction of extensor muscles and facilitates contraction of flexor muscles via corticoreticular pathways. If these cortical controls are interrupted, the unchecked descending pontine and medullary pathways make extensor motor neurons hyperexcitable, producing increased muscle tone, a condition called *spasticity*. The level of the lesion determines which muscles manifest spasticity.

Medial Descending Brain Stem Pathways

The medial indirect activation pathways include the medullary reticulospinal, vestibulospinal, and tectospinal tracts. They have several features in common: (1) they are in the ventral and ventrolateral white matter of the spinal cord; (2) they end bilaterally in the ventromedial part of the gray matter that contains long- and intermediate-projecting propriospinal neurons; (3) they synapse directly on motor neurons of neck, back, and proximal extremity muscles; (4) they show a high degree of collateralization, with axons spreading widely in the area of termination; (5) they receive input from premotor cortical areas; and (6) their distribution overlaps that of the ventral corticospinal tract.

The *medullary reticulospinal tract* arises from neurons in the reticular formation. The reticular formation is a field of dispersed cells or small nuclei in between large nuclei and tracts throughout the medulla and the pontine tegmentum. In addition to mediating ascending sensory activity and consciousness as described in other chapters, the reticular formation has complex effects on spinal cord motor neurons. The medullary reticulospinal tract arises from an inhibitory area of the reticular formation in the ventromedial part of the caudal medulla. Activity in this region produces mixed effects, most frequently inhibition of extensor motor neurons and excitation of flexors. It also inhibits tendon reflexes. This region depends on descending stimulation from supratentorial motor structures; that is, inhibi-

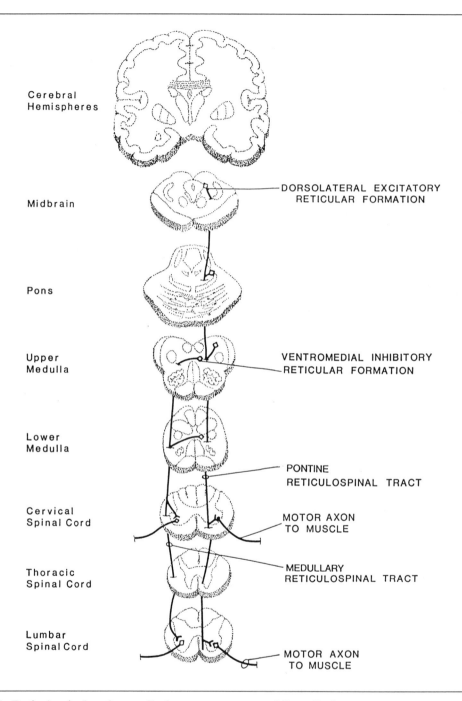

Fig. 8-12. Reticulospinal pathways. Both tracts are present bilaterally but are shown only on one side. The pontine reticulospinal tract arising from the excitatory dorsolateral reticular formation in the pons is shown on the right. The medullary reticulospinal tract arising from the inhibitory ventromedial reticular formation is shown on the left.

tion by reticulospinal pathways requires their excitation by rostral motor areas. Medullary reticulospinal fibers are crossed and uncrossed and descend in the spinal cord in the ventral part of the lateral funiculus. They terminate in the dorsolateral part of the ventral horn, in the same area where the corticospinal tract terminates (Fig. 8-12).

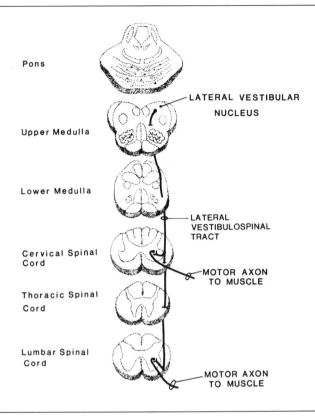

Pons

LATERAL VESTIBULAR
NUCLEUS

Upper Medulla

Lower Medulla

LATERAL
VESTIBULOSPINAL
TRACT

Cervical Spinal
Cord

MOTOR AXON
TO MUSCLE

Thoracic Spinal
Cord

Lumbar Spinal
Cord

MOTOR AXON
TO MUSCLE

Fig. 8-13. The vestibulospinal tract arising from the lateral vestibular nucleus is bilateral but is shown on only one side.

The *vestibulospinal tract* arises from the vestibular nuclei. The vestibular system consists of a group of brain stem nuclei that receive sensory input from the vestibular apparatus and the cerebellum and that in turn project to brain stem, cerebellar, and spinal cord areas.

The lateral vestibular nucleus is the source of the major vestibular projection to spinal motor neurons. This nucleus receives primary afferent input from the vestibular nerve and other input from the cerebellum. Activity in the nucleus produces excitation of extensor motor neurons; its effects on flexor motor neurons are generally significant. Descending discharges through this system are seen in the tendency to fall after rapid whirling. The *vestibulospinal tract,* which originates from cells in the lateral vestibular nucleus, descends mostly uncrossed in the ventral funiculus of the spinal cord. These fibers terminate in the ventromedial portion of the ventral horn on both alpha and gamma motor neurons. Other, less important vestibulospinal fibers descend crossed in the ventral funiculus of the spinal cord as a caudal extension of the medial longitudinal fasciculus to the rostral portions of the spinal cord (Fig. 8-13).

The *tectospinal tract* is believed to be important in mediating reflex movements of the head in response to visual or auditory stimuli (Fig. 8-14). This tract originates from cells in the superior colliculus, crosses in the brain stem, and descends near the medial longitudinal fasciculus. In the spinal cord, it travels in the ventral funiculus and does not extend below the cervical levels. Fibers terminate in the ventromedial regions along with the vestibulospinal tract.

Lateral Descending Brain Stem Pathways

The lateral indirect activation pathways include the rubrospinal tract, from the red nucleus, and the pontine reticulospinal tract, from the dorsolateral pontine reticular for-

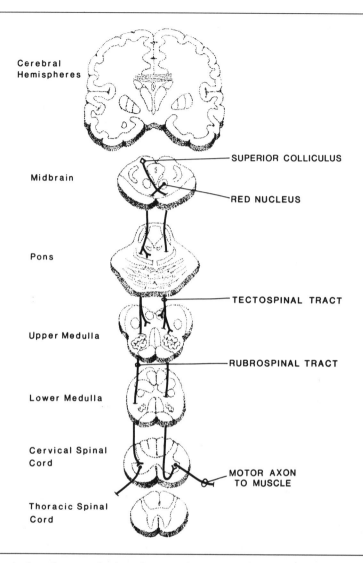

Cerebral Hemispheres

Midbrain

SUPERIOR COLLICULUS

RED NUCLEUS

Pons

TECTOSPINAL TRACT

Upper Medulla

RUBROSPINAL TRACT

Lower Medulla

Cervical Spinal Cord

MOTOR AXON TO MUSCLE

Thoracic Spinal Cord

Fig. 8-14. Rubrospinal and tectospinal pathways, though both bilateral, are shown unilaterally. Rubrospinal tract is shown descending on the left. It arises in red nucleus on opposite side. Tectospinal tract is shown descending on right after arising in colliculus on left.

mation. These tracts share several features: (1) they descend in the contralateral dorsolateral fasciculus of the spinal cord; (2) they terminate in the dorsal and lateral part of the intermediate gray matter, which contains short-projecting propriospinal neurons; (3) they have monosynaptic connections with motor neurons innervating distal extremity muscles; (4) their axons have little collateralization; (5) they receive input from primary motor cortex; and (6) their termination overlaps that of the lateral corticospinal tract.

The cells of origin of the pontine reticulospinal tract are primarily in the pons but extend from the midbrain into rostral medulla. Activity in this part of the reticular formation produces excitation of extensor motor neurons and inhibition of flexor motor neurons and is manifested as postural tone. Pontine reticulospinal fibers originating from cells in the excitatory, dorsolateral reticular formation descend uncrossed in the medial part of the ventral funiculus of the spinal cord. They terminate in the ventromedial part of the ventral horn, mainly on interneurons and gamma motor neurons (see Fig. 8-12).

The *rubrospinal tract* originates in the *red nucleus*, and the fibers immediately decussate in the ventral tegmental decussation to descend on the opposite side. The tract occupies about the same position as the lateral corticospinal tract with which its fibers intermingle in the spinal cord. The sites of termination are much the same, but few *rubrospinal fibers* reach the lower spinal cord, so that the main rubrospinal influence is on flexor muscles of the upper extremities (see Fig. 8-14).

The red nucleus receives cortical projections that are somatotopically organized and provides another indirect path from the cortex to the spinal cord. Other input (cerebellum and basal ganglia) can modify the descending activity in the red nucleus. The rubrospinal tract is not well defined in humans; although some authors consider it rudimentary, others think it projects through the length of the spinal cord. It consists mainly of small fibers. The rubrospinal tract, unlike the other indirect pathways, has different effects on the motor neurons to the arms and the legs. It facilitates activity in arm flexors but has little effect on leg muscles.

The *propriospinal pathways* are made up of short axons that arise from neurons in the dorsal portion of the ventral horn and that extend a few segments dorsally or ventrally in the cord. They make connections primarily with interneuronal pools in the ventral horn to coordinate the activities of muscle groups innervated at different levels of the spinal cord.

Effects on the Final Common Pathway

In general, the response of a gamma motor neuron (see Final Common Pathway section) to a particular stimulus is the same as that of the corresponding alpha motor neuron; that is, both gamma and alpha neurons innervating extensor muscles are excited by the vestibulospinal tract and the pontine reticulospinal tract. However, gamma motor neurons have lower response thresholds to all forms of stimulation than do alpha motor neurons, so

that stimuli insufficient to produce alpha motor neuron discharge may be sufficient to discharge the gamma motor neurons, whereas a stimulus just adequate to discharge alpha motor neurons may exert a pronounced effect on gamma motor neurons.

As true with other inputs to the ventral horn cells, the effects differ for flexor and extensor neurons as well as for neurons innervating the arm and leg. Lesions that damage most or all the corticoreticular fibers above the midbrain and red nucleus produce increased extensor tone in the legs and increased flexor tone in the arms (decorticate posture), because of loss of inhibition of all descending pathways. Lesions at the level of the midbrain below the red nucleus remove arm flexor excitation and result in excitation of all extensor muscles and a generalized increase in extensor tone (decerebrate posture). Lesions below the medulla produce loss of all the descending input (generalized flaccidity).

Clinical Correlations

The clinical effects of damage to the descending indirect pathways are largely a function of two complicating factors. First, the fibers of these pathways are not in well-defined bundles and therefore are not damaged selectively; they are sufficiently widespread so that significant effects occur only with large lesions, which almost always also cause damage to the corticospinal pathways. Second, the clinical findings with major damage to these or other pathways change with time because of the development of *denervation hypersensitivity*. The loss of all or most of the afferent input to a cell or groups of cells gradually results in an increased response to stimuli that normally would evoke a lesser response. This is best exemplified in major, acute lesions of the spinal cord.

If the spinal cord is transected, all long descending pathways to the alpha and gamma motor neurons are destroyed. A large proportion of the input to these cells is lost, and they become inactive; clinically, all motor activity is markedly reduced or lost, along with all reflexes. Tone is flaccid. But these changes persist for only a few weeks or months. There remain significant inputs to the motor neurons in the spinal cord, including the local sensory input from the periphery and from other parts of the spinal cord. With time the neurons recover their excitability and become hyperexcitable. Postural and voluntary activities remain lost, but local tendon reflexes and other cord reflexes are preserved and become overactive. At times, more complex reflexes, like withdrawal of a limb from pain, occur and are mediated by local spinal cord connections.

Lesions in the lower brain stem that are severe enough to damage the reticular formation and vestibular nuclei are not compatible with life, and specific syndromes of destruction of the descending indirect pathways at this level are not seen. However, with major damage at higher levels to the descending pathways from the cerebral hemispheres, patients manifest findings that depend on the indirect pathways. Loss of forebrain control of the inhibitory reticular formation, which inhibits extensor neurons and excites flexor neurons, results in overactivity of the extensor neurons under the drive of the excitatory reticular formation and vestibular nuclei. The clinical findings are those of increased extensor tone and increased reflexes. The importance of the vestibular nuclei in this increase in extensor tone can be shown by destruction of the vestibular nuclei, which results in a marked reduction in extensor hyperactivity. In addition to increased tone and reflexes, patients with indirect pathway damage have *spasticity*, an increase in resistance to passive movement of an extremity, which subsides with continued pressure. The reduction in tone is the clasp-knife response.

Bilateral damage to the indirect activation pathways in the midbrain below the red nucleus produces extensor spasticity of all extremities. This condition is called *decerebrate posture* and occurs in humans with massive cerebral trauma, anoxic damage, or midbrain destructive lesions. Lesions large enough to produce decerebrate posture also produce coma. Decerebrate posture is due to the release of reticulospinal and vestibulospinal excitation when the inhibitory drive of forebrain structures on the medullary reticular formation is lost. If damage occurs above the level of the red nucleus, the excitatory drive of the red nucleus on the flexor neurons of the upper

extremity with inhibition of the extensor neurons results in flexor rather than extensor spasticity in the arms. Flexor spasticity in the arms with extensor spasticity in the legs is called *decorticate posture*. Decorticate posture occurs with indirect activation pathway (upper motor neuron) damage above the level of the red nucleus.

Hemiplegia and Hemiparesis

Lesions of the motor pathways of the cerebral hemispheres are common and are called *upper motor neuron lesions*. Because of the intermingling of the direct and indirect pathways, they only rarely are damaged selectively. The clinical findings, therefore, are usually a combination of the effects already described for lesions of the direct and indirect activation pathways. The combined paralytic and release phenomena are exemplified by a lesion in the internal capsule. Such a lesion produces a characteristic pattern of impaired motor activity on one side of the body. If paralysis is severe, the pattern is called a *hemiplegia*. If mild, it is called a *hemiparesis*. The typical findings of hemiparesis are as follows:

Movement. Motor activity is slowed, and weakness is present in a characteristic distribution: the upper portion of the face is spared, while the lower portion is weak contralateral to the lesion. Volitional facial movements are weak, while emotional and associated movements such as smiling are spared or exaggerated. There may be slight weakness of the palate contralateral to the lesion and a tendency for the tongue to deviate on protrusion to the side of the hemiplegia. In the upper extremity, the weakness affects the extensor muscles more than the flexors, whereas in the lower extremity the flexors are weaker than the extensors. Skilled, delicate, precision movements are chiefly affected. The fingers, therefore, are particularly involved. There is also greater weakness of extension of the wrist and elbow and of abduction and elevation of the shoulder. In the lower limb, the weakness involves chiefly the dorsiflexors of the toes and ankle, the flexors of the knee, and the flexors of the hip.

Movements tend to be massive and crude.

Table 8-3. Origins of Signs with an Upper Motor Neuron Lesion

Direct activation pathway damage	Indirect activation pathway damage
Hypotonia	Clonus
Loss of fine, skilled movement	Increased tone of arm flexors and leg extensors
Distal weakness	Spasticity (with clasp-knife response)
Absent abdominal reflexes	Decorticate or decerebrate posture
Babinski's sign	Hyperactive stretch reflexes
Hyporeflexia	

The patient may be unable to carry out selective movements; for instance, he or she may be able to flex and extend all the fingers together but not individually, and on an attempt to dorsiflex the ankle, may also flex the knee. The patient walks with a characteristic circumduction of the affected leg. Movements that the patient is unable to carry out voluntarily may occur reflexly; when the patient yawns or is tickled, the paretic upper limb may elevate and the fingers extend and abduct. Involuntary associated movements also occur in the paralyzed limb when powerful movements are carried out on the nonparalyzed side.

Muscle Tone and Posture. There is myotatic hyperreflexia with an upper motor neuron lesion, which is expressed as increased muscle stretch reflexes and an increased resistance to passive movement (spasticity). There is overactivity of the spinal reflexes that maintain upright posture and a corresponding increase of tone in the antigravity muscles. In humans, the *antigravity muscles* are the flexors in the upper limb and the extensors in the lower limb. Lesions of the upper motor neuron result in a characteristic posture: the upper limb is adducted and flexed at the elbow, wrist, and fingers; the lower limb is adducted and extended at the hip and knee. The response to passive movement includes the clasp-knife response, in which the increased resistance to passive movement, present with initial stretch, subsides with continued stretch. Large, acute, supratentorial lesions may produce a transient flaccid paralysis.

Impaired speech also occurs with upper motor neuron lesions. Because of bilateral innervation of bulbar muscles, these findings are most common with bilateral disease. They are referred to as *spastic dysarthria*, characterized by a harsh, labored, slow, monotonous, and weak speech with poor articulation.

Reflexes. The stretch reflexes in upper motor neuron disease differ from normal in that the threshold is lowered and the response is exaggerated and more protracted (hyperreflexia). When the stretch reflexes occur in series, *clonus* (repeated jerking of the muscle) occurs, each relaxation initiating another contraction. (Clonus must be distinguished from the clonic, jerking movements in a seizure.) The abdominal and cremasteric reflexes are impaired or lost, but Babinski's sign appears.

The sources of these phenomena are listed in Table 8-3.

Final Common Pathway

The final common pathway is the peripheral effector mechanism by which all motor activity is mediated. It includes interneurons and motor neurons in the ventral horn of the spinal cord and the axons of the motor neurons that extend peripherally via nerves to innervate muscles. These motor neurons are called *alpha motor neurons* or *alpha efferents*. The alpha efferents innervate the muscle fibers that are responsible for skeletal muscle contraction.

Anatomy

The basic functional component of the final common pathway is the *motor unit*. The concept of the *motor unit*, that is, a ventral horn cell (alpha motor neuron) and the muscle fibers innervated by it, is a physiologic one, developed largely as a result of the work of Sir Charles Sherrington and his colleagues on the reflex activity of the spinal cord. By definition, each unit consists of the cell body of a motor neuron, its single axon (which leaves the spinal cord in the ventral root and extends through the peripheral nervous system before ramifying to innervate the muscle fibers in a

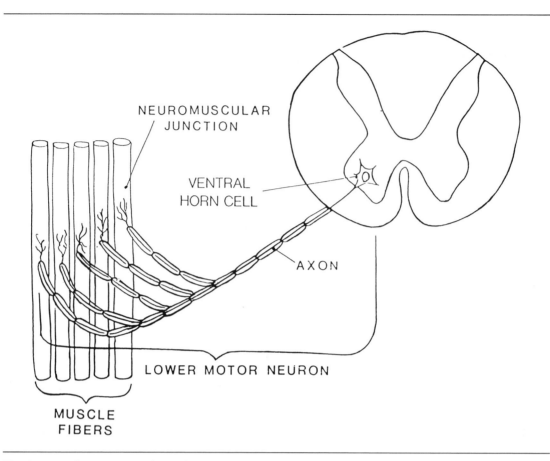

NEUROMUSCULAR
JUNCTION

VENTRAL
HORN CELL

AXON

LOWER MOTOR NEURON

MUSCLE
FIBERS

Fig. 8-15. A single motor unit and its components: the lower motor neuron and muscle fibers innervated by it. The final common pathway contains hundreds of thousands of such units innervating skeletal muscle.

particular muscle), and all the muscle fibers innervated by the terminal axons (Fig. 8-15).

Ventral Horn Cells
The cell bodies of lower motor neurons lie in the ventral horn of the spinal cord. They are relatively large (50 to 80 μm) and are arranged in well-defined columns that extend through many spinal segments and the brain stem. These are called *alpha motor neurons*. There are other, smaller neurons in the ventral horns that are more diffusely arranged, the interneurons and gamma motor neurons. *Gamma motor neurons* innervate muscle spindles. The *interneurons* integrate the activity from the direct and indirect pathways and peripheral sensory input. The motor units of craniofacial muscles have their motor neurons in the brain stem. Destruction of the ventral horn cell of a

motor unit results in degeneration of the axon and loss of innervation of the muscle fibers of that motor unit. The muscle becomes weak or paralyzed, and the muscle fibers atrophy.

Motor Axons
Motor axons (nerve fibers) are large myelinated fibers, 6 to 20 μm in diameter, located in the peripheral nerves. The large myelinated motor nerve fibers of most nerves innervating muscle have axons of two sizes because of the presence of two distinct fiber types in these nerves. Nearly half of the fibers are the large alpha motor fibers that innervate muscle fibers (extrafusal muscle fibers); the others are the gamma motor fibers to the muscle spindles (intrafusal muscle fibers). The gamma motor axons originate from the smaller neurons in the ventral horn of the spinal cord and are of

smaller caliber (6 to 10 μm) than alpha motor axons.

Branching of motor nerve fibers occurs along the course of nerves at the nodes of Ranvier and is greatest distally in the muscle. Each terminal ramification of a nerve fiber ends at a *neuromuscular junction*, a motor end-plate on a single muscle fiber. The nerves that go to muscle also contain many sensory fibers arising mainly from the muscle spindles. Mild damage to the motor axons in the peripheral nerve can block the conduction of action potentials to the muscle; severe damage can produce wallerian degeneration of the axon distal to the site of the lesion. In either instance, muscle function is lost.

The Neuromuscular Junction
The points of contact between the terminal ramifications of motor axons and muscle fibers innervated by them are known as *motor end-plates*, or *neuromuscular junctions*. Each motor end-plate is a composite structure belonging partly to the motor axon and partly to the muscle fiber. The terminal axon lies in a hollow indentation of the surface of the muscle fiber, the *synaptic gutter*. The membrane of the nerve terminal and that of the muscle fiber are separated by a narrow space, the *synaptic cleft*. The nerve terminal holds many vesicles that contain the neurotransmitter acetylcholine.

Organization of Muscle Fibers in a Motor Unit
The nerve terminals of a single motor axon innervate muscle fibers that may be distributed widely throughout the muscle, intermingling with muscle fibers innervated by other neurons. A muscle may contain from 50 to 1,000 motor units.

The size of a motor unit is determined by the number of extrafusal fibers innervated by a single motor neuron. This is expressed as the *innervation ratio*, the number of muscle fibers per axon. Muscles concerned with fine movements have smaller innervation ratios than those that perform cruder movements. The motor units of the powerful limb muscles, for example, each contain from 500 to 2,000 muscle fibers. In contrast, motor units in intrinsic hand muscles have innervation ratios of only 10 to 50, and eye muscles have ratios of 3 to 10.

After destruction of isolated ventral horn cells, for example, as in poliomyelitis, reinnervation of some of the denervated fibers may occur by branching of the remaining motor nerve fibers. These new collateral sprouts of intact axons form new motor end-plates on the denervated muscle fibers, resulting in an increase in the number of muscle fibers in the remaining motor units and, thus, an increase in the innervation ratio.

Muscle Fiber Structure
Muscle fibers of skeletal muscles are long cylindrical structures, each of which is a syncytium containing hundreds of nuclei. These nuclei are situated near the surface of the fiber adjacent to the sarcolemmal sheath. In transverse sections, the fibers are seen as rounded or polygonal structures. The cytoplasm of the muscle fiber contains mitochondria, sarcoplasmic reticulum, and *myofibrils*, the contractile elements of the muscle. The myofibrils have a banded structure that subdivides them into units called sarcomeres. A *sarcomere* is the distance between two well-defined cross striations on the muscle fiber, the *Z bands*. On electron microscopic examination, the myofibrils are found to consist of filaments of the proteins actin and myosin, whose arrangement in the myofibrils is responsible for the cross striation.

Individual muscle fibers may be several centimeters long. They may run from one end of the muscle to the other, or they may be attached to tendinous insertions within the muscle. The fibers are arranged in groups, or *fasciculi*, each of which is a bundle of parallel fibers bound together and surrounded by connective tissue containing blood vessels and nerves. Adult muscle fibers range from 30 to 90 μm in diameter. Differences in fiber diameter between different muscles and between the muscles of different people occur because of differences in build and muscular development. The size of muscle fiber also depends on the activity of the muscle and on *trophic factors* released from the nerve terminals. Lack of use causes muscle fibers to shrink, but they do so more severely and rapidly with immobilization or with loss of innervation. In cases of loss of innervation, this loss of size, or *atrophy*, of the fiber is limited to the muscle fibers that were innervated by the damaged neuron. In abnormalities of the muscle itself, atrophy involves all fibers in the muscle.

Physiology

The motor unit is the physiologic unit of reflex and voluntary contraction. Under normal conditions, the motor unit behaves in an all-or-none manner, which means that an impulse in the motor nerve fiber produces an action potential in and synchronous contraction of all the muscle fibers it supplies. Thus, the resulting contraction of the motor unit is the sum of the mechanical responses of the component muscle fibers.

Activation of a lower motor neuron in the spinal cord or brain stem by any of the three sources of input produces an action potential that spreads to each of the terminal branches of the motor axon in the muscle. Each of these axons releases the neurotransmitter *acetylcholine*, which diffuses rapidly across the synaptic cleft and acts on the postsynaptic membrane of the muscle fiber to produce an end-plate potential. The end-plate potential initiates an action potential in the muscle fiber, which then spreads along the entire length of the muscle fiber. The electrical currents generated by the muscle action potential invade the depths of the muscle fiber via a tubular system to "turn on" the contractile mechanism that produces the actual twitch of the muscle. This sequence of steps converts the activation of motor neurons to muscle contraction.

In the normal activation of lower motor neurons, the neurons discharge repetitively at rates of 5 to 20 per second. At these rates, the twitch of slow muscles is not completed before the next action potential arrives, so that smooth movements or steady contractions can be obtained from repetitive action potentials. Normal movements involve the coordinated activity of hundreds to thousands of motor units in many muscles. The speed and strength of a movement are controlled by the number of motor units active, their rate of firing, and the characteristics of the motor units activated.

Units with low innervation ratios are needed for some tasks. For example, extrinsic ocular muscles, which must fixate accurately, need very fine control and therefore have low innervation ratios. The number of muscle fibers in a motor unit is also related to the load that it must move. For example, to move the mass of the lower limb even slightly requires the simultaneous action of many muscle fibers; consequently, in the muscles responsible for such movements, high innervation ratios are found. Because activation of a normal ventral horn cell results in contraction of all the muscle fibers in the motor unit, gradation of contraction is accomplished by varying the frequency of firing of single motor units and the number of motor units activated. When effort is increased, more motor units are brought into action.

In general, the motor units in limb muscles may be divided into two groups according to their speed of contraction: fast twitch and slow twitch. The distinction is based on the differences in time from the start of the contraction to the time at which the motor unit develops its peak tension in response to a single stimulus. In a typical fast-twitch motor unit, this contraction time is approximately 25 milliseconds, while in a slow-twitch unit, the time is approximately 75 milliseconds. The motor nerve innervating the muscle fibers of the motor unit determines the twitch time by some trophic (chemical) substance liberated at the nerve endings independently of acetylcholine, by the pattern of nerve impulses reaching the motor end-plate, or by a combination of these.

Slow-twitch motor units tend to be found in certain muscles, for example, the soleus muscle. This has led to the use of the term *slow muscle*. Other muscles containing predominantly fast-twitch motor units are designated *fast muscles*. The segregation of more motor units of a particular speed into certain muscles is of functional significance. It is generally agreed that slow limb muscles, like the soleus muscle, subserve a predominantly postural role, while the fast limb muscles are concerned more with phasic, voluntary movements. However, fast- and slow-twitch motor units are intermingled in most muscles.

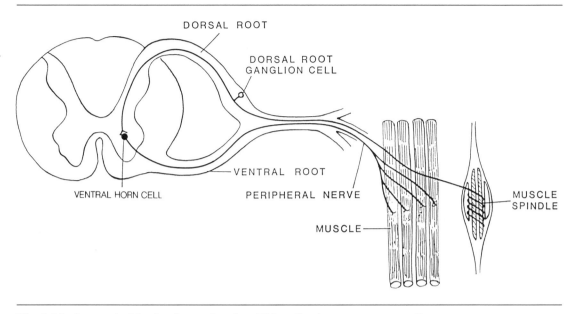

Fig. 8-16. Anatomical basis of stretch reflex. This reflex is a two-neuron reflex mediated by stretch receptors in the muscle spindle, sensory axons with their cell bodies in the dorsal root ganglion, a synapse in the spinal cord, and an anterior horn cell innervating the striated muscle.

Local Reflexes

Three local reflexes involving the final common pathway are of particular importance: the stretch reflex, the lengthening reflex, and Renshaw inhibition. Of these, the stretch reflex is the most clinically important because it is the basis of the neurologic testing of tendon reflexes. The *stretch reflex* is a simple two-neuron reflex elicited by stimulation of a muscle spindle and ending with activation of the motor unit (Fig. 8-16).

The Muscle Spindles

Striated muscles are rich in sensory receptors and contain muscle spindles, Golgi tendon organs, and bare nerve endings. Of these sensory organs, the muscle spindles are the most complex and best understood. The *muscle spindle* is a group of specialized muscle fibers with two types of sensory receptors, the *primary* and *secondary endings*, which measure the length and velocity of stretch in a muscle. The muscle spindle fibers are referred to as intrafusal fibers (inside the muscle spindle) in contrast to the extrafusal fibers, which make up the bulk of the muscle.

The muscle spindles are arranged in parallel with the extrafusal muscle fibers. Each spindle is surrounded by a connective tissue capsule that connects the spindle to the origin and insertion of the muscle. Within the connective tissue capsule are two types of intrafusal muscle fibers, the large-diameter, longer *nuclear bag* fibers and the smaller *nuclear chain* fibers. The former have a number of nuclei close together in the middle, while in the latter, the nuclei are distributed evenly throughout the length of the muscle fiber (Fig. 8-17).

The *primary sensory ending*, or *annulospiral ending*, of the muscle spindle forms a spiral around both the nuclear bag fibers and the nuclear chain fibers. This sensory ending gives rise to large-diameter, fast-conducting afferent nerve fibers (type Ia), which end monosynaptically in the spinal cord on the motor neurons of the muscle of origin and synergistic muscles. Collateral branches from the primary afferent fibers pass up the posterior columns to other levels and also connect via interneurons to the motor neurons of antagonistic muscles. The spindle *secondary sensory endings*, or *flower spray endings*, are almost exclusively on nuclear chain

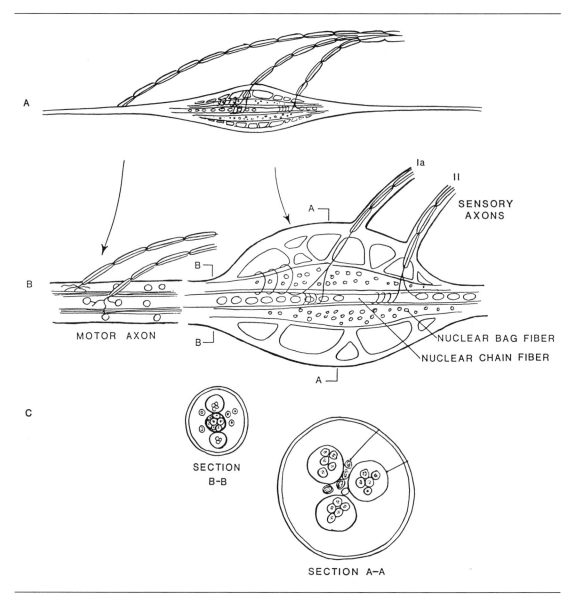

Fig. 8-17. Muscle spindle. A. Entire spindle with axons innervating it. B. Detailed longitudinal view of spindle at its center and at one end. C. Cross-sectional view of spindle at middle (*A-A*) and end (*B-B*).

fibers. They give rise to smaller diameter and therefore slower conducting (type II) afferent axons, which connect with motor neurons only via interneurons. Primary and secondary afferents from the muscle spindle make up a large proportion of the direct sensory input to the final common pathway.

Both primary and secondary sensory endings are sensitive to stretch in the intrafusal fibers. They may be activated by stretch of the skeletal muscle containing the spindle or by contraction of the intrafusal muscle fibers in the spindle. Because of differences in viscosity, the two types of intrafusal fibers differ in their response to stretch, and their discharges are divided into dynamic (phasic) and static (tonic) phases. The former occurs during the period of stretching; the latter occurs while the sensory endings are held stretched (Fig. 8-18).

The action potentials from the type Ia mus-

Fig. 8-18. Responses of afferent fibers from muscle spindle. A. Length of muscle containing muscle spindle. Muscle length is changed with various waveforms of stretch. B. Response of type Ia afferent fibers from primary ending of spindle. C. Response of type II afferent fibers from secondary ending of spindle. Type Ia afferents respond to rapid stretch; type II afferents respond to length.

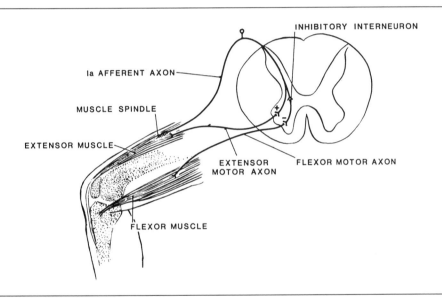

Fig. 8-19. Central connections of a type Ia afferent fiber from muscle spindle. Spindle activity activates the muscle and inhibits the antagonist.

cle spindle afferents are excitatory to the ventral horn cells that innervate synergistic muscles and are inhibitory to antagonistic muscles (Fig. 8-19). Thus, sudden activation of the spindles in a muscle results in a brisk muscle contraction. The response of the primary endings in the muscle spindle to a quick stretch is the basis of stretch reflexes, called *myotatic reflexes*, in which the physician taps a tendon with a reflex hammer and produces a stretch of the muscle. The resulting discharge of a large number of type Ia afferents is sufficient to activate the anterior horn cells on which these afferents end and to cause a muscle twitch.

Therefore, loss of either the afferent fibers or the lower motor neuron results in a loss of myotatic reflexes.

A common clinical test is to gauge the resistance of a muscle to passive movement. Normally, when the examiner moves a limb and a muscle is stretched, there is a mild resistance to the passive movement, referred to as *muscle tone*. Tone is due partly to the intrinsic elasticity of the tissue, but it is also a result of the activation of motor units with stretching of the muscle spindles. An increase in the input to the alpha or gamma motor neurons results in an increase in muscle tone (hyper-

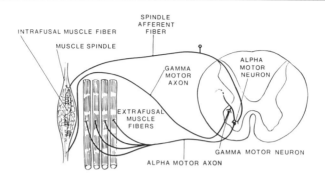

Fig. 8-20. Gamma motor system. Contraction of intrafusal fibers by gamma motor neurons can maintain a muscle spindle at proper length to respond to muscle stretch, even though the muscle changes length.

tonia). A reduction in either the afferent input from the muscle spindles or the efferent activity of the lower motor neurons results in a decrease of muscle tone (hypotonia).

The central connections of the type II axons from the secondary spindle endings are more complex than those of the primary endings. Like the type Ia endings, they have excitatory connections with synergistic muscles and have inhibitory connections with antagonistic muscles so that they may participate in the myotatic reflexes. However, they also have more widespread, polysynaptic connections that have a longer duration of action, which may be part of flexion reflexes in which a limb is withdrawn from noxious stimuli.

The type II axons also participate in the clasp-knife reflex. The increased tone in patients with upper motor neuron lesions decreases with passive stretch of the muscle. This reduction in tone has been likened to the rapid snapping shut of a pocketknife (clasp knife). The reduction in hypertonia with muscle stretching is length dependent; that is, the tone decreases in direct proportion to the increase in muscle length. Muscle length is signaled by the secondary muscle spindle endings, which therefore mediate the clasp-knife reflex.

For a muscle spindle to respond appropriately to a stretch or change in muscle length, the spindle length must be adjusted as the length of the muscle changes. This is accomplished through a separate motor innervation of the spindle fibers. The motor innervation of

the intrafusal muscle fibers is known as the *fusimotor system* (and comes from gamma motor neurons) (Fig. 8-20). The neuromuscular terminations of the fusimotor system are of two types: *plate endings* and *trail endings*. The former are discrete single endings, and the latter are diffuse multiple endings. These endings can preferentially increase either the phasic (changing) discharge from the muscle spindle or the tonic (maintained) discharge. The independent motor control of the two types of intrafusal muscle fibers allows independent control of the spindle's phasic and tonic discharges. Such control is of considerable importance in maintaining stability of the stretch reflex during movements.

During muscle contraction, the type Ia fiber discharge would be completely suppressed by "unloading" if the gamma motor neuron were not simultaneously active. Therefore, gamma motor neurons are coactivated with the alpha motor neurons to a muscle in order to maintain the spindle receptor sensitivity to unexpected movements (Fig. 8-21).

Muscle spindles are not distributed equally throughout the muscles. More are present in slow muscles, such as the soleus, than in fast muscles, such as the gastrocnemius. Within the spinal cord, there is a concentration of monosynaptic spindle afferents on the synergistic slow motor neurons. The spindle mechanism is thus of greater importance in control of the tonic activity of slow muscles.

Another important sensory structure in muscle is the *Golgi tendon organ*, a sensory

Fig. 8-21. Effect of gamma motor neuron activation. A. Length of muscle (muscle contraction) as it actively contracts. B. Action potential discharges in type Ia afferent fibers during muscle contraction without gamma motor neuron activation. C. Type Ia afferent firing during muscle contraction with gamma motor neuron activation.

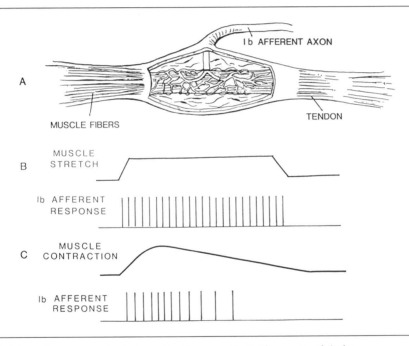

Fig. 8-22. Golgi tendon organ. A. Schematic diagram. B. Action potentials in afferents from Golgi tendon organ are shown as muscle is passively stretched. C. Afferent activity with active muscle contraction.

receptor with type Ib axons; it is sensitive to tension and is located in the tendon. Because it is in series with the extrafusal muscle fibers, the Golgi tendon organ increases its discharge rate in response to an increase in tension, whether generated by passive stretch or active muscle contraction (Fig. 8-22). This is in contrast to the muscle spindle, which is in parallel with the extrafusal muscle fibers and increases its discharge rate with passive stretch of the muscle but not with muscle contraction (Fig. 8-23).

Through interneurons, the Golgi tendon organ inhibits the motor neurons to the same muscle and synergistic muscles and excites motor neurons to antagonistic muscles (see Fig. 8-23). The Golgi tendon organ thereby provides a direct tension feedback mechanism for either increases or decreases in tension.

Renshaw loops originate as collateral

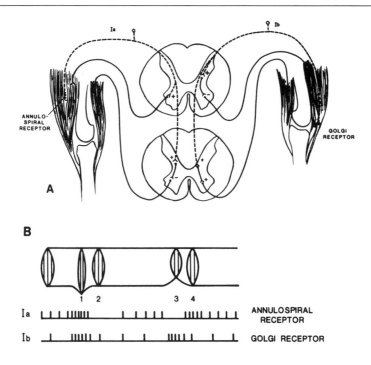

Fig. 8-23. Muscle spindle and Golgi tendon organ. A. Central connections of types Ia and Ib afferents. On left, the type Ia connections produce excitation (+) of synergistic muscles (myotatic reflex) and inhibition (−) of antagonistic muscles through inhibitory interneurons. On right, the type Ib connections produce inhibition of synergistic muscles through an inhibitory interneuron (−). B. Effects of passive muscle stretch (*1*) and active muscle contraction (*3*) on action potential firing in type Ia axons from muscle spindle and type Ib axons from tendon organ (*2* and *4* indicate resting muscle state).

branches from the axons of alpha motor neurons. The axon branches synapse with interneurons (the Renshaw cells) that inhibit the motor neurons of synergistic muscles. Activity in such a loop temporarily inhibits the motor neurons. The function of the Renshaw loop is probably to stabilize the discharge frequency of motor neuron pools and generally to prevent the neurons from discharging at excessive rates. The Renshaw loops originate mainly from the motor neurons innervating fast-twitch motor units but act primarily on the smaller alpha motor neurons that innervate slow-twitch skeletal muscle fibers. The primary function of slow motor units is to subserve static postural functions, and the primary function of the fast motor units is to produce phasic movements. The asymmetric Renshaw inhibitory distribution thus also acts to subdue the postural stretch reflexes in slow

muscle during the activity of phasic motor neurons.

Integration in the Final Common Pathway

We have just discussed some of the input that impinges on the motor neuron: afferent activity from the muscle spindles, the Golgi tendon organs, and the Renshaw cells. In addition to sensory input, the ventral horn cells receive input from three other major sources: the direct activation pathway, the indirect activation pathway, and other segments of the spinal cord. Each of these sources may transmit excitatory or inhibitory impulses to the final common pathway, which are integrated by the ventral horn cells before they respond. Table 8-4 summarizes the major spinal reflexes.

Table 8-4. Major Spinal Cord Reflexes

	Stretch	Lengthening	Other
Sensory axon type	Ia	Ib	II
Receptor	Muscle spindle	Golgi tendon organ	Muscle spindle, joint receptor, pacinian corpuscle, other receptors
Stimulus	Changes in muscle length	Muscle tension	Multiple
Interneurons	Ia interneuron	Ib interneuron	Interneuron pool
Effect on motor neurons	Monosynaptic excitation of agonist	Disynaptic inhibition of agonist	Excitation of ipsilateral flexors
	Disynaptic inhibition of antagonist	Di/trisynaptic excitation of antagonist	Inhibition of ipsilateral extensors

Clinical Correlations

Diseases may affect the final common pathway at the level of the ventral horn cell, the axon, or the muscle fiber. However, damage to all these sites has common clinical features that permit the clinician to identify disease of the motor unit. These include weakness, atrophy, loss of reflexes, and loss of tone. Other features that may indicate abnormal function of the motor unit include fasciculations, cramps, and excessive contraction.

In the weakness or paralysis due to final common pathway disease, there is an inability to obtain voluntary contraction, a loss of involuntary movements, and a loss of reflex contraction of the muscle. The weakness occurs either because the action potentials cannot be transmitted to the muscle owing to disease of the lower motor neuron or because diseased muscle fibers cannot respond to the action potentials of the lower motor neurons.

The strength of a muscle is generally proportional to its size: an elderly lady has less strength than a young weight lifter, although both have normal muscle function. A physician must evaluate strength in proportion to size. The loss of muscle bulk in disease is referred to as *atrophy* and is often found with weakness due to disease of the final common pathway. Two types of atrophy must be differentiated. The first, *neurogenic atrophy*, occurs with loss of innervation, when a muscle undergoes atrophy and is weak (out of proportion to its size). The second, *disuse atrophy*, occurs with lack of use of the muscle. In disuse atro-

phy, strength is appropriate to the size of the muscle. Disuse atrophy is not a sign of disease of the neuromuscular system, whereas neurogenic atrophy is. Atrophy may also occur in muscle disease.

In general, if the lower motor neurons are lost, reflexes, in particular the tendon reflexes, are also lost. They are most consistently lost if the disease process damages the afferent fibers of the reflex arc. Disruption of the reflex arc also results in loss of the normal tone or response to passive movement. This state is called *flaccidity*, and the weakness with disease of the final common pathway is *flaccid paralysis*.

Weakness, flaccidity, and atrophy also occur in the face, tongue, and pharyngeal muscles, with disease of the lower motor neurons in the brain stem. This results in a characteristic breathy, imprecise, nasal speech called *flaccid dysarthria* (dysarthria = abnormal utterances).

Diseases of the motor unit also may be associated with excessive activity or spontaneous firing, with a low threshold for discharge. This may take the form of a single, spontaneous discharge of a motor unit, a *fasciculation*. A fasciculation can be seen on the surface of the skin as a brief, localized twitch. A continuous, high-frequency discharge of fascicles of muscle fibers is a cramp. Both may be manifestations of disease or may be due simply to "physiologic irritability," such as can occur after excessive exertion. After destruction of the lower motor neuron, the muscle fibers that have lost their innervation generate slow re-

Table 8-5. Findings on Neurologic Examination of Motor Function Related to the Divisions of the Motor System at the Four Levels of the Nervous System

	Level of damage			
	Peripheral	Spinal	Posterior fossa	Supratentorial
Final common pathway	Weakness, atrophy, hyporeflexia, hypotonia, absent abdominal reflexes, cramp, and fasciculation	Weakness, atrophy, hyporeflexia, hypotonia, absent abdominal reflexes, cramp, and fasciculation	Weakness, atrophy, and fasciculation	
Direct activation pathway		Weakness, loss of abdominal reflex, and Babinski's sign	Weakness, loss of abdominal reflex, Babinski's sign, hyporeflexia, and hypotonia	Weakness, loss of abdominal reflex, Babinski's sign, seizure, apraxia, hyporeflexia, and hypotonia
Indirect activation pathway		Hyperreflexia, clonus, spasticity, and clasp-knife reflex	Hyperreflexia, clonus, spasticity, clasp-knife reflex, and decerebrate posture	Hyperreflexia, clonus, spasticity, clasp-knife reflex, apraxia, decorticate posture
Cerebellar control circuit			Ataxia, dysmetria, dyssynergia, intention tremor, past pointing, rebound, hyporeflexia, and hypotonia	Ataxia
Basal ganglia control circuit				Rigidity, athetosis, dystonia, chorea, hemiballismus, hyperkinesia, and resting tremor

petitive action potentials and contract regularly, a process called *fibrillation*. Fibrillations are not visible through the skin.

Motor System Examination

Movement in the normal person involves the simultaneous, coordinated activities of all the major divisions of the motor system. Therefore, these are tested together in the neurologic examination. The examination is best organized into separate evaluation of strength, reflexes, coordination, gait, tone, and muscle bulk and observation for abnor-

mal movements. The changes in each of these with disease in each division of the motor system are outlined in Table 8-5.

Strength

Strength testing evaluates the power of muscle groups in performing specific actions. Strength depends on age, occupation, physical activity, and muscular development. It may be apparently reduced in patients with bone deformity, pain, or a lack of understanding of the test. Because the object of strength testing is to detect disease of the neuromuscular system, these extraneous factors must be excluded. Strength cannot be graded as abnormal on the basis of an absolute measure of force. It must be judged for each person on the basis of age and all the other variables noted.

Strength is tested by having the patient resist pressure initiated by the examiner. The position of the extremity during testing is of great importance in isolating the action of specific muscle groups and in providing optimal leverage. Each muscle group should be tested in the position that best isolates its function and puts it at a relative mechanical disadvantage (partially contracted position). Force should not be applied suddenly but should be applied gradually to a maximum.

There are several systems for grading strength (or weakness). A simple and universally understood one uses a verbal description:

Normal. Level of strength expected for that person.

Mild weakness. Level of strength less than expected but not sufficient to impair any daily function.

Severe weakness. Strength sufficient to activate the muscle and move it against gravity but not against any added resistance.

Complete paralysis. No detectable movement.

The following muscle groups are tested as part of a general neurologic examination. The individual muscles participating in these functions will be discussed in Chapter 13 (The Peripheral Level).

Facial muscles. Upper and lower facial muscles are tested separately by having the patient wrinkle the forehead, squeeze the eyes shut, and show the teeth.

Neck muscles. The patient resists attempts by the examiner to flex and extend the neck by exerting pressure on the occiput and forehead, respectively.

Arm abductors. The patient holds the arms laterally at right angles to the body while the examiner pushes down on the elbows.

Elbow flexors and extensors. With the elbow bent at a right angle, the patient resists attempts to straighten it out (flexing to prevent extension) and to bend it (extending to prevent flexion).

Wrist extensors. The patient holds the wrist straight with knuckles up, while the examiner attempts to depress it.

Finger flexors. The patient resists attempts to straighten the fingers of a clenched fist (or squeezes two of the examiner's fingers in his or her hand).

Trunk flexors. The patient attempts to do a sit-up from a supine position with the legs extended.

Hip flexors. In a sitting position, the patient holds the knee up off the chair against resistance; supine, the patient keeps the knee pulled up to the chest.

Hip extensors. Prone, the patient holds the bent knee off the examining table; supine, the patient resists attempts to lift the leg straight off the examining table; these are the major muscles used in arising from a squatting position (with knee extensors).

Knee flexors. The patient resists attempts to straighten the knee from a 90-degree angle position.

Knee extensors. The patient resists attempts to bend the knee from a 90-degree angle position; these are major muscles used in arising from squatting.

Ankle plantar flexors. The patient's ability to rise onto the toes of one foot or to walk on toes is assessed. This ability is too powerful to test by hand unless it has been severely weakened.

Ankle dorsiflexors. The patient holds the ankle in a resting 90-degree angle position against attempts to depress it.

Reflexes

Two major types of reflexes are tested in the neurologic examination: stretch reflexes and superficial (cutaneous) reflexes. The former depend on a rapid, brisk stretch of the muscle, whereas the latter depend on an uncomfortable stimulus to the skin. Correct positioning and application of the stimulus are extremely important in eliciting reflexes. There are also significant variations among patients and even of a reflex in a single patient on repeated testing. Therefore, much experience with normal reflexes is required before the presence of abnormality can be assessed.

The jaw, biceps, triceps, knee, and ankle reflexes are the most important muscle-stretch reflexes. The patient must be completely relaxed in the testing of all these reflexes.

Jaw jerk. The examiner's index finger is placed lightly on the patient's mandible below the lower lip. It is then tapped briskly with the reflex hammer. The reflex is a brisk jaw closure.

Biceps jerk. The patient's elbow is bent to 90-degree angle position with the forearm resting on the lap or on the examiner's arm. The examiner's thumb is placed on the patient's biceps tendon with slight pressure. The thumb is then tapped firmly and briskly with the reflex hammer. The reflex is a quick biceps muscle contraction with tendon (and forearm) movement.

Triceps jerk. The patient's elbow is bent to 90-degree angle position with the forearm hanging limply, supported at the elbow by the examiner's hand. A firm, brisk tap is applied directly to the tendon of the triceps, 1 to 3 cm above the olecranon. The elbow extends in this reflex.

Knee jerk. The patient's knee is bent to 90 degrees in the sitting position. A firm, brisk tap is applied to the quadriceps tendon 0.5 to 1.0 cm below the patella. The knee extends in this reflex.

Ankle jerk. The patient's ankle is passively bent to 90 degrees and held by the examiner in that position. The examiner gives a firm, brisk tap to the Achilles tendon 2 to 3 cm above the heel. The foot plantar flexes in the reflex.

Abdominal reflex. The patient lies supine with the abdomen relaxed. By means of a sharp object, the skin of the patient's abdomen is scraped quickly and lightly in each quadrant along a line toward the umbilicus. The umbilicus moves toward the stimulus.

Plantar responses. The sole of the patient's foot is scratched firmly with a blunt instrument such as a key. The stimulus is begun at the heel and smoothly carried forward along the lateral border of the sole to the base of the toes and then medially to the base of the great toe. A normal response is curling of the toes. Babinski's sign is extension of the great toe and fanning of the other toes.

Coordination

The ability to coordinate the movements of multiple muscle groups can be observed during ordinary activity, such as shaking hands, talking, dressing, and writing. Specific tests allow assessment of coordination in localized areas. All may be done with the patient sitting or supine, and each should be done individually for all four extremities.

Finger-to-nose testing. The patient is asked to touch alternately his or her own nose and the examiner's finger with the tip of his or her own index finger. The examiner's finger should be far enough away so that the patient must fully extend the arm. Test this with the patient's eyes open and then closed.

Heel-to-shin testing. The patient places the heel carefully on the opposite knee and slides it slowly along the edge of the tibia to the ankle and back up to the knee again.

Rapid alternating testing. The patient pats each hand or foot as rapidly and regularly as possible against a firm surface. A more difficult variation requires alternately patting the front and back of the hand on the knee as rapidly and regularly as possible.

Gait and Station

Tests of gait and station involve all areas of the motor system. Various patterns of gait abnormality occur with different disorders. The test of gait and station is perhaps the single most useful motor system test and should be observed in all patients.

Gait. The patient walks normally back and forth at a moderate rate; he or she then walks on heels, toes, and tandem along a straight line, touching heel to toe; the patient then hops on each leg.

Station. The patient is asked to stand with the feet together, first with the eyes open and then with the eyes closed. There should be little or no sway.

Muscle Tone

The elbows, wrists, and knees are passively flexed and extended with the patient completely relaxed. There should be only a minimal smooth resistance to the movement.

Muscle Bulk

All major muscle groups should be examined for signs of focal atrophy. The diameters of the extremities may be measured and compared with each other.

Abnormal Movements

Because many motor disorders are manifest as abnormal involuntary movements, the patient should be examined undressed, both sitting and supine and fully relaxed for such movements. Fasciculations in particular require careful observation of each area under good lighting.

Objectives

1. Draw the pathways and name the major nuclei in the direct and indirect activation pathways, the final common pathway, and the control circuits.
2. Describe the function of each of the divisions (direct activation system, indirect activation system, control systems, and final common pathway) of the motor system. Identify pathways acting on the motor unit and describe their effects.
3. Describe the reflex arc and its function in the motor system.
4. Name the symptoms and signs resulting from disease of the motor system and identify the major division of the motor system in which a lesion causing them would be located.
5. Describe the mechanisms by which each of the signs of motor dysfunction occurs.

Clinical Problems

1. A 26-year-old housewife began having infrequent, brief episodes of twitching of her left hand 10 months ago. These ceased 4 months ago, but she then noted clumsiness when using her left hand. This progressed to moderate weakness and a "peculiar" feeling in her hand. In the past month, she began having headaches.

On examination, she was lethargic but otherwise mentally intact. There was mild swelling of the optic disks bilaterally. She had a mild droop of the lower part of her face on the left, moderate weakness and slowing of rapid alternating movements of the left hand, and a circumduction gait on the left. Reflexes were hyperactive in the left arm and leg, with Babinski's sign on the left. Muscle tone was increased on the left. Sensation was normal except for inability to recognize some objects in her left hand.
   a. Identify the level, side, and type of lesion.
   b. Which spinal cord tracts would show wallerian degeneration?
   c. How does the firing rate of the gamma motor neurons to left-side extremity muscles compare with normal?
   d. What were the transient episodes?
   e. Would the jugular compression test be useful?
2. A 23-year-old woman has a slowly progressive disorder that first began in high school when she was noted to be "fidgety." She did well in school and worked as a secretary for 3 years. During this time, she experienced gradually increasing jerking movements of her arms and face, and her speech became slurred, to the point that she was no longer able to work. During the past 2 years, her gait has become unsteady and her movements have slowed. She also has had occasional, uncontrollable, flailing movements of her arms. During the past year, her memory has been poor and her intellectual capabilities have deteriorated.

On neurologic examination, she had occasional, coarse, asymmetric jerks of the upper extremities and neck, with some grimacing. Sensation, strength, and reflexes were unremarkable. Her tone was increased, with rigidity in all extremities. She had a coarse intention tremor of both arms.
   a. Identify the level, side, and type of disease.
   b. What major divisions of the motor system are involved?
   c. What two general types of cause must be considered in this disorder?
   d. Name the structures in the diseased pathways.

e. What are the signs of basal ganglia disease?

3. A 21-year-old single woman was found lying unresponsive in bed by her girlfriend, who had stopped off in the morning to drive her to work. She called for an ambulance and brought the patient to the hospital. The following facts were obtained from the friend on questioning. The patient had been in good health. She was well the evening before. She was apparently taking no medications, and no empty or partially filled bottles were in evidence. There were no signs of a struggle or violence and no suicide note. She was in bed as though she had been asleep. There were no unusual findings about the patient: no blood, urine, feces, or injuries. But her skin had a peculiar pink appearance.

On examination she was unresponsive to all but painful stimuli, to which she responded with decerebrate posturing, with her arms, legs, and neck stiffly extended. Her eyes apparently did not respond to threatening stimuli but appeared to close randomly. Her jaw was tightly clenched. There were bilateral extensor plantar responses. Her respirations were irregular. Tone was generally increased with some lengthening reaction. Reflexes were generally hyperactive. All other aspects of the examination were within normal limits.

a. Identify the level, side, and most likely type of disease.

b. What other types of disorders can have this temporal profile?

c. There is evidence of involvement of which components of the motor system?

d. How is decerebrate rigidity produced?

e. Which sensory receptors are responsible for a clasp-knife reflex?

4. A 9-year-old boy had a mild "cold," which a day later was associated with fever and severe aching muscle pains, especially in his back. He was generally weak, but by the fourth day, he noted an inability to move his right leg and the fingers of his left hand. Lumbar puncture revealed that the CSF was clear and colorless, with a sugar level of 68 mg per deciliter, a protein level of 86 mg per deciliter, and 46 lymphocytes per mi-croliter. His generalized symptoms cleared over the next week.

On examination at 3 weeks, there was almost complete paralysis of his right leg, moderate weakness of his left arm, and mild weakness of other muscles, including the facial muscles. Results of sensation and coordination tests were normal — where he was able to perform them. Reflexes were hypoactive in the right leg, which was flaccid. There was atrophy of all muscles, most strikingly in the right leg and left arm.

a. Identify level, side, and type of disease.

b. Are the spinal fluid findings of any help in identifying the disease?

c. Which component of the motor system is involved?

d. What are the signs of disease in this component?

e. List the major inputs to the final common pathway.

5. A 58-year-old banker suddenly lost the ability to speak, and within a few minutes he was unable to move his right arm. On examination later in the day, there had been no progression in symptoms. He appeared to understand what he was told, but he could not answer questions. In attempting to speak, he uttered nonsense words or garbled words. A very few words came out correctly, such as "hello." His right arm was paralyzed, and the right cheek and right side of his mouth drooped. Forehead movements were normal. Leg strength was normal. Deep tendon reflexes were hypoactive in his right arm but normal elsewhere. He seemed to recognize sensations everywhere. Results of coordination tests were normal, except in the right arm. His gait was normal. Optic fundi were normal.

a. Identify the level, side, and type of lesion.

b. Specifically, what component and what site in the motor system are involved?

c. How do plantar responses and abdominal reflexes change with lesions in this division?

d. What term is used to describe this speech disorder?

e. Why was forehead movement on the right normal?

6. A 7-year-old boy with a history of chronic recurrent otitis media awoke one morning complaining of headache. At school, he was noted to be awkward and to have trouble using his right hand. By the next day, he was unable to hold a glass of milk in his right hand without spilling it, and he veered to the right when walking.

On examination, his neck was slightly stiff, though his fundi were normal. He had an intention tremor of his right arm and leg, with marked dysmetria of these extremities on finger-to-nose and heel-to-shin testing. Reflexes on the right were slightly hypoactive. Sensation was normal.

a. Identify the level, side, and type of lesion.

b. Why should you hesitate to do a lumbar puncture?

c. Which component of the motor system is involved?

d. Which fiber pathways in this component decussate?

e. What are the functional subdivisions of this component of the motor system?

Additional Reading

Albin, R. L., Young, A. B., and Penney, J. B. The functional anatomy of basal ganglia disorders. *Trends Neurosci.* 12:366, 1989.

Alexander, G. E., and Crutcher, M. D. Functional architecture of basal ganglia circuits: Neural substrates of parallel processing. *Trends Neurosci.* 13:266, 1990.

Asbury, A. K., McKhann, G. M., and McDonald, W. I. (eds.). *Diseases of the Nervous System: Clinical Neurobiology.* Philadelphia: Saunders, 1992. Vol. I, pp. 123–353.

Burke, D., and Gandevia, S. C. Peripheral Motor System. In G. Paxinos (ed.), *The Human Nervous System.* San Diego: Academic Press, 1990. pp. 125–145.

DeLong, M. R., and Georgopoulos, A. P. Motor Functions of the Basal Ganglia. In J. M. Brookhart, et al. (eds.), *Handbook of Physiology.* Section 1: *The Nervous System.* Vol. II: *Motor Control, Part 2.* Bethesda, Maryland: American Physiological Society, 1981. pp. 1017–1061.

Dum, R. P., and Strick, P. L. Premotor Areas: Nodal Points for Parallel Efferent Systems Involved in the Central Control of Movement. In D. R. Humphrey and H. J. Freund (eds.), *Motor Control: Concepts and Issues.* Chichester: John Wiley & Sons, 1991. pp. 383–398.

Dyck, P. J., et al. (eds.). *Peripheral Neuropathy* (3rd ed.). Philadelphia: Saunders, 1993.

Engel, A. G., and Banker, B. Q. (eds.). *Myology: Basic and Clinical.* New York: McGraw-Hill, 1992.

Graybiel, A. M. Dopaminergic and Cholinergic Systems in the Striatum. In A. R. Crossman and M. A. Sambrook (eds.), *Neural Mechanisms in Disorders of Movement.* London: Libbey, 1989. pp. 3–16.

King, J. S. (ed.). *New Concepts in Cerebellar Neurobiology.* New York: Liss, 1987.

Kuypers, H. G. J. M. Anatomy of the Descending Pathways. In J. M. Brookhart et al. (eds.). *Handbook of Physiology.* Section 1: *The Nervous System.* Vol. II: *Motor Control, Part 1.* Bethesda, Maryland: American Physiological Society, 1981. pp. 597–666.

Lemon, R. The output map of the primate motor cortex. *Trends Neurosci.* 11:501, 1988.

— 9 —

The Internal Regulation System

The internal regulation system is phylogenetically the oldest functional system. It is a critical component of the central core of neurons and pathways that control automatic functions necessary for *life and survival of the species*. The internal regulation system controls visceral, endocrine, and behavioral functions that maintain the internal environment of the body in response to internal and external changes. The neural components are located at supratentorial, posterior fossa, spinal, and peripheral levels. The most important functions of the internal regulation system are (1) maintenance of *homeostasis*, or the internal environment, for cell function, (2) integration of adaptative responses to external and internal stimuli, including reactions to fear and stress, (3) drinking, feeding, and sexual behaviors, (4) modulation of pain sensation, and (5) regulation of immune function.

The internal regulation system performs all these important functions through three components: (1) the *autonomic nervous system*, including pathways innervating the heart, smooth muscle, visceral organs, blood vessels, skin, and eye; (2) the *neuroendocrine system*, including circulating hormones from the pituitary gland and the peripheral endocrine organs; and (3) connections with the *somatic motor system* for expression of complex behaviors such as feeding and drinking and of automatic motor functions such as respiration and swallowing.

Overview

The internal regulation system consists of (1) integrating-coordinating circuits, (2) visceral, humoral, and external inputs, and (3) autonomic (visceral motor), neuroendocrine, and somatic motor outputs (Fig. 9-1).

The *integrating-coordinating circuits* form a functional unit located at the supratentorial, posterior fossa, spinal, and peripheral levels (Table 9-1 and Fig. 9-2). At the *supratentorial level*, the internal regulation system includes the *prefrontal* and *insular cortices*, the *basal forebrain*, and the *preoptic-hypothalamic area*. The prefrontal cortex and insula are involved in high-order visceral sensory and motor functions. The amygdala is critical for initiation of responses associated with emotion. The preoptic-hypothalamic area plays a central role in homeostasis.

At the *posterior fossa level*, the internal regulation system includes the periaqueductal gray matter of the midbrain, visceral sensory relay nuclei, particularly the nucleus of the tractus solitarius, autonomic centers of the reticular formation, and cranial parasympathetic nuclei. The periaqueductal gray matter is important for integration of autonomic, motor, and pain-controlling mechanisms associated with response to external stressors, reproduction, and defense behavior. The nucleus of the tractus solitarius is the first relay station for cardiovascular, respiratory, and other visceral afferents. Its main functions are initiation of cardiovascular and respiratory reflexes and transference of visceral sensory information to other components of the internal regulation system. Neurons of the medullary reticular formation, particularly ventrolateral medulla, maintain such vital functions as vasomotor tone and respiration. The cranial parasympathetic nuclei contain efferent neurons impor-

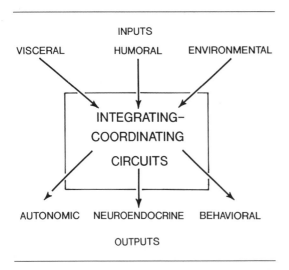

Fig. 9-1. Organization of input, integrating-coordinating, and output components of the internal regulation system.

tant for control of the pupil, lacrimation, salivation, and visceral organs. The most important output originates from the medullary nuclei that project through the vagus nerve.

At the *spinal level*, the internal regulation system includes the *intermediolateral cell column* (containing thoracolumbar sympathetic and sacral parasympathetic neurons), *phrenic* and other *respiratory motor neurons*, and *sphincter motor neurons* in the sacral cord.

The *autonomic ganglia, peripheral endocrine organs*, and *local circuits* form the internal regulation system at the *peripheral level*.

The integrating-coordinating circuits receive three types of input: visceral, humoral, and exteroceptive (Table 9-2). Visceral receptive inputs are carried by *general visceral afferent pathways*, which transmit information from visceral receptors via spinal or medullary afferents. Brain stem afferents are carried by the glossopharyngeal nerve (cranial nerve

Table 9-1. Functional Anatomy of the Internal Regulation System

Level	Area	Function
Supratentorial		
Telencephalon	Amygdala	Emotional response (fear)
Diencephalon	Preoptic-hypothalamic area	Homeostasis
		Neuroendocrine control
		Arousal
		Circadian rhythms
		Reproduction
		Feeding and drinking behavior
		Integrated response to stress
		Immunomodulation
Posterior fossa		
Midbrain	Periaqueductal gray matter	Central control of pain
		Response to stress
Pons	Parabrachial complex	Visceral sensory relay
		Micturition
		Respiration
Medulla	Nucleus of the tractus solitarius	First visceral sensory relay
		Integration of brain stem reflexes
		Respiration
	Ventrolateral reticular formation	Vasomotor tone
		Sympathetic activation
		Respiration
		Control of hypothalamic function
	Vagal nuclei	Preganglionic parasympathetic
Spinal		
Spinal cord	Intermediolateral column	Preganglionic sympathetic and parasympathetic

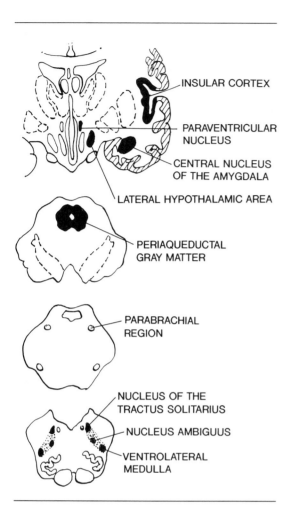

Fig. 9-2. Principal components of the central integrating-coordinating circuits of the internal regulation system. All these areas are reciprocally connected and contain various neurotransmitters.

INSULAR CORTEX

PARAVENTRICULAR NUCLEUS

CENTRAL NUCLEUS OF THE AMYGDALA

LATERAL HYPOTHALAMIC AREA

PERIAQUEDUCTAL GRAY MATTER

PARABRACHIAL REGION

NUCLEUS OF THE TRACTUS SOLITARIUS

NUCLEUS AMBIGUUS

VENTROLATERAL MEDULLA

Table 9-2. Input to the Internal Regulation System

Input	Source
Visceral	Visceral mechanoreceptors and chemoreceptors
Humoral	Blood temperature, osmolarity, glucose level
	Steroid hormones
	Circulating peptides and monoamines
	Cerebrospinal fluid pH
Exteroceptive	Olfaction
	Taste
	Visual
	Vestibular
	Somatic sensory (pain)

IX) and the vagus nerve (cranial nerve X) and synapse in the nucleus of the tractus solitarius.

Humoral inputs include changes in the composition of blood and cerebrospinal fluid detected by *central chemosensitive zones* and *circumventricular organs.*

Exteroceptive sensory input is relayed to the paralimbic areas of the brain.

The three *effector mechanisms* of the internal regulation system are the *visceral motor, endocrine,* and *somatic motor* systems (Table 9-3).

The *visceral motor,* or *autonomic, output* includes the *sympathetic* and the *parasympathetic* outflows. These are two-neuron pathways that synapse in the *autonomic ganglia.*

Preganglionic sympathetic neurons form functional units at segments T-1 to L-3 of the spinal cord, the *thoracolumbar outflow.* Preganglionic parasympathetic neurons are located in the brain stem and in segments S-2 to S-4 of the sacral cord, the *craniosacral outflow.* The neurotransmitter of the preganglionic fibers is *acetylcholine,* which acts primarily on nicotinic receptors in the autonomic ganglia (Fig. 9-3). Postganglionic sympathetic neurons use the neurotransmitter *norepinephrine,* which acts on adrenergic receptors. Postganglionic parasympathetic neurons use acetylcholine, which acts on muscarinic receptors in target organs. Sympathetic and parasympathetic outputs are continuously active and exert complementary effects in control of the heart and other viscera, blood vessels, and pupillary muscles.

The *humoral,* or *endocrine, output* is mediated by circulating hormones, including peptides secreted by the hypothalamic-pituitary area and hormones secreted by peripheral endocrine cells.

The *somatic motor output* is mediated via connections with the motor system, *central pattern generators* of the medullary reticular formation (which control respiration and swallowing), and the *sphincter motor neurons.*

Circuits of the internal regulation system integrate neural and humoral inputs with neural and humoral outputs. This is critical for *tonic maintenance* of vital functions, *reflex adjustments* for homeostasis, and complex

Table 9-3. Output Mechanisms of the Internal Regulation System

Output	Central relay	Effector mechanism
Visceral motor	General visceral efferent column of brain stem and spinal cord	Sympathetic and parasympathetic visceral motor pathways
Neuroendocrine	Hypothalamic-pituitary area	
	Magnocellular system	Vasopressin/oxytocin
	Parvocellular system	Anterior pituitary hormones
	Peripheral endocrine organs	Endocrine cells of adrenal gland, pancreas, kidney, and gut
Somatic motor	Pattern generators of medulla and pons	Automatic motor patterns
	Circuits of limbic system	Complex motivated behavior

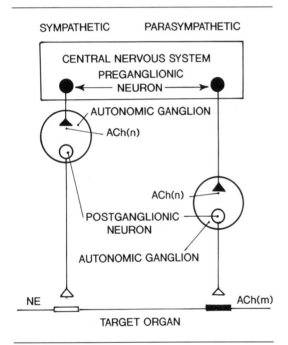

Fig. 9-3. General organization of the sympathetic and parasympathetic outputs of the internal regulation system. (*ACh* = acetylcholine; *NE* = norepinephrine; (*n*) = nicotinic receptors; (*m*) = muscarinic receptors.)

adaptive responses to change in the internal and external environments.

Abnormal function in the internal regulation system produces several different clinical manifestations. Hypothalamic lesions disrupt control of temperature regulation, water balance, appetite, and endocrine and reproductive functions. With medullary lesions, respiration or vasomotor tone may not be sustained. Central or peripheral autonomic failure produces orthostatic hypotension, inability to sweat, impotence, bladder dysfunction, and abnormal gastrointestinal motility.

Integrating-Coordinating Circuits

The *integrating-coordinating circuits* of the internal regulation system are represented at all levels of the nervous system (see Table 9-1). The integrating-coordinating circuits are characterized by reciprocal interactions mediated by several neurotransmitters. Amino acids transmit fast, point-to-point excitatory or inhibitory signals. Monoamines, including catecholamines, and neuropeptides modulate neuronal excitability in central autonomic circuits. Monoamines and neuropeptides may also act by volume transmission, that is, diffusion through the brain extracellular fluid to act on neuronal targets at a distance.

The main interconnecting pathways of the internal regulation system include the afferent and efferent connections of the amygdala, the *medial forebrain bundle*, which interconnects the basal forebrain, preoptic-hypothalamic area, and midbrain, and the *periventricular system*, also called the *dorsal longitudinal fasciculus*, which carries descending inputs to brain stem and spinal cord autonomic nuclei (Fig. 9-4). The medial forebrain bundle and the periventricular system are bidirectional, multisynaptic pathways of the inner tube consisting of unmyelinated or small myelinated axons. Through the medial forebrain bundle, the internal regulation system is interconnected with the diffusely projecting cholinergic and monoaminergic nuclei of the brain

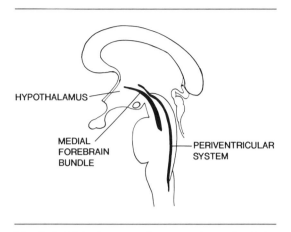

Fig. 9-4. Main input and output channels of the internal regulation system.

stem and forebrain involved in behavioral state control.

Supratentorial Level

At the supratentorial level, the internal regulation system includes visceral areas of the cerebral cortex, amygdala and associated areas of the basal forebrain, and effector nuclei of the preoptic-hypothalamic area.

Cerebral Cortex

Cortical areas involved in high-order autonomic control include the *insular, orbitofrontal, anterior cingulate,* and *medial temporal cortices* (Fig. 9-5). These are known as *paralimbic areas* and have connections with the amygdala, hippocampus, and neocortical association areas.

Fig. 9-5. Telencephalic components of the internal regulation system. A. The insular cortex is the primary visceral sensory area. B. The amygdala is involved in emotions.

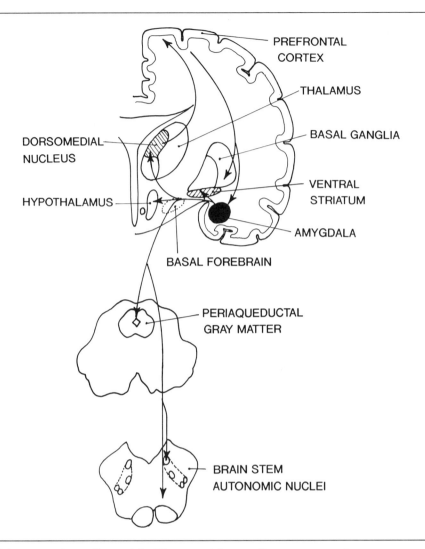

Fig. 9-6. Main connections of amygdala. The amygdala coordinates autonomic, motor, and cognitive aspects of emotional responses.

The paralimbic areas channel exteroceptive information to the amygdala, hypothalamus, and other components of the internal regulation system. The insula is a primary visceral sensory area and receives general visceral and taste information. The orbitofrontal and cingulate cortices initiate various autonomic responses. These cortical regions are connected with the amygdala and hypothalamus directly or through limbic relay nuclei in the thalamus.

Amygdala

The *amygdala* is critical for initiation and expression of *emotional responses*. It provides emotional significance to internal and exter-

nal stimuli and initiates the appropriate autonomic and motor responses. These functions depend on connections of the amygdala with *cholinergic neurons* of *basal forebrain* that mediate arousal, the *ventral striatum*, involved in motivated behavior, and the *hypothalamus*, *periaqueductal gray matter*, and *brain stem autonomic nuclei*, including those in ventrolateral medulla (Fig. 9-6).

Preoptic-Hypothalamic Region

The preoptic area and the hypothalamus form a functional unit critical for homeostasis. They receive humoral, visceral, and exteroceptive information and compare this infor-

Table 9-4. Functional Anatomy of the Preoptic-Hypothalamic Area

Zone	Function
Periventricular	Autonomic
	Circadian rhythms
	Neuroendocrine
Medial	Homeostasis
	Reproduction
Lateral	Arousal
	Motivated behavior

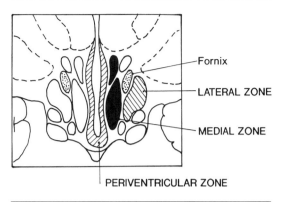

Fig. 9-7. Functional zones of hypothalamus.

mation with a predetermined *set point*. They then initiate compensatory autonomic, humoral, and behavioral responses to regulate the internal milieu around this set point.

The preoptic-hypothalamic area is subdivided into three longitudinally arranged functional zones: the periventricular, medial, and lateral zones (Table 9-4 and Fig. 9-7). The *periventricular zone* contains nuclei involved in neuroendocrine control, biologic rhythms such as circadian rhythms, and complex autonomic responses. The *medial zone* contains nuclei that are critical for homeostasis, energy metabolism, and reproduction. The *lateral hypothalamic zone* participates in arousal, motivated behavior, and autonomic control.

Important hypothalamic nuclei in the periventricular zone include the *suprachiasmatic nucleus* involved in circadian rhythms, the *paraventricular nucleus* involved in integrated hormonal and autonomic responses to stress, and the *arcuate*, or *infundibular*, *nucleus*, which together with the paraventricular nucleus controls anterior pituitary function.

The medial zone contains several nuclear groups, including the *medial preoptic–anterior hypothalamic region*, which contains sensor neurons for blood temperature, osmolarity, and glucose. Other nuclei in the medial zone are the dorsomedial (autonomic responses to stress) and ventromedial (reproductive behavior) nuclei. The *lateral zone*, or *lateral hypothalamic area*, contains the *tuberomammillary nuclei*, which project diffusely to the cerebral cortex and are involved in arousal. The lateral hypothalamic area contains the medial forebrain bundle, which includes dopaminergic pathways of the reward system of the brain involved in motivated behavior.

The *autonomic output* of the hypothalamus originates from several regions, particularly the *paraventricular nucleus*, the *lateral hypothalamic area*, and the *dorsomedial nucleus*. These regions contain intermixed populations of neurons that project directly to lower autonomic centers, including the nucleus of the tractus solitarius, medullary reticular formation, and preganglionic sympathetic and parasympathetic neurons (Fig. 9-8).

The *neuroendocrine output* is mediated via two systems. The *magnocellular system* includes neurons of the *supraoptic* and *paraventricular nuclei* that secrete *vasopressin* (*antidiuretic hormone*) and *oxytocin* (Fig. 9-9A). The *parvocellular*, or *tuberoinfundibular*, *system* includes neurons in the *preoptic*, *paraventricular*, and *arcuate nuclei* that secrete *releasing* or *inhibiting factors* to control anterior pituitary function (Fig. 9-9B). The interactions of the hypothalamus with the endocrine system are mediated via several feedback mechanisms (Fig. 9-10).

The *hypothalamic outputs* important in behavior are mainly the connections of the lateral hypothalamic area with the cerebral cortex, basal forebrain, and somatic motor circuits. These outputs are involved with control of arousal and complex motor behavior (Fig. 9-11).

Posterior Fossa Level

The brain stem components of the internal regulation system include the *periaqueductal gray matter* of the midbrain, the *parabrachial region*

PARAVENTRICULAR NUCLEUS

LATERAL HYPOTHALAMIC AREA

PERIAQUEDUCTAL GRAY MATTER

PARABRACHIAL REGION

NUCLEUS OF THE TRACTUS SOLITARIUS

NUCLEUS AMBIGUUS

VENTROLATERAL MEDULLA

INTERMEDIOLATERAL CELL COLUMN

Fig. 9-8. Important sources of autonomic outputs of hypothalamus. The hypothalamic area contains mixed populations of neurons controlling sympathetic or parasympathetic outputs.

of the pons, the *nucleus of the tractus solitarius*, *autonomic centers* of the reticular formation of the medulla and pons, and *preganglionic parasympathetic cranial nerve nuclei* of the midbrain, pons, and medulla (Table 9-5).

The *periaqueductal gray matter* coordinates motor and autonomic responses to stressful external stimuli and plays a critical role in central inhibitory control of pain transmission. The *parabrachial region*, located in the dorsal pons close to the superior cerebellar peduncle (brachium conjunctivum), relays in-

put from the nucleus of the tractus solitarius to rostral visceral sensory areas and contains important "premotor" autonomic neurons. The *nucleus of the tractus solitarius* is the first brain stem station for the termination of visceral afferents. It has two important functions: it is the site of initiation and integration of many autonomic reflexes, and it provides input to all areas of the autonomic core, particularly the hypothalamus.

Complex networks of neurons in the brain stem reticular formation, referred to as *centers*, control preganglionic visceral motor neurons and respiratory and sphincter motor neurons. These neurons are concentrated in the parabrachial region, the nucleus of the tractus solitarius, and the ventrolateral medulla. The ventrolateral medulla contains several groups of neurons that have spontaneous activity and provide continuous excitation to motor neurons that sustain vasomotor tone and respiration.

The *micturition centers*, located near the parabrachial region, include neurons that control bladder and sphincter function. The respiratory groups contain inspiratory or expiratory neurons that project to spinal phrenic and intercostal respiratory motor neurons, respectively. Brain stem respiratory neurons located in the parabrachial region, nucleus of the tractus solitarius, and ventrolateral medulla are called *pontine* (*pneumotaxic center*), *dorsal*, and *ventral respiratory groups*, respectively. A group of interneurons close to the ventral respiratory group is critical for generation of respiratory rhythm.

An important group of *vasomotor neurons* in the rostral ventrolateral medulla projects directly to sympathetic preganglionic neurons and maintains basal arterial blood pressure, mediates sympathetic reflexes, and serves as the relay station for many pathways affecting the sympathetic system. The ventrolateral medulla, in the region of the *nucleus ambiguus*, also contains *cardiovagal neurons* that control heart rate.

The portion of medullary reticular formation that extends from the nucleus of the tractus solitarius to the ventrolateral medulla is called the *intermediate reticular zone*. It contains interneurons that coordinate various respiratory and cardiovascular reflexes. Med-

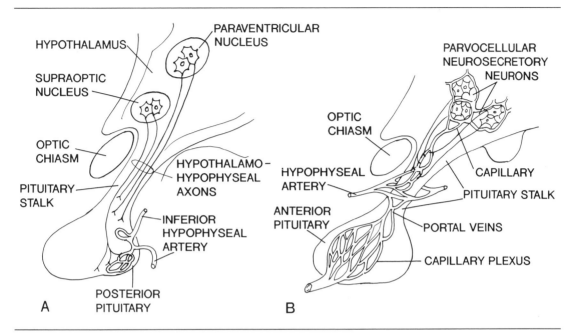

Fig. 9-9. A. Magnocellular hypothalamic neurosecretory system. Supraoptic and paraventricular nuclei contain separate groups of neurons that produce vasopressin or oxytocin and transport them to the posterior pituitary for release into the general circulation. B. Parvocellular hypothalamic neurosecretory system. The nuclei produce releasing or inhibiting factors controlling secretory cells in the anterior pituitary.

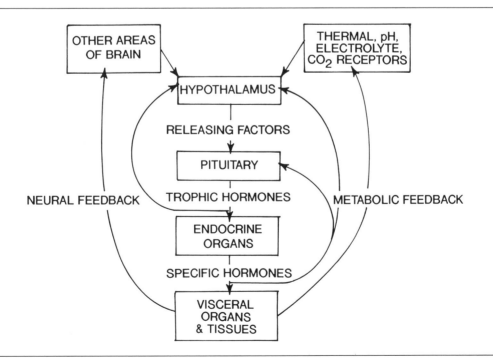

Fig. 9-10. Interactions of hypothalamus and endocrine system. Direct arrows indicate control, and loops show feedback pathways.

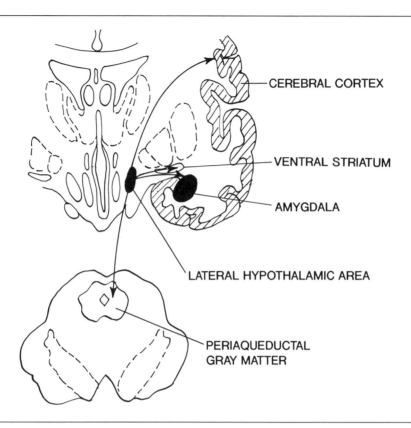

Fig. 9-11. Hypothalamic outputs important in behavior. Lateral hypothalamic areas project to the cerebral cortex for behavioral arousal and to the ventral striatum, amygdala, and midbrain locomotor region to mediate behavioral responses.

Table 9-5. Autonomic Regions of the Brain Stem

Level	Region	Function
Midbrain	Periaqueductal gray matter	Pain control
		Defense reaction
Pons	Parabrachial region	Micturition center
		Pneumotaxic center
Medulla	Nucleus of the tractus solitarius	Relay of visceral afferents
		Cardiovascular reflex center
		Dorsal respiratory group
	Ventrolateral reticular formation	
	Rostral	Premotor sympathetic neurons
		Ventral respiratory group
	Caudal	Ventral respiratory group
		Visceral sensory relay
	Dorsal motor nucleus	Preganglionic vagal
	Nucleus ambiguus	Preganglionic vagal

ullary vasomotor, cardiomotor, and respiratory neurons and control networks are intermingled, functionally related, and have reciprocal connections. The descending brain stem pathways for control of breathing, blood pressure, sweating, and micturition run in the ventral half of the white matter of the lateral columns of the spinal cord.

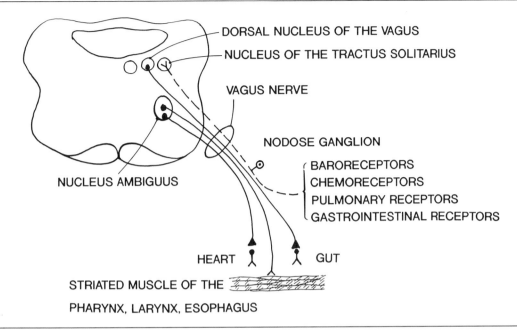

DORSAL NUCLEUS OF THE VAGUS

NUCLEUS OF THE TRACTUS SOLITARIUS

VAGUS NERVE

NODOSE GANGLION

BARORECEPTORS
CHEMORECEPTORS
PULMONARY RECEPTORS
GASTROINTESTINAL RECEPTORS

NUCLEUS AMBIGUUS

HEART   GUT

STRIATED MUSCLE OF THE
PHARYNX, LARYNX, ESOPHAGUS

Fig. 9-12. Components of the vagus nerve. Most fibers of the vagus nerve are afferent.

Autonomic Output Neurons in the Brain Stem

The autonomic output neurons of the brain stem occupy the *general visceral efferent column* in the midbrain, pons, and medulla. These neurons are preganglionic parasympathetic neurons located in the nuclei of cranial nerves III (oculomotor nerve), VII (facial nerve), IX (glossopharyngeal nerve), and X (vagus nerve). The most important autonomic output from the brain stem is carried by the vagus nerve and originates from the *dorsal vagal nucleus* and the *nucleus ambiguus* (Fig. 9-12). Vagal output controls respiratory, cardiovascular, and gastrointestinal functions.

Spinal Level

Spinal components of the internal regulation system include *preganglionic visceral motor neurons* and *somatic motor neurons* that innervate respiratory and external sphincter muscles. Preganglionic autonomic neurons occupy the *intermediolateral cell column* of the gray matter and include the *thoracolumbar* (*sympathetic*) *cell group* and the *sacral* (*parasympathetic*) *cell group*. These neurons are the final common pathway for central control of visceral function. Preganglionic sympathetic neurons are organized in separate functional units (sudomotor, vasomotor, visceral motor), which generate integrated responses throughout the body for control of blood pressure, heart rate, body temperature, and other functions. Sacral parasympathetic neurons control rectal, bladder, and sexual function via *sacral parasympathetic reflexes.*

Respiratory motor neurons include inspiratory neurons at spinal levels C-3 and C-4, which innervate the diaphragm via the phrenic nerve, and intercostal motor neurons at spinal levels T-1 to T-10, which innervate intercostal and abdominal muscles. *Sacral motor neurons* located at the level of S-2 to S-4 innervate the pelvic floor muscles and the external sphincters and are an integral part of reflexes controlling bladder, rectal, and sexual function.

Peripheral Level

Visceral sensory and humoral inputs may initiate visceral motor or endocrine responses via reflex mechanisms that are integrated peripherally. These reflexes may be integrated locally at the level of the target organs, at the level of the autonomic ganglia (ganglion reflexes), and at the level of the peripheral endocrine organs. Local reflexes are typical of the *enteric nervous system*, which is located in the wall of the gut. It contains afferent neurons, interneurons, and efferent neurons that respond to local mechanical and chemical influences and control peristalsis and secretions in the gastrointestinal tract. Ganglion reflexes generate topographically restricted visceral motor responses. Inputs integrated at the level of the *peripheral endocrine organs* produce widespread humoral influences.

Input to the Internal Regulation System

Afferents from Visceral Organs

General Characteristics

Visceral receptors generally are mechanoreceptors or chemoreceptors located in the muscular wall and in the mucosal and serosal surfaces of internal organs, blood vessels, and pleural and peritoneal cavities. Most visceral receptors have low spontaneous activity, are slowly adapting, and are innervated by small myelinated and unmyelinated fibers. Visceral afferents, similar to somatic afferents, have cell bodies in the dorsal root ganglia or cranial nerve ganglia. The density of innervation of the viscera is low compared with that of skin and deep somatic tissues. This explains the vague spatial resolution of visceral sensation.

Unmyelinated visceral afferents contain several combinations of neuropeptides and, as nociceptive afferents do, may release neuropeptides centrally (to transmit visceral sensory information) and locally (via axon reflexes to produce vascular and secretory changes at the level of the site of stimulation).

Visceral afferents have two functions. They provide input to central structures for conscious sensation of visceral stimuli, and they initiate visceral reflexes. Most visceral afferent information is concerned with unconscious monitoring of the internal milieu and is used to produce reflex adjustments of visceral function through visceral efferents. General visceral afferent signals follow three main routes. Some remain in the peripheral organ to mediate local reflexes, some provide collateral input to autonomic ganglion cells to mediate ganglion reflexes, and some enter the central nervous system at the level of the spinal cord or brain stem.

In the central nervous system, visceral afferents either synapse on second-order neurons that project to higher levels to initiate integrated arousal, autonomic, and humoral responses or synapse (directly or through interneurons) on visceral or somatic motor neurons to initiate visceral-visceral or visceral-somatic reflexes. General visceral afferents may be subdivided into two groups: afferents that enter the central nervous system at the spinal level (Fig. 9-13) and those that enter at the brain stem, or posterior fossa, level (Table 9-6).

Spinal Visceral Afferents

Spinal visceral afferents are carried by *thoracolumbar* (*sympathetic*) and *sacral* (*parasympathetic*) *nerve trunks*. They have an important role in nociceptive (visceral pain) and nonnociceptive visceral sensation and in spinal visceral-somatic and visceral-visceral reflexes (Fig. 9-14). Spinal afferents have their cell bodies in dorsal root ganglia. They pass through the paravertebral ganglia via the sympathetic and sacral parasympathetic nerve trunks and join the spinal roots to enter the spinal cord. The afferents of an organ terminate mainly in one or two segments of the spinal cord, although there is some overlap between afferents from different organs. Some primary afferents may branch peripherally to supply both visceral and somatic structures, and some may enter the spinal cord through the ventral roots.

In the spinal cord, visceral afferents branch extensively to provide divergent input to many dorsal horn neurons and interneurons. They synapse on the so-called *viscerosomatic neurons* in the dorsal horn and intermediate gray matter. These special second-order neurons receive convergent inputs from visceral and somatic afferents.

Visceral sensation is carried mainly via ventrolateral pathways in the spinal cord, including the spinothalamic and spinoreticular pathways, which transmit *visceral pain*, and the spinosolitary and spinomesencephalic pathways, which may activate descending input that inhibits pain transmission in the dorsal horn. Pathways for visceral sensation are

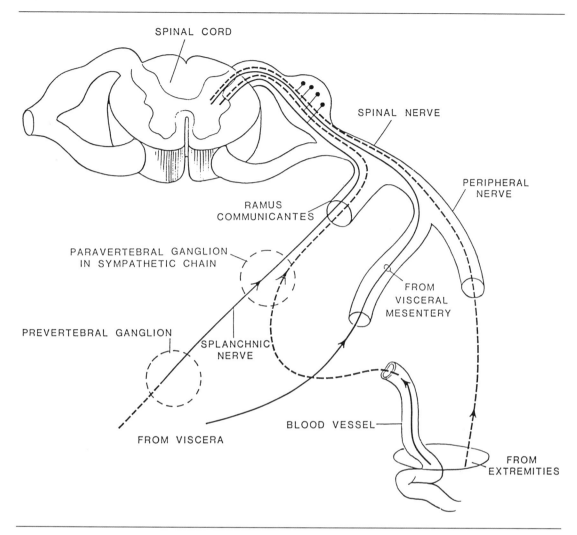

Fig. 9-13. Visceral afferents reach spinal cord by several pathways. Afferents travel directly via peripheral nerves or indirectly through sympathetic paravertebral or prevertebral ganglia, whether coming from the extremities or the viscera.

Table 9-6. Spinal and Brain Stem Visceral Afferents

	Spinal afferents	Brain stem afferents
Nerve trunk	Sympathetic Sacral parasympathetic	Cranial parasympathetic (CN IX and X)
First-order neuron	Dorsal root ganglion	Nodosum ganglion (CN X) Petrosal ganglion (CN IX)
First central relay	Dorsal horn	Nucleus of the tractus solitarius
Mediation of visceral pain	Yes	No
Reflex function	Generally excitatory	Generally inhibitory

CN = cranial nerve.

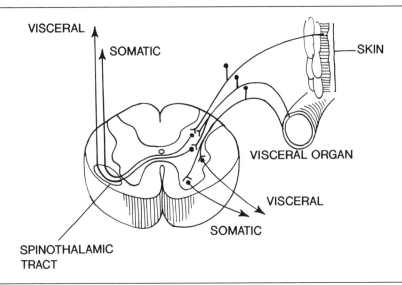

Fig. 9-14. Visceral afferents make multiple spinal cord connections. Local reflexes are mediated via visceral and somatic motor neurons. Synapses with secondary neurons carry information to the brain in association with the spinothalamic tract. Some of the visceral afferents may end on secondary neurons in the somatic sensory system as well, resulting in referred pain.

pathways of the inner tube of the neuraxis. Some information may be carried by the dorsal columns, including sensations related to micturition, defecation, and gastric distention. Visceral sensory input is relayed in the *midline thalamic nuclei* and terminates in the *insular cortex.*

Visceral sensory spinothalamic and spinoreticular pathways send numerous collaterals to the ventral medullary reticular formation, which initiates visceral-visceral and visceral-somatic reflexes and gives rise to descending reticulospinal pathways controlling pain transmission in the dorsal horn, and to brain stem, hypothalamic, and limbic regions to initiate adaptative, affective, autonomic, and neuroendocrine responses.

Spinal visceral afferents have an exclusive role in transmission of *visceral pain.* Visceral pain may be initiated from mechanoreceptors (signaling visceral distention), chemoreceptors, or thermoreceptors; it is relayed centrally, but there is no clear topographic representation of the viscera. Unlike somatic pain, visceral pain is generally vague and poorly localized — being described as abdominal, thoracic, or pelvic rather than being localized to a

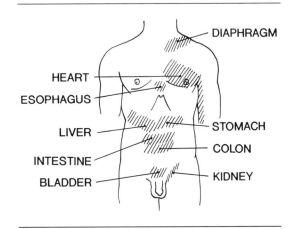

Fig. 9-15. Shading shows dermatomal areas in which pain is felt with disease in visceral organs (referred pain).

specific organ. It commonly activates autonomic and somatic reflex responses. Visceral pain is often referred to overlying or nearby somatic structures; this is called *referred pain* (Fig. 9-15). Referred pain may be due to convergence of visceral and somatic afferents onto a common viscerosomatic neuron pool in the spinal cord.

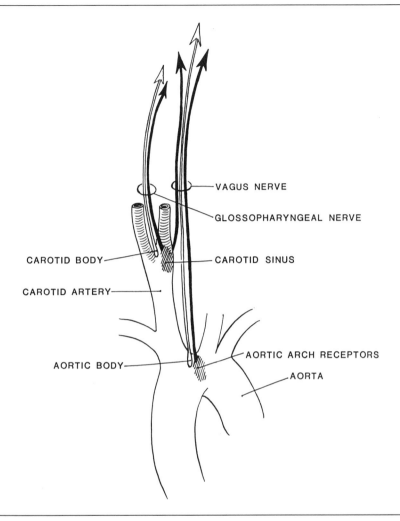

Fig. 9-16. Mechanoreceptors in carotid sinus and aortic arch respond to blood pressure changes. Chemoreceptors in carotid and aortic bodies respond to changes in partial pressure of oxygen and carbon dioxide in the blood.

Brain Stem Visceral Afferents

Brain stem visceral afferents are carried by the vagus and glossopharyngeal nerves. *Vagal afferents*, with cell bodies in the nodose ganglion, carry information from gastrointestinal, tracheobronchial, and cardiopulmonary mechanoreceptors and chemoreceptors and from aortic baroreceptors and chemoreceptors. *Glossopharyngeal afferents*, with cell bodies in the petrosal ganglion, carry input from baroreceptors and chemoreceptors in the carotid sinus and carotid body, respectively (Fig. 9-16). Vagal and glossopharyngeal

afferents relay on the *nucleus of the tractus solitarius*. This nucleus transmits visceral information to other brain stem autonomic nuclei, hypothalamus, amygdala, medial thalamus, and insular cortex.

Vagal and glossopharyngeal afferents initiate several important medullary cardiovascular and respiratory reflexes. Brain stem visceral afferents have a minor role in visceral sensation and do not mediate visceral pain, although they may trigger central pain-controlling mechanisms. Together with taste and trigeminal afferents, brain stem visceral afferents are also important for initiating such automatic motor acts as swallowing, vomiting, and coughing. These complex motor acts involve *central pattern generators* in the lateral reticular formation of the medulla.

Humoral Input

Humoral input to the internal regulation system may arise from the *blood*, the *cerebrospinal fluid*, or the *circumventricular organs*.

Direct Effects of Blood Composition
Changes in blood glucose, blood gases, electrolytes, temperature, osmolarity, and steroid hormones exert influence at all levels of the internal regulation system. For example, the hypothalamus, medulla, and pancreas contain glucoreceptors, and the skin, viscera, spinal cord, brain stem, and hypothalamus contain thermoreceptors. Some chemical stimuli may act only on specific receptors. For example, a decrease in arterial oxygenation activates mainly chemoreceptors in the carotid body. Steroids exert a widespread influence because steroid hormone receptors are widely distributed in the central nervous system.

Composition of the Cerebrospinal Fluid
Changes in pH and partial pressure of carbon dioxide in the cerebrospinal fluid are detected by *central chemosensitive areas* of the ventral surface of the medulla. The cerebrospinal fluid also contains neuropeptides that are released from the hypothalamic-pituitary area and that can exert marked effects throughout the neuraxis.

Circumventricular Organs
Circumventricular organs are specialized structures located in the walls of the ventricles. They characteristically contain fenestrated capillaries and lack a blood-brain barrier (see Chapter 6, The Cerebrospinal Fluid System). Circumventricular organs detect chemical changes in the blood and cerebrospinal fluid and relay this information to the rest of the internal regulation system. For example, the *area postrema* in the walls of the fourth ventricle mediates the emetic effects of dopamine and other substances. Another cir-

cumventricular organ, the *subfornical organ*, located in the anterior wall of the third ventricle immediately below the fornix, mediates the important effects of circulating angiotensin II and natriuretic peptides on blood pressure, thirst, and sodium balance.

Exteroceptive Input

The internal regulation system receives input from sensory pathways and from association areas of the cerebral cortex.

Pain and Temperature
Spinoreticular and trigeminoreticular pathways relay nociceptive and thermal information to central autonomic circuits in the ventral medulla, dorsal pons, periaqueductal gray matter, hypothalamus, and amygdala and initiate suprasegmental somatic-visceral reflexes. Connections with the medial thalamus and limbic cortex are important for the affective component of visceral pain.

Special Somatic Afferents
Visual input reaches the suprachiasmatic nucleus of the hypothalamus and is important in circadian rhythms. Vestibular input, through connections of the vestibular nuclei and the fastigial nucleus of the cerebellum with the area postrema and the nucleus of the tractus solitarius, mediates vomiting and other manifestations of acute vestibular dysfunction.

Taste and Olfaction
Input from the *taste buds* is transmitted via the facial, glossopharyngeal, and, to a lesser extent, vagus nerves to the rostral portion of the nucleus of the tractus solitarius and relayed to the medial thalamus and then to insular cortex. Olfactory input reaches the anterior medial temporal cortex.

Cortical Input
Information relayed to the cerebral cortex by different sensory pathways is integrated in cortical association areas. This highly integrated exteroceptive and interoceptive information is sent by these cortical areas to the *paralimbic areas* of the cerebral cortex, including the *orbitofrontal*, *anterior cingulate*, *insular*, *parahippocampal*, and *temporopolar*

Table 9-7. Comparison Between the General Visceral Efferent System and the General Somatic Efferent System

	Visceral	Somatic
Activity	Tonic, slow, diffuse	Phasic, fast, local
Output	Two neurons (preganglionic and post-ganglionic)	One neuron (alpha motor neuron)
Efferent axon	Small myelinated	Large myelinated
Effector neurotransmitter	Acetylcholine (muscarinic) Norepinephrine (adrenergic)	Acetylcholine (nicotinic)
Effectors		
Type	Heart, smooth muscle, glands	Striated muscle
Spontaneous activity	Yes	No
Effect of denervation	Supersensitivity	Paralysis, atrophy

regions. These regions project to the amygdala and the hypothalamus, which are involved in elaborating the emotional aspects of sensation.

Output of the Internal Regulation System

General Visceral Efferents

General Organization
General visceral efferents are contained in the sympathetic and parasympathetic divisions of the autonomic nervous system. Autonomic influences are more continuous and generalized and have a longer latency and duration than the effects of the somatic efferent system. The differences between the functional organization of the efferent systems are summarized in Table 9-7.

The tonic activity of visceral efferents is due to spontaneous discharge of reticular pacemaker neurons in the brain stem. The visceral output involves a *two-neuron pathway*, with at least one synapse in the *autonomic ganglia*.

Preganglionic Component
The preganglionic neurons occupy the general visceral efferent column of the brain stem and spinal cord. The preganglionic sympathetic neurons are located in the intermediolateral cell column of spinal segments T-1 to L-3 (*thoracolumbar outflow*). The preganglionic parasympathetic neurons are located in the brain stem and in spinal segments S-2 to S-4 (*craniosacral outflow*).

Preganglionic autonomic neurons, similar to somatic motor and branchial motor neurons, originate from the basal plate and use *acetylcholine* as their primary neurotransmitter. Their axons emerge from the brain stem or spinal cord as small myelinated fibers and pass through peripheral nerves to the autonomic ganglia.

Autonomic Ganglia
The peripheral autonomic ganglia are not only synaptic relay stations but also sites of complex interactions affecting the transmission of preganglionic input to postganglionic neurons. Acetylcholine, the neurotransmitter of preganglionic sympathetic and parasympathetic fibers, primarily produces a fast excitation of ganglion neurons via *nicotinic receptors* and slow inhibitory and slow excitatory postsynaptic potentials via *muscarinic receptors*.

Autonomic ganglion neurons, like dorsal root ganglion neurons, originate from the neural crest. Their axons, called *postganglionic fibers*, are *unmyelinated* and contain varicosities from which acetylcholine or norepinephrine is released together with neuropeptides and other cotransmitter agents.

Visceral Plexuses
Visceral plexuses are complex networks of neurons and axons that travel from one area to another. Nearly all these plexuses consist of four main elements: preganglionic parasympathetic efferents, postganglionic sympathetic efferents, primary visceral afferents, and clus-

ters of peripheral sympathetic or parasympathetic ganglion cells.

Autonomic Neurotransmission

The autonomic terminals are varicosities that release neurotransmitter to interact with receptors at specific postjunctional sites and at extrajunctional sites in the membrane.

The primary postganglionic sympathetic neurotransmitter is *norepinephrine*, which acts via different subtypes of *adrenergic receptors*. As an exception, the sympathetic input to sweat glands is mediated by acetylcholine.

Norepinephrine is mainly inactivated through reuptake by presynaptic terminals. Norepinephrine is metabolized by the enzymes monoamine oxidase and catechol-*O*-methyltransferase.

The primary postganglionic parasympathetic neurotransmitter is *acetylcholine*, which acts via different subtypes of *muscarinic* receptors. Acetylcholine is rapidly hydrolyzed by *acetylcholinesterase*. Adrenergic and muscarinic receptors are G-protein–linked receptors that initiate slow onset and relatively persistent electrical and biochemical effects in their targets. In addition to acetylcholine or norepinephrine, postganglionic autonomic terminals release other cotransmitter substances, including adenosine triphosphate (ATP) and neuropeptides.

Modulation of Autonomic Neurotransmission

Autonomic neurotransmission is modulated by inhibitory feedback effects of norepinephrine or acetylcholine acting via presynaptic autoreceptors, effects of neuropeptide cotransmitters, local factors (for example, histamine, serotonin, prostaglandins, and kinins), and circulating hormones.

Sympathetic Outflow

Descending Pathways

Descending inputs to preganglionic sympathetic neurons originate from several sources, particularly the hypothalamus and ventral medulla. These inputs are neurochemically complex — they contain excitatory amino acids, monoamines, and several neuropeptides — and innervate functionally different subsets of preganglionic sympathetic neurons.

The rostral ventrolateral medulla provides the critical input for tonic maintenance of sympathetic vasomotor activity. Descending sympathetic pathways occupy a narrow band in the lateral column of the spinal cord. This input has three main functions: (1) to provide tonic excitation of preganglionic sympathetic neurons, (2) to mediate reflex and adaptive influences on sympathetic activity, and (3) to allow a functionally selective, rather than massive, sympathetic discharge.

Preganglionic Sympathetic Neurons

Preganglionic sympathetic neurons are located in the *intermediolateral cell column of spinal segments T-1 to L-3* (Fig. 9-17). They are organized into different *preganglionic sympathetic functional units* that control specific targets and are under specific control of hypothalamic and brain stem areas.

Preganglionic sympathetic fibers have a segmental organization, but their distribution does not follow the dermatomal pattern of somatic nerves. Thus, preganglionic neurons in spinal segments T-1 to T-2 innervate the head and neck; T-3 to T-6, the upper extremities and thoracic viscera; T-7 to T-11, the abdominal viscera; and T-12 to L-2, the lower extremities and pelvic and perineal organs.

Preganglionic sympathetic axons are myelinated, exit through the ventral roots, and pass via the *white rami communicantes* of the corresponding spinal nerve to reach the *paravertebral sympathetic chain*. At this level, preganglionic fibers may (1) synapse on a postganglionic neuron at the same level, (2) branch and run rostrally and caudally in the sympathetic chain to synapse on a large number of postganglionic neurons, (3) pass through the paravertebral chain without synapsing and form the *splanchnic nerves* that innervate *prevertebral ganglia*, or (4) pass through the chain as splanchnic nerves to innervate the *adrenal medulla* (Fig. 9-18). The adrenal medulla, a homologue of sympathetic ganglia, releases its neurotransmitters, mainly epinephrine, into the bloodstream.

Sympathetic Ganglia

Sympathetic ganglia can be subdivided functionally into two classes: *paravertebral* (or sympathetic trunk) *ganglia* and *prevertebral*

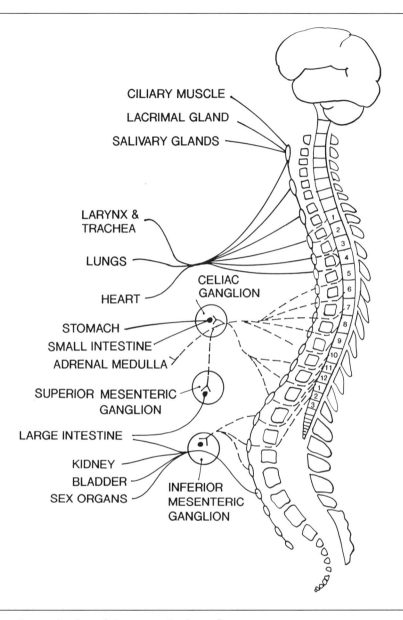

CILIARY MUSCLE

LACRIMAL GLAND

SALIVARY GLANDS

LARYNX & TRACHEA

LUNGS

CELIAC GANGLION

HEART

STOMACH

SMALL INTESTINE

ADRENAL MEDULLA

SUPERIOR MESENTERIC GANGLION

LARGE INTESTINE

KIDNEY

BLADDER

SEX ORGANS

INFERIOR MESENTERIC GANGLION

Fig. 9-17. General organization of the sympathetic outflow system.

(or autonomic plexus) *ganglia* (Table 9-8 and Fig. 9-18).

Paravertebral ganglia provide long postganglionic unmyelinated axons to all sympathetically innervated tissues and organs except those in the abdomen, pelvis, and perineum. These fibers follow three main courses: perivascular, spinal, and visceral.

Perivascular fibers course along arterial trunks and branches. For example, the axons from the superior cervical ganglion (spinal segments T-1 to T-2) provide pupillodilator and sudomotor innervation to the face and follow the course of branches of the internal and external carotid arteries, respectively. Spinal fibers join the peripheral spinal (somatic) nerves via the gray rami communicantes. Thus, the distribution of postganglionic sympathetic fibers is similar to that of the corresponding somatic nerve. For example, axons from the stellate ganglion innervate the upper extremity via branches of the

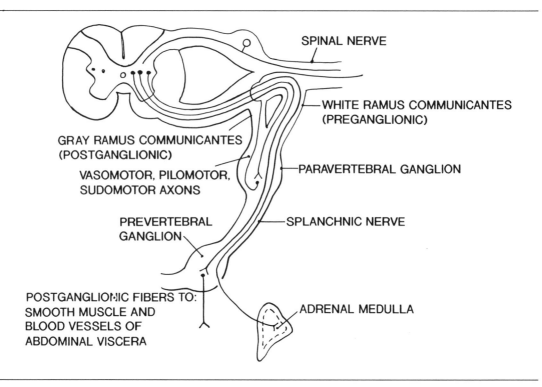

Fig. 9-18. Organization of the prevertebral and paravertebral sympathetic outflow.

brachial plexus. Sympathetic fibers traveling in somatic nerve trunks provide *vasomotor, sudomotor,* and *pilomotor* innervation to the extremities and trunk. Visceral fibers from the lower cervical and upper thoracic ganglia innervate the heart via the cardiac plexus to produce cardiac stimulation or reach the tracheobronchial tree via the pulmonary plexus to produce bronchodilatation.

Prevertebral ganglia are anterior to the abdominal aorta, close to the origin of the celiac and mesenteric arteries, and innervate all abdominal, pelvic, and perineal organs. Their preganglionic inputs are carried by the *splanchnic nerves.* Preganglionic input from spinal segments T-5 to L-2 are carried by the splanchnic nerves, which traverse the diaphragm to enter the *celiac* and *superior mesenteric ganglia.* These ganglia contribute postganglionic sympathetic fibers to the *celiac plexus,* which innervates all abdominal viscera except the descending colon. The celiac plexus also carries the preganglionic in-

put to the adrenal medulla. Sympathetic input produces *splanchnic vasoconstriction, inhibition of secretion and motility of the gut,* and *secretion of epinephrine, renin,* and *glucagon.*

Preganglionic input from spinal segments L-1 to L-3 is carried by the *lumbar splanchnic nerves,* which synapse in the *inferior mesenteric ganglion.* This provides postganglionic input to the *hypogastric plexus,* which innervates the descending colon and pelvic and perineal organs (rectum, bladder, and genitalia). This input *inhibits muscle contractility,* allowing storage of urine and feces, and produces *contraction of the vas deferens.* Thus, this sympathetic input is necessary for *ejaculation.*

Sympathetic Neurotransmission
Norepinephrine is the primary postganglionic sympathetic neurotransmitter in all organs except sweat glands, which receive sympathetic

Table 9-8. Functional Organization of the Sympathetic Outflow

Spinal segment	Ganglion	Pathway	Organ	Effect
PARAVERTEBRAL GANGLION				
T-1	Superior cervical	Perivascular (internal carotid)	Pupil	Dilatation (mydriasis)
T-2	Superior cervical	Perivascular (external carotid)	Facial sweat glands	Sweating Vasoconstriction
T-2 to T-6	Stellate	Gray rami (brachial plexus)	Upper extremity	Vasoconstriction in skin Piloerection Sweating
T-9 to L-1	Lumbosacral	Gray rami (lumbosacral plexus) Perivascular	Lower extremity	Vasodilatation in muscle
T-2 to T-8	Upper thoracic	Cardiac plexus	Heart	Stimulation
		Pulmonary plexus	Tracheobronchial tree	Bronchodilatation
PREVERTEBRAL GANGLION				
T-6 to T-10	Celiac	Celiac plexus	Gastrointestinal tract	Inhibition of peristalsis and secretion
T-11 to L-1	Superior mesenteric	Celiac plexus	Gastrointestinal tract	
T-12 to L-1	Celiac	Celiac plexus	Kidney	Vasoconstriction Renin secretion
T-10 to L-1	Celiac	Celiac plexus	Adrenal gland	Epinephrine secretion
T-12 to L-2	Inferior mesenteric, hypogastric	Hypogastric plexus	Rectum Bladder Sex organs	Retention of feces Retention of urine Ejaculation

cholinergic innervation. Epinephrine released by the adrenal medulla acts as a neurohormone that amplifies sympathetic responses. The effects of norepinephrine and epinephrine are mediated by *alpha-* and *beta-adrenergic receptors*. Alpha receptors mediate constriction of smooth muscle in blood vessels and visceral sphincters. Beta receptors mediate cardiac stimulation, relaxation of visceral smooth muscle and some vascular smooth muscle, and metabolic and endocrine effects (Table 9-9).

Postganglionic sympathetic fibers also release *ATP* and *neuropeptide Y* in addition to *norepinephrine*. Neuropeptide Y is a potent vasoconstrictor; it also modulates noradrenergic transmission by inhibiting presynaptic release and by potentiating postsynaptic effects of norepinephrine.

Parasympathetic Outflow

Cranial Parasympathetic Outflow
Input to cranial parasympathetic nuclei originates in the hypothalamus and the amygdala and descends close to sympathetic pathways in the lateral tegmentum.

The *cranial parasympathetic neurons* are located in the *general visceral efferent column* of the midbrain, pons, and medulla. Their preganglionic axons are components of cranial nerves III, VII, IX, and X (Fig. 9-19). The effects of parasympathetic outputs are summarized in Table 9-10. Parasympathetic output carried in cranial nerve III produces *constriction of the pupil* and *accommodation of the lens*. The output carried in cranial nerves VII and IX stimulates *secretion of lacrimal and salivary glands*.

Table 9-9. Peripheral Autonomic Effects

	Sympathetic		Parasympathetic
	Alpha receptor	Beta receptor	Muscarinic receptor
Heart			
Heart rate		Increases	Decreases
Atrioventricular conduction		Increases	Decreases
Contractility		Increases	Antagonizes
Smooth muscle			
Pupil	Dilatation		Constriction
Lens			Accommodation
Bronchial		Dilatation	Constriction
Gastrointestinal			
Motility		Decreases	Increases
Sphincter		Increases	Decreases
Bladder			
Detrusor		Relaxation	Contraction
Sphincter	Constriction		Relaxation
Sex organs	Ejaculation		Erection
Blood vessels			
Arteries	Constriction (skin, gut, kidney)	Dilatation (muscle, heart)	Dilatation (gut, genital)
Veins	Constriction		
Pilomotor	Contraction		
Glands			
Salivary/lacrimal	Inhibits		Stimulates
Bronchial	Inhibits		Stimulates
Gastrointestinal	Inhibits		Stimulates
Sweat			Stimulates*
Metabolism		Glycogenolysis	Insulin secretion
		Lipolysis	
		Renin secretion	

*Postganglionic *sympathetic fibers* that innervate sweat glands are *cholinergic* axons.

Cranial nerve X, or the *vagus nerve*, provides the most widespread brain stem parasympathetic output. Vagal preganglionic neurons are located in the *dorsal motor nucleus*, which controls respiratory and abdominal viscera, and in the region of the *nucleus ambiguus*, which innervates the heart. The vagus nerve provides input to terminal parasympathetic ganglia located in or near the target organs. Its main effects are *cardioinhibitory*, *visceral motor*, and *secretomotor*. The cardiac vagus exerts a beat-to-beat control of heart rate. The abdominal vagus facilitates the processes of digestion, absorption, and utilization of nutrients. The vagus nerve innervates neuronal plexuses of the enteric nervous system and stimulates (1) esophageal motility, gastric evacuation, and coordinated peristalsis along the gut, (2) secretion of electrolytes and digestive enzymes by the stomach, liver, pancreas, and intestine, and (3) secretion of insulin and other gastrointestinal peptides.

Sacral Parasympathetic Outflow

The preganglionic neurons are located in the lateral gray matter of *spinal segments S-2 to S-4*. Their axons pass via the ventral roots to the *pelvic splanchnic nerves* (nervi erigentes), which join the inferior hypogastric (pelvic) plexus. The sacral parasympathetic system is critical for *defecation, micturition, and erection*.

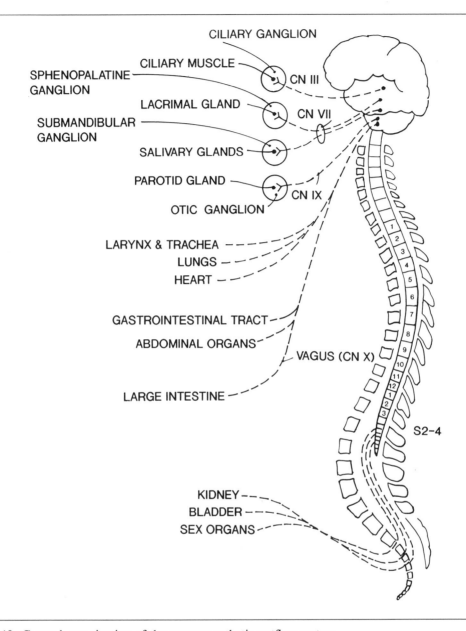

Fig. 9-19. General organization of the parasympathetic outflow system.

Parasympathetic Neurotransmission

Acetylcholine is the primary postganglionic parasympathetic neurotransmitter at all parasympathetic neuroeffector junctions. It acts via different subtypes of *muscarinic receptors* (see Table 9-9). These receptors mediate cardiac inhibition, increased contractility of visceral smooth muscle, relaxation of sphincters and visceral blood vessels, and increased secretion of exocrine glands. Postganglionic cholinergic fibers that innervate the exocrine glands also contain *vasoactive intestinal polypeptide*, a potent vasodilator that potentiates the secretomotor effect of acetylcholine. Postganglionic parasympathetic neurons that innervate smooth muscle may also produce *nitric oxide*, which has a potent vasodilator effect and appears to be critical for erection. Nitric oxide is abundant in intrinsic neurons of the gut.

Table 9-10. Functional Organization of the Parasympathetic Outflow

	Nucleus	Nerve	Ganglion	Effect
Cranial division				
Midbrain	Edinger-Westphal	CN III	Ciliary	Pupilloconstriction
				Accommodation
Pons	Superior salivary	CN VII	Sphenopalatine	Lacrimation
			Submandibular	Salivation (submaxillary and sublingual glands)
Medulla	Inferior salivary	CN IX	Otic	Salivation (parotid gland)
	Dorsal motor	CN X	Near end organs	Bronchoconstriction
				Bronchosecretory
				Gastrointestinal peristalsis and secretion
	Ambiguus	CN X	Near end organs	Decreases heart rate and conduction
Sacral division				
Segments S-2 to S-4	Intermediolateral column	Pelvic Splanchnic	Near end organs	Emptying of bladder and rectum
				Erection

CN = cranial nerve.

Table 9-11. Comparison Between Sympathetic and Parasympathetic Systems

	Sympathetic	Parasympathetic
Function	Energy expenditure, emergency	Protective, restorative
Effect	Generalized, long lasting	Local, short lasting
Preganglionic neuron	Thoracolumbar cord, T-1 to L-3	Cranial nerves III, VII, IX, X Sacral cord, S-2 to S-4
Ganglion	Paravertebral Prevertebral	Near end organ
Preganglionic myelinated fiber	Short	Long
Preganglionic neurotransmitter	Acetylcholine	Acetylcholine
Postganglionic unmyelinated fiber	Long	Short
Distribution	Throughout body	Specific organs
Innervation of limbs	Yes	No
Postganglionic neurotransmitter	Norepinephrine (except in sweat glands)	Acetylcholine
Receptors	Alpha- and beta-adrenergic	Muscarinic
Neurotransmitter inactivation	Slow	Fast
Cotransmitter	Neuropeptide Y	Vasoactive intestinal polypeptide
	ATP	ATP

Functional Aspects of Autonomic Control of Visceral Function

The sympathetic outflow responds to stress and facilitates the expenditure of energy. It is particularly active during emotion, fear, cold, exercise, and pain. The parasympathetic outflow, on the other hand, promotes restoration and conservation of energy stores and is most active during rest and sleep (Table 9-11).

The sympathetic system may be widely activated; it has widespread influence and relatively long-lasting effects, especially during *fight* or *flight reactions*. The parasympathetic system has more discrete, localized, and shorter lasting effects. The widespread effects of the sympathetic system may be explained by the considerable divergent output of the preganglionic neurons and by the amplification effects of circulating epinephrine. Also, the longer duration of sympathetic responses may be due to the slower inactivation of norepinephrine by reuptake and metabolism, as compared with the rapid inactivation of acetylcholine by acetylcholinesterase.

Most visceral organs have a dual sympathetic and parasympathetic control. However, peripheral blood vessels, pilomotor muscles, sweat glands, and the spleen receive only sympathetic innervation. Parasympathetic control predominates in the salivary glands, sinoatrial node, and gastrointestinal tract. Sympathetic-parasympathetic interactions are not simply antagonistic but functionally complementary. For example, parasympathetically mediated erection is complemented by sympathetically mediated ejaculation. The interactions between the sympathetic and parasympathetic systems may occur at the level of the central nervous system, autonomic ganglia, neuroeffector junction, or target organ.

Visceral Effectors

The autonomic effectors include the specialized and contractile tissue of the heart, the smooth muscle, and the glandular epithelia. Smooth muscle and cardiac muscles, unlike striated muscle, exhibit the properties of *automatism*, *adaptation*, and *intramural conduction*. Automatism is the ability to sustain rhythmic contractions in the absence of innervation and is due to generation of impulses by a pacemaker area. This activity tends to spread to other cells, may shift from one region to another, and is affected by autonomic neurotransmitters, local conditions (temperature, pH, and ion concentration), local neurochemicals, and circulating hormones. Adaptation is the ability of smooth muscle to modify its rhythmicity and contractility in response to mechanical factors, such as stretch or distention of an organ. Intramural conduction involves transmission of electrical input between syncytial fibers through gap junctions (as in the heart and blood vessels) or through local intramural connections (as in the gut).

Whereas the main consequences of dener-

vation in striated muscle are paralysis and atrophy, most autonomic effectors develop *denervation supersensitivity* in response to postganglionic denervation. Denervation supersensitivity is the exaggerated response to the specific neurotransmitter. This phenomenon is clinically important because it indicates a postganglionic lesion.

Humoral Output of the Internal Regulation System

In addition to the fast, short-lasting influences mediated through the autonomic output, the internal regulation system produces longer latency and more prolonged responses via humoral output. This output arises from two main sources: the *hypothalamic-pituitary axis* and the *peripheral endocrine organs*.

Hypothalamic-Pituitary Axis

The neuroendocrine, or humoral, output of the hypothalamus is mediated through two neurosecretory systems: the *magnocellular hypothalamohypophyseal system*, which produces *vasopressin* and *oxytocin*, and the *parvocellular tuberoinfundibular system*, which produces *releasing factors* and *inhibiting factors* (regulatory hormones) that regulate anterior pituitary function.

Peripheral Endocrine Organs

Autonomic and pituitary outputs affect the function of peripheral endocrine organs, including the thyroid gland, endocrine pancreas, juxtaglomerular apparatus of the kidney (renin secretion), steroid-producing endocrine glands (adrenal cortex and gonads), and peptide-producing endocrine cells of the gastrointestinal tract. All these peripheral humoral mediators may exert direct effects on target organs, produce local modulation of target responses to autonomic inputs, and influence central neural structures.

Somatic Motor Output

The internal regulation system has important connections with the motor system at all levels of the neuraxis. At the supratentorial level, connections of the lateral hypothalamus and the amygdala with the ventral striatum are important for complex motor behavior. At the posterior fossa level, connections between the nucleus of the tractus solitarius and the central pattern generators of the medullary reticular formation coordinate cranial nerve motor neurons involved in vomiting and respiration. At the spinal level, hypothalamic and brain stem inputs may affect somatic motor respiratory and sphincter motor neurons.

Input-Output Integration in the Internal Regulation System

The most characteristic feature of the internal regulation system is the interactions between visceral sensory, humoral, and somatic sensory inputs and visceral motor (autonomic), endocrine, and behavioral outputs. This interaction occurs at all levels, particularly in the hypothalamus, brain stem, and spinal cord.

Hypothalamic Level

The *paraventricular nucleus* of the hypothalamus is an important output region and is critical for homeostasis and integrated responses to stress. It receives visceral sensory input from the nucleus of the tractus solitarius and the ventrolateral medulla, humoral input from the subfornical organ, and somatic sensory input via spinothalamic pathways or connections with the limbic lobe. The paraventricular nucleus initiates integrated responses to stress. It contains (1) magnocellular neurons that secrete vasopressin and thus regulate water balance, (2) parvocellular neurons that secrete corticotropin-releasing hormone, which stimulates the pituitary-adrenal axis and thus controls glucose metabolism and immune function, (3) central autonomic neurons that project to visceral motor nuclei of the brain stem and spinal cord, and (4) neurons that project to the dorsal horn of the spinal cord to inhibit pain transmission.

Brain Stem Level

The medulla is the site of reflex mechanisms critical for control of respiration and circulation. Medullary reflex circuits have several general features. The *afferent limb* of cardiovascular and respiratory reflexes mediated by the medulla involves input from cardiovascular and pulmonary mechanoreceptors and chemoreceptors carried by the vagus and glossopharyngeal nerves and integrated in the nucleus of the tractus solitarius. The *efferent limb* is mediated by vasomotor, cardiovagal, or respiratory neurons in ventrolateral medulla and their corresponding spinal outputs. Interneurons in the intermediate medullary reticular formation coordinate the interactions between the nucleus tractus solitarius and neurons in ventrolateral medulla. Vasomotor, cardiovagal, and respiratory medullary neurons form an integrated *cardiorespiratory network*, which is coordinated by local interneurons. Medullary cardiovascular and respiratory neurons are affected by humoral influences, including blood-borne chemicals that act on chemoreceptors in the *area postrema*, a circumventricular organ in the floor of the fourth ventricle. Also, changes in the pH of the cerebrospinal fluid are detected by neurons in the *central chemosensitive zone* of the ventral surface of the medulla. Finally, medullary reflexes may be affected by influences from the hypothalamus and amygdala, which may inhibit or facilitate these reflexes during complex adaptive responses such as exercise and emotion.

Spinal Level

Preganglionic sympathetic neurons are organized into different sympathetic functional units. These include skin vasomotor, muscle vasomotor, visceral motor, pilomotor, and sudomotor units. Therefore, preganglionic neurons do not discharge massively but control specific targets. Thus, instead of there being a generalized sympathetic tone, there is coordinated activity of specific subsets of sympathetic neurons. For example, the sympathetic response to life-threatening conditions includes vasoconstriction in the skin and splanchnic vessels, vasodilatation in skeletal muscle, piloerection, sweating, and release of epinephrine. This is different from the response to a change in posture from supine to standing, which includes predominantly vasoconstriction in skeletal muscle and to a lesser extent in skin but no release of epinephrine, pupil dilatation, or piloerection. In humans, sympathetic nerve activity in skeletal muscle is finely regulated by baroreflex activity, whereas sympathetic activity in the skin is regulated mainly by environmental temperature and emotional state.

Preganglionic sympathetic motor neurons differ from somatic motor neurons in several important respects: (1) the preganglionic neurons are organized symmetrically and control ipsilateral targets, except those innervating prevertebral ganglia that control the intestine and pelvic viscera, (2) there may be functional asymmetry, for example, preganglionic neurons on the right side of the upper thoracic cord control heart rate, whereas those on the left side control cardiac contractility, and (3) preganglionic neurons are segmentally organized, but a given sympathetic ganglion receives preganglionic input from several segments.

Activity of preganglionic sympathetic neurons depends on supraspinal and segmental inputs. Several parallel pathways descending from the hypothalamus and brain stem exert specific modulatory influences on selective populations of preganglionic neurons. This is critical for their coordinated action. Preganglionic neurons are the efferent limb of various sympathetic reflexes. These reflexes are triggered by skin, muscle, or visceral afferents that are in dorsal roots and that generally stimulate preganglionic neurons through local interneurons. The segmental reflexes are controlled by suprasegmental input. For example, innocuous stimulation of the skin or distention of the bladder in normal subjects produces minimal change in preganglionic activity. However, in patients with lesions at a high level in the spinal cord in which descending pathways are interrupted, innocuous stimuli trigger massive sympathetic excitation, including intense sweating, muscle and skin vasoconstriction, tachycardia, and hypertension.

Preganglionic parasympathetic neurons are restricted to spinal segments S-2 to S-4. They innervate the colon, bladder, and sexual organs. Their function involves reciprocal interactions with sacral somatic motor neurons that innervate the sphincters and pelvic floor muscles. Parasympathetic neurons are *excited*, whereas sphincter somatic motor neurons are *inhibited* during micturition and defecation. The opposite occurs during times of storage of urine and feces.

Specific Circuits

Control of the Pupil

The diameter of the pupil is controlled by the balanced activity of two sets of muscles: the *constrictor muscle*, a circular band of muscle fibers, and the *dilator muscle*, a radial band of muscle fibers. The *constrictor muscle* is innervated by the *parasympathetic system*, and the *dilator muscle* is innervated by the *sympathetic system*. Pupillary constriction is called *miosis*, and pupillary dilatation is *mydriasis*.

Parasympathetic Pathway

The parasympathetic pathway for pupillary constriction is a two-neuron system. Preganglionic axons from the *Edinger-Westphal nucleus* of the midbrain are carried in the *oculomotor nerve* and relay in the *ciliary ganglion* in the orbit. Postganglionic neurons innervate the constrictor (and the ciliary muscle) via the *short ciliary nerves*.

Sympathetic Pathway

The sympathetic pathway for pupillary dilatation is a three-neuron system. The first neuron is located in the *hypothalamus* and projects through the *dorsal longitudinal fasciculus*. The second neuron is a preganglionic sympathetic neuron in the *ciliospinal center* in the intermediolateral cell column at spinal levels T-1 and T-2. Preganglionic axons enter the sympathetic chain and ascend in the sympathetic trunk to synapse on a third (or postganglionic) neuron, which is in the *superior cervical ganglion*. Postganglionic fibers follow the course of the internal carotid artery and ophthalmic artery to innervate the dilator muscle through the *long ciliary nerves*.

Pupillary Reflexes

Unlike other smooth muscles, pupillary constrictors and dilators do not demonstrate automatic activity in the absence of innervation. The size of the pupil is a function of the relative activity of parasympathetic and sympathetic influences (Fig. 9-20).

The pathway for pupillary constriction is activated by either stimulation with light (*light reflex*) or near vision (*accommodation*). The pathway for the light reflex is discussed

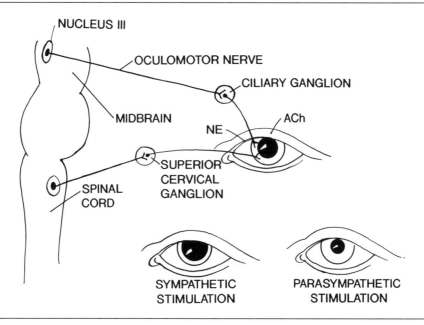

Fig. 9-20. Effects of sympathetic and parasympathetic activity on pupil size. (*ACh* = acetylcholine; *NE* = norepinephrine.)

further in Chapter 15 (The Posterior Fossa Level). Briefly, it involves afferents in the optic pathway, a synapse in the midbrain, excitatory input to the Edinger-Westphal nucleus, and efferent axons to the constrictor muscle via the oculomotor nerve and ciliary ganglion. Decussation of the pathway allows stimulation of either eye to produce both an *ipsilateral*, or *direct*, *response* and a *contralateral*, or *consensual*, *response*. The *accommodation reflex* is integrated at the level of the oculomotor nucleus and consists of *miosis, gaze convergence,* and *increased curvature of the lens.* Pretectal lesions may result in lack of pupillary response to light but spare pupillary constriction with accommodation.

The pathway for pupillary dilatation is activated mainly by the hypothalamus. The *ciliospinal reflex* consists of pupillary dilatation evoked by noxious cutaneous stimulation, such as pinching the face or neck.

Cardiovascular Control

The autonomic nervous system controls cardiac output and peripheral resistance through its effects on the heart, peripheral vessels, and circulating hormones such as vasopressin and angiotensin II.

Parasympathetic Control

Parasympathetic control of the heart is exerted primarily by neurons in the region of the *nucleus ambiguus* of the medulla and is carried by the vagus nerve. The vagal innervation of the heart decreases heart rate, delays atrioventricular conduction, and antagonizes the stimulating sympathetic effects of myocardial contractility. Vagal influence on the sinus node predominates over that of the sympathetic innervation and allows control of heart rate on a beat-to-beat basis. Vagal effects on heart rate vary during the respiratory cycle and are less marked during inspiration than expiration. This results in inspiratory tachycardia and expiratory bradycardia, known as *respiratory sinus arrhythmia*. This is an important index of cardiovagal function.

Sympathetic Control

Sympathetic output controls the heart and the blood vessels. Basal sympathetic vasomotor activity originates primarily from *rostral ventrolateral medulla*. Sympathetic output produces (1) increase in heart rate, atrioventricular conduction, and cardiac contractility via beta receptors, (2) constriction of blood vessels in the skin, kidney, and abdomen via alpha receptors, and (3) dilatation of cardiac and skeletal muscle blood vessels via beta receptors. Constriction of abdominal blood vessels is very important in preventing a decrease in arterial pressure while changing from a supine to a standing position (orthostatic hypotension). Humoral mechanisms, including vasopressin and the renin-angiotensin-aldosterone system, allow longer lasting control of arterial pressure.

Cardiovascular Reflexes

Cardiovascular control centers in the medulla are regulated primarily by two types of influences: by hypothalamic and other descending inputs and by various cardiovascular reflexes integrated at the medullary level. Cardiovascular reflexes include the *arterial baroreflex*, *arterial chemoreflex*, and *cardiopulmonary reflexes*. They originate from mechanoreceptors or chemoreceptors in the carotid sinus, aortic arch, and cardiac atria and ventricles. Baroceptor and chemoreceptor inputs from the carotid sinus or the aortic arch are carried to their first central relay station (second neuron), the *nucleus of the tractus solitarius*, by afferent branches of the glossopharyngeal and vagus nerves. The cell bodies of these afferents are in the petrosal and nodose ganglia. Inputs from cardiac receptors are carried by either vagal or spinal (sympathetic trunk) afferents. All cardiovascular medullary reflexes are mediated directly or indirectly through the connections of the nucleus of the tractus solitarius with the cardiovagal and sympathoexcitatory neurons in ventrolateral medulla. The arterial baroreflex is a critical buffering mechanism for preventing fluctuations of arterial pressure. This reflex is responsible for rapid adjustments of arterial pressure when adopting erect posture. The carotid sinus and aortic baroreceptors are stimulated by an increase in arterial pressure. Baroreceptor stimulation excites the nucleus of the tractus solitarius, which in turn stimulates cardiovagal neurons and inhibits vasomotor neurons. This produces reflex bradycardia and vasodilatation and a decrease of arterial pressure to basal level. On the contrary, a decrease in arterial pressure decreases baroreceptor activity, which results in compensatory tachycardia and vasoconstriction.

Thermoregulation

Changes in body temperature are detected by thermoreceptors in the skin, viscera, spinal cord, brain stem, and, most important, in the hypothalamus. Two regions of the hypothalamus have a major role in thermoregulation: the *preoptic-anterior hypothalamic area* and the *posterior hypothalamic area*. The preoptic-anterior hypothalamic area contains sensor neurons that detect changes in blood temperature and initiate responses leading to heat loss, for example, skin vasodilatation and sweating. The posterior hypothalamic region may integrate the thermoregulatory "set point" and be involved in responses leading to heat gain, such as vasoconstriction and shivering. There are several effector mechanisms for thermoregulatory control: (1) somatic motor (shivering and behavior in response to thermal discomfort), (2) humoral-metabolic (increased basal metabolism and lipolysis), and (3) autonomic (mainly via effectors in the skin).

Sympathetic innervation of the skin is important in thermoregulation. It includes adrenergic vasoconstrictor, cholinergic sudomotor, adrenergic pilomotor, and vasodilator efferents. The most important effects are regulation of blood flow in the skin and sweating. Exposure to cold temperatures produces skin vasoconstriction (pallor) and piloerection, whereas warm temperatures elicit sweating and vasodilatation. Thermoregulatory sweating is mediated by sympathetic cholinergic muscarinic innervation of the eccrine sweat glands. Emotional stimuli (fear, anxiety) and severe decrease in arterial pressure (as in shock) activate vasoconstrictor and sudomotor fibers, resulting in cold, clammy skin.

Control of the Bladder

The control of bladder function is integrated at spinal, posterior fossa, and supratentorial levels.

Spinal Level

At the spinal level, the control of the bladder is exerted via the sacral parasympathetic, lumbar sympathetic, and sacral somatic outputs (Table 9-12 and Fig. 9-21). The *sacral parasympathetic*

Table 9-12. Innervation of the Bladder

Division	Spinal level	Nerve	Neurotransmitter	Receptor	Mechanism	Effect
Parasympathetic	S-2 to S-4	Pelvic	Acetylcholine	Muscarinic	Contraction of detrusor	Bladder emptying
					Relaxation of sphincter	Bladder emptying
Sympathetic	T-11 to L-2	Hypogastric	Norepinephrine	Beta	Relaxation of detrusor	Retention of urine
				Alpha	Contraction of bladder neck	Retention of urine
Somatic	S-2 to S-4	Pudendal	Acetylcholine	Nicotinic	Contraction of external sphincter	Retention of urine

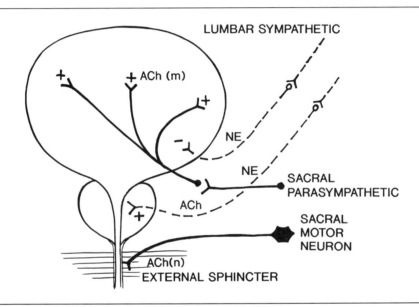

Fig. 9-21. Innervation of the bladder. (*ACh* = acetylcholine; *NE* = norepinephrine; (*n*) = nicotinic receptors; (*m*) = muscarinic receptors.)

output (spinal segments S-2 to S-4), carried via the *pelvic nerve*, is mediated by *muscarinic cholinergic receptors* in the bladder and promotes *bladder emptying*, or *micturition*, by activating the bladder detrusor muscle and relaxing the bladder neck. Sacral parasympathetic mechanisms are critical for bladder function. Lesions of the sacral cord or the cauda equina abolish the micturition reflex. Muscarinic blockade produces urinary retention.

The *lumbar sympathetic output* (spinal segments T-11 to L-2), carried by the hypogastric nerves, produces both relaxation of the detrusor muscle (beta receptors) and contraction of the bladder neck, or internal sphincter (alpha receptors). These actions favor storage of urine. Sympathectomy, unlike parasympathetic denervation, does not significantly affect bladder function.

The *sacral somatic motor output* (motor neurons in spinal segments S-2 to S-4), carried by the pudendal nerve, stimulates the external sphincter via *nicotinic cholinergic receptors* and also promotes urine storage.

Posterior Fossa Level

The *micturition centers* are located in the pons and include at least two different regions: a

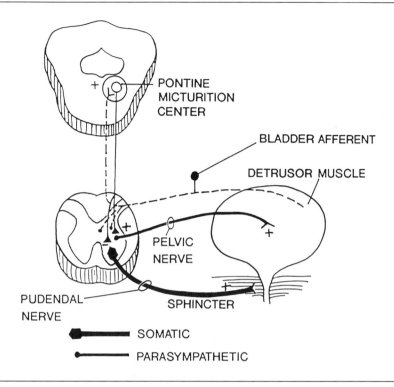

Fig. 9-22. Micturition reflex pathways.

medial region that gives rise to excitatory input to sacral parasympathetic (micturition) neurons and a lateral region that sends excitatory input to sacral somatic motor neurons (sphincter motor neurons) (Fig. 9-22). During micturition, the medial region is activated and inhibits the lateral region. Thus, sacral preganglionic neurons are activated, and sphincter motor neurons are inhibited. This activity produces coordinated bladder contraction and sphincter relaxation, resulting in bladder emptying. Interruption of descending pathways from the pontine micturition centers to the sacral cord, as in cases of spinal cord lesions, may produce incoordinated activity of these effectors, or *detrusor-sphincter dyssynergia*.

Supratentorial Level
Activity of the micturition centers is controlled by input from the hypothalamus and the medial frontal cortex. Cortical input is responsible for voluntary control of the initiation and the cessation of micturition. This control may be interrupted by lesions involv-

ing the medial frontal lobes, for example, hydrocephalus and tumors. The result is involuntary micturition that is referred to as *uninhibited bladder.*

Reflex Control of the Bladder
Reflex control of the bladder is initiated by input from volume and tension receptors in the muscular wall and carried by the pelvic nerve (spinal segments S-2 to S-4), pain receptors in the submucosa of the base of the bladder and carried by the hypogastric nerve (spinal segments L-1 to L-3), and muscle proprioceptors in the external sphincter and pelvic floor carried by the pudendal nerve (spinal segments S-2 to S-4) (see Fig. 9-22).

If the neuraxis is intact, micturition primarily involves a supraspinal spinopontospinal reflex that is triggered by stimulation of tension receptors and that is responsible for the coordinated activity of the detrusor and sphincter muscles. If the suprasegmental pathways are interrupted, micturition occurs via segmental spinospinal sacral reflexes that are triggered by perineal or nociceptive stimulation, but bladder and sphincter contractions are not well coordinated (detrusor-sphincter dyssynergia).

Lumbar sympathetic neurons mediate visceral-sympathetic reflexes that are inhibitory. Afferent fibers that are activated by low increases in bladder pressure enter the sacral cord, ascend to the lumbar cord, and stimulate sympathetic efferents that inhibit the detrusor muscle and activate the bladder neck. This promotes *continence*.

In summary, during storage of urine, bladder distention triggers low-level firing of bladder afferents. This stimulates sympathetic outflow, causing contraction of the bladder outlet and inhibition of the detrusor, and pudendal (somatic motor) outflow to the external sphincter. These *spinal guarding reflexes* preserve *continence*. At the onset of micturition, intense activity in bladder afferents activates the pontine micturition center, which simultaneously activates the detrusor and inhibits the spinal guarding reflexes, thus favoring *bladder emptying*.

Reproductive Function

The control of reproductive function includes behavioral, hormonal, and autonomic mechanisms. Sexual and reproductive functions involve interactions among paralimbic, limbic, preoptic-hypothalamic, brain stem, and spinal autonomic centers. The preoptic-anterior hypothalamic region is *sexually dimorphic* (larger in men) and controls sex behavior and release of gonadotropins. In contrast, the arcuate nucleus exerts a tonic, dopamine-mediated inhibition of prolactin release. Both regions are targets of feedback regulation by sex hormones. The autonomic control of sex organs is mediated by the pelvic plexus. In men, sacral parasympathetic output is critical for erection. This involves relaxation of erectile tissue and vasodilatation; these effects may be mediated by nitric oxide or vasoactive intestinal polypeptide (or both) released from parasympathetic neurons. Lumbar sympathetic input produces an alpha-adrenergic-mediated contraction of the vas deferens, which is necessary for ejaculation. In women, parasympathetic input produces increased vaginal secretion and engorgement of the cli-

toris, whereas sympathetic input facilitates contraction of the cervix and vagina.

Enteric Nervous System

The *enteric nervous system* is a separate division of the autonomic nervous system. It contains a large number of neurons located in the submucosal plexus and the myenteric plexus in the wall of the gut. These plexuses include afferent (sensory) neurons that are stimulated by intestinal distention, excitatory and inhibitory interneurons, and motor neurons. Excitatory and inhibitory motor neurons coordinate peristalsis along the gut. Secretory motor neurons control gastrointestinal exocrine secretions. These neurons contain several neuropeptides in various combinations in addition to acetylcholine, gamma-aminobutyric acid, ATP, and nitric oxide. Enteric neurons are controlled by the vagus and the prevertebral sympathetic ganglia. Prevertebral ganglia are the site of integration of preganglionic, primary visceral, and enteric sensory inputs. Prevertebral reflexes are stimulated by intestinal distention. Input from enteric cholinergic and primary afferent (peptidergic) axons stimulates noradrenergic ganglion cells, which in turn inhibit myenteric motor neurons, thus providing feedback to reduce the mechanosensitivity of the gut.

Clinical Correlations

Diseases involving the internal regulation system may produce (1) level-specific syndromes, (2) isolated disorders of a particular autonomic effector, or (3) diffuse autonomic failure.

Level-Specific Syndromes

Supratentorial Level
Seizures originating in temporal or frontal limbic and paralimbic areas may produce vegetative auras (olfactory or gastric sensations), autonomic phenomena (tachycardia, pallor or flushing, pupillary dilatation), emotions (anxiety or fear), or complex motor automatisms. Hypothalamic disorders produce complex autonomic and neuroendocrine disturbances that are associated with abnormal thermoreg-

Table 9-13. Large Dilated Pupil

	Preganglionic	Postganglionic	Pharmacologic blockade
Cause	Lesion of oculomotor nerve	Lesion of ciliary ganglion	Muscarinic blockade
Direct light reflex	No	No	No
Consensual reflex	No	No	No
Contralateral eye reflexes	Yes	Yes	Yes
Response to muscarinic agonists (pilocarpine)			
Low dose	No	Yes	No
High dose	Yes	Yes	No

ulation, osmolarity, and food intake. The hypothalamus exerts a tonic inhibitory control on the secretion of prolactin. Thus, lesions that interrupt hypothalamic-pituitary connections produce *hyperprolactinemia*, with galactorrhea, amenorrhea, and infertility. Secreting pituitary tumors may produce hyperprolactinemia, gigantism, and hypercorticalism. Pituitary or hypothalamic lesions may also produce *pituitary insufficiency*. Insufficient secretion of vasopressin (antidiuretic hormone) produces *diabetes insipidus*. Excessive secretion of this hormone produces the *syndrome of inappropriate release of antidiuretic hormone.*

Brain Stem Level

Brain stem lesions may produce life-threatening disorders affecting respiration (sleep apnea) or cardiovascular disorders (paroxysmal hypertension, intractable hypotension, or cardiac arrhythmias).

Spinal Level

Lesions of the upper spinal cord may interrupt bulbospinal pathways for tonic autonomic control, thus producing respiratory arrest, hypotension, absence of sweating, and urinary retention. Chronic spinal lesions may result in autonomic hyperreflexia, because of lack of modulation by structures above the spinal level.

Peripheral Level

Interruption of either preganglionic or postganglionic output may produce localized or generalized failure of autonomic effectors. An important aspect of peripheral lesions is the development of denervation supersensitivity, which may be useful in localizing the lesion.

Output-Specific Syndromes

Pupil

A unilateral, large pupil commonly results from underactivity of *ipsilateral parasympathetic outflow.* The lesion may occur at the level of the preganglionic neuron (oculomotor nerve), the postganglionic nerve (ciliary ganglion), or receptor (muscarinic blockade) (Table 9-13).

A unilateral small pupil is commonly due to underactivity of the *ipsilateral sympathetic outflow.* Miosis is commonly associated with ptosis (lid droop due to sympathetic denervation of the tarsal muscle) and facial anhydrosis (loss of sweating), a combination known as *Horner's syndrome* (Table 9-14). This syndrome can be caused by (1) central lesions that involve the hypothalamospinal pathway, (2) preganglionic lesions (for example, compression of the sympathetic chain by a tumor in the apex of the lung), or (3) postganglionic lesions at the level of the internal carotid plexus (for example, a tumor in the cavernous sinus).

Cardiovascular Circuits

Baroreceptor dysfunction may produce severe hypertension, arterial pressure fluctuations, or syncope. Lesions involving cardiovascular regulatory centers, descending vasomotor pathways to the spinal cord, or peripheral sympathetic fibers cause *orthostatic hypoten-*

Table 9-14. Unilateral Horner's Syndrome

	Lesion		
	Central pathway for pupillary dilatation	Preganglionic	Postganglionic
Facial sweating	Abnormal	Abnormal	Normal
Response to drugs inhibiting norepinephrine uptake (cocaine)	No or variable	No	No
Response to drugs causing release of norepinephrine (methamphetamine)	Yes	Yes	No
Supersensitivity to sympathetic agonists	No	No	Yes
Example of lesion	Dorsolateral medulla	Stellate ganglion	Cavernous sinus

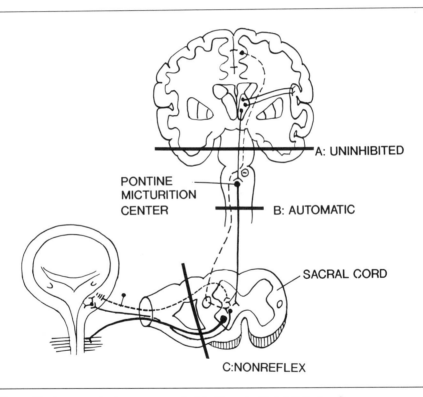

Fig. 9-23. Sites of lesions producing neurogenic bladder. A. Uninhibited reflex bladder. B. Automatic reflex bladder. C. Nonreflex bladder.

sion, a severely disabling symptom of autonomic failure.

Thermoregulation

Sympathetic denervation may produce warm, dry skin, whereas sympathetic hyperactivity produces coldness and sweating. Diffuse sudomotor failure may result in intolerance to heat.

Bladder

Disturbances at different levels of the system for bladder control result in the development of *neurogenic bladder* (Fig. 9-23). Two types of neurogenic bladder occur: *reflex*, or *upper motor neuron type*, and *nonreflex*, or *lower motor neuron type*. The terms *reflex* and *nonreflex* denote presence or absence, respectively, of bulbocavernous and anal reflexes (Table 9-15).

Table 9-15. Neurogenic Bladder

| | Bladder type | | | | |
| | Reflex (upper motor neuron) | | Nonreflex (lower motor neuron) | | |
	Uninhibited	Automatic	Autonomic	Motor	Sensory
Initiate voiding	Normal	Decreased	Decreased	Decreased	Normal
Inhibit voiding	Decreased	Decreased	Decreased	Decreased	Decreased
Incontinence	Yes	Yes	Yes	Yes	Yes
Retention	No	Yes	Yes	Yes	Yes
Sensation	Normal	Decreased	Decreased	Normal	Decreased
Anal and bulbocavernous reflexes	Yes	Yes	No	No	No
Examples of lesions	Hydrocephalus	Spinal cord lesion (trauma)	Cauda equina lesion	Motor nerve roots	Dorsal root ganglia, sensory nerve roots (tabes dorsalis)

The two types of reflex bladders include *uninhibited bladder* and *automatic bladder. Uninhibited bladder* occurs with lesions of the medial frontal cortex and is associated with urinary incontinence but not retention, because of preservation of detrusor-sphincter synergy. *Automatic bladder* occurs with lesions of the spinal cord that interrupt the pathway from the pontine micturition centers. Automatic bladder is associated with urgency, frequency, incontinence, urinary retention, and detrusor-sphincter dyssynergia. Nonreflex type of neurogenic bladder, such as occurs with lesions of the cauda equina, is characterized by urinary retention and overflow incontinence.

Sexual Function

Hypothalamic-pituitary dysfunction may produce amenorrhea, impotence, or infertility. Impotence is also a common manifestation of generalized autonomic failure, lower spinal cord lesions, and peripheral autonomic nerve disease.

Gastrointestinal Function

Dysfunction of the enteric nervous system may result in protracted vomiting, impairment of gastric evacuation, diarrhea, or severe constipation.

Generalized Autonomic Failure

Generalized autonomic failure affects pupillary, cardiovascular, sweating, bladder, sexual, and gastrointestinal functions in several combinations and may occur as a manifestation of central or peripheral lesions. Central lesions occur in neurodegenerative disorders that affect preganglionic autonomic neurons and occasionally sphincter motor neurons and respiratory circuits. Peripheral lesions involve autonomic ganglia or, more commonly, small unmyelinated postganglionic fibers, as in diabetes.

Examination of Visceral Function

The internal regulation system affects all major organ systems via both visceral motor and humoral outputs. The function of each effector system is described above. A number of visceral functions are mediated by cranial nerves and are considered in detail in Chapter 15 (The Posterior Fossa Level). A limited but important number of specific functions should be tested as part of the neurologic history and examination of visceral function.

Clinical Evaluation

The clinical evaluation of the internal regulation system should include appropriate inquiry into a history of autonomic symptoms and examination of autonomic function in each of the areas listed below.

Pupil

Because the size and symmetry of the pupils and their reaction to light depend on the balance of sympathetic and parasympathetic inputs, these features should be carefully noted. Normal pupils are equal in size (2–4 mm in diameter) and react briskly to light in either eye.

Cardiovascular Function

Pulse and blood pressure in supine and standing positions can reflect alterations in neural input and must be part of each examination. A pronounced decrease in arterial pressure when the patient is standing, called *orthostatic hypotension*, particularly when not associated with compensatory increase in heart rate, indicates a dysfunction in the afferent, central, or efferent components of the baroreceptor reflex. Lack of heart rate variability with deep respiration (respiratory sinus arrhythmia) indicates failure of the vagal control of the heart.

Thermoregulation

Skin temperature and sweating are controlled by the sympathetic fibers. A search should be made for the localized absence of sweating, asymmetrical skin temperature or color, and absence of normal oral and conjunctival moisture.

Bladder

The clinical evaluation of neurogenic bladder includes (1) assessment of the ability to voluntarily control initiation or interruption of micturition and bladder sensation, (2) examination of reflexes integrated at the level of the conus medullaris and mediated by sensory and motor roots in the cauda equina (the *bulbocavernous* and *anal reflexes*, which are somatic reflexes integrated at spinal levels S-2 to S-4, and the *scrotal* and *internal anal reflexes*, which are autonomic reflexes integrated at spinal levels S-2 to S-4 and T-12 to L-2, respectively), (3) evaluation of perianal sensation, and (4) quantitation of residual volume, either by palpation and percussion of the bladder for evidence of abnormal bladder distention or by post-void residual after catheterization.

Laboratory Evaluation

Pharmacologic testing with adrenergic and cholinergic agonists is useful for detecting lack of response or denervation supersensitivity of effector organs. These tests are used commonly to assess pupillary control, sweating, and cardiovascular function. *Denervation supersensitivity* is a manifestation of postganglionic, as opposed to preganglionic, autonomic failure.

Pupil

Pharmacologic testing with local instillation of drugs that affect sympathetic neurotransmission in the pupil helps to localize lesions responsible for Horner's syndrome (see Table 9-14).

Cardiovascular Function

Cardiovascular reflex tests used to study patients with autonomic failure include (1) blood pressure and heart rate responses to *head-up tilt*, (2) heart rate fluctuations during deep breathing, or *respiratory sinus arrhythmia*, and (3) *Valsalva maneuver* (Table 9-16). During head-up tilt, hypotension with no

Table 9-16. Findings with Clinical Testing for Autonomic Failure

| | Sympathetic dysfunction | | Cardiovagal dysfunction |
	Central	Peripheral	
Response to head-up tilt			
Blood pressure	Orthostatic hypotension	Orthostatic hypotension	Variable
Heart rate	No increase	No increase	No increase
Respiratory sinus arrhythmia	Normal	Normal	Abnormal
Valsalva maneuver	Abnormal	Abnormal	Abnormal
Thermoregulatory sweat test	Abnormal	Abnormal	Normal
Acetylcholine sudomotor axon reflex	Normal	Abnormal	Normal

compensatory tachycardia indicates failure of the afferent, central, or efferent components of the baroreflex arc. Lack of heart rate fluctuations during deep breathing indicates cardiovagal failure. The Valsalva maneuver, a voluntary expiration against resistance, is a complex test that evaluates reflex cardiovagal and sympathetic vasomotor and cardiomotor responses to a transient decrease in cardiac output.

Sweating

The sympathetic innervation of the skin is tested by determining the patient's ability to sweat. The distinction between central and peripheral causes of sudomotor failure can be made by combining the *thermoregulatory sweat test* and the *acetylcholine sudomotor axon reflex test*. The thermoregulatory sweat test is a test of central and peripheral pathways that measures the sudomotor response to an increase in body temperature. The quantitative sudomotor axon reflex test stimulates receptors in sympathetic sudomotor terminals through local application of acetylcholine. Abnormal results on the thermoregulatory sweat test but normal findings with the quantitative sudomotor axon reflex test indicate central sudomotor failure. Abnormal findings with both tests indicate a peripheral lesion (see Table 9-16).

Bladder

Clinical evaluation of neurogenic bladder is complemented by urodynamic evaluation, including cystometrography, measurement of bladder pressure and urinary flow, and electromyography of the external sphincter.

Sex Organs

Evaluation of impotence includes measuring levels of such hormones as prolactin and testosterone and performing the penile tumescence test during sleep.

Gastrointestinal Tract

Motor function of the gut is tested by measuring the magnitude, frequency, rhythm, and distribution of peristaltic waves with pressure transducers.

Objectives

1. Describe the main functions and the general organization of the internal regulation system.
2. List the main components of the central circuits of the internal regulation system at supratentorial, posterior fossa, and spinal levels.
3. List the main functions of the paralimbic cortex, amygdala, hypothalamus, nucleus of the tractus solitarius, ventrolateral medulla, cranial parasympathetic nuclei, intermediolateral cell column, and sympathetic ganglia.
4. Describe the organization and function of spinal and brain stem visceral afferents. List the location and function of the circumventricular organs.
5. Differentiate sympathetic pathways from parasympathetic pathways by their location, function, and pharmacology.
6. List the main differences between the somatic and visceral motor systems with regard to organization of output, neurotransmission, characteristic of the effectors, and consequences of denervation.
7. List the main humoral and somatic motor output mechanisms of the internal regulation system.
8. Describe the clinical effects of lesions of the hypothalamus, medullary reticular formation, oculomotor nerve, superior cervical and stellate ganglia, and conus medullaris.
9. List sites at which lesions can produce abnormalities of the pupil, and describe the types of abnormalities seen with each lesion.
10. List the sites at which lesions can produce bladder disorders and the type of neurogenic disorder produced by a lesion at each site.

Clinical Problems

1. A 52-year-old man was referred for evaluation because of blackouts. The spells began a year before admission and were becoming more frequent. They occurred only

when he arose from a supine or sitting position to a standing one and were most severe in the morning. This change in position precipitated a giddy feeling in his head and dimness of vision and often was followed by complete loss of consciousness. No convulsive movements were observed and shortly after hitting the floor he regained consciousness, only to pass out again if he got up too quickly.

In addition to this primary symptom, the patient complained that during the last 3 years, he had gradually become sexually impotent. He also noted that he felt very uncomfortable in hot weather and did not perspire as he had before. Occasionally, fever would develop during hot weather, with no evidence of infection.

On examination, blood pressure was recorded at 130/70 mm Hg when the patient was supine. When he sat up, it decreased to 110/50 mm Hg. When he stood, it was 70/30 mm Hg, and he began to complain of faintness. Pulse rate was 82 to 90 per minute during the entire episode. The skin was warm and dry and remained so after many minutes in a hot examining room. Results of the rest of the physical examination were normal.

a. What is the site of the lesion?
b. What is the type of lesion?
c. Which of the patient's symptoms could be due to a disorder of sympathetic efferents?
d. What effect would pilocarpine (which directly stimulates sweat glands) have on this patient?
e. Which of the following may result in hypotension?
   (1) Spinal cord lesion at T-2
   (2) Fear
   (3) Peripheral nerve disease
   (4) Micturition

2. A 51-year-old tree trimmer had gradually experienced difficulty with urination during a 6- to 9-month period. He felt less urge to urinate, had difficulty in starting, and voided only small amounts. Recently, incontinence and a urinary tract infection had developed.

On examination, he had decreased anal sensation with absent anal and bulbo-cavernous reflexes. His bladder was distended, but he was unable to empty it.

a. What is the location of the lesion?
b. What is the type of lesion?
c. What type of bladder disturbance is this?
d. What abnormalities of sexual function might be expected?

3. A 37-year-old man who had had a thyroid carcinoma completely resected had a 2-month progressive history of left shoulder pain, with no motor or sensory symptoms.

Examination revealed drooping of the left eyelid, the left pupil smaller than the right (though both reacted normally to light), and dry skin on the left side of his face.

a. What is the location of the lesion?
b. What is the type of lesion?
c. What structure is most likely involved?
d. Does the lesion involve sympathetic or parasympathetic fibers?
e. List the structures where these pathways could be damaged to produce a similar syndrome.
f. In this patient, a drug that releases norepinephrine from nerve terminals has no effect. What does this indicate?
g. If a drug that causes the release of norepinephrine from nerve terminals evokes pupillary dilatation, where is the lesion most likely located?

4. An elderly retired oil tycoon was brought to the emergency room complaining of severe cramping abdominal pain, vomiting, diarrhea, and shortness of breath. He was able to relate that he became ill about half an hour after ingestion of a hearty meal served to him by his young bride of only a month. The meal consisted of steak smothered in mushrooms, mashed potatoes, and home-canned green beans. His spouse had complained of not feeling well before dinner and had not eaten at all.

Examination revealed marked tearing. The pupils were pinpoint in size. The patient was salivating profusely. Pulse rate was 50 per minute. Examination of the chest revealed diffuse rales in inspiration and wheezing in expiration. Auscultation of the abdomen revealed markedly active bowel sounds, and the examination was frequently interrupted by the patient's urgent need for a bedpan.

  a. What is the location of the lesion?

  b. What is the type of lesion?

  c. Is the disorder due to an abnormality in the sympathetic or parasympathetic pathway?

  d. What is the most likely cause of the disorder?

  e. What would be the effect of a cholinergic blocking agent on the pupils?

  f. Give examples of situations in which emotional activity in the limbic system alters function in the following organs:

    (1) Heart

    (2) Gastrointestinal tract

    (3) Urinary tract

    (4) Skin

    (5) Lacrimal glands

5. A 14-year-old boy was examined because of a discharge from his nipples that began 4 months ago. Additional questioning elicited a 2-year history of headaches when supine, a 20-lb weight gain, and recently lethargy and irritability.

Examination revealed mild obesity and sallow skin. He moved slowly, had a hoarse voice, and no secondary sexual characteristics. There was a clear discharge from both nipples. Examination of the cranial nerves showed only partial loss of vision in the temporal fields bilaterally.

  a. What are the level and site of the lesion?

  b. What is the type of lesion?

  c. Which neural structures are involved?

  d. What receptors are found in this area?

  e. What mechanism produces most of the symptoms?

Additional Reading

Bannister, R., and Mathias, C. J. (eds.). *Autonomic Failure: A Textbook of Clinical Disorders of the Autonomic Nervous System* (3rd ed.). Oxford: Oxford University Press, 1992.

Dinner, D. S. (ed.). The autonomic nervous system. *J. Clin. Neurophysiol.* 10:1, 1993.

Feldman, J. L. Neurophysiology of Breathing in Mammals. In V. B. Mountcastle, F. E. Bloom, and S. R. Geiger (eds.), *Handbook of Physiology.* Section 1, The Nervous System. Vol. 4, Intrinsic Regulatory System of the Brain. Bethesda, MD: American Physiological Society, 1986. Pp. 463-524.

Loewy, A. D., and Spyer, K. M. (eds.). *Central Regulation of Autonomic Functions.* New York: Oxford University Press, 1990.

Low, P. A. (ed.). *Clinical Autonomic Disorders: Evaluation and Management.* Boston: Little, Brown, 1993.

Swanson, L. W. The hypothalamus. In A. Björklund and T. Hökfelt (eds.), *Handbook of Chemical Neuroanatomy.* Amsterdam: Elsevier, 1987. Vol. 15, Pp. 1-124.

Törk, I., et al. Autonomic Regulatory Centers in the Medulla Oblongata. In G. Paxinos (ed.), *The Human Nervous System.* San Diego, CA: Academic, 1990. Pp. 221-259.

— 10 —

The Consciousness System

Chapter 7, The Sensory System, describes the major afferent pathways that provide the central nervous system with direct access to information about the external environment. These pathways are located in the outer tube portion of the central nervous system. In parallel with these pathways at the posterior fossa and supratentorial levels is another ascending system, the consciousness system, which is located primarily in the inner tube portion of the central nervous system. This system extends from the medulla to the cerebral cortex.

The consciousness system is a diffuse system that regulates consciousness, attention, and the wake-sleep states and modulates cortical reactivity to stimuli. Although the sensory pathways and the consciousness system both transmit sensory information to the cerebral cortex, the primary afferent pathways do so by means of direct pathways that are located in the outer tube and specific thalamic nuclei that project primarily to the sensory cortex. In contrast, the pathways of the consciousness system modulate activity via diffuse multineuronal pathways located in the inner tube and that project either directly to the cerebral cortex or indirectly by way of thalamic nuclei.

In this chapter, the anatomy and physiology of the consciousness system, its role in the regulation of wakefulness and sleep, and pathologic states of altered consciousness, which are a reflection of deranged activity within the system, are described.

Overview

The consciousness system is a diffuse multineuronal, polysynaptic system located in the brain stem, diencephalon, and cerebral hemispheres. Structures in the system are (1) portions of the brain stem reticular formation, (2) the neurochemically defined nuclear groups of the brain stem, (3) thalamic nuclei, (4) basal forebrain area, (5) ascending projections to the thalamus and cerebral cortex, and (6) widespread areas of the cerebral cortex. The control of the behavioral states of consciousness, attention, and wakefulness and sleep is related to specific changes in neural activity in the brain stem and basal forebrain that result in functional changes in thalamic and cortical circuits.

The reticular formation consists of multiple aggregates of neurons that receive and integrate information from many areas of the neuraxis, including the sensory system, cerebral cortex, basal forebrain, hypothalamus, and cerebellum. The reticular formation also sends projections to widespread areas of the cerebral cortex, either directly or indirectly through the thalamic nuclei, as well as to the motor and internal regulation systems. The neurochemically defined nuclear groups of the reticular formation consist of the cholinergic and monoaminergic nuclei. The latter includes the norepinephrine, serotonin, and histamine cell groups. The reticular formation can modify various neural activities directly or indirectly through connections with the thalamus and can selectively modulate the activity of the cortex and its reactivity to stimuli.

Proper functioning of the consciousness system and hence the regulation of consciousness and attention are predicated on a continuous interaction between the cerebral cortex, basal forebrain, thalamus, and brain stem reticular structures.

The electrical activity of a neuronal aggregate such as the cerebral cortex is a reflection of its own intrinsic activity and of ascending influences, primarily from the thalamus and reticular activating system.

The *electroencephalogram* (EEG) is a means of recording cortical activity. The waveforms that are seen represent summations of the postsynaptic, dendritic potentials generated near the surface in response to the intrinsic, neuronal electrical activity of the cerebral cortex as modified by input from subcortical structures. The EEG thus can provide information not only about cortical functioning but also about activity throughout the consciousness system.

Consciousness is an awareness of environment and self and is achieved through the action of the projections of the reticular activating system and basal forebrain on the cortex. The process of *attention* by which normal persons can focus their thoughts on specific information is achieved by the modulation of neuronal input to the cortex through the reticular activating system and basal forebrain, which permits persons to direct their attention to specific aspects of the environment without being continually distracted by multiple simultaneous stimuli.

Sleep is a normal cyclic physiologic alteration of consciousness, which is readily reversed by appropriate stimuli. It has been divided into two stages, rapid eye movement and nonrapid eye movement sleep. *Rapid eye movement* (REM) *sleep* is characterized by rapid eye movements, muscle twitches, decreased muscle tone, dreaming, and an EEG pattern resembling that of a waking recording. *Nonrapid eye movement* (non-REM) *sleep* is characterized by the absence of rapid eye movements, reduced body movements, and an EEG pattern showing the characteristic waveforms of the sleep state.

Pathologic processes that destroy or depress function of the reticular formation, of the ascending projectional pathways, or of both cerebral hemispheres produce alterations in consciousness. Examples of states of altered consciousness include *coma*, a state of extended unconsciousness from which the patient cannot be aroused; *confusional states*, in which the patient is disoriented, is inattentive, and cannot think clearly; *concussion*, a brief loss of consciousness after a blow to the head from which the patient recovers without neurologic sequelae; *seizure*, a transient alteration in brain function due to excessive neuronal discharge, which, when generalized and involves the consciousness system, causes loss of consciousness; and *syncope*, a transient loss of consciousness due to widespread neuronal ischemia.

Evaluation of a patient with a disorder of consciousness requires analysis of associated neurologic signs to determine whether the responsible lesion is (1) located at the supratentorial level, (2) located at the posterior fossa level, or (3) diffusely distributed at both levels.

Anatomy of the Consciousness System

Structures of the consciousness system include portions of the brain stem reticular formation, the basal forebrain, the neurochemically defined nuclear groups of the brain stem and basal forebrain, the thalamus, the ascending projectional pathways, and widespread areas of the cerebral cortex (Fig. 10-1).

Reticular Formation

The reticular formation is a complex aggregate of large multipolar and small round neurons and their axons diffusely distributed in cellular clusters throughout the central tegmental portions of the brain stem, extending from the decussation of the pyramids in the medulla to the basal forebrain area and thalamus. The brain stem portions of the reticular formation are located in the core of the neural tube (inner tube). This is the phylogenetically older part of the brain stem that consists of various nuclear groups and multisynaptic pathways. The diffuse arrangement of the multipolar neurons and the many interconnections of the reticular formation allow a single reticular neuron to make synaptic contact with many afferent fibers. This arrangement gives rise to the term "reticular" ("forming a network"). With phylogenic advancement, this centrally located network becomes sur-

Fig. 10-1. Lateral view of the brain showing the components of the consciousness system.

rounded by structures serving specific functions within the motor and sensory systems. Functionally, the reticular formation can be divided into a *lateral receptive area*, which receives collateral branches from ascending sensory pathways, and a *medial projectional area*, from which efferent pathways arise.

Afferent pathways to the reticular formation (Fig. 10-2) consist of (1) collateral branches from the primary ascending tracts of the sensory system (spinothalamic and lemniscal pathways), which synapse with cells in the reticular formation, (2) fibers from the cerebral cortex, consisting of corticoreticular fibers from widespread cortical areas as well as collateral branches from the corticospinal and corticobulbar tracts of the motor system, (3) fibers from other structures, including the cerebellum, basal ganglia, hypothalamus, cranial nerve nuclei, and the colliculi, and (4) visceral afferents from the spinal cord and cranial nerves.

The efferent pathways project rostrally to the forebrain and caudally to the spinal cord. In addition to the ascending projections of the reticular formation in the consciousness system, the other projections convey information to the motor and internal regulation systems (Fig. 10-3). By means of these multiple connections and pathways, the reticular formation can integrate information from various levels of the neuraxis and thereby regulate and modify the activities of the nervous system.

Neurochemically Defined Nuclear Groups of the Brain Stem and Basal Forebrain

The important groups of cells in the reticular formation that are involved with the control of the different behavioral states of wakefulness and sleep are characterized by their neurotransmitters and consist of cholinergic groups and monoaminergic groups (Table 10-1).

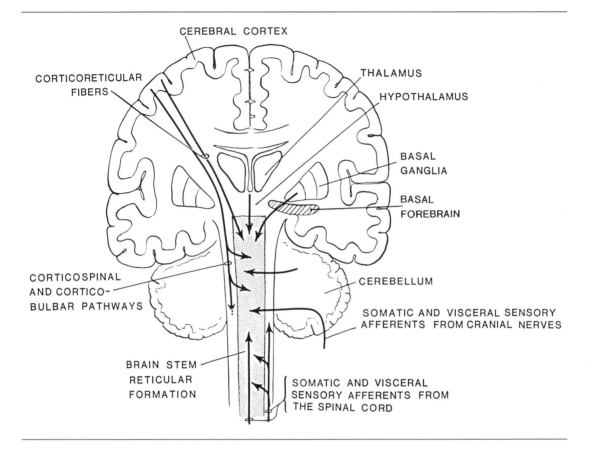

Fig. 10-2. Input to the brain stem reticular formation.

The *cholinergic nuclear groups* of neurons are located in the *basal forebrain* area and in the dorsal tegmentum of the upper pons and midbrain (referred to as the *mesopontine tegmentum*) and form an anatomical functional unit that has projections to the cortex via the medial forebrain bundle. The cholinergic structures of the basal forebrain, including the nucleus basalis (of Meynert) and the medial septal nuclei, send diffuse projections to the cerebral cortex. These projections are critical for regulation of behavioral functions, including cortical arousal, wakefulness, sensory processing, learning, and memory. In addition to direct action on the cerebral cortex, a portion of the basal forebrain neurons projects to the reticular nucleus of the thalamus and to other thalamic nuclei. Cholinergic input to the thalamic reticular nucleus modulates the activity of the thalamus and the thalamocortical projections to the cerebral cortex. The cholinergic neurons of the basal forebrain thus project di-

rectly to the cerebral cortex or to the reticular thalamic nucleus. Cholinergic neurons are also located in the mesopontine tegmentum. They also project to the thalamus and the basal forebrain. Thus, the ascending cholinergic pathways from the brain stem project to the cerebral cortex via the basal forebrain or via the thalamus, which in turn can affect cortical activity.

The *monoaminergic groups* that are important in regulating behavioral states and state-dependent activity are the *norepinephrine, serotonin*, and *histamine nuclear groups*. These neurochemically defined nuclear groups are located in the brain stem and hypothalamus and send projections to the basal forebrain and cerebral cortex via the medial forebrain bundle and fornix.

The *norepinephrine cells* are located in the *locus ceruleus*, which is in the lateral part of the upper pons and lower midbrain (Fig. 10-4). The locus ceruleus is a group of mela-

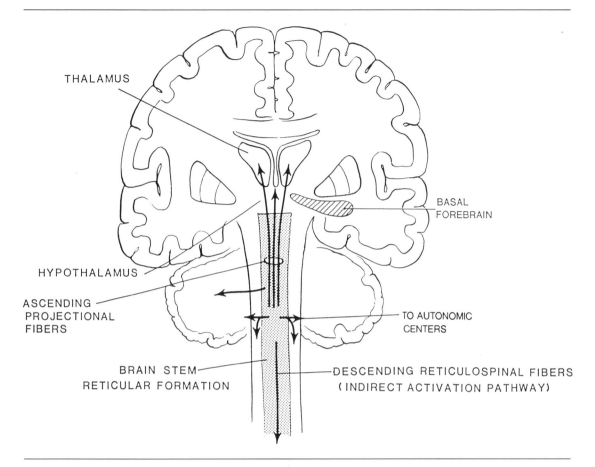

Fig. 10-3. Output pathways of brain stem reticular formation.

Table 10-1. Neurochemically Defined Nuclear Groups

Neurotransmitter	Location of nuclear group	Modulates
Acetylcholine	Dorsal tegmentum of pons and midbrain	Wakefulness
	Basal forebrain	REM sleep
Monoamines		
Norepinephrine	Locus ceruleus	Wakefulness and attention
Serotonin	Raphe nuclei	Non-REM sleep
Histamine	Hypothalmus	Wakefulness

nin pigmented cells rich in norepinephrine; it has a slightly bluish appearance in fresh specimens, hence, the name. The locus ceruleus is one of the principal brain stem nuclei that contain norepinephrine neurons and that send projections to areas that mediate responses to sensory stimuli, including the thalamus, hypothalamus, basal forebrain, cerebral cortex, cerebellum, and spinal cord.

The neurons of the locus ceruleus increase their activity in response to new and challenging stimuli and thus play an important role in the mechanism of arousal and attention.

The *serotonergic neurons* form the *raphe nuclei*, which are located in the median area of the brain stem (see Fig. 10-4). The rostral group (upper pons and midbrain) gives rise

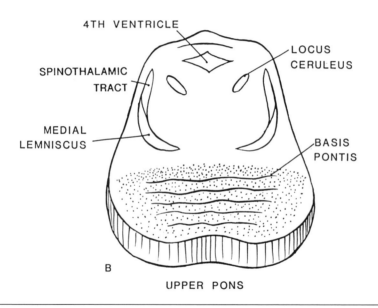

Fig. 10-4. Location of raphe nuclei and nucleus of the tractus solitarius at level of medulla (A) and locus ceruleus at level of upper pons (B).

to ascending projections to the thalamus, hypothalamus, basal forebrain, and cerebral hemispheres. The caudal group (lower pons and medulla) gives rise to descending projections to the spinal cord and other areas of the brain stem. The serotonergic neurons facilitate sleep and thus exert a widespread influence on various areas of the central nervous system.

The *histamine neurons* are located in the *posterior lateral hypothalamus*. They enhance arousal mechanisms and wakefulness.

Thalamus

The thalamus is the gateway to the cerebral cortex and subserves two important roles. It acts as a relay station (relaying information to and from the cortex), and it filters and modulates the flow of information to the cortex from other areas.

The thalamus is subdivided into several groups of neurons, each containing *relay*, or *projectional*, *neurons* and local *interneurons*. Functionally, the thalamic nuclei are subdi-

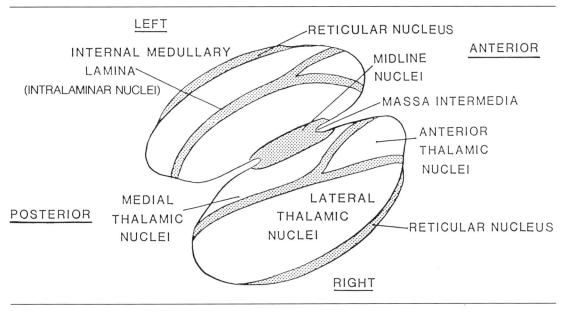

Fig. 10-5. Dorsolateral view of the thalamus with nonspecific thalamic nuclei (*stippled*). (Redrawn from F. H. Netter. *The Ciba Collection of Medical Illustrations.* Vol. I, The Nervous System. Summit, N.J.: Ciba Pharmaceutical Products, 1962. P. 48.)

vided into (1) specific thalamic nuclei, which are associated with the sensory and motor systems and have reciprocal connections with localized areas of the cerebral cortex, and (2) nonspecific thalamic nuclei, which receive afferent input from other thalamic nuclei, the reticular formation, and the basal forebrain and in turn project to all areas of the cerebral cortex via the diffuse thalamic projection system. The nonspecific thalamic nuclei include the midline nuclei (located near the massa intermedia), the intralaminar nuclei (located in the internal medullary lamina, a band of myelinated fibers separating the anterior, medial, and lateral thalamic nuclei), and the reticular nucleus (located on the lateral margin of the thalamus) (Fig. 10-5). The reticular nucleus projects to other thalamic nuclei but not to the cerebral cortex. Interactions between the reticular nucleus and other thalamic nuclei are important for regulation of the thalamocortical circuits. Diffuse projections from the thalamic nuclei that connect the reticular system and other brain stem structures to widespread areas of the cortex have a critical role in regulating the electrical activity of the ce-

rebral cortex and in modifying the states of consciousness and alertness (Fig. 10-6).

Basal Forebrain Area

The *basal forebrain* area consists of a group of structures located at the ventral and medial aspects of the cerebral hemispheres. It includes the *nucleus basalis* (of Meynert), the *septal nuclei*, and the rostral part of the *medial forebrain bundle* (Fig. 10-7). The nucleus basalis consists mainly of cholinergic neurons and sends extensive projections to widespread areas of the cerebral cortex. It serves as the major source of extrathalamic input to cortical areas. The medial forebrain bundle is a major tract that runs from the midbrain tegmentum through the lateral hypothalamus into the septum, preoptic area, hypothalamus, basal olfactory region, and cingulate gyrus. This bundle represents the most rostral extent of the reticular system and contains ascending and descending fibers that interconnect the brain stem and telencephalon. Many of the cholinergic and monoaminergic fibers that originate in the brain stem send projections to cortical regions through the medial forebrain bundle.

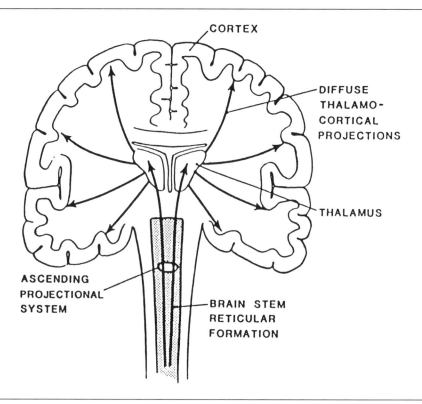

Fig. 10-6. Diffuse thalamocortical projections of the consciousness system.

Ascending Pathways to the Cerebral Cortex

The activating influences of the reticular formation and other brain stem structures are transmitted to the cortex by two main types of projectional pathways: thalamocortical pathways and extrathalamic pathways that involve the basal forebrain and medial forebrain bundle (Table 10-2).

The thalamic relay nuclei receive information from specific afferent pathways in the outer tube of the brain stem. The thalamic relay nuclei, in turn, send projections to specific topographic areas of the cerebral cortex. The thalamocortical inputs are phasic and dependent on the arrival of input from the specific afferent pathways. The thalamus not only acts as a relay station but also enhances or attenuates neuronal activity that is transmitted to the cerebral cortex.

The extrathalamic pathways originate from cholinergic and monoaminergic neuronal groups that are located primarily in the brain

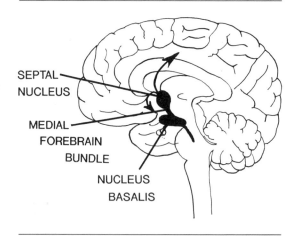

Fig. 10-7. Lateral view of the brain showing the basal forebrain area.

stem and the basal forebrain. These include norepinephrine neurons in the locus ceruleus, serotonergic neurons in the raphe nuclei, histamine neurons in the lateral hypothalamus, and cholinergic neurons in the mesopontine tegmentum and basal forebrain area. These

Table 10-2. Ascending Pathways of the Consciousness System

	Thalamocortical pathways	Extrathalamic pathways
Input from	Sensory relay nuclei in spinal cord and brain stem	Cholinergic and monoaminergic neuron groups in brain stem and basal forebrain
Projectional pathway	Thalamic radiation	Medial forebrain bundle
Projects to	Specific topographic areas of cortex	Widespread areas of cortex and thalamus
Function	Relay information to cerebral cortex Filter flow of information to cortex	Modulate activity of cortex and thalamus
Activity	Phasic/excitatory	Tonic-continuous Modulatory
Dependent on	Specific afferent stimulation	Behavior state (wake-sleep)

structures send projections to widespread areas of the cerebral cortex by way of the medial forebrain bundle. In addition, they send projections to the thalamus, which in turn sends projections to the cerebral cortex. Thus, cholinergic and monoaminergic neurons exert a continuous, tonic modulatory influence on cortical and thalamic neurons dependent on the behavioral state (wake or sleep) of the person. Because of the simultaneous effect on the thalamus and the cerebral cortex, the state-dependent changes in cholinergic and mono-aminergic neuronal neurochemical groups cause global changes in cortical activity.

Cerebral Cortex

Although many specific functions, such as somatic sensation and vision, are relayed and integrated in specific areas, no single area of cortex is responsible for the maintenance of consciousness. Indeed, because of the widespread interconnections between the nonspecific thalamic nuclei and the cerebral cortex, all areas of cortex appear to participate in consciousness and are therefore considered part of the consciousness system.

Physiology of the Consciousness System

Neurophysiology of Single Cells

As described in Chapter 5 (Diagnosis of Neurologic Disorders: Transient Disorders and Neurophysiology), neurons generate two types of potentials: synaptic potentials and action potentials.

Synaptic Potential (Dendritic Potential)

The *synaptic* or *dendritic potential* is a local potential generated in the dendritic portion of the nerve cell as a result of a neurotransmitter interacting with the cell membrane (Fig. 10-8). Synaptic potentials are localized, nonpropagated, graded fluctuations of the dendritic membrane potential and can be excitatory (EPSPs) when the neurotransmitter causes a depolarization in the cell membrane or inhibitory (IPSPs) when the neurotransmitter causes a hyperpolarization of the cell membrane. The duration of these potentials is usually 15 to 20 milliseconds, and they do not have a refractory period.

Action Potential

The action potential usually arises from the axon hillock of the neuron and propagates along the axon (see Fig. 10-8). (In some instances, it can also arise from the dendrite or cell body.) The action potential occurs only when the neuronal membrane is depolarized beyond a critical (threshold) level. The spike discharge is brief (usually less than 1 msec). It is an all-or-none phenomenon propagated down the axon and followed by a temporary refractory period (see Fig. 10-8).

Neurophysiology of Neuronal Aggregates

Neurons in the central nervous system and cerebral cortex do not function in isolation but function as part of neuronal aggregates.

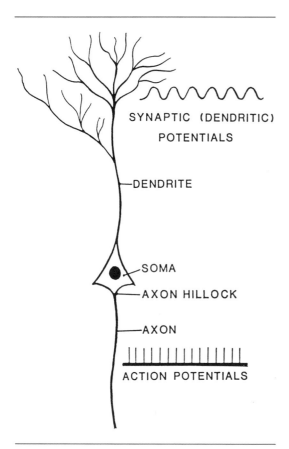

Fig. 10-8. Diagram of a cortical neuron showing synaptic potentials generated in a dendrite and action potentials generated in an axon.

These neurons have rich synaptic interconnections, and the electrical activity of the aggregate reflects the summated effect of all the dendritic potentials and action potentials occurring within that aggregate. This activity is recorded as complex waveforms rather than as the simple spikes of single cells. The cortex generates these electrical waves in response to local activity within the neuronal aggregate and to input from both the specific and the nonspecific nuclei of the thalamus. Because the thalamic nuclei have widespread connections with the cerebral cortex, they can exert a strong influence on cortical activity. They can act to excite, inhibit, or promote widespread synchronization of cortical neuronal activity.

The electrical activity of the cerebral cortex can be detected by the EEG, which records cortical activity from electrodes placed on the scalp. This brain-wave activity consists of continuous rhythmic or arrhythmic oscillating waveforms that vary in frequency, amplitude, polarity, and shape. These electrical potentials are usually in the range of 20 to 50 µV. The activity seen on the EEG (Fig. 10-9) reflects the summation of synaptic potentials of many dendrites lying near the surface of the cortex. The fluctuation of the EEG is due to varied excitatory and inhibitory synaptic potentials impinging on the dendritic membranes.

Cortical neuronal activity is modulated by synaptic input from other cortical neurons, the basal forebrain, and the thalamus. Thalamic influences determine the intrinsic resting frequencies of the brain waves because structures in the thalamus serve as the "pacemakers" in producing widespread synchronization and rhythmicity of cortical activity over the cerebral hemispheres.

Electrical stimulation of the thalamus alters the EEG pattern. A low-frequency stimulus produces a more rhythmic and synchronized EEG pattern, whereas a high-frequency stimulus results in a low-amplitude, arrhythmic, desynchronized pattern.

Functions of the Consciousness System

The consciousness system is responsible for the maintenance of consciousness, attention, and regulation of the wake-sleep states.

Consciousness

This is a subjective state defined as an "awareness of environment and self." It implies an awake and alert condition in which the person is capable of perceiving his or her internal and external environments and, if the motor system is intact, of responding in an appropriate manner to input stimuli. There are two aspects of consciousness: (1) the *content of consciousness*, representing cognitive mental functions that reflect the activity of the cerebral cortex, and (2) *arousal* and *wakefulness*, which are dependent on the reticular activating system and its projections and which in turn are activated by direct stimulation, sensory stimuli, or cortical influences.

Direct electrical stimulation of the reticular formation in a sleeping animal results in a state of behavioral arousal, indicated by open-

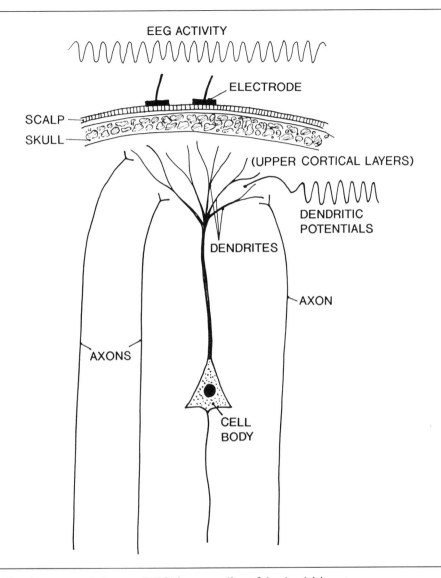

Fig. 10-9. The electroencephalogram (EEG) is a recording of the dendritic potentials in the upper cortical layers as they appear on the scalp.

ing of the eyes, turning of the head, and movement of the limbs. Associated with this is a change in the EEG from a synchronous slow-wave sleep pattern to the low-voltage, fast pattern of the waking state.

The reticular formation receives sensory input via collateral branches from every major sensory pathway, which keeps the reticular activating system in an excited state and in turn activates the cortex to maintain wakefulness. The importance of sensory influences in maintaining a wakeful state is illustrated by the progressive decrease in the degree of wakefulness that occurs with loss or reduction in sensory input. If the consciousness system is intact, then stimulation of the reticular activating system results in an arousal response; however, if a portion of the consciousness system is destroyed, particularly the rostral part of the brain stem and thalamus, a permanent "sleep" state ensues.

Activating influences of the reticular formation and other brain stem structures are transmitted to the cerebral cortex by way of the medial forebrain bundle or the thalamus. This system may be activated by sensory stimuli.

Norepinephrine neurons in the locus ceruleus increase their firing in response to new and challenging stimuli and are involved with the processes of arousal and attention. There is also a tonic state of activation that maintains wakefulness and cortical excitability. Neurons primarily involved with this function are the cholinergic neurons in the basal forebrain and the cholinergic and monoaminergic neurons in the mesopontine tegmentum that project to the basal forebrain and that are tonically active during wakefulness. Histamine neurons in the posterior lateral hypothalamus are also involved in wakefulness.

All areas of the brain stem reticular formation and basal forebrain involved with the consciousness system have multiple sensory inputs and reciprocal projections with the cerebral cortex. Electrical stimulation of certain cortical areas, such as the orbitofrontal area and superior temporal gyrus, evokes an arousal response. Emotional stimuli such as anger and fear also act as powerful stimulants to the consciousness system.

The state of wakefulness and alertness thus is achieved by the consciousness system through the action of the reticular activating system and basal forebrain on the cerebral cortex; the reticular activating system, in turn, is activated by activity in the sensory pathways and by fibers from the cerebral cortex and hypothalamus.

Attention

The consciousness system not only determines the state of alertness and wakefulness but also influences the degree of overall attentiveness to the environment and perception of specific sensory modalities. The cholinergic neurons of the basal forebrain facilitate sensory processing of cortical neurons and the response to specific sensory stimuli. The activity of the basal forebrain neurons is influenced by input from the ascending pathways of the brain stem and can cause a localized or generalized activation of different cortical areas. The consciousness system also modulates cortical reactivity to stimuli by facilitating or inhibiting transmission of neural impulses of the sensory system through the thalamus. The various projections of the consciousness system act on relay nuclei in the thalamus to make them more or less receptive to sensory stimuli. Thus, the thalamus acts as a mechanism to enhance or attenuate responses to incoming stimuli and to direct attention to specific input while suppressing other incoming signals. Electrical activity reaching the cerebral cortex via specific sensory pathways is not perceived unless it is followed by activity via the diffuse projection paths. For example, reading a book, a person is absorbed by the words on the page and is not aware of body contact with the chair or outside noises. The consciousness system, in response to cortical reticular direction, selectively sends "alerting" signals to the cortex receiving the visual input and suppresses sensory input in auditory or somatic pathways. The consciousness system thus acts in an adaptive manner to prevent the cortex from being overwhelmed and to permit selective attention to specific external and internal stimuli.

Sleep States

Consciousness may be altered by several conditions. One normal physiologic alteration is that associated with sleep, which is defined as a cyclic, temporary, and physiologic loss of consciousness that is readily, promptly, and completely reversed by appropriate stimuli. Recent studies have shown that sleep is an active phenomenon in which hypnogenic areas of the brain and neurochemical substances actively promote sleep and inhibit the arousal system.

The structures involved with sleep include the raphe nuclei in the upper medullary and lower pontine areas of the reticular formation of the brain stem, the nucleus of the tractus solitarius in the medulla, the locus ceruleus in the lateral portion of the upper pons and lower midbrain (see Fig. 10-4), the lateral pontine reticular formation ventral to the locus ceruleus, the anterior portion of the hypothalamus, the reticular nucleus of the thalamus, and the basal forebrain-preoptic area (Fig. 10-10). These structures modulate sleep by producing excitation of other areas of the brain associated with sleep and by actively inhibiting areas of the reticular system that are responsible for maintaining a wakeful state. Destruction of these areas can result in decreased sleep.

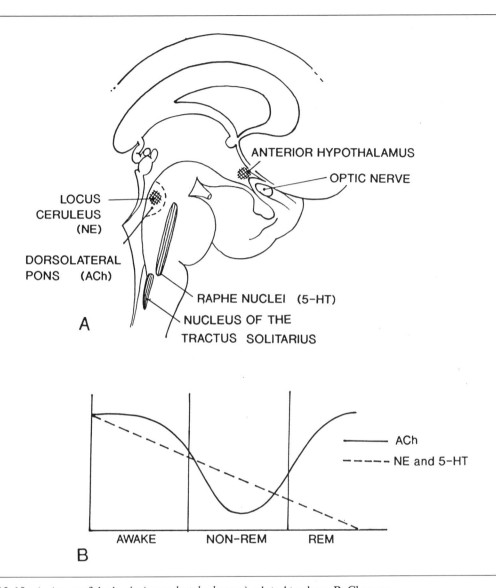

Fig. 10-10. A. Areas of the brain (*cross-hatched areas*) related to sleep. B. Changes in neurochemical activity during wake-sleep states. (*ACh* = acetylcholine; *5-HT* = serotonin; *NE* = norepinephrine.)

Two distinctive patterns of sleep are seen in normal persons: rapid eye movement (REM) sleep and nonrapid eye movement (non-REM) sleep (Table 10-3). *REM sleep* is sleep in which there are rapid conjugate eye movements; fluctuations of body temperature, blood pressure, heart rate, and respiration; a decrease in muscle tone; muscle twitches; and penile erection. This is also the stage of sleep in which dreams occur. An EEG recorded during REM sleep shows a low-amplitude fast pattern resembling that of a person in an alert state with the eyes open (Fig. 10-11). Because of the above characteristics, REM sleep is also known as *paradoxical, active,* or *dream* sleep.

Non-REM sleep is sleep during which there are no rapid eye movements. There is a widespread decrease in brain activity. Vital signs and autonomic activity are more stable. During non-REM sleep, the EEG shows different patterns, depending on the depth of sleep (see Fig. 10-11). During drowsiness, the EEG shows a low-amplitude background with an attenuation of rhythmic activity. During light-

Table 10-3. Characteristics of the Two Major Patterns of Sleep (REM and non-REM)

Sleep activity	REM sleep	Non-REM sleep
Eye movements	Rapid	Slow (during drowsiness)
Body movements	Muscle twitches	Muscle relaxation
Muscle tone	Decreased	Some tone in postural muscle groups
Vital signs	Fluctuating	Stable
Penile erection	Common	Rare
Dreams	Common	Rare
EEG	Low-voltage pattern	Spindles, V waves, K complexes, slow waves
Percentage in adults	20	80
Percentage in infants	50	50

Fig. 10-11. EEG patterns of wakefulness and different levels of sleep. The awake EEG is recorded from occipital areas with the eyes closed. With the eyes open, the EEG resembles the REM sleep pattern.

to-medium levels of sleep, specific EEG waveforms (sleep spindles, V waves, and K complexes) are present. *Sleep spindles* are sinusoidal waveforms ranging from 10 to 14 Hz and are usually present over the frontal head regions. *V waves* (vertex waves) are high-amplitude, sharp waveforms occurring over the frontal and parietal regions. *K complexes* are a combination of V waves and spindle activity and often signify a partial arousal response in the EEG. During deep levels of sleep, widespread high-amplitude slow waves are present.

Non-REM sleep is the predominant type of sleep in adults and accounts for 75 to 80 percent of the nocturnal sleep pattern, while REM sleep accounts for only 20 to 25 percent. In newborn infants, however, 50 percent of sleep is REM sleep. During a night's sleep in adults, non-REM sleep occurs first and generally lasts for 60 to 90 minutes. It is then interrupted by a REM period, which may last from several minutes to one-half hour and which is followed by another non-REM period. A total night's sleep usually consists of four to six such cycles of alternating non-REM and REM sleep.

Experimental data indicate that non-REM and REM sleep are produced by different anatomical, physiologic, and neurohumoral systems.

Non-REM sleep is mediated by a widespread system that consists of multiple groups of neurons located in the anterior hypothalamus, the basal forebrain-preoptic area, and the brain stem, including the dorsal medullary reticular formation and the nucleus of the tractus solitarius.

REM sleep is mediated by a more discrete system in the pons and includes the dorsolateral pontine reticular formation, particularly the region just ventral and lateral to the locus ceruleus. The dorsolateral pontine neurons, interacting with other neurons in the brain stem and forebrain, are involved with the reciprocal activation and deactivation of the neuronal groups that mediate REM sleep. The norepinephrine cells in the locus ceruleus and the serotonergic cells in the dorsal raphe nuclei become inactive during REM sleep; they are the "REM off-cells." Neurons in the region just ventral and lateral to the locus ceruleus, however, fire at faster rates during REM sleep and are called the "REM on-cells." This is the area most critical for REM sleep: it induces the neuronal changes mediating REM sleep.

Table 10-4. Neuronal Firing During Wakefulness and Sleep

	Cholinergic neurons	Monoaminergic neurons
Wake	Increases	Increases
Non-REM sleep	Decreases	Decreases
REM sleep	Increases	Decreases

Wake-Sleep States

The mechanisms governing wake-sleep states are not precisely defined; however, it is apparent that multiple structures and neurohumoral agents interact to regulate the cyclic alterations between the wake and the sleep states (see Fig. 10-10).

Cholinergic neuronal activity is increased during wakefulness and REM sleep and decreased during non-REM sleep. The activity of the monoaminergic neurons (norepinephrine and serotonin) is increased before arousal, is decreased before the onset of non-REM sleep, and is minimal or ceases during REM sleep (Table 10-4). The initiation of sleep and the transition between the various stages of sleep and wakefulness occur as a sequence of reciprocal activation and inhibition of the different structures involved with wake-sleep states.

In the wake state, neurons of the cerebral cortex and brain stem are in an excited and aroused state and are receptive to sensory input. This excited state is maintained by the activity of the cholinergic neurons in the reticular formation and the basal forebrain. In addition, the norepinephrine neurons of the locus ceruleus increase the activity of the cortical and brain stem structures in response to alerting stimuli. Histamine neurons in the posterior hypothalamus also enhance the state of wakefulness.

In non-REM sleep, the wake mechanisms are deactivated or inhibited, and there is decreased responsiveness to external stimuli. The neurons mediating non-REM sleep (located in the raphe nuclei, the nucleus of the tractus solitarius, the reticular nucleus of the thalamus, the basal forebrain, and the anterior hypothalamus) become more active, while other neurons of the reticular formation become deactivated. Sleep is also facilitated by serotonergic neurons that decrease sensory input and inhibit motor activity.

REM sleep is mediated by brain stem structures that include the midbrain reticular formation, the area ventral and lateral to the locus ceruleus, and the brain stem tegmentum. Cholinergic neurons are active during REM sleep, maintaining cortical activity. However, spinal motor neurons are inhibited during REM sleep, resulting in atonia. In other words, the brain is active during REM sleep but is disengaged from the rest of the body.

Sleep and wakefulness are circadian rhythms that occur approximately every 24 hours. Many other biologic systems, such as hormonal secretion, follow a similar pattern. The circadian rhythms are controlled by a pacemaker, the "biological clock," located in the suprachiasmatic nuclei of the hypothalamus.

Clinical Correlations

Sleep Disorders

Narcolepsy is a disorder of sleep control mechanisms characterized by excessive sleepiness. The patient falls asleep spontaneously and precipitously at any time during the day. These episodes are most frequent during monotonous situations. In addition, the patient may have cataplexy, sleep paralysis, or hypnagogic hallucinations. *Cataplexy* is an abrupt loss of muscle tone that may cause the patient to fall suddenly to the ground. Cataplexy is often precipitated by emotional events such as laughter, fright, or excitement.

Sleep paralysis occurs during the transition between wakefulness and sleep and is a temporary state of the inability to move. *Hypnagogic hallucinations* are false visual or auditory perceptions that occur just before the patient falls asleep and often in conjunction with sleep paralysis. These findings probably reflect a disorder of REM sleep. Most patients with narcolepsy have no known structural lesion, and neurologic examination reveals no abnormality.

Sleep apnea is a condition in which the patient stops breathing when asleep. This may be due to upper airway obstruction or depression of central respiratory mechanisms. After a period of apnea, which may last for 1 minute or more, the patient with obstructive sleep apnea

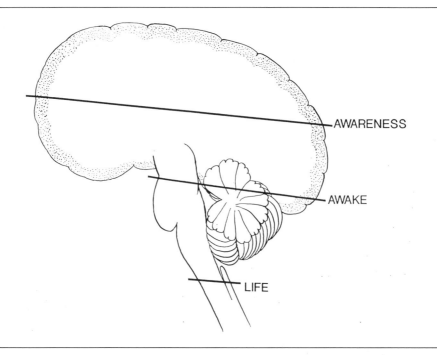

Fig. 10-12. The levels responsible for awareness, wakefulness, and life functions.

arouses from sleep with noisy gasping respirations. When the patient goes back to sleep, the cycle is repeated. As a result, the patient has a decreased amount of sleep and is excessively drowsy when awake.

Periodic limb movement disorder consists of periodic or repetitive stereotyped flexion-extension movements of the limbs, usually the legs, which occur during sleep and cause intermittent arousal or awakening.

Somnambulism (*sleep walking*) and *sleep terrors* are other types of sleep disorder. They occur predominantly during deep levels of non-REM sleep.

Prolonged sleep deprivation can cause decreased vigilance and attention span, poor performance of tasks, increased irritability, diplopia, unsteadiness, slurring of speech, hallucinations, illusions, and, occasionally, psychotic behavior.

Disorders of Consciousness

Consciousness is a function of the combined activity of the reticular activating system and the cerebral cortex. Major damage to or depression of the brain stem and/or bilateral

hemispheric dysfunction results in pathologic alteration in consciousness, or *loss of consciousness*. The loss of consciousness may be transient or prolonged and may vary from mildly increased sleepiness to deep coma.

Lesions that alter consciousness are located at the supratentorial or posterior fossa level. Interruption of the reticular activating system or its projections to the cortex produces different effects on consciousness, awareness, the wake-sleep states, and life functions, depending on the level of involvement (Fig. 10-12).

With nonfatal destruction of the high cervical spinal cord or spinomedullary junction, the consciousness system remains intact. Therefore, the wake and sleep states are present clinically and electrographically. Arousal occurs in response either to sensory stimuli from the cranial nerves or to stimulation of the reticular formation.

If damage occurs at the midpontine pretrigeminal level, just rostral to the trigeminal nerve entry zone and above the medullary and pontine sleep centers, there will be a persistent EEG pattern of wakefulness, consisting of low-voltage fast activity characteristic of an awake state.

A lesion at the midbrain level results in a "sleep state" in which neither sensory stimuli nor direct stimulation of the reticular formation or thalamus will produce an arousal response.

Bilateral lesions that affect the ascending pathways in the region of the diencephalon (thalamus and hypothalamus) produce a state of sustained somnolence, with the EEG showing diffuse slow-wave activity.

Focal or unilateral lesions of the cerebral hemispheres do not result in loss of consciousness as long as the projections of the consciousness system to at least one cerebral hemisphere are intact. However, if there is bilateral destruction of the cerebral hemispheres, there is no longer a substratum for consciousness, and unconsciousness ensues.

Thus, the more rostral portions of the consciousness system, in particular the area above the trigeminal nerve entry zone, are critical for maintaining alertness and consciousness. However, portions of the reticular system of the lower pons and medulla seem to have important influences on certain stages of sleep, although they do not seem to be directly required for the maintenance of consciousness.

Degrees of Altered Consciousness

Regardless of the cause, various degrees of altered consciousness result from lesions affecting this system. *Coma* is a state of extended unconsciousness in which the patient is unarousable and shows little or no spontaneous movement and little or no alerting response to painful or noxious stimuli. Often the muscle-stretch reflexes, the plantar responses, and the pupillary and light reflexes are depressed or absent. Vital signs are usually altered, particularly with lesions affecting the brain stem; the patient has a slow and variable pulse rate and a periodic respiratory pattern.

In *stupor*, the patient often shows a moderate amount of spontaneous movement and can be aroused to respond purposefully to afferent stimuli. If sufficiently aroused, the patient can give a brief response to questions or simple commands.

Obtundation is a state in which alertness of the patient is mildly to moderately decreased. When left undisturbed, the patient falls asleep; when aroused, he or she shows a slowed or reduced response to all forms of stimuli.

In *somnolence*, the patient is easily aroused and shows appropriate verbal and motor responses to sensory stimuli. When the stimulus stops, the patient drifts back to sleep.

Confusion is a transient state, distinct from dementia, in which there is a progressive decline in cognitive functions in the presence of normal consciousness. Level of attention is decreased and the ability to think clearly is impaired. Responses to verbal stimuli are slowed, and the patient is less able to recognize and understand what is going on in the environment.

Delirium is an agitated state of confusion associated with *illusions* (false interpretations or misrepresentations of real sensory images), *hallucinations* (false sensory perceptions for which there are no external bases), and *delusions* (false beliefs or misconceptions that cannot be corrected by reason).

Sleep, in contrast to the pathologic alterations previously described, is a normal physiologic state, but one that also can be associated with pathologic involvement of the consciousness system. The sleeping person, as compared with one in coma, is fully aroused by appropriate stimuli. During sleep, the eyes are closed, the muscles are relaxed, and the cardiac output, pulse rate, blood pressure, and respiration are decreased.

Causes of Loss of Consciousness

The consciousness system may suffer either from physiologic alterations of function that produce a transient loss of consciousness or from structural lesions that result in a persistent loss of consciousness. A transient disturbance of consciousness occurs as a result of (1) concussion, (2) a generalized seizure, (3) syncope, or (4) a metabolic encephalopathy.

Concussion is a brief loss of consciousness, usually occurring after a sudden blow to the head. Although the patient is unconscious, arousal by vigorous stimuli is often possible. After return of consciousness, there is some confusion and *amnesia* (loss of memory) that persist for a variable period afterward, but usually there are no permanent neurologic sequelae. Mechanisms postulated to cause the transient loss of consciousness include (1) a sudden increase in pressure in the region of neurons critical for consciousness, (2) cerebral ischemia, (3) sudden depolarization or hyperpolarization (or both) of neurons, and (4) transient alteration in neuronal functioning secondary to mechanical distortion of neurons or axons. Although no gross neuropathologic change is usually apparent, diffuse axonal injury and individual neuronal alterations have been found on microscopic examination, especially in the region of the brain stem reticular formation.

Seizures (convulsions) are transient episodes of supratentorial origin in which there is an abrupt and temporary alteration in cerebral function. Seizures may consist of abnormal movements (such as tonic or clonic movements), an abnormal sensation (such as paresthesias or visual hallucination), or a disturbance in behavior or consciousness. They are caused by a spontaneous, excessive discharge of cortical neurons, which may occur as a result of an increase in neuronal excitability, an excessive excitatory synaptic input impinging on the nerve cells, or a decrease in normal inhibitory mechanisms.

Seizures can be either focal or generalized. A *focal* seizure, also called *partial* seizure, involves only a localized area of the cortex. Partial seizures have been subdivided into simple partial seizures, in which there is no loss of consciousness, and complex partial seizures, in which there is some alteration of consciousness. A *generalized* seizure involves widespread and bilateral areas of both hemispheres simultaneously. It may have some spread to the thalamus and reticular activating system and, therefore, is associated with a loss of consciousness.

Syncope (fainting) is a transient loss of consciousness due to a decrease in cerebral blood flow and ischemia of the entire brain. This occurs as a result of decreased cardiac output, slowing of the heart rate, or pooling of blood in the periphery. The loss of consciousness is usually brief (a matter of seconds to minutes) and is preceded by light-headedness, weakness, giddiness, sweating, and dimming of vision. During this time, the patient is pale and sweaty; pulse is weak, and blood pressure is reduced. Syncope accompanied by brief generalized tonic, clonic, or tonic-clonic movements is called *convulsive syncope.*

Several systemic disorders produce *metabolic encephalopathy*, which diffusely affects the consciousness system and causes a transient alteration in consciousness, often without localizing signs. Hypoglycemia, hyponatremia, and drug overdosage are common causes of metabolic encephalopathy.

Structural lesions can result in persistent impairment of consciousness or in coma. Although we use the general term *coma* in this discussion, stupor and somnolence are also produced by identical disease processes. Coma results from lesions that involve the reticular formation and its projectional systems or the cerebral hemispheres bilaterally.

Direct damage or depression of the consciousness system in the posterior fossa or diencephalon may occur from infarction, hemorrhage, neoplasia, trauma, metabolic disturbances, and anesthetic agents and drugs. Unilateral lesions of the cerebral hemispheres do not cause coma if the consciousness system is intact. However, coma does result from bilateral lesions that diffusely affect the cerebral hemispheres, such as encephalitis, meningitis, subarachnoid hemorrhage, metabolic disturbances (such as hypoglycemia), hypoxia, some degenerative diseases, and certain drugs.

Indirect involvement of the consciousness system also can result in coma. This involvement is usually the result of mass lesions that, although extrinsic to the consciousness system, compress or distort the diencephalon and brain stem. Common examples are mass lesions of the posterior fossa (for example, a cerebellar neoplasm) or expanding unilateral cerebral masses that result in herniation of the brain contents and secondary compression of diencephalic or midbrain structures (see Chapter 15, The Posterior Fossa Level, for further discussion).

In summary, coma can be produced by:

1. Focal lesions of the posterior fossa that involve the brain stem.
2. Focal supratentorial lesions, if they are of such magnitude as to directly or indirectly involve the deep midline diencephalic structures necessary for the maintenance of consciousness.

3. Diffuse lesions, generally of an anoxic, toxic-metabolic, or inflammatory nature, capable of causing widespread depression.

The Electroencephalogram

The EEG is a useful adjunct to neurologic diagnosis. Electrical activity recorded by the EEG from the cerebral cortex is classified into four main types, depending on the frequency or number of waveforms per second (hertz) (Fig. 10-13).

Fig. 10-13. Four basic EEG frequencies.

1. *Beta activity* is low-amplitude fast activity occurring at a frequency of more than 13 Hz. This type of activity is usually seen over the anterior head regions.
2. *Alpha activity* is rhythmic activity at a frequency of 8 to 13 Hz. These rhythms occur in the posterior head regions and are the predominant background activity during the relaxed waking state when the eyes are closed (Fig. 10-14). With eye opening or with attention, there is attenuation of the rhythmic alpha background and replacement by a low-voltage pattern.
3. *Theta activity* ranges from 4 to 7 Hz and may be normal when present in a child or in an adult in a drowsy state, but when present in a fully awake adult, it is abnormal.
4. *Delta activity* is the slowest waveform, occurring at a frequency of less than 4 Hz. This activity is normal when present in an infant or in a sleeping adult but is abnormal under any other circumstances.

The EEG is helpful in studying normal physiologic activities; however, it attains its greatest usefulness in detecting abnormalities of cerebral functioning. The EEG reflects the intrinsic cortical activity as modified by subcortical

Fig. 10-14. Normal EEG pattern during wakeful state, showing presence of alpha activity in the posterior head region. (In each EEG illustration, electrical activity is a bipolar recording of the potential difference between electrodes, indicated by letters and numbers to the left of each line. Location of each electrode is shown on the diagram of the head.)

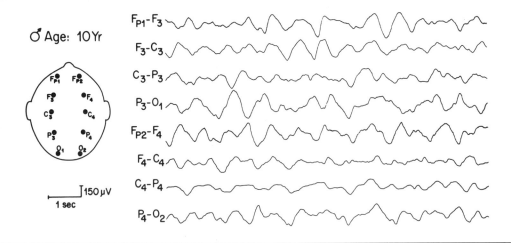

Fig. 10-15. EEG of a comatose patient with encephalitis, showing widespread delta slowing.

structures (the thalamus and the ascending projections of the ascending reticular activating system). An EEG abnormality therefore occurs as a result of a disturbance of (1) cortical neuronal activity, (2) subcortical structures that regulate cortical neuronal activity, and (3) the thalamocortical projection pathways.

The two main types of EEG abnormalities are slow-wave abnormalities and epileptiform abnormalities; both can be either focal or generalized. A focal EEG abnormality indicates a localized disturbance of cerebral function, while a generalized EEG abnormality indicates a bilateral and diffuse disturbance of cerebral function or a disturbance that is projected to the surface from subcortical structures. The EEG thus helps distinguish between a focal and a generalized disturbance of cerebral function and in determining the level of the brain involved.

In coma secondary to diffuse cerebral disease, the EEG shows widespread, generalized slowing (Fig. 10-15), with the degree of slowing often paralleling the degree of coma. When there is dysfunction of subcortical structures, the EEG shows different types of abnormalities, depending on the level of the neuraxis involved. With diencephalic or midbrain involvement, the EEG shows intermittent, rhythmic slow waves occurring bilaterally and synchronously over both hemispheres. If the pons or lower brain stem is involved, the EEG may contain alpha activity and resemble a

normal waking record, but unlike the normal alpha rhythm in an alert person, this activity does not show normal reactivity to light, noise, or noxious stimuli. In addition, there may be cyclic sleep patterns consisting of sleep spindles, V waves, and delta waves. When there are focal cerebral lesions, focal slowing is seen on the EEG (Fig. 10-16). If the primary cerebral lesion is large enough to distort or to cause a pressure effect on diencephalic or mesencephalic structures, the EEG may show intermittent, widespread, rhythmic slow-wave abnormalities in addition to the focal slow-wave abnormality.

In the diagnosis of seizure disorders, the EEG shows epileptiform abnormalities consisting of sharp waves, spikes, or spike and slow-wave discharges that may occur in a focal or generalized manner (Fig. 10-17). During an actual seizure, these occur in a sustained, repetitive, and rhythmic fashion (Fig. 10-18).

Brain Death

Brain death occurs when neural damage is irreversible, and although cardiac activity may be present, there no longer is evidence of cerebral function. The patient is unresponsive and shows no spontaneous movement or behavioral response to external stimuli. The absence of brain stem function is manifested by loss of respiratory activity and all brain stem reflexes. Absence of cerebral function can be confirmed by blood flow studies that show cessation of blood flow in

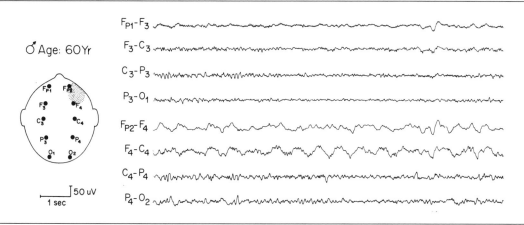

Fig. 10-16. EEG showing focal delta waves over the right frontal area (*stippled in diagram*) due to right frontal tumor.

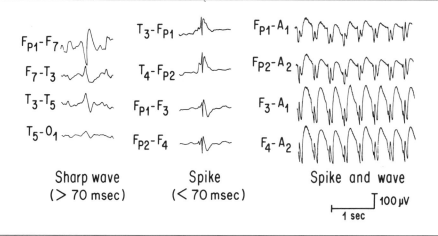

Fig. 10-17. Three types of epileptiform discharges. The sharp-wave discharge (*left*) was recorded from the left temporal region. The spike (*center*) and spike and (slow) wave discharges (*right*) were recorded from widespread areas of cortex.

the brain or by the EEG, which shows a flat pattern with no sign of electrocerebral activity. Because brain function is markedly depressed by certain anesthetic agents and other drugs, they also can produce a flat EEG. This cause should be excluded before concluding that irreversible brain death is present.

Neurologic Examination of the Consciousness System

Examination of the patient with altered consciousness represents a challenge to the physi-

cian. The situation is often emergent, and the patient is frequently uncooperative. Furthermore, assessment of the functions of the consciousness system alone seldom provides sufficient information for anatomicopathologic diagnosis, and one must rely on other associated clues from the history and results of physical examination to determine the location and cause of the responsible lesion.

Assessment of the Consciousness System

Involvement of the consciousness system is evaluated by noting the patient's ability to per-

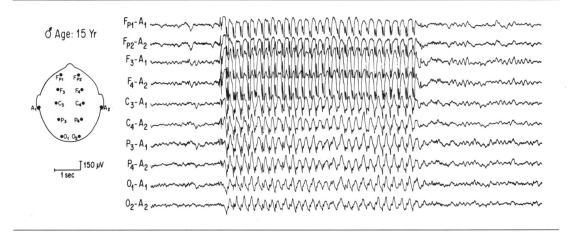

Fig. 10-18. Generalized 3-Hz spike-and-wave discharge with an absence seizure, during which the patient was unresponsive.

ceive and attend to the external environment. The degree of coma is determined by the patient's response to stimuli, such as touch, pinprick, calling the patient's name, a handclap, or some other form of loud noise. If the patient is unresponsive to milder forms of stimulation, then noxious or painful stimuli, such as pinching or deep pressure in sensitive areas, are used. The patient's response is observed to define the presence of delirium, confusion, somnolence, stupor, or coma (as described above), any of which would suggest some involvement of the consciousness system. However, from this evaluation one cannot determine the site or nature of the involvement.

Anatomicopathologic Diagnosis

Lesions affecting the consciousness system are located at the supratentorial or posterior fossa (or both) levels; therefore, one must seek clues that suggest involvement at these levels by noting the vital signs (pulse, blood pressure, respiration, temperature) and examining motor, sensory, and cranial nerve functions. Precise anatomical localization is seldom necessary, but some attempt should be made to apply the general principles of anatomical diagnosis described in Chapter 3 (Diagnosis of Neurologic Disorders: Anatomical Localization) to decide whether the responsible lesion is located at (1) the supratentorial level, (2) the posterior fossa level, or (3) if it is diffusely distributed at both levels.

This seemingly crude localization is actually extremely useful in the clinical setting, and when combined with information about the temporal evolution of the illness, it is used (as described in Chapter 4, Diagnosis of Neurologic Disorders: Neurocytology and Pathologic Reactions of the Nervous System) to establish a cause (vascular, inflammatory, toxic-metabolic, traumatic, neoplastic, or degenerative). Judicious selection of appropriate ancillary studies such as radiography, neuroimaging studies, blood studies, EEG, and cerebrospinal fluid examination is often required to establish a precise anatomico-pathologic diagnosis.

Objectives

1. Describe the anatomy of the consciousness system, with special reference to the reticular formation, the thalamic nuclei, the ascending projectional system, the basal forebrain, the cerebral cortex, and the neurochemically defined nuclear groups.
2. List the major connections (input and output) of the reticular formation.
3. Describe the projectional pathways of the consciousness system to the cortex.
4. Describe and differentiate the electrical activity of single neurons and neuronal aggregates.
5. Describe the two main types of sleep patterns, the differences between them, and

the anatomical regions involved with the sleep states.

6. Define and list the characteristics of each of the following: narcolepsy, delirium, confusion, somnolence, stupor, coma, concussion, seizure, and syncope.

7. State the anatomical locations of lesions that result in loss of consciousness, and give examples of specific disease processes that affect each area.

8. Describe the neurophysiologic basis of the EEG and the fundamental waking and sleeping patterns, and describe how the EEG is useful in evaluating patients with disorders of consciousness.

Clinical Problems

1. A 56-year-old diabetic man became confused and then unresponsive over a period of several hours. He had given himself his usual injection of insulin on awakening in the morning. Because of an upset stomach, he failed to eat anything during the day. When brought to the emergency room, he was comatose but was without localizing neurologic signs.
   a. What is the anatomicopathologic diagnosis?
   b. What portions of the consciousness system are involved?
   c. What is the precise etiologic diagnosis?
   d. What changes might be found in the EEG?

2. A 74-year-old woman with a history of hypertension had a sudden onset of a severe, right-sided headache, followed by weakness of the left side of her face and body and somnolence. When hospitalized 1 hour later, she had severe weakness on the left side of the body and face and decreased sensation on the left side of the body and face. During the next few hours, she became progressively less responsive and finally comatose.
   a. Prior to the patient's entering the hospital, what would be the most appropriate anatomicopathologic diagnosis?
   b. What is the nature of the pathologic lesion?
   c. What is the mechanism for her becoming comatose?
   d. What changes would be expected in the EEG?

3. A 38-year-old woman had a 3-year history of generalized grand mal seizures. On the day of admission to the hospital, she was found unresponsive on the floor of her living room. When brought to the emergency room, she was stuporous, with continuous bilateral convulsive movements of the face and upper and lower extremities. These subsided, and within 24 hours, the results of the neurologic examination were normal.
   a. What is the anatomicopathologic diagnosis?
   b. What changes might be seen in the EEG during the seizure?
   c. List six types of conditions that cause generalized seizures.
   d. If focal seizures were also present in this patient, would that influence your choice as to their possible cause?

Additional Reading

Culebras, A. (ed.). The neurology of sleep. *Neurology* 42 (Suppl 6), 1992.

Engel, J., Jr. *Seizures and Epilepsy.* Philadelphia: Davis, 1989.

Fisch, B. J. *Spehlmann's EEG Primer* (2nd ed.). Amsterdam: Elsevier, 1991.

Guilleminault, C., and Baker, T. L. Sleep and electroencephalography: Points of interest and points of controversy. *J. Clin. Neurophysiol.* 1:275, 1984.

Guyton, A. C. *Basic Neuroscience: Anatomy and Physiology.* Philadelphia: Saunders, 1987.

Kandel, E. R., Schwartz, J. H., and Jessell, T. M. (eds.). *Principles of Neural Science* (3rd ed.). New York: Elsevier, 1991.

Kryger, M. H., Roth, T., and Dement, W. C. *Principles and Practice of Sleep Medicine.* Philadelphia: Saunders, 1989.

Napier, T. C., Kalivas, P. W., and Hanin, I. (eds.). *The Basal Forebrain: Anatomy to Function.* New York: Plenum, 1991.

Plum, F., and Posner, J. B. *The Diagnosis of Stupor and Coma* (3rd ed.). Philadelphia: Davis, 1980.

Siegel, J. M. Mechanisms of sleep control. *J. Clin. Neurophysiol.* 7:49, 1990.

— 11 —

The Vascular System

The blood vessels to an organ provide it with a relatively constant supply of oxygen and other nutrients and a means for removal of metabolic wastes. Failure to meet these vital requirements results in disease in that organ. Because of the unique structure and organization of the nervous system, localized abnormalities in blood supply may produce devastating alterations in neural function. In this chapter, the normal anatomy and physiology of the vascular supply to neural tissue and the clinical manifestations of pathologic processes affecting this system are described.

Of all neurologic diseases likely to be encountered, cerebrovascular disease (stroke) is among the most common. Cerebrovascular disease represents a major cause of disability and death throughout the world. In the United States, stroke ranks third as a cause of death (heart disease is first; cancer is second; accidents are fourth). The amount of money spent annually on diagnosis, treatment, and rehabilitation is extremely high and because the majority of stroke victims survives the acute phase of illness and may live for years thereafter in a disabled condition, the social and economic impact of stroke is immeasurable.

Vascular disease involving cerebral vessels is no different from vascular disease involving other organ systems. The processes of atherosclerosis and thromboembolism differ little whether they involve the cerebral, peripheral, or coronary circulation. However, understanding the clinical problems in patients with cerebrovascular disease depends on a more detailed understanding of activities that are unique to the nervous system.

In the other longitudinal systems already discussed, the manifestations of disease are a direct result of damage to neural tissue within that system. The vascular system, however, is a supporting system, and diseases of the vascular system will be manifest as secondary alterations in function in other neural systems. The vascular cause of disease is identified by the characteristic temporal profile of sudden onset and rapid evolution of symptoms involving other systems.

Overview

In order to sustain aerobic metabolism, the brain is supplied by two major arterial systems. Much of the cerebral hemispheres is supplied by the carotid arterial system, while the entire posterior fossa, occipital lobes, and portions of the temporal lobes are supplied by the vertebrobasilar system. A series of anastomotic channels, including the circle of Willis located at the base of the brain, interconnect these two systems. Derivatives of the outer tube of the neuraxis receive their blood supply from large circumferential vessels, whereas derivatives of the inner tube are supplied by smaller penetrating arteries and arterioles.

Lesions involving the carotid arterial system may alter function in the distribution of any or all of its three clinically important branches: ophthalmic artery, anterior cerebral artery, and middle cerebral artery. Therefore the various combinations of hemiparesis, hemisensory deficit, monocular visual loss, homonymous hemianopia, and aphasia are suggestive of a lesion in this system. Lesions involving the vertebral and basilar arteries may alter function in the distribution of any or all of their clinically important branches,

Table 11-1. Correlation of Vascular and Parenchymal Disease

Type of vascular disease	Resultant parenchymal lesion	
	Focal	Diffuse
Occlusive-ischemic	Infarct (nonmass)	Anoxic encephalopathy
Hemorrhagic	Intracerebral hemorrhage (mass)	Subarachnoid hemorrhage

which include those to the brain stem, to the cerebellum, and to the occipital and temporal lobes via the posterior cerebral artery. The various combinations of diplopia, dysarthria, dysphagia, and disequilibrium, associated with hemiparesis, hemisensory deficit, or homonymous hemianopia, are suggestive of a lesion in the vertebrobasilar system.

The blood supply to the spinal cord is via the anterior spinal artery and paired posterior spinal arteries (branches of the vertebral arteries and descending aorta), and the vascular supply to the peripheral nerves is usually via nutrient vessels from accompanying major arterial channels.

Cerebral blood flow is normally maintained at a relatively constant rate of approximately 50 to 55 ml/100 g brain tissue per minute by a process of *autoregulation* and can thereby compensate for fluctuations in perfusion pressure and cerebrovascular resistance. Reduction in blood flow below a critical threshold level results in ischemia and infarction. Several neurogenic, chemical, and metabolic factors interact to regulate cerebral blood flow in normal and pathologic states.

The clinical pattern seen with disease in the cerebrovascular system is distinctive. The cardinal identifying feature is its *acute* onset. The symptoms produced are a reflection of the location and nature of the pathologic process. The symptoms of vascular disease may be either focal or diffusely distributed and result from parenchymal dysfunction secondary to the primary pathologic change in the blood vessels or circulatory system. The parenchymal lesions, which are the result of either occlusive-ischemic or hemorrhagic disease processes, may be of a mass or a nonmass type (Table 11-1).

Occlusive-Ischemic Vascular Disease

When a portion of neural tissue is deprived of its blood supply, *ischemia* develops. If the nor-

mal protective mechanisms are insufficient to compensate for this deprivation, death of tissue, *infarction*, results. The process of metabolic failure leading to cell death involves the cessation of blood flow, loss of energy, and neuronal depolarization. The resultant release of glutamate, entry of calcium ions into the cell, generation of oxygen free radicals and nitric oxide, and the activation of proteases and lipases all contribute to cell breakdown and infarction. The clinical symptoms reflect tissue damage in the regions of ischemia and infarction. Disease of a blood vessel may result in local thrombus formation, which may progress to occlusion, *thrombosis*, of the vessel; or a portion of the thrombus (embolus) may break loose and lodge in a more distal portion of the circulation. Both processes may result in localized areas of neural tissue being deprived of blood supply, and both may produce a focal destructive lesion (infarct). Atherosclerosis is by far the most important disease process responsible for thromboembolic disease; it is not, however, the only disease process responsible for it. Ischemia also may occur without occlusive disease if there is hemodynamic failure of the circulatory system (as might be seen with cardiac disease or profound hypotension). This type of ischemia also may result in infarction, but the defect is usually diffusely distributed throughout the brain as *anoxic encephalopathy*.

Hemorrhagic Vascular Disease

A diseased blood vessel may rupture and leak, producing *hemorrhage*. Depending on the site of accumulation of the blood, focal or diffuse neurologic symptoms may result. Blood that extravasates throughout the subarachnoid space is a *subarachnoid hemorrhage* and results in diffuse neurologic signs. Subarachnoid hemorrhage is commonly the result of trauma, rupture of an intracranial aneurysm, or bleed-

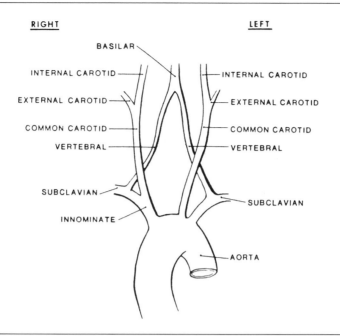

RIGHT   LEFT

BASILAR

INTERNAL CAROTID ———   ——— INTERNAL CAROTID

EXTERNAL CAROTID ———   ——— EXTERNAL CAROTID

COMMON CAROTID ———   ——— COMMON CAROTID

VERTEBRAL ———   ——— VERTEBRAL

SUBCLAVIAN ———

                                           ——— SUBCLAVIAN
INNOMINATE ———

                                           ——— AORTA

Fig. 11-1. Major arteries supplying supratentorial and posterior fossa levels.

ing from an arteriovenous malformation. Blood that accumulates within the substance of the brain is an *intracerebral hemorrhage* and results in signs of a focal, mass lesion. Intracerebral hemorrhage is commonly the result of hypertensive arteriolar disease or bleeding from an arteriovenous malformation.

Radiographic examination of the cerebral blood vessels by injection of a radiopaque substance into the arterial system (cerebral angiography), magnetic resonance angiography and imaging, and computerized tomography are important neurodiagnostic techniques that are used to identify vascular and other intracranial disease processes.

Anatomy of the Vascular System

Blood Supply to the Brain

All the arteries that supply the supratentorial and posterior fossa levels arise from the aortic arch (Fig. 11-1). The innominate (brachiocephalic) artery divides into the right common carotid and the right subclavian arteries. The left common carotid artery arises directly from the apex of the aortic arch. The right and

left common carotid arteries ascend in the neck lateral to the trachea. Slightly below the angle of the jaw each vessel bifurcates into the internal and external carotid arteries.

The *internal carotid* artery on each side enters the skull, without branching, through the carotid canal located in the petrous portion of the temporal bone. After entering the cranium, each internal carotid artery forms an S-shaped curve, the carotid siphon, and lies within the cavernous sinus. As it leaves the cavernous sinus to enter the subarachnoid space at the base of the brain, it gives rise to the *ophthalmic artery*, an important anastomotic communication with branches of the external carotid artery. Each internal carotid artery then divides into an anterior cerebral artery and a middle cerebral artery (Fig. 11-2).

The *vertebral arteries* arise as the first branches of the right and left subclavian arteries. Each artery ascends through foramina in the transverse processes of the upper six cervical vertebrae, curves behind the articular process of the atlas, pierces the dura, and enters the subarachnoid space at the level of the upper cervical spinal cord. The vertebral arteries enter the cranial cavity through the foramen magnum. The vertebral arteries are subject to

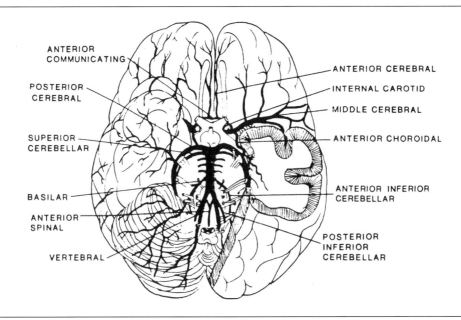

Fig. 11-2. Principal arterial vessels on basal aspect of brain. Portions of the left temporal lobe and the left cerebellar hemisphere have been removed. (Redrawn from B. Pansky and E. L. House. *Review of Gross Anatomy* [3rd ed.]. New York: Macmillan, 1975.)

normal anatomic variations; the left vertebral artery frequently arises directly from the arch of the aorta. In addition, the two vertebral arteries are often of unequal caliber.

The vertebral arteries enter the cranium and ascend on the ventrolateral surface of the medulla oblongata (see Fig. 11-2). At the lower border of the pons, they unite to form the *basilar artery*. At the level of the midbrain, the basilar artery divides into the right and left posterior cerebral arteries.

Circle of Willis

At the base of the brain, surrounding the optic chiasm and pituitary stalk, anastomotic connections occur between the internal carotid and vertebrobasilar arterial systems. This ringlike series of vessels is called the *circle of Willis* (Fig. 11-3) and consists of the *anterior communicating artery*, which unites the two anterior cerebral arteries, and the *posterior communicating arteries*, which join the internal carotid arteries with the posterior cerebral arteries. The circle of Willis is subject to frequent anatomical variation, and a "normal" circle is seen in only approxi-

mately 50 percent of the population. Common variations in the circle occur when the posterior cerebral arteries arise directly from the internal carotid via an enlarged posterior communicating artery, when one or both posterior communicating arteries are absent, and when there are multiple small anterior communicating arteries.

Blood Supply to the Outer Tube and Inner Tube of the Neuraxis

In developing a scheme of neural organization, the concept of an outer tube and an inner tube was presented. This concept is further reflected in the vascular supply to the brain. The outer tube, containing elements of the phylogenetically newer somatic longitudinal systems, receives its blood supply from the large anastomotic circumferential arteries that are easily seen in the subarachnoid space. These vessels are responsive to chemical and metabolic regulation and are susceptible to the pathophysiologic processes of atherosclerosis and thromboembolism, often resulting in large areas of infarction. In contrast, the blood supply to the phylogenetically older inner tube, containing the diffuse internal regu-

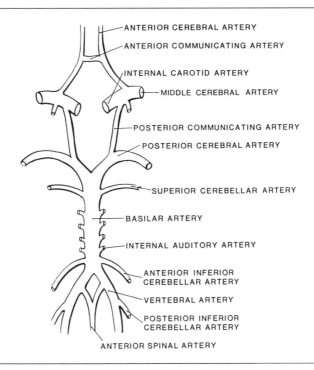

ANTERIOR CEREBRAL ARTERY

ANTERIOR COMMUNICATING ARTERY

INTERNAL CAROTID ARTERY

MIDDLE CEREBRAL ARTERY

POSTERIOR COMMUNICATING ARTERY

POSTERIOR CEREBRAL ARTERY

SUPERIOR CEREBELLAR ARTERY

BASILAR ARTERY

INTERNAL AUDITORY ARTERY

ANTERIOR INFERIOR CEREBELLAR ARTERY

VERTEBRAL ARTERY

POSTERIOR INFERIOR CEREBELLAR ARTERY

ANTERIOR SPINAL ARTERY

Fig. 11-3. Major intracranial arteries and circle of Willis (anterior cerebral, anterior communicating, posterior communicating, and posterior cerebral arteries).

lation and consciousness systems, is from penetrating vessels and end arterioles. These vessels are less responsive to chemical and metabolic regulation and are susceptible to the pathologic changes accompanying blood pressure change, which predispose to small (*lacunar*) infarction and intracranial hemorrhage.

Blood Supply to the Cerebral Hemispheres
The supratentorial level is provided with blood from the anterior, middle, and posterior cerebral arteries (Fig. 11-4). The *anterior cerebral artery* supplies the medial surface of the cerebrum and the superior border of the frontal and parietal lobes. The *middle cerebral artery* supplies most of the lateral surface of the cerebral hemispheres, including the lateral portions of the frontal lobe, the superior and lateral portions of the temporal lobes, and the deep structures of the frontal and parietal lobes. The *posterior cerebral artery* supplies the entire occipital lobe and the inferior and medial portions of the temporal lobe. The deeper structures of the cerebral hemispheres

are supplied by penetrating branches of the larger arteries. Of notable importance are the perforating *lenticulostriate arteries*, which supply the basal ganglia and internal capsule, and the perforating branches of the posterior cerebral artery, which supply the thalamus (Fig. 11-5).

Anastomoses and Collateral Circulation
Extensive communications exist between the arterial systems that supply the brain. Because of the potential for additional circulation through these alternate channels, occlusion of one or more intracranial or extracranial vessels may occur at times, with few or no resultant neurologic signs and symptoms. The major anastomotic channels are (1) the circle of Willis; (2) corticomeningeal anastomoses — communications of the three major cerebral vessels on the surface of the hemispheres at the junctional zones of the areas supplied by these vessels; and (3) anastomoses between extracranial and intracranial arteries. The most significant in the last group occur in the regions of the face and orbit where the ophthal-

Fig. 11-4. Areas of distribution of anterior, middle, and posterior cerebral arteries to the base of the cerebral hemispheres.

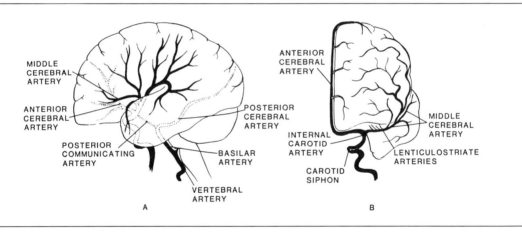

Fig. 11-5. Course and distribution of major supratentorial arteries in a lateral view (A) and an anteroposterior view (B).

mic artery, a branch of the internal carotid artery, communicates with the superficial temporal and facial branches of the external carotid artery. Occasionally, anastomoses between the external carotid and vertebral arteries occur in the neck.

Blood Supply to the Posterior Fossa

The structures contained in the posterior fossa (midbrain, pons, medulla, and cerebellum) are supplied by branches of the vertebral and

basilar arteries (see Fig. 11-2). Although there are numerous branches from these vessels, the pattern of blood supply from these branches is relatively constant (Fig. 11-6). At each level of the brain stem, short *median* and *paramedian perforating branches* arise and supply a zone on either side of the midline. The paramedian area of the caudal medulla is supplied by the *anterior spinal artery*, which arises from the union of branches from each vertebral artery. The paramedian area at higher levels is sup-

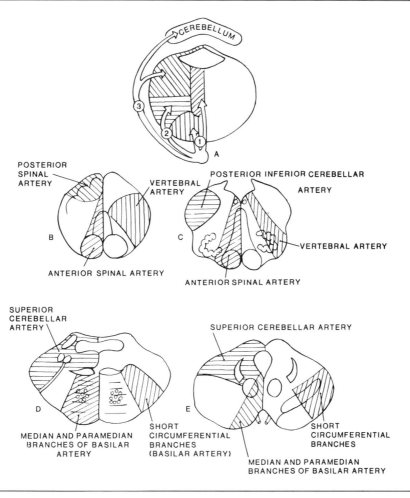

Fig. 11-6. Blood supply to posterior fossa. A. General pattern of blood supply. Arising from the basilar artery are (*1*) short median and paramedian branches supplying blood to the medial tegmentum and base of the brain stem, (*2*) short circumferential branches supplying blood to the ventrolateral tegmentum, and (*3*) long circumferential branches supplying blood to the dorsolateral tegmentum and the cerebellum. The areas of distribution of specific arteries are shown in the caudal medulla (B), medulla (C), rostral pons (D), and mesencephalon (E).

plied by penetrating branches of the basilar artery. An intermediate zone, situated more laterally at each level, is supplied by *short circumferential branches* of the vertebrobasilar system. The lateral areas of the brain stem and the cerebellum are supplied by three pairs of *long circumferential arteries*. The *posterior inferior cerebellar arteries* arise from the vertebral arteries and supply the lateral medulla and posterior inferior aspect of the cerebellum. The *anterior inferior cerebellar artery* is a branch of the basilar artery and supplies the lateral aspect of the pons and the anterior infe-

rior cerebellum. The *superior cerebellar artery* is a branch of the basilar artery and supplies the lateral midbrain and superior surface of the cerebellum.

Functional Anatomy of the Cerebral Vasculature

Clinically, the distribution of a presumed arterial lesion can be inferred by relating the observed signs and symptoms to the anatomy of the cerebral vessels. Although precise localization to a specific blood vessel is at times desirable, it is *essential* to be able to determine whether a lesion lies in the distribution of either the carotid or the vertebrobasilar arterial systems.

Lesions involving the internal carotid artery may alter function in the distribution of any or all of its three clinically important branches: (1) the ophthalmic artery, producing ipsilateral monocular loss of vision; (2) the anterior cerebral artery, producing contralateral weakness and sensory loss primarily in the leg; and (3) the middle cerebral artery, producing contralateral weakness and sensory loss maximal in the face and arm and to a lesser degree in the leg. If the optic pathways are involved, a contralateral homonymous hemianopia may be produced. With dominant hemisphere lesions, there may be involvement of speech areas, which will result in aphasia.

The various combinations, therefore, of hemiparesis, hemisensory deficit, monocular visual loss, homonymous hemianopia, and aphasia are suggestive of a lesion in the carotid arterial system.

Lesions involving vertebral and basilar arteries may alter function in the distribution of any or all of their clinically important branches: (1) branches to the brain stem itself, resulting in loss of brain stem function, cranial nerve abnormalities with or without hemiparesis, and hemisensory deficits; (2) branches to the cerebellum, resulting in ataxia and disequilibrium; and (3) posterior cerebral artery, resulting in unilateral or bilateral hemianopia.

The various combinations, therefore, of diplopia, dysarthria, dysphagia, and disequilibrium associated with hemiparesis, hemisensory deficit, and homonymous hemianopia are suggestive of a lesion in the vertebrobasilar arterial system.

Blood Supply to the Spinal Cord

The spinal cord is supplied with arterial blood by one anterior and two posterolateral vessels that run along the length of the cord and by an irregular plexus of segmentally arranged vessels that encircle the cord and interconnect the major vessels (Fig. 11-7). The *anterior spinal artery* is a single vessel lying in the ventral median fissure. It arises from a pair of small branches of the vertebral arteries that fuse along the caudal medulla and descend along

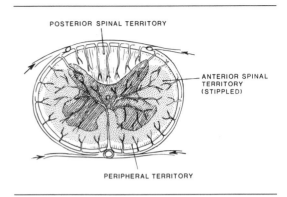

Fig. 11-7. Schematic transverse section of spinal cord illustrating the areas of supply of the anterior and posterior spinal arteries and the peripheral zone supplied by the circumferential vessels.

the cervical spinal cord (see Fig. 11-2). A series of six to eight ventral radicular arteries arising from the intercostal, lumbar, and sacral arteries connect with the anterior spinal artery at various levels along the length of the spinal cord (Fig. 11-8). The largest of these radicular arteries enters at the low thoracic or upper lumbar region. Because of this uneven blood supply, the spinal cord is most vulnerable to ischemia at the midthoracic and upper lumbar levels, as shown by the stippled areas in Figure 11-8. Sulcal branches of the anterior spinal artery pass alternately to the right and left at each segment to supply blood for the interior of the spinal cord (see Fig. 11-7).

The *posterior spinal arteries* are paired structures that run along the posterolateral aspect of the cord near the dorsal roots. They receive contributions from the posterior radicular arteries (Fig. 11-9) and supply the dorsal funiculus and dorsal gray horns (see Fig. 11-7).

Vascular diseases of the spinal cord are less common than similar processes in the posterior fossa or cerebrum. When ischemic disease occurs, however, it is most often confined to the distribution of the anterior spinal artery, where it produces loss of motor function and loss of pain and temperature sensation below the lesion; the functions associated with the dorsal columns are spared (see Fig. 11-7).

Blood Supply to Peripheral Structures

All neural structures must receive adequate arterial blood supply in order to sustain life

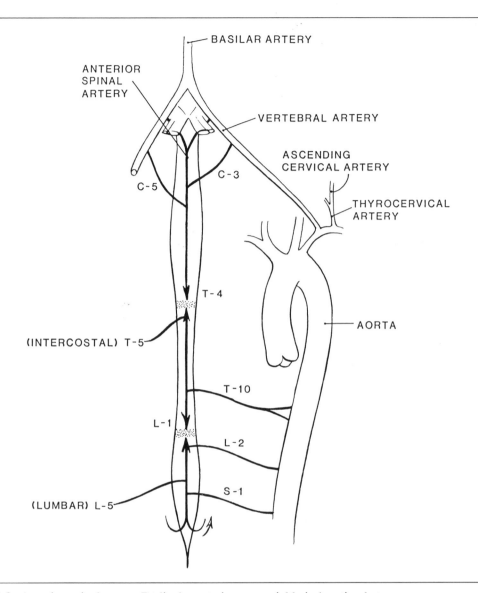

Fig. 11-8. Anterior spinal artery. Radicular arteries are variable in location but are shown here at C-3, C-5, T-4, T-10, L-2, L-1, and S-1. Stippled areas indicate zones of marginal blood supply. (Redrawn from B. Pansky and E. L. House. *Review of Gross Anatomy* [3rd ed.]. New York: Macmillan, 1975.)

and maintain their integrity. The axons traveling to the periphery are gathered into bundles or fascicles that have a connective tissue covering. Within this covering, along the entire course of the nerve, is a rich and highly anastomotic plexus of small arterioles derived from the branches of the major extremity vessels (Fig. 11-10). This dense anastomosis renders the peripheral nerve relatively immune to ischemic vascular disease. Such abnormality, when noted in peripheral neural structures, is usually associated with either direct compression of nerve or with multiple segmental vascular lesions from small vessel arterial disease.

Venous Drainage of the Central Nervous System

The venous drainage of the brain is divided into superficial and deep systems. The cortex and outer half of the white matter drain into the superficial system of veins located over the

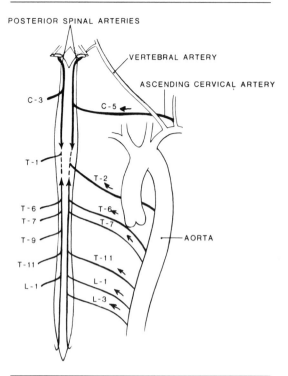

POSTERIOR SPINAL ARTERIES

VERTEBRAL ARTERY

ASCENDING CERVICAL ARTERY

C-3

C-5

T-1

T-2

T-6

T-6

T-7

T-7

T-9

AORTA

T-11

T-11

L-1

L-1

L-3

Fig. 11-9. Posterior spinal arteries supply blood to the posterior aspect of spinal cord. They receive blood from radicular arteries at multiple levels. (Redrawn from B. Pansky and E. L. House. *Review of Gross Anatomy* [3rd ed.]. New York: Macmillan, 1975.)

convexity of the brain in the subarachnoid space. The superficial veins of the superior half of the brain drain into the *superior sagittal sinus*; those from the inferior half drain into the *lateral sinuses*. The deep white matter and deep nuclei of the brain drain into the deep venous system, which includes the *great cerebral vein of Galen, inferior sagittal sinus*, and *straight sinus*. From these venous channels, blood empties into the transverse sinuses, the sigmoid sinuses, and ultimately the jugular veins (Fig. 11-11). Veins on the inferior surfaces of the cerebrum terminate directly or indirectly in the *cavernous sinus*, an important dural structure located on either side of the pituitary fossa containing the carotid artery; cranial nerves III, IV, and VI; and branches of cranial nerve V.

The spinal cord is drained by an anastomotic venous plexus surrounding the dural sac. Veins drain outward along both the dorsal and ventral roots into this plexus, which has numerous connections with the veins of the thoracic, abdominal, and pelvic cavities.

Physiology of the Vascular System

Cerebral Blood Flow

For normal neural function, adequate blood flow and oxygenation must be maintained. The

Fig. 11-10. Blood supply to peripheral nerve. Multiple anastomotic channels are derived from regional arteries.

VEIN

EPINEURIUM

PERINEURIUM

FASCICLE

PERFORATING ARTERIOLE AND CAPILLARY PLEXUS

REGIONAL ARTERY

NUTRIENT ARTERY

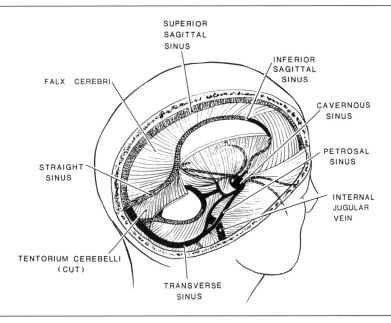

Fig. 11-11. Dura mater and its major sinuses. Dorsolateral view illustrating falx cerebri, tentorium cerebelli, and dura lining base of skull. The dural venous sinuses are stippled or black.

normal blood flow through the brain is approximately 750 ml per minute, or about 50 to 55 ml/100 g brain tissue per minute. Although the brain constitutes only 2 percent of the body weight, it receives 15 percent of the cardiac output and utilizes 20 percent of the oxygen consumed in the basal state. The total oxygen consumption of the brain is approximately 50 ml per minute, or 3.7 ml/100 g brain tissue per minute. Any decrease in the amount of available oxygen provided to the brain reduces neural activity. Under normal conditions, the total oxygen consumption and blood flow to the brain are nearly constant. Cortical gray matter with its increased metabolic demand has about six times the blood flow of white matter. Local changes in blood flow may occur with the changing demands of varying neural activity.

In any hemodynamic system, blood flow is directly proportional to the perfusion pressures and inversely proportional to the total resistance of the system. For the brain, this can be expressed by the following equation:

$$\text{Cerebral blood flow} \approx \frac{\text{mean arterial pressure} - \text{central venous pressure}}{\text{cerebrovascular resistance}}$$

A number of factors can modify cerebral blood flow by altering different elements in the equation above. These have been arbitrarily divided into two groups: (1) extracerebral factors and (2) intracerebral factors (Table 11-2).

Extracerebral Factors
Factors outside the cranial cavity that modify or regulate the cerebral blood flow are primarily related to the cardiovascular system and include the systemic blood pressure, the efficiency of cardiac function, and the viscosity of the blood. The principal force in maintaining the cerebral circulation is the pressure difference between the arteries and the veins. Because under normal circumstances, cerebral venous pressure is low (approximately 5 mm Hg), the arterial blood pressure becomes the most important factor in maintaining cerebral blood flow. Variations in systemic arterial blood pressure do not, however, ordinarily produce changes in cerebral blood flow in healthy persons if the intrinsic regulatory mechanisms are intact, unless the mean arterial pressure decreases to less than 50 to 70 mm Hg. The systemic arterial blood pressure is dependent on the efficiency of cardiac function (cardiac out-

Table 11-2. Factors Regulating Cerebral Blood Flow (CBF)

Factors	Increased CBF	Decreased CBF
Extrinsic		
Systemic blood pressure		Mean arterial pressure < 50 to 70 mm Hg
Cardiovascular function		Cardiac arrhythmias; orthostatic hypotension; loss of carotid sinus and aortic arch reflexes
Blood viscosity	Anemia	Polycythemia
Intrinsic		
State of the cerebral vasculature	Arteriovenous malformation	Atherosclerosis
Intracranial CSF pressure		Increased intracranial pressure
Cerebral autoregulatory mechanisms		
Myogenic factors	Decreased intraluminal pressure (vasodilation)	Increased intraluminal pressure (vasoconstriction)
Neurogenic factors	Parasympathetic stimulation (vasodilation)	Sympathetic stimulation (vasoconstriction)
Biochemical-metabolic factors	Increased carbon dioxide (vasodilation)	Decreased carbon dioxide (vasoconstriction)
	Decreased oxygen (vasodilation)	Increased oxygen (vasoconstriction)
	Decreased pH (acidosis) (vasodilation)	Increased pH (alkalosis) (vasoconstriction)
	Lactic acid (vasodilation)	

put) and the peripheral vasomotor tone or resistance. These are governed principally by autonomic control from the vasomotor center in the medulla. Alterations in cardiac rhythm and myocardial function or the presence of cardiac disease may result in changes in cardiac output that may secondarily influence cerebral blood flow. Baroreceptors in the carotid sinus and aortic arch participate in reflexes that mediate cardiovascular tone and help to maintain a constant blood pressure. Advancing age, the presence of atherosclerosis, and certain drugs may alter these reflex mechanisms, and a simple physiologic act such as assuming an upright posture may result in severe orthostatic hypotension and pronounced reduction in cerebral blood flow (causing fainting or syncope). In addition, the viscosity of the blood may alter cerebral blood flow; severe anemia may increase flow as much as 30 percent, while polycythemia may decrease flow by more than 50 percent.

Intracerebral Factors

The state of the cerebral vasculature also can influence cerebral blood flow. Widespread intracranial arterial disease increases cerebrovascular resistance and can result in a reduction in cerebral blood flow, whereas pathologic processes that are associated with a rapid shunting of blood from arteries to veins (such as occurs with an arteriovenous malformation) may produce both an increase in total cerebral blood flow and a local reduction in tissue perfusion.

Any increase in intracranial pressure is transmitted directly to the low-pressure venous system and increases cerebral venous pressure, thus decreasing cerebral blood flow. In pathologic states that are frequently accompanied by an increase in intracranial pressure (see Chapter 6, The Cerebrospinal Fluid System), this reduction in blood flow may further accentuate the signs and symptoms produced by the primary lesion.

Regulation of Cerebral Blood Flow

Several factors can modify cerebral blood flow. These include (1) neurogenic control, (2) chemical factors, (3) metabolic regulation, and (4) autoregulation.

Neurogenic Control

Although the extracranial and intracranial arteries are richly supplied by a neural network, neurogenic factors do not seem to play as great a role in the regulation of cerebral blood flow as chemical and metabolic factors. Neurogenic control can be viewed as both extrinsic and intrinsic to the brain.

1. Extrinsic neurogenic control is provided by postganglionic fibers from the superior cervical sympathetic ganglion that innervate the carotid and vertebral arteries and their major intracranial branches. Norepinephrine released from these sympathetic fibers produces vasoconstriction. The main role of this neurogenic control is to protect capillaries against hyperperfusion whenever blood pressure is increased. Parasympathetic fibers travel in the facial and superficial petrosal nerves to innervate cerebral blood vessels of large and small diameter. These fibers use acetylcholine as a transmitter. Fibers from the facial nerve are a source of nitric oxide, a potent vasodilator substance. Fibers from the trigeminal ganglion that use substance P and calcitonin gene-related peptide also innervate cerebral vessels and produce vasodilatation and increased permeability.
2. Intrinsic neurogenic control of the cerebral circulation is provided by pathways originating in the brain stem and by interneurons in the cerebral cortex. The major brain stem pathways are from (a) the locus ceruleus, whose neurons use norepinephrine to produce microcirculatory vasodilatation, (b) the raphe nuclei, whose neurons use serotonin, a vasoconstrictor substance, and (c) the fastigial nuclei of the cerebellum. Activation of cortical interneurons containing neuropeptide Y produces local vasoconstriction, but activation of ones containing vasoactive intestinal peptide causes local vasodilatation.

Chemical Factors

In contrast to the modest effects of neurogenic control, chemical-metabolic factors exert a strong influence on cerebral blood flow. *Carbon dioxide*, a substance that rapidly diffuses across the blood-brain barrier and an end product of cerebral metabolism, is also the most potent physiologic and pharmacologic agent that influences cerebral blood flow. Cerebral blood vessels react rapidly to any change in local carbon dioxide tension ($PaCO_2$). Any increase in $PaCO_2$ produces vasodilatation and increased cerebral blood flow, whereas a decrease in $PaCO_2$ has the opposite effect. The cerebral circulation reacts to *oxygen* in the reverse manner; a reduction in local oxygen tension (PaO_2) produces vasodilatation and increased cerebral blood flow, and an increase in PaO_2 produces vasoconstriction and a decrease in cerebral blood flow. The exact mechanism by which these agents exert their effects on cerebral blood vessels is unknown. They may act directly on the smooth muscle of the vessel wall, indirectly via neurogenic chemoreceptors, or by producing alterations in brain hydrogen ion concentration (pH). A reduction in brain pH (acidosis) from any cause produces vasodilatation and increased cerebral blood flow, whereas an increase in brain pH (alkalosis) is associated with vasoconstriction and decreased cerebral blood flow. *Lactic acid*, which is produced by the shift to anaerobic metabolism in regions of ischemia, is therefore a potent vasodilator.

Metabolic Regulation

Under normal conditions, cerebral blood flow is coupled directly to neuronal metabolic activity, with a linear increase or decrease in cerebral blood flow resulting from a corresponding change in brain metabolic activity. This coupling of blood flow occurs with a short latency of 1 to 2 seconds and is a strictly regional effect, producing little alteration in overall total blood flow despite measurable local change. Local metabolic coupling can be demonstrated during sleep, during various sensorimotor tasks, and in pathologic conditions such as coma and seizure. The mechanism of metabolic coupling involves vasodilator metabolites such as adenosine, potassium and hydrogen ions, prostaglandins, oxygen free radicals, and the vasodilatory transmitters (acetylcholine and vasoactive intestinal polypeptide).

Autoregulation

The normal brain has the ability to regulate its own blood supply (*autoregulation*) in response to changes in the arterial blood pressure and metabolic demand. *Autoregulation* is defined as the ability of an organ (for example, the brain) to maintain its blood flow constant for all but the widest extremes in perfusion pressure. Autoregulation of the cerebral blood flow occurs when the mean arterial blood pressure is between 60 and 150 mm Hg; below 60 mm Hg, blood flow decreases, and above 150 mm Hg, blood flow increases.

The brain can accomplish autoregulation by using myogenic, neurogenic, and chemical-metabolic mechanisms. Autoregulation occurs in both large and small arterioles. Cerebral vessels, like other hollow organs that contain smooth muscle, can alter their diameter in response to intraluminal pressure. This effect (known as the "Bayliss effect") results in vasoconstriction with increased intraluminal pressure and in vasodilatation with a decrease in pressure. Therefore, autoregulation is primarily a pressure-controlled myogenic mechanism that operates independently but synergistically with other neurogenic and chemical-metabolic factors.

Autoregulation is thus a major homeostatic and protective mechanism. In normal persons, autoregulation prevents alteration in cerebral blood flow despite variations in systemic blood pressure or regional increases in metabolic demand on the brain. In the situation of regional increase in metabolism, a corresponding increase in carbon dioxide results, to produce local vasodilatation and increased blood flow, thus accommodating the increased metabolic demand. In certain disease states associated with vascular occlusion, an area of regional ischemia develops because of the reduction in available blood supply; intraluminal pressure decreases, oxygen is no longer available, $PaCO_2$ increases, lactate is produced, and the tissue becomes acidotic. All these factors produce vasodilatation of nearby vessels and may provide an increase in blood flow to an area of ischemia. In certain situations, this is sufficient to increase regional cerebral blood flow and to prevent infarction; in other situations, it may reduce the size of the resultant infarct. In a region of cerebral infarction, these protective mechanisms have reduced cerebrovascular resistance to a very low value. Because there is little acute change in

the central venous pressure, the major determinant of blood flow in the region of ischemic tissue becomes the mean arterial blood pressure. The proper maintenance of systemic blood pressure, therefore, may be of prime importance in the treatment of ischemic infarcts, and any pronounced reduction in systemic pressure or the presence of cerebral edema (which will secondarily increase venous pressure) may further alter cellular function.

Cerebral Metabolism

High metabolic activity and high oxygen consumption characterize cerebral metabolism. A constant supply of energy is necessary for the support of neuronal and neurologic functions. These vital energy-dependent processes include the establishment of membrane potentials, maintenance of transmembrane ionic gradients, membrane transport, and the synthesis of cellular constituents such as proteins, nucleic acids, lipids, and neurotransmitters. The energy needed is supplied in the form of high-energy phosphate bonds from adenosine triphosphate (ATP), which is synthesized in the brain, as in other organ systems, through the glycolytic pathway, the Krebs' (citric acid) cycle, and the respiratory (electron-transport) chain (Table 11-3).

Under aerobic conditions, glucose is effectively metabolized through the glycolytic pathway, citric acid cycle, and respiratory chain to yield 38 moles of ATP per mole of glucose. Under anaerobic conditions, the Krebs' (citric acid) cycle and respiratory chain cannot be activated (because of lack of oxygen); therefore, the pyruvate derived from glycolysis is metabolized to lactate and yields only 2 moles of ATP per mole of glucose. Another source of high-energy phosphate bonds is *creatine phosphate*. This compound, which is even more abundant than ATP in the brain, is used to regenerate ATP from adenosine diphosphate (ADP) and is thus important for maintaining the level of tissue ATP. Although glycogen is present and the brain is capable of its rapid synthesis and breakdown, the role of glycogen in brain metabolism is not completely understood and the extent of its participation in the production of high-energy phos-

Table 11-3. Glucose Metabolism

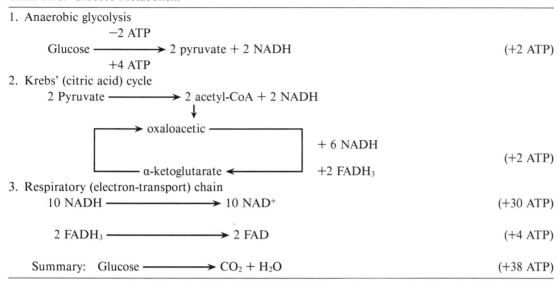

1. Anaerobic glycolysis

$$\text{Glucose} \xrightarrow[\text{+4 ATP}]{\text{−2 ATP}} \text{2 pyruvate + 2 NADH} \qquad (\text{+2 ATP})$$

2. Krebs' (citric acid) cycle

$$\text{2 Pyruvate} \longrightarrow \text{2 acetyl-CoA + 2 NADH}$$

oxaloacetic

α-ketoglutarate

+ 6 NADH

+2 FADH$_3$

(+2 ATP)

3. Respiratory (electron-transport) chain

$$\text{10 NADH} \longrightarrow \text{10 NAD}^+ \qquad (\text{+30 ATP})$$

$$\text{2 FADH}_3 \longrightarrow \text{2 FAD} \qquad (\text{+4 ATP})$$

$$\text{Summary:} \quad \text{Glucose} \longrightarrow CO_2 + H_2O \qquad (\text{+38 ATP})$$

phate bonds through glycogenolysis in the brain is not known. However, regardless of the existence of glycogen and the possible participation of amino acids in the processes of oxidative phosphorylation, *glucose is the basic substrate for brain metabolism.*

Pathophysiology

Reversible alteration in cell function due to lack of oxygen results in *ischemia*, and irreversible alteration results in *infarction*. After vessel occlusion and deprivation of blood flow to the brain, a series of events unfold (the "ischemic cascade") that consist of the following alterations and lead ultimately to neuronal dysfunction and death:

1. Cerebral blood flow and cerebral oxygen and glucose consumption decrease in the center of the ischemic area. These functions are less impaired at the periphery of the ischemic area (the "ischemic penumbra") where there are accompanying functional changes (for example, the electroencephalogram is isoelectric at flow rates less than 15 ml/100 g per minute) but where blood flow is sufficient to prevent irreversible cell damage.

2. Local autoregulatory mechanisms are impaired, and local responsivity of vessels to chemical and metabolic changes and to alterations in perfusion pressure is lost.

3. Anaerobic glycolysis is initiated as the vital substrates, oxygen and glucose, are decreased and brain glycogen content falls. Tissue lactate increases but pH decreases, and a zone of hyperemia and increased perfusion develops in the periphery of the ischemic zone.

4. Substrate depletion leads to failure of mitochondrial function and inefficient ATP generation, with leakage of potassium ions from cells and the intracellular accumulation of sodium, chloride, and calcium ions and free fatty acids. The net effect is neuronal depolarization, loss of the transmembrane potential, and increase in tissue water. This also produces impairment of ATP-dependent neurotransmitter reuptake.

5. Energy loss also results in increased release of excitatory neurotransmitters such as glutamate. The neurotoxic effect of this large accumulation of glutamate in the extracellular space is exerted through activation of *N*-methyl-D-aspartate (NMDA) receptors, causing increased permeability to sodium ions, cellular swelling and lysis, and massive entry of calcium ions into the postsynaptic neuron. Additional calcium-induced release of excitatory neurotransmitters during the ischemic process heightens neuronal necrosis.

6. The increase in intracellular calcium activates phospholipases and proteases and

generates oxygen free radicals and nitric oxide. This leads to membrane, mitochondrial, and microtubular damage and eventually cell destruction.

If the period of ischemia is short and the supply of high-energy phosphate bonds can be reestablished, neuronal function can resume. The local accumulation of adenosine, potassium, and hydrogen, which occurs in response to the production of lactic acid, produces local vasodilatation in an attempt to restore an adequate blood supply. However, if the cell continues to be deprived of its nourishment, catabolic and morphologic changes occur in the neuron. Initially, the cell begins to swell (acute cell change); if its metabolic needs are not met, the cell becomes irreversibly damaged. This is referred to as *infarction*, the morphologic correlate of which is *ischemic cell change* (described in Chapter 4, Diagnosis of Neurologic Disorders: Neurocytology and Pathologic Reactions of the Nervous System). If the area of infarction is large, other cellular elements and the blood-brain barrier will be affected. In the region of maximal change, there is death and destruction of cells. With the catabolic changes and breakdown in the blood-brain barrier, the water content of the tissue increases. The associated *brain edema* may further impair the function of cells in the regions surrounding the infarction. After scavenger cells enter the area and the cellular debris is removed, a cystic cavity remains.

In conditions of partial ischemia, the decline of high-energy phosphate bonds is less precipitous, and the irreversible damage occurs only after a more prolonged period of ischemia. Thus, in *cerebral hypoxia*, because there is an abundant supply of glucose, the metabolic changes are similar to those of anoxia but lesser in extent. However, if the hypoxia is prolonged, the accumulation of lactate due to accelerated glycolysis becomes significant, and ischemia and infarction may result.

In *hypoglycemia*, the brain is supplied with adequate oxygen but lacks glucose as a substrate. Hypoglycemia produces a different metabolic pattern than that seen in cerebral ischemia. In hypoglycemia, the brain can maintain high-energy phosphate bonds through the utilization of creatine phosphate

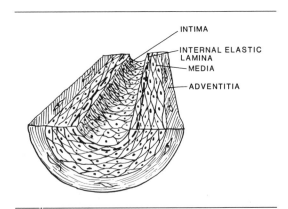

Fig. 11-12. Cross section of normal arterial wall; note intima, internal elastic lamina, media, and adventitia.

and other substances. Although function is temporarily altered, if the glucose deficiency is not present for a prolonged period, then catabolic changes are not produced and recovery can occur upon reversal of the hypoglycemic state.

Pathology of the Vascular System

The symptoms and signs produced by vascular disease are a reflection of altered neuronal function in focal or diffuse areas of the nervous system. The location and nature of the underlying neural-parenchymal lesion are directly related to the abnormalities found in the blood vessels or circulatory system. Therefore, this discussion of the pathology of the vascular system considers (1) the major derangements involving blood vessels and (2) the neural-parenchymal lesions produced by these vascular abnormalities.

Vascular Pathology

Normal Arterial Histology
The normal arterial wall contains three distinct layers (Fig. 11-12): (1) the *intima*, a layer of endothelial cells surrounding the vessel lumen with a small amount of extracellular connective tissue, the internal elastic lamina; (2) the *media*, a layer of diagonally oriented smooth muscle cells surrounded by collagen and mucopolysaccharides; and (3) the *adventitia*, the outermost layer, containing fibroblasts and smooth muscle cells intermixed with bun-

Fig. 11-13. Angiographic study showing aneurysm (*arrow*) that arose from internal carotid–posterior communicating artery junction.

dles of collagen and mucopolysaccharides. An external elastic lamina is generally not found in cerebral arteries.

Intracranial Arterial Aneurysms

An *aneurysm* is an abnormal, localized dilatation of the arterial lumen. The most commonly encountered type is a round or oval-shaped, berry-like structure that arises at the bifurcation of cerebral vessels (Fig. 11-13). The majority of cerebral aneurysms are located in the anterior half of the circle of Willis, with the most favored sites being the internal carotid–posterior communicating artery junction, the anterior cerebral–anterior communicating artery junction, and the middle cerebral artery bifurcation. Perhaps secondary to a developmental anomaly, a ballooning of the intima is seen associated with a defect in the media and internal elastic lamina (Fig. 11-14). Varying in size from 1 to more than 10 mm, these lesions occasionally produce symptoms by exerting pressure on adjacent structures but more often present with rupture and bleeding into the subarachnoid space or brain (Fig. 11-15). Occasionally, aneurysms arise secondary to destruction of the arterial wall by atherosclerosis (atherosclerotic aneurysm) or to infected emboli arising from the heart (septic or mycotic aneurysm).

Fig. 11-14. Aneurysm (*right*) of internal carotid artery (*left*). Note abrupt termination of media and internal elastic lamina of carotid artery at neck of aneurysm. (Elastic stain; ×4.)

Arteriovenous Malformations

Arteriovenous malformations are developmental abnormalities that are often encountered in young adults. They result from defective communication between arteries, capillaries, and veins, with dilatation of one or more of the vascular elements, thus forming a variable-sized meshwork of tortuous blood vessels (Figs. 11-16 and 11-17). The walls of these abnormal vessels may be thin (and predisposed to rupture) or they may be hypertrophic. Rapid shunting of blood generally occurs and may produce a chronic ischemic state in the neighboring brain. Depending on the location and structure of the malformation, there may be associated seizures and focal neurologic deficit, infarction, or bleeding into the subarachnoid space or brain.

Atherosclerosis

A generalized vascular derangement of unknown but probably multifarious causes, atherosclerosis is the most important pathologic lesion responsible for cerebral infarction. The basic pathologic lesion is the atherosclerotic plaque. Although secondary changes may occur in other layers of the vessel wall, the intima is the layer that is principally involved in atherogenesis. Injury to the arterial wall causes focal desquamation of endothelial cells and exposes subendothelial connective tissue to circulating platelets. Stimulated by the denuded surface, platelets aggregate and adhere

Fig. 11-15. Coronal section of hemispheres showing large ruptured aneurysm of the left internal carotid artery associated with subarachnoid and intraventricular hemorrhage.

Fig. 11-16. Angiograms showing large arteriovenous malformation. *Left*, antero-posterior view. *Right*, lateral view.

Fig. 11-18. Cross section of atherosclerotic plaque in carotid artery. Arterial wall necrosis with mural thrombosis and stenosis of lumen is seen. (H & E; ×3.5.)

Fig. 11-17. Arteriovenous malformation of left parietal lobe. Note tangled mass of dilated vessels in roughly wedge-shaped area pointing toward ventricle, with degeneration of cerebral tissue between vessels. Celloidin section. (Luxol fast-blue stain; ×1.)

to the arterial wall. The process of platelet aggregation releases substances that, in association with certain lipids, induce smooth muscle and endothelial proliferation to form an elevated fibrous plaque that protrudes slightly into the arterial lumen. Although these early atherogenic lesions may regress, with further arterial injury the process is repeated, and the plaque becomes altered by ulceration, increased lipid content, hemorrhage, cell necrosis, mural thrombosis, and calcification to form the typical atherosclerotic plaque with narrowing (stenosis) or occlusion of the arterial lumen (Fig. 11-18). Clinically, many of the so-called risk factors for atherogenesis are also factors that have been shown experimentally to be capable of producing chronic injury to the arterial wall: increased shear stress hypertension, hyperlipidemia, and diabetes.

The basic processes of platelet aggregation and release and secondary plaque formation can be inhibited by certain drugs. Platelet-vessel wall interaction is influenced by the selective oxygenation of arachidonic acid in both the platelet and the vascular endothelium. In the platelet, thromboxane synthase converts prostaglandin H_2 to thromboxane A_2, which is a potent aggregator of platelets as well as a constrictor of arterial conductance vessels. Vascular endothelium, however, metabolizes prostaglandin H_2 to prostacyclin, a compound that antagonizes platelet aggregation and dilates blood vessels. These observations suggest that pharmacologic agents that selectively inhibit thromboxane synthase or facilitate the biosynthesis of prostacyclin might be beneficial in preventing the thromboembolic complications of atherosclerosis. Although the optimal pharmacologic agent is not yet available, drugs such as acetylsalicylic acid are beneficial.

The vascular endothelium itself is a source of vasoactive substances. Endothelium-derived relaxing factors such as nitric oxide produce vasodilatation. Endothelium-derived constricting factors such as the endothelin group of peptides are potent vasoconstrictors.

Atherosclerosis tends chiefly to affect large-caliber blood vessels; in the cerebral circulation, both the intracranial and the extracranial arteries may be involved (Fig. 11-19). Al-

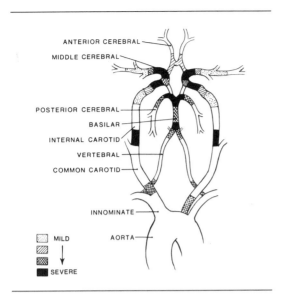

Fig. 11-19. Location and severity of atherosclerotic lesions in major extracranial and intracranial vessels. (Redrawn from R. Escourolle and J. Poirier. *Manual of Basic Neuropathology.* Translated by L. J. Rubinstein. Philadelphia: Saunders, 1973.)

though minimal patchy involvement of the carotid and vertebral arteries is seen, significant stenosis or occlusion commonly occurs at selected sites. The carotid arteries, in their extracranial portion, tend to develop atherosclerotic plaques at the carotid bifurcations and in the proximal portions of the internal carotid arteries, whereas the vertebral arteries are especially likely to develop lesions at their sites of origin from the subclavian arteries. Atherosclerosis of the intracranial arteries is usually limited to the larger arteries related to the circle of Willis and is found most frequently in the internal carotid, proximal middle cerebral, vertebral, and basilar arteries. The smaller distal branches of the major cerebral arteries are seldom involved by gross atheromatous plaques.

The relative importance of the intracranial compared with the extracranial arteries in the pathogenesis of cerebral ischemia is not known. Localized atheromatous plaques may occur in either site, produce focal thrombosis, and reduce blood flow distal to the lesion. This mechanism may be responsible for producing some types of cerebral infarction.

An additional danger is the development of local intraarterial thrombosis, with subsequent *embolization* to distal vessels (Fig. 11-20). These changes are frequently noted when there are lesions at the carotid bifurcation and other extracranial sites. Therefore, although it was formerly assumed that thrombosis of an intracranial artery was the most common cause of cerebral infarction, it has now become evident that atherosclerotic involvement of extracranial vessels with distal embolization is probably of equal significance; in fact this may represent the major pathogenetic mechanism for the production of transient ischemic attacks. Atherosclerotic narrowing of extracranial or cerebral vessels may lead to

Fig. 11-20. Mechanism of thromboembolism secondary to atherosclerosis. (Redrawn from R. Escourolle and J. Poirier. *Manual of Basic Neuropathology.* Translated by L. J. Rubinstein. Philadelphia: Saunders, 1973.)

Fig. 11-21. Hypertensive fibrinoid necrosis. Note irregular degeneration and dilatation of wall associated with infiltration by fibrinoid material and lymphocytes. (H & E; ×100.)

cerebral ischemia and infarction, with or without actual thrombosis, if there is a sudden hemodynamic reduction in cerebral blood flow in an area of the brain where the blood supply is already marginal.

Fibrinoid Necrosis

A segmental, nonatherosclerotic arteriopathy, fibrinoid necrosis (also referred to as lipohyalinosis and arteriolar sclerosis), involves primarily smaller intraparenchymal blood vessels and is found almost exclusively in the brains of hypertensive patients. The lesion is characterized by the presence of a fibrinoid material and lipid-laden macrophages in the subintimal layer of cerebral vessels (Fig. 11-21). It is postulated that sustained elevations in blood pressure result in further arterial disorganization. Some of these lesions show progressive luminal obliteration and eventually result in small areas of infarction called *lacunae*, but others produce progressive weakening of the vessel wall and microaneurysm formation and eventually rupture and produce an intracerebral hemorrhage.

Other Types of Blood Vessel Lesions

Other pathologic processes that may result in disease of intracranial arteries and veins can produce local thrombosis and resultant infarction or hemorrhage. Common examples include (1) inflammatory involvement of cere-

bral blood vessels, *arteritis*, which may occur secondary to infectious processes (syphilis, pyogenic meningitis) or may accompany certain systemic disorders (lupus erythematosus, periarteritis nodosa); (2) certain hematologic disorders (polycythemia, sickle cell disease); and (3) emboli of various types arising from distant sources (usually the heart).

Neural-Parenchymal Pathology

The neural-parenchymal lesions produced by the vascular lesions just discussed are of two major types: (1) hemorrhage and (2) infarction. Lesions of both types are common at the supratentorial and posterior fossa levels but less frequent at the spinal level. Symptomatic vascular disease involving the peripheral level is distinctly rare and generally occurs with lesions involving smaller arteries and arterioles that secondarily alter the blood supply to peripheral nerves.

Hemorrhagic Lesions

Pathologic examination reveals that nontraumatic intracranial hemorrhagic disease may be defined by its anatomical location. It is usually found within the subarachnoid space as *subarachnoid hemorrhage* (refer to Fig. 6-14), within the parenchyma of the brain as *intracerebral hemorrhage* (Fig. 11-22), or as a combination of the two. Hemorrhage in either of these locations may be produced by various pathophysiologic mechanisms, the most common being (1) rupture of an intracranial aneurysm, usually producing subarachnoid hemorrhage (occasionally with an associated intracerebral hemorrhage); (2) rupture of an intraparenchymal vessel, usually producing a variably sized, blood-filled mass lesion (intracerebral hemorrhage), which often has some extension of bleeding into the ventricles; and (3) bleeding from an arteriovenous malformation, commonly producing either a subarachnoid hemorrhage or an intracerebral hemorrhage, alone or in combination.

Infarction

With prolonged tissue ischemia, permanent pathologic change occurs in neuronal function and structure. In the presence of diffuse oxygen deprivation, wide areas of cerebral cortex

Fig. 11-22. Massive left intracerebral hemorrhage with intraventricular rupture in hypertensive patient.

(which is more sensitive to metabolic alteration than other cerebral structures) have evidence of necrosis and cell loss, *anoxic encephalopathy* (Fig. 11-23). More commonly, the area of infarction is localized to the distribution of a diseased blood vessel (Fig. 11-24). In that region, softening and necrosis with *ischemic cell change* (see Chapter 4, Diagnosis of Neurologic Disorders: Neurocytology and Pathologic Reactions of the Nervous System) are observed. The size of the infarct varies; smaller lesions (0.5 to 10 mm) are often referred to as *lacunar infarctions* and are common in the brains of hypertensive patients (Fig. 11-25). On occasion, especially with large infarctions, the original nonmass lesion may become edematous and assume the characteristics of a mass lesion. With the passage of time, the necrotic tissue in an infarcted area is removed by phagocytes and replaced by a cavity containing cystic fluid surrounded by an area of glial tissue (Fig. 11-26).

Clinical Correlations

Risk Factors for Stroke

The goal of medical therapy in cerebrovascular disease is prevention. Epidemiologic studies have identified numerous factors, including hyperlipidemia, obesity, diabetes, and excessive smoking, that appear to be associated with atherosclerosis. Because atherosclerosis is a major cause of stroke, many of these same factors are present in the stroke-prone profile. There are, in addition, three highly specific factors that have been shown to be associated with a greatly increased risk of stroke but more importantly to result in a significant decrease in stroke incidence when promptly recognized and treated. These factors include (1) transient focal ischemic attacks, (2) hypertension, and (3) certain cardiac disorders.

Fig. 11-23. Diffuse hypoxic brain damage in patient who survived 7 months in coma after cardiac arrest. Note infarction of cerebral cortex and basal ganglia. Cortical infarction is maximal in arterial border zones and depths of sulci.

Transient Focal Ischemic Attacks

These spells are defined as brief (less than 24 hours, usually 5 to 30 minutes) episodes of focal neurologic dysfunction of abrupt onset, which clear without permanent neurologic deficit. These episodes may occur in the distribution of either the carotid or the vertebrobasilar arterial system. There are many theories as to the cause of these ischemic events, but current evidence suggests that the majority are caused by emboli that arise from a proximal ulcerated atherosclerotic plaque. Lesions in the region of the carotid bifurcation are a common source of transient ischemic attack. *Amaurosis fugax* (fleeting blindness) is a related episode consisting of transient monocular blindness that often arises from temporary alteration of the retinal blood supply caused by ipsilateral carotid artery disease. These events must be recognized because be-

tween 20 and 35 percent of patients experiencing these transient episodes subsequently have permanent cerebral infarction.

Hypertension

Sustained elevation in systemic blood pressure increases the risk of subsequent stroke by at least four times when compared with normotension. Hypertension of even modest degree exerts its effect on the cerebral vasculature by two distinct mechanisms: (1) acceleration of atherosclerosis — hypertensive patients of any age have a greater amount of atherosclerotic disease than do nonhypertensive persons and hence are at a higher risk for the forms of atherothrombotic disease previously described, and (2) initiation of pathologic change in small arterioles (fibrinoid necrosis). This type of arterial degeneration is found almost exclusively in hypertensive pa-

Fig. 11-24. Acute infarction in middle cerebral artery distribution. Note swelling and cortical discoloration and petechial hemorrhages in infarcted territory, with marked shift of midline structures.

tients and seems to be the vascular lesion that predisposes to both lacunar infarction and intracerebral hemorrhage. (Intracerebral hemorrhage in the absence of an arteriovenous malformation is seldom found in normal, nonhypertensive patients.)

Certain Forms of Cardiac Disease

Valvular heart disease of various types, endocarditis, and various cardiac arrhythmias (primarily atrial fibrillation) are associated with intracardiac thrombus formation. Because a large proportion of the cardiac output supplies the cerebrum, the nervous system remains a major target organ for all forms of cardiac emboli.

Generalized Cerebral Ischemia — Syncope

Under normal circumstances, cerebral blood flow remains relatively constant in spite of mi-

nor fluctuations in blood pressure. When systemic blood pressure decreases to extremely low levels and the cerebral autoregulatory mechanisms are no longer effective, a state of generalized cerebral ischemia develops. The momentary giddiness and light-headedness occasionally experienced when a person abruptly assumes an upright posture is an example of this. If cerebral perfusion remains inadequate, syncope results and consciousness is lost. States of decreased cardiac output, hypotension from many causes, vagal hyperactivity, and impairment of sympathetic vasomotor reflex activity are common causes of syncope, which should not be confused with a transient ischemic attack as previously defined. Transient ischemic attack is a *focal* ischemic event, syncope is a *generalized* ischemic event that occurs as a result of vastly different pathogenetic mechanisms and has a different

Fig. 11-25. Small, old cystic infarcts (lacunae) in basal ganglia bilaterally in hypertensive patient.

prognosis. In the presence of severe focal intracranial vascular disease, syncope may infrequently be associated with focal neurologic signs and symptoms.

Radiographic Anatomy — Angiography

In living patients, we do not have an opportunity to examine the cerebral blood vessels directly but rely on a procedure called *angiography*. High-resolution images of the cerebrovascular anatomy are obtained by cannulation of an extracranial artery and injection of a radiopaque material. As the contrast medium is carried through the cerebral circulation, serial radiographs are obtained in both the lateral and anteroposterior projections. The contrast medium outlines the interior of the blood vessels, and the arterial, capillary, and venous phases of the circulation can be assessed.

The normal vascular anatomy as seen in a conventional cerebral angiogram is illustrated in Figure 11-27. Deviations from the normal vascular pattern may be indicative of disease and should be correlated with the clinical history and examination. Images of lower resolution, primarily displaying the larger arterial vessels, can be produced by magnetic resonance imaging or by electronic enhancement of radiographs obtained after the intravenous injection of contrast medium (digital subtraction angiography). This technique, which alleviates the potential risks of an arterial puncture, is, at times, a useful alternative to conventional angiography in selected patients (Fig. 11-28). Three major types of change may be seen on the angiogram: structural abnormalities of vessels, alterations in position of vessels, and alterations in flow patterns.

Structural Abnormalities of Vessels
Stenosis (narrowing) of the dye column or occlusion (nonfilling) of a vessel may be seen. Vascular malformations and aneurysms are examples of this type of change. Collections of abnormal vessels may be demonstrated within neoplasms,

Fig. 11-26. Old infarct (20 years) in middle cerebral artery territory. Damaged brain tissue has been completely absorbed, leaving cystic area traversed by glial-vascular membranes. Note relatively intact middle cerebral artery within the area of infarction.

in particular gliomas, meningiomas, and metastatic lesions, and these collections may be responsible for a so-called tumor blush or stain seen as an area of increased dye concentration.

Alterations in Position of Vessels

Mass lesions commonly produce displacement of vessels. Such displacement may be local and result in delineation of the mass or be distant and indirect; examples of the latter include shift of the anterior cerebral artery with anteriorly placed lesions or of the internal cerebral vein with more posteriorly placed lesions. At times, such a shift or displacement of vessels is associated with a stain or blush; in other instances, as with subdural hematoma, only the shift is recognized, the lesion itself being represented by an avascular area. In hydrocephalus, the vessels may be stretched out over the dilated ventricular system.

Alterations in Flow Patterns

Changes in the circulatory pattern may be evident as an expression of abnormal vascular shunts, as with arteriovenous malformations or

in some tumors. Collateral flow patterns may be identified in instances of thrombosis of major arteries as, for example, through the ophthalmic artery in instances of carotid artery occlusion; diminution or absence of flow is found distal to the site of vascular occlusion itself. A general slowing of the circulation may be noted when the intracranial pressure is elevated.

Measurement of Ocular Arterial Pressure

Vessel stenosis must be greater than 60 or 70 percent before flow is reduced and distal arterial pressure is lowered. An inference can be made about the presence of such a lesion by demonstrating a reduction in blood pressure along a distal segment of that artery. Thus, severe stenosis of the subclavian artery lowers the brachial blood pressure. Similarly, severe stenosis of the internal carotid artery lowers the ipsilateral ophthalmic or retinal artery pressure. A variety of simple and safe *noninvasive techniques* (ophthalmodynamometry, oculoplethysmography) are now available. Unilateral reduction in ocular arterial pressure is a reliable indi-

Fig. 11-27. Arteriographic anatomy. A, B. Lateral views. C, D. Anteroposterior views. (*1*) Internal carotid artery, (*2*) vertebral artery, (*3*) basilar artery, (*4*) branches of anterior cerebral artery, (*5*) branches of middle cerebral artery, (*6*) branches of posterior cerebral artery, (*7*) posterior communicating artery, and (*8*) anterior communicating artery.

cator of the presence of a highly stenotic or occlusive lesion in the ipsilateral carotid system and may be of value in the assessment of patients with suspected carotid arterial disease.

Computerized Tomography

Computerized tomography is a radiographic technique capable of visualizing intracranial anatomy and pathology and has proved to be helpful in the assessment of patients with cerebrovascular disease. As shown in Figure 11-29, areas of infarction (A) often appear as regions of reduced attenuation, whereas regions of hemorrhage (B) show increased attenuation. At times, after subarachnoid hemorrhage, there is sufficient blood in the subarachnoid spaces to be identified by this technique (C). Enhancement of the vascular structures of the brain can be achieved by the injection of intravenous contrast material and can be used to identify large vascu-

Fig. 11-28. Intravenous digital subtraction angiography showing the major extracranial arteries. A. Normal; (*1*) right vertebral artery, (*2*) right common carotid artery, (*3*) left vertebral artery, and (*4*) left common carotid artery. B. Note arrows pointing to a high-grade stenosis of the right internal carotid artery.

lar anomalies such as the arteriovenous malformation shown in D.

Magnetic Resonance Imaging

Magnetic resonance imaging is another imaging technique that can provide useful information about the status of the cerebral vasculature and brain parenchyma. This technique is becoming more widely available for the assessment of patients with all types of neural and cerebrovascular disorders.

Examination of the Vascular System

Because "vascular" refers to both an anatomical system and an etiologic category, its evaluation requires both historical data and information obtained from the physical examination. Patients with cerebrovascular disease may present with a wide range of symptoms of diverse causes. The evaluation of such patients should be designed to enable the clinician to determine (1) the nature of the presenting symptoms and signs; (2) the type, location, and extent of the pathologic process in the neural parenchyma; (3) the type, location, and

extent of the pathologic process in the vasculature; and (4) the pathophysiologic mechanism responsible for the observed symptoms and signs. Usually this evaluation can be accomplished with reasonable accuracy through detailed history and physical examination, aided by the judicious selection of certain ancillary diagnostic studies.

Historical Aspects

From the history, it is possible to determine if a problem is vascular and if the primary pathologic process is hemorrhage or infarction and to define the likely pathophysiologic mechanism responsible for the problem.

The judgment as to whether a problem is vascular is made almost exclusively from the *temporal profile;* the onset, evaluation, and course of the presenting symptoms. An acute onset with rapid evolution (minutes to hours) to maximal deficit implies a vascular cause. In the absence of a history of a clearly defined acute onset, the diagnosis of nontraumatic cerebrovascular disease must remain uncertain.

Patients with symptoms of acute onset may

Fig. 11-29. Computerized tomography. A. Infarction in left middle cerebral artery distribution. B. Area of hemorrhage in right occipital lobe. C. Blood in the basilar cisterns. D. Large, predominantly left frontal arteriovenous malformation on a contrast-enhanced scan.

be seen at any stage in the development of their symptoms. Some patients have symptoms that have resolved completely by the time they present for evaluation. They may describe the focal symptoms of transient ischemic attacks, but such events must be distinguished from seizures, labyrinthine distur-

bances, migraine, and generalized ischemic disorders (syncope).

Patients with symptoms of acute onset may progress and display increasing deficit while undergoing evaluation (a progressing stroke); but with these patients, careful historical inquiry must be undertaken to uncover the possibility of an underlying neoplasm, other mass lesions (that is, subdural hematoma), or superimposed metabolic or inflammatory encephalopathy.

Finally, the condition of some patients with symptoms of acute onset may have stabilized with residual deficit or may show some improvement at the time of evaluation. Most of these patients will have a *completed stroke*. Again, historical inquiry must be directed toward uncovering the pathophysiologic mechanism responsible for the deficit and must take into account other intracranial processes that could account for the symptoms.

The distinction between hemorrhage and infarction, although of major clinical importance and readily made in most cases, may be difficult in certain instances. The onset of symptoms in association with severe headache, though not invariably associated with hemorrhage, favors a hemorrhagic process. If the primary pathologic lesion is located at the supratentorial level (rather than posterior fossa), the presence of alteration in consciousness, stupor, or coma coincident with or shortly after the onset of symptoms favors the diagnosis of hemorrhagic disease.

When hemorrhage is suspected, a clinical determination of the location of the hemorrhage is often possible. The early absence of focal neurologic symptoms favors a subarachnoid hemorrhage and, in the absence of trauma, suggests the possibility of a ruptured intracranial aneurysm. The presence of focal neurologic symptoms suggests an intracerebral hemorrhage. In patients with suspected intracerebral hemorrhage, a history of significant, untreated hypertension renders the diagnosis more likely. In its absence, one must consider either the possibility of a ruptured aneurysm with associated intracerebral hemorrhage or a parenchymal hemorrhage secondary to an arteriovenous malformation (which also can present as a subarachnoid hemorrhage). The history of preexistent focal seizures, localized headache, or previous intracranial bleeding supports the diagnosis of an arteriovenous malformation.

When an ischemic process is suspected, it is necessary first to distinguish between carotid and vertebrobasilar arterial system disease. Although in most patients ischemic lesions are related to atherosclerosis, the patient's entire medical and neurologic history should be used to determine whether the symptoms are a result of (1) intracranial pathologic processes involving large-caliber or small-caliber arteries and arterioles, (2) thromboembolic disease in the major extracranial vessels, (3) emboli arising from distant sources (most often the heart), or (4) other systemic disorders.

The Neurovascular Examination

The physical evaluation of patients with suspected cerebrovascular disease must include, in addition to a general physical examination and more detailed study of neurologic function, an assessment of the neurovascular system. Cerebrovascular disease seldom occurs in isolation; the basic pathologic process often exerts its effect on multiple target organs, and therapeutic intervention can be planned only after consideration of the general well-being of the patient. A careful cardiac, pulmonary, and peripheral vascular examination (including recording of pulse rate and rhythm and measurement of the brachial blood pressures bilaterally and in the lying and standing positions) is particularly essential. In addition, the degree to which underlying disorders such as hypertension, diabetes, hyperlipidemia, and hematologic abnormalities may be contributing to the production of cerebrovascular symptoms must be determined.

The neurovascular examination includes examination of neck flexion for evidence of nuchal rigidity in patients with suspected hemorrhagic disease and three additional procedures designed to provide evidence of disease in the cerebrovascular system: auscultation of the head and neck, palpation of the cephalic vessels, and neuroophthalmologic examination.

Auscultation of the Head and Neck

The examiner should gently apply the stethoscope over the great vessels arising from the aortic arch, the carotid bifurcations, the orbits, and the skull, listening for evidence of bruits. A *bruit* is an abnormal pulsatile sound indicating turbulent blood flow through a vessel. It is usually, but not always, associated with stenosis of that vessel. A bruit may be

Fig. 11-30. Small cholesterol embolus seen in distal arteriole of optic fundus of patient with atherosclerosis of proximal internal carotid artery.

audible over an area of abnormal arteriovenous communication and may at times be heard over an anatomically normal vessel if there is turbulent flow.

Palpation of the Cephalic Vessels

Gentle palpation of the carotid arteries in the neck and of the superficial temporal arteries anterior to the ear should be performed. Altered pulsation, especially if unilateral, is usually indicative of proximal obstructive vascular disease. Although palpation of the peripheral pulses is an important part of the assessment of the general vascular system, palpation of the carotid pulses is less reliable and carries with it the potential danger of dislodging material from an atheromatous plaque. If pulsation of a carotid artery cannot be felt on gentle palpation, vigorous compression will add little diagnostic information.

Neuroophthalmologic Examination

The optic fundus should be examined in all patients, because this provides valuable information about intracranial vascular disease. Atherosclerosis, hypertension, diabetes, and other systemic disorders produce recognizable retinal and vascular changes. Subhyaloid (preretinal) hemorrhages may be seen in patients with subarachnoid hemorrhage. Evidence of retinal embolic events in the form of retinal infarcts and of cholesterol (Fig. 11-30),

platelet-fibrin, or calcific emboli may be seen in patients with carotid occlusive disease. These intraarterial fragments are presumed to result from an ulcerated atheromatous lesion in the circulation proximal to the ophthalmic arteries, and their presence correlates well with demonstrable lesions in the ipsilateral internal carotid artery.

Objectives

1. Define ischemia, infarction, intracerebral hemorrhage, subarachnoid hemorrhage, aneurysm, arteriovenous malformation, embolus, transient ischemic attack, syncope, angiogram, and bruit.
2. Describe the methods of formation and the role of ATP in brain metabolism.
3. Describe the mechanisms of cell damage that occur with ischemia.
4. Define autoregulation, and list or discuss the factors that can alter cerebral blood flow.
5. Identify the following major vessels, and list the symptoms that *might* develop in a patient with a lesion of the affected artery:
   a. Vertebral arteries
   b. Posterior communicating artery
   c. Common and internal carotid arteries
   d. Anterior cerebral arteries
   e. Middle cerebral arteries
   f. Basilar artery
   g. Posterior cerebral artery
6. Given a patient protocol:
   a. Recognize when the problem suggests cerebrovascular disease, and list those aspects of the protocol that led to this conclusion.
   b. Localize the area of abnormality to a specific area of the neuraxis, and identify whether that area of abnormality falls within the distribution of the internal carotid, vertebrobasilar, or spinal arterial systems.
   c. Decide if the basic pathologic mechanism is hemorrhage or infarction, and state the reasons for your choice.

Clinical Problems

1. A 16-year-old boy with endocarditis noted the sudden onset of complete visual loss;

within minutes, this partially cleared, and he noted only a loss of vision in the left half of the visual field of each eye. He had improved slightly when he reached the hospital, but examination still revealed a left homonymous hemianopia.

  a. What is the anatomicopathologic nature of the lesion?

  b. What is the location of the lesion with respect to its vascular supply? Why did you make this choice?

  c. What is the pathologic term that describes the parenchymal lesion?

  d. What is the pathophysiologic mechanism responsible for the symptoms?

  e. What biochemical changes have taken place in the region of the lesion?

2. A 65-year-old woman suddenly experienced the onset of severe weakness on her left side, loss of feeling on her left side, and an inability to see in the left half of her visual fields. Examination revealed weakness of face, arm, and leg, increased reflexes with a Babinski's sign on the left, sensory loss on the left side, and a left homonymous hemianopia. A right carotid bruit was noted.

  a. What is the anatomicopathologic nature of the lesion?

  b. What is the location of the lesion with respect to its vascular supply?

  c. What is the pathologic term that describes the parenchymal lesion?

  d. What is the pathophysiologic mechanism responsible for the symptoms?

  e. In the region immediately surrounding the lesion, the blood vessels are maximally dilated: true or false?

3. A 55-year-old hypertensive man noted the sudden onset of severe headache on the left side, loss of speech, and right hemiparesis. Within minutes, he became somnolent. Examination in the emergency room 30 minutes later revealed a comatose patient with a blood pressure of 220/120 mm Hg, a dense right hemiparesis with increased reflexes on the right, and bilateral Babinski's signs. A radiograph of the skull showed a 7-mm shift of the pineal gland from left to right.

  a. What is the anatomicopathologic nature of the lesion?

  b. What is the pathologic term that describes the parenchymal lesion?

  c. What are three common causes of this type of parenchymal lesion?

  d. What clinical signs suggest the pathologic diagnosis?

  e. What other noninvasive diagnostic test would be useful in defining the pathologic lesion?

4. A 50-year-old man experienced the sudden onset of vertigo. Examination revealed dysarthria, difficulty in swallowing, a left Horner's syndrome, left palatal weakness, and loss of pain sensibility over the left face and the right limbs and trunk. He had coarse ataxia and incoordination of his left arm.

  a. What is the anatomicopathologic nature of the lesion?

  b. What is the location of the lesion in respect to its vascular supply?

  c. What is the pathologic term that describes the parenchymal lesion?

  d. What is the pathophysiologic mechanism responsible for the symptoms?

  e. List the tract or nucleus responsible for each of the symptoms or signs in this patient.

5. A 62-year-old man suffered frequent, highly stereotyped episodes. He suddenly felt giddy and light-headed, lost consciousness, and fell to the ground. A physician observed one of his spells and noted that during the episode there was no peripheral pulse, and the blood pressure was too low to be detected. Both blood pressure and peripheral pulse returned to normal coincident with the patient's regaining consciousness.

  a. What is the anatomicopathologic nature of the lesion?

  b. What is the pathophysiologic mechanism responsible for the symptoms?

  c. Define autoregulation.

  d. Under normal physiologic conditions, which of the following could be expected to produce cerebral vasodilation: inhalation of oxygen; 20 percent decrease in arterial blood pressure; 20 percent increase in arterial blood pressure; inhalation of carbon dioxide?

  e. How do these spells differ from transient ischemic attacks?

6. A 38-year-old man suddenly experienced a severe headache associated with nausea, vomiting, and neck stiffness. When examined 2 hours later, he was somnolent but easily aroused. He had no focal neurologic findings but had marked nuchal rigidity. Lumbar puncture revealed grossly bloody cerebrospinal fluid.

   a. What is the anatomicopathologic nature of the lesion?

   b. What is the pathophysiologic mechanism responsible for the symptoms?

   c. How would you determine whether the bloody cerebrospinal fluid was due to a traumatic puncture?

Additional Reading

Adams, R. D., and Victor, M. *Principles of Neurology* (4th ed.). New York: McGraw-Hill, 1989. Pp. 617–692.

Barnett, H. J. M., and Hachinski, V. C. (eds.). Cerebral ischemia: Treatment and prevention. *Neurol. Clin.* 10(1), 1992.

Kety, S. S., and Schmidt, C. F. The nitrous oxide method for the quantitative determination of cerebral blood flow in man: Theory, procedure and normal values. *J. Clin. Invest.* 27:476, 1948.

Meyer, F. B., et al. Focal cerebral ischemia: Pathophysiologic mechanisms and rationale for future avenues of treatment. *Mayo Clin. Proc.* 62:35, 1987.

Powers, W. J. Cerebral hemodynamics in ischemic cerebrovascular disease. *Ann. Neurol.* 29:231, 1991.

Scheinberg, P. The biologic basis for the treatment of acute stroke. *Neurology* 41:1867, 1991.

— 12 —

The Neurochemical Systems

The nervous system uses chemical substances for transmission of information and for maintenance of neuronal function. Transmission of information in all the systems studied involves chemical synapses that use various neurochemical mediators. On the basis of their biochemical and functional characteristics, these mediators can be classified into different groups referred to as *neurochemical systems*. Neurochemical systems include amino acid, acetylcholine, monoamine, and neuropeptide systems.

Overview

Neurochemical Systems

Neuroactive substances can be subdivided into four main categories, according to their biochemical and functional characteristics: amino acids, acetylcholine, monoamines, and neuropeptides (Table 12-1). These substances may produce fast neuronal excitation or inhibition, referred to as *classic neurotransmission*, or they may modulate the excitability and responsiveness of neurons to stimuli, referred to as *neuromodulation*. In addition, neurochemical systems may produce long-term effects on neuronal activity critical for neural development, learning, and response to injury. Thus, they are important for plasticity in the nervous system.

Amino acids include excitatory amino acids, such as *L-glutamate*, and inhibitory amino acids, such as *gamma-aminobutyric acid (GABA)* and *glycine*. *L-Glutamate* is the most important excitatory neurotransmitter

in all rapidly conducting relay pathways of the motor and sensory systems of the outer tube of the central nervous system, including the corticospinal, lemniscal, spinothalamic, and special somatosensory pathways. L-Glutamate produces fast or prolonged synaptic excitation and triggers various calcium-dependent processes in the target cells, including production of nitric oxide. L-Glutamate also has a major role in synaptic plasticity during development and in the processes of learning and memory. *GABA* is the most important inhibitory neurotransmitter in the central nervous system and is found mainly in inhibitory interneurons, as well as in projection neurons of the circuits of the basal ganglia and cerebellum. *Glycine* is located in inhibitory interneurons in the spinal cord and brain stem.

Acetylcholine is an important neurotransmitter in both the central and peripheral nervous systems. In the central nervous system, it is present in diffusely projecting neurons of the basal forebrain and mesopontine tegmentum, in local interneurons, and in spinal and cranial motor neurons (see Table 12-1). At the peripheral level, acetylcholine is the neurotransmitter of skeletal neuromuscular junctions, autonomic ganglia, and parasympathetic neuroeffector junctions. Central cholinergic mechanisms are important for memory, arousal, and REM sleep. Peripherally, acetylcholine mediates activation of skeletal muscles and visceral effectors.

Monoamines include *catecholamines* (dopamine, norepinephrine, epinephrine), *serotonin*, and *histamine*. These substances are present in neurons that are located in re-

Table 12-1. Main Features of Neuroactive Agents

Neuroactive agent	Main source	Function	Inactivation
L-Glutamate	Excitatory projection neurons	Fast excitation	Reuptake
Gamma-aminobutyric acid (GABA)	Inhibitory interneurons	Fast/slow inhibition	Reuptake
Acetylcholine	Basal forebrain	Modulation	Acetylcholinesterase
	Mesopontine tegmentum		
	Motor neurons	Fast excitation	
Monoamines	Brain stem and hypothalamic diffuse systems	Modulation	Reuptake Monoamine oxidase Catechol-*O*-methyltransferase
Neuropeptides	Local and diffuse systems in hypothalamus, limbic, autonomic, and pain circuits	Long-lasting modulation	Peptidases

stricted areas of the brain stem and hypothalamus and that have abundant projections throughout the central nervous system. They modulate ongoing synaptic activity in the brain and spinal cord, and their effects are mediated by various subtypes of receptors, which mediate complex excitatory or inhibitory synaptic interactions.

Dopamine is located in neurons of the substantia nigra pars compacta and in other neurons of the midbrain and hypothalamus. It is important for motor control and endocrine regulation. *Norepinephrine* and epinephrine are located in the central and peripheral nervous systems. In the central nervous system, norepinephrine neurons form two systems: the *locus ceruleus system* in the pons and the *lateral tegmental system* in the lower pons and medulla. (The latter system also contains epinephrine-synthesizing neurons.) In the periphery, norepinephrine is the primary neurotransmitter of postganglionic sympathetic pathways. *Serotonin* is located in the raphe nuclei of the brain stem and histamine in neurons of the lateral hypothalamus, specifically the tuberomammillary nucleus. Central catecholaminergic, serotonergic, and histaminergic systems are important for control of arousal, attention, emotion, and affect.

Neuropeptides include several families of genetically related substances. In the central nervous system, neuropeptides are most abundant in the hypothalamus and limbic system and in the autonomic and pain-processing pathways of the brain stem. Hypothalamic

peptidergic neurons tend to project throughout the central nervous system, whereas those in other regions are primarily local circuit neurons. Peripherally, neuropeptides are present in unmyelinated nociceptive afferents, postganglionic parasympathetic and sympathetic fibers, and enteric neurons. Neuropeptides frequently coexist with other neurotransmitters and act as cotransmitters involved in presynaptic and postsynaptic modulation. They have a slow onset and produce prolonged and potent effects.

In addition to acting at the site of release, monoamines and neuropeptides may diffuse through the extracellular fluid of the central nervous system to influence neurons located at a distance, a process called *volume transmission*. Volume transmission affects not only neurons but also glial cells and blood vessels and is important for coupling neuronal activity with regional cerebral blood flow and metabolism. Also, neuropeptides may be released into the peripheral circulation and act as hormones.

Functional and Anatomical Organization of the Neurochemical Systems

Neurochemical systems are functionally organized into three main patterns of neuronal connectivity: *relay systems*, *diffuse systems*, and *local circuits*.

Relay systems are located in the outer tube of the central nervous system and include the direct sensory and motor pathways (Table

Table 12-2. Functional Organization of the Neurochemical Systems

	Relay systems (outer tube)	Diffuse systems (inner tube)
Pathway	Direct	Indirect
Type of information	Fast Point-to-point Excitation or inhibition	Slow, modulation
Neurotransmitter	Excitatory amino acids (L-glutamate) Inhibitory amino acids (GABA)	Acetylcholine Monoamines Neuropeptides
Receptor mechanism	Opening of neurotransmitter-linked ion channel	G-protein-mediated opening or closing of voltage-gated channels
Effect on neurons	Rapid transmission of excitatory or inhibitory signals	Modulation of neuronal excitability
Function	Sensory and motor control	Visceral control Arousal and attention
Systems	Motor system Sensory system	Internal regulation system Consciousness system

12-2). They are involved in fast sequential transmission of precise, point-to-point information via excitatory relay neurons that use L-glutamate or other excitatory amino acids. Local interneurons contain GABA and control information processing at each relay station. Interruption of any link in a motor or sensory relay pathway incapacitates the whole system and is the basis for most focal neurologic signs.

Diffuse systems consist of neuronal groups of the inner tube of the central nervous system, specifically in the brain stem, basal forebrain, and hypothalamus. These neurons contain acetylcholine, monoamines, or neuropeptides and send diffuse axonal projections to modulate global excitability of neurons at all levels of the nervous system (see Table 12-2). Diffuse systems are important for regulation of arousal-attention processes, emotion, and homeostasis via both synaptic and volume transmission. Alteration of these systems produces profound changes in the state of alertness, attention, emotion, behavior, visceral, and endocrine control.

Local circuit neurons have connections mainly within the immediate vicinity of their location and regulate the flow of information in relay systems and diffuse systems. Local neurons in the relay stations of the direct systems mainly use GABA. Local neurons may use many other transmitters, including gly-cine, glutamate, acetylcholine, and neuropeptides.

The neurochemical systems are involved in the pathophysiology of many neurologic diseases. Excitatory amino acids may cause neuronal injury (referred to as *excitotoxicity*), which may be responsible for neuronal death in acute conditions such as stroke and in chronic neurodegenerative disorders such as Huntington's disease and Alzheimer's disease. Impairment of GABAergic inhibition may cause seizures and other motor disorders. Defective cholinergic transmission in the cerebral cortex produces memory deficits or confusional state. Impairment of dopamine circuits for motor control results in movement disorders. Disorders of norepinephrine and serotonin mechanisms may be involved in sleep and psychiatric disorders. Neuropeptides may be involved in neuroendocrine, autonomic, and neurogenic pain disorders.

Neurochemical Systems

The different neurochemical systems vary in their distribution, mechanism of action, and function. Amino acids are the most abundant neurotransmitters in the central nervous system and are used for fast neurotransmission in most clinically relevant pathways. Monoamines are less abundant and produce more prolonged effects that are important for modification of neural responses to amino acid neurotransmitters; their effect depends on the behavioral state. Neuropeptides are the least abundant but are very potent and produce responses that have a long latency and prolonged responses.

Excitatory Amino Acids

L-Glutamate and L-aspartate are the neurotransmitters used by most excitatory neurons in the central nervous system.

Biochemistry
L-Glutamate is formed by intermediate metabolism of glucose via precursors of the Krebs' cycle (particularly alpha-ketoglutarate). It may also be synthesized from glutamine. The synaptic effects of L-glutamate are terminated by its presynaptic reuptake via a sodium ion/ATP-dependent pump.

Anatomical Distribution
L-Glutamate is the neurotransmitter for (1) pathways from the cerebral cortex (corticospinal, corticostriate pathways), (2) intrahemispheric and interhemispheric association pathways, (3) hippocampal circuits, (4) primary afferents and somatosensory and special sensory (visual, auditory) pathways, (5) cerebellar afferents, and (6) excitatory interneurons.

Receptor Mechanisms
Virtually all fast excitation in the central nervous system is mediated by excitatory amino acid receptors, of which there are several subtypes. The best characterized are AMPA (alpha-amino-3-hydroxy-5-methylisoxazole-4-propionate) receptor, NMDA (N-methyl-D-aspartate) receptor, and the metabotropic receptors. The AMPA receptor is diffusely distributed in the central nervous system and produces fast excitation, primarily through opening of sodium ion channels. The NMDA receptor is coupled to an ion channel that allows influx of calcium and sodium ions and produces prolonged bursts of depolarization. Activation of NMDA receptors is voltage-dependent, because at normal resting membrane potential, the channel is blocked by

magnesium ions. This blockade is removed by depolarization. In many brain regions, AMPA and NMDA receptors are coupled functionally, and AMPA receptor-mediated depolarization may remove the magnesium ion blockade of NMDA receptors, allowing NMDA channels to open and calcium ions to enter. NMDA receptors are modulated by glycine; this amino acid is critical for activation of NMDA receptors. The metabotropic receptor is a G-protein-linked receptor that triggers calcium ion release from intracellular stores.

Intracellular calcium ions play a crucial role in mediating many of the effects of excitatory amino acids. The AMPA receptor-mediated depolarization opens voltage-gated calcium ion channels, the NMDA receptor allows direct influx of calcium ions through its channel, and the metabotropic receptor triggers release of calcium ions from intracellular stores. Increased levels of intracellular calcium have important consequences, including prolonged depolarization bursts, long-lasting changes in synaptic efficacy (known as *synaptic plasticity*), and, in pathologic conditions, calcium-mediated excitotoxic neuronal injury. The effects of intracellular calcium depend on its interaction with several target proteins and its activation of several enzymatic cascades, including phospholipases and proteases. Important effects are activation of arachidonic acid cascade and synthesis of nitric oxide. Nitric oxide acts as a short-acting messenger molecule that may diffuse retrogradely to affect the presynaptic neuron and other, neighboring neurons. Also, it may play a critical role in synaptic plasticity and mediation of neuronal injury.

Functions
Excitatory amino acids are important in learning and memory through a mechanism known as *long-term potentiation*. Long-term potentiation is a long-lasting facilitation of excitatory amino acid transmission after repeated activation of excitatory amino acid pathways. This effect has been best characterized in hippocampal circuits. Long-term potentiation may involve both postsynaptic and presynaptic mechanisms. Postsynaptic long-term potentiation involves activation of NMDA receptors, entry of calcium ions, and phos-

phorylation of receptor proteins in the dendritic spines of the target cell. Presynaptic long-term potentiation involves increased release of L-glutamate.

Inhibitory Amino Acids

GABA (found throughout the central nervous system) and glycine (found mainly in the spinal cord and brain stem) account for most of the inhibitory synapses in the central nervous system.

Biochemistry
The main source of GABA is glucose. The synthesis and metabolism of GABA are intimately linked with those of L-glutamate and involve interactions between GABAergic neurons and astrocytes. In GABAergic terminals, GABA is synthesized from L-glutamate by action of *glutamic acid decarboxylase*. After release, GABA undergoes reuptake both by GABAergic terminals and astrocytes and is then metabolized through the Krebs' cycle to reconstitute L-glutamate. In astrocytes, glutamate is used to fixate ammonia to form glutamine by action of glutamine synthetase. This process is important for ammonia detoxification. In neurologic conditions associated with high ammonia levels, such as liver disease, there is compensatory hypertrophy of astrocytes.

Anatomical Distribution
GABA is present in two main classes of neurons: in inhibitory interneurons in local circuits (throughout the central nervous system) and in projection neurons in circuits of the basal ganglia and cerebellum.

Receptor Mechanisms
The inhibitory actions of GABA are mediated by two classes of receptor: GABA$_A$ and GABA$_B$ receptors. Activation of GABA$_A$ receptors triggers influx of chloride ions, which brings the membrane potential close to -75 mV. In most neurons, this results in fast hyperpolarization, but in primary afferents in the spinal cord, it causes depolarization (primary afferent depolarization). GABA$_A$ mechanisms are inhibitory because they stabilize the membrane potential so that the membrane is unable to respond to stimuli, a process known as *shunting inhibition*. GABA$_A$ responses are potentiated by benzodiazepines and barbiturates, drugs commonly used for treatment of neurologic and psychiatric disorders. GABA$_B$ receptors are G-protein-linked receptors. They produce an increase in potassium ion conductance, which results in slow synaptic inhibition.

Both types of GABA receptor may mediate postsynaptic and presynaptic inhibition. Postsynaptic GABA$_A$ input to the axon hillock (the site of spike generation) controls the global output of the neuron, whereas individual GABAergic terminals may have localized effects in dendritic microcircuits. The slow hyperpolarizing GABA$_B$ effect modulates the overall level of excitability of the neuron. Presynaptic GABA$_A$ and GABA$_B$ receptors decrease neurotransmitter release.

Functions
Inhibitory GABAergic interneurons participate in local feedforward and feedback circuits, which are important for spatial and temporal restriction of excitation in the central nervous system. In brain regions, including the cerebral cortex, glutamatergic input produces not only monosynaptic excitation of the target neuron but also disynaptic fast inhibition through activation of local GABAergic interneurons. This excitation-inhibition sequence ensures that the transmission is extremely brief and localized. This is critical for sensory discrimination and fine motor control. In addition, local GABAergic inhibition may decrease activation of NMDA receptors and dendritic voltage-dependent calcium ion channels and thus prevent *burst firing* or *epileptic neuronal discharges* (Fig. 12-1).

In the basal ganglia and cerebellum, serial GABAergic inhibitory synapses are the basis of the process of *synaptic disinhibition*. In these circuits, GABAergic neurons exert a tonic inhibition on their targets. Thus, GABAergic input to these tonic inhibitory neurons produces transient disinhibition and increased activity of the effector neurons.

Glycine is an important inhibitory neurotransmitter in interneurons in the ventral horn of the spinal cord and in the brain stem. The actions of glycine, like those of GABA, are

FEEDBACK
INHIBITION

FEED FORWARD
INHIBITION

GABA

GABA

GLUTAMATE

GLUTAMATE

A   B

Fig. 12-1. Interactions between excitatory (glutamate) neurons and afferents and local inhibitory (GABA) interneurons. A. GABA interneurons activated by collaterals of projection neurons produce recurrent (or feedback) inhibition of neuronal output. B. Interneurons activated by collaterals of afferents produce feedforward inhibition. Both mechanisms restrict discharge of the projection neuron spatially and temporally.

mediated through receptors linked to a chloride ion channel.

Acetylcholine

Acetylcholine is an important neurotransmitter in both the central and peripheral nervous systems.

Biochemistry

Acetylcholine is synthesized from acetyl coenzyme A and choline by the enzyme choline acetyltransferase. The synaptic actions of acetylcholine are rapidly terminated through hydrolysis by acetylcholinesterase (Table 12-3).

Choline acetyltransferase   Acetylcholinesterase
↓   ↓
Acetyl coenzyme A + Choline → Acetylcholine → Choline + Acetate

Drugs that inhibit acetylcholinesterase (*anticholinesterase agents*) markedly potentiate cholinergic transmission.

Anatomical Distribution

Acetylcholine is an important neurotransmitter at synapses in the central and peripheral nervous systems. In the central nervous system, it is contained in five types of neurons: (1) projection neurons in the basal forebrain (Fig. 12-2), (2) projection neurons in the mesopontine tegmentum (Fig. 12-3), (3) interneurons in the striatum, cerebral cortex, and other areas, (4) motor neurons in the brain stem and spinal cord, and (5) preganglionic autonomic neurons in the brain stem and spinal cord.

Receptor Mechanisms

The effects of acetylcholine are mediated by two classes of receptor: *nicotinic* receptors and *muscarinic* receptors. Nicotinic receptors are ion channel receptors, and their activation opens a cation channel that allows influx of sodium ions, producing fast excitatory postsynaptic potentials. Nicotinic receptors mediate the rapid excitatory effects of acetylcholine at the skeletal neuromuscular junction (motor end-plate) and the autonomic ganglia. Muscarinic receptors belong to the family of G-protein-coupled receptors that mediate slow postsynaptic (modulatory) responses. *Muscarinic receptors mediate most of the effects of acetylcholine in the central nervous system.* In the periphery, they mediate the effects of acetylcholine at parasympathetic neuroeffector junctions. There are different subtypes of muscarinic receptors; some mediate slow excitation via a decrease in potassium currents, and others slow inhibition via an increase in these currents. Muscarinic autoreceptors in cholinergic terminals inhibit the release of acetylcholine.

Functions

The most common effect of acetylcholine in the brain is excitation, mediated largely by muscarinic receptors. Cholinergic neurons in the basal forebrain, including the nucleus basalis, are important for cortical activation and memory processing. Cholinergic neurons in the mesopontine tegmentum project to the thalamus and activate thalamocortical circuits involved in arousal and REM sleep. Cholinergic interneurons in the striatum may participate in the control of posture and movement. Acetylcholine is the neurotrans-

Table 12-3. Comparison of Cholinergic and Monoaminergic Systems

System	Location of neurons	Precursor	Enzyme for synthesis	Inactivation
Cholinergic				
Acetylcholine	Basal forebrain Mesopontine tegmentum Motor neurons Preganglionic and postganglionic parasympathetic neurons	Choline	Choline acetyltransferase	Acetylcholinesterase
Monoaminergic				
Dopamine	Substantia nigra Ventral tegmental area	Tyrosine	Tyrosine hydroxylase	Reuptake Monoamine oxidase Catechol-*O*-methyltransferase
Norepinephrine	Locus ceruleus Lateral pontomedullary tegmentum	Tyrosine	Tyrosine hydroxylase Dopamine β-hydroxylase	Reuptake Monoamine oxidase Catechol-*O*-methyltransferase
Epinephrine	Lateral pontomedullary tegmentum	Tyrosine	Tyrosine hydroxylase Dopamine β-hydroxylase Phenylethanolamine-*N*-methyltransferase	Monoamine oxidase Catechol-*O*-methyltransferase
Serotonin	Raphe nuclei	Tryptophan	Tryptophan hydroxylase	Monoamine oxidase
Histamine	Tuberomammillary nucleus	Histidine	Histidine decarboxylase	Monoamine oxidase Histamine-*N*-methyltransferase

mitter of all motor neurons of the brain stem and spinal cord, including skeletomotor neurons, branchiomotor neurons, and preganglionic autonomic neurons. The main effect of these cholinergic neurons is fast synaptic excitation mediated by nicotinic receptors. Acetylcholine is also the neurotransmitter in postganglionic parasympathetic pathways, which innervate the heart, glandular tissue, and smooth muscle of all viscera via muscarinic receptors.

Monoamines

General Characteristics
Central monoaminergic systems include neuronal groups containing catecholamines, serotonin, or histamine (see Table 12-3). These systems have several characteristics in common: (1) restricted localization of cell bodies in specific regions of the brain stem and hypothalamus, (2) diffuse projections throughout the central nervous system via axon collaterals, (3) neurotransmitter biosynthesis dependent on specific enzymes and synaptic uptake of dietary amino acid precursors, (4) presynaptic inhibition of neuronal activity and neurotransmitter release via autoreceptors, (5) termination of neurotransmitter action by presynaptic reuptake and enzymatic degradation, (6) frequent coexistence with neuropeptides, (7) slow tonic neuronal activity dependent on the behavioral state of the person (sleep-wake cycle, attention), (8) synaptic effects mediated by various subtypes of G-protein-linked receptors, (9) modulatory, or "gain setting," influence on their neuronal targets, and (10) interaction of neurochemicals on a single target.

Catecholamine Biochemistry
Catecholamines include *dopamine, norepinephrine,* and *epinephrine.* These substances are synthesized from the amino acid L-tyrosine. The rate limiting step is mediated by *tyrosine hydroxylase.*

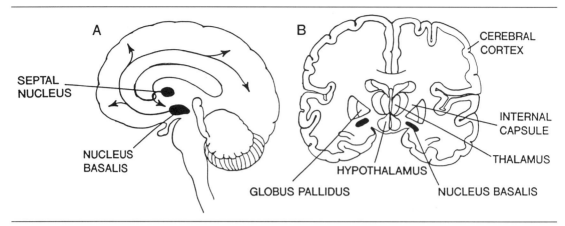

Fig. 12-2. Distribution of cell bodies and projections of the cholinergic system of basal forebrain. A. Sagittal view of projections from nucleus basalis to cerebral cortex and from septal nuclei to hippocampus. B. Coronal section showing the location of the nucleus basalis underneath the globus pallidus.

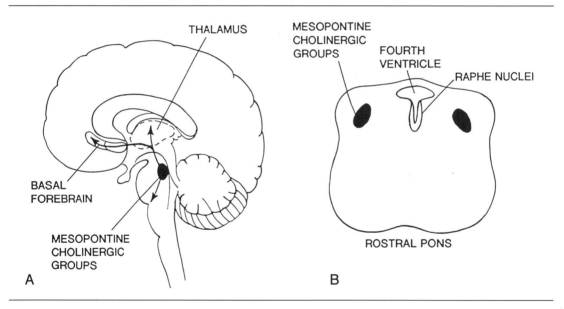

Fig. 12-3. Distribution of cell bodies and projections of mesopontine cholinergic neurons. A. Sagittal view of projections to thalamus. B. Cross section showing location of cholinergic neurons in rostral pons.

The most important mechanism for termination of the synaptic effect of catecholamines is specific sodium ion/ATP-dependent presynaptic reuptake. The enzymatic catabolism of catecholamines involves two classes of enzymes: monoamine oxidases and catechol-*O*-methyltransferase. Monoamine oxidases are mitochondrial enzymes that inactivate intraneuronal catecholamines that are free in the terminals after reuptake and include two classes, A and B. Catechol-*O*-methyltransfer-

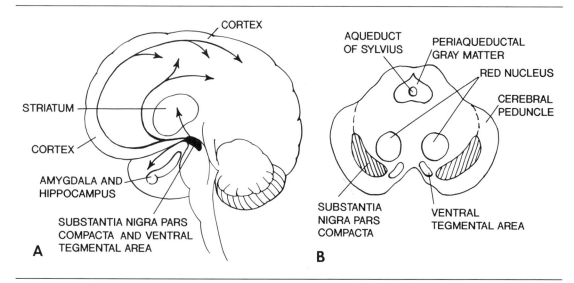

Fig. 12-4. Distribution of cell bodies and projections of mesotelencephalic dopaminergic neurons. A. Sagittal view of projections from substantia nigra pars compacta and adjacent ventral tegmentum to striatum and cerebral cortex. B. Cross section showing location of dopaminergic cell bodies in ventral tegmentum of midbrain.

ase acts on extraneuronal catecholamines. The principal metabolites of catecholamines result from the combined action of monoamine oxidase and catechol-*O*-methyltransferase. The principal metabolite of dopamine is homovanillic acid. The principal metabolite of norepinephrine and epinephrine in the central nervous system is 3-methoxy-4-hydroxyphenylethyleneglycol, and in the periphery, it is vanillylmandelic acid.

Dopamine

Anatomical Distribution
Dopamine is located in two main groups of central neurons: a mesencephalic group and a hypothalamic group. The mesencephalic dopaminergic group includes the substantia nigra pars compacta and the ventral tegmental area (Fig. 12-4). These neurons are interdigitated and form the mesotelencephalic dopaminergic system. This system includes (1) the nigrostriatal pathway that projects from the substantia nigra pars compacta to the caudate and putamen, (2) the mesolimbic pathway that projects from the ventral tegmental area to the limbic striatum (nucleus accumbens), amygdala, and hippocampus,

and (3) the mesocortical pathway that projects to the prefrontal and association cortices.

Hypothalamic dopaminergic neurons are located in the tuberoinfundibular area (which controls pituitary function) and in the lateral hypothalamus.

Receptor Mechanisms
The effects of dopamine are mediated by various subtypes of dopamine receptor, including the D_1 and D_2 receptor subfamilies. Both receptor subtypes are abundant in the striatum. D_2 receptors are also inhibitory presynaptic autoreceptors and produce feedback inhibition of neuronal activity and dopamine release. There are complex interactions between D_1 and D_2 receptor mechanisms.

Functions
The nigrostriatal pathway modulates basal ganglia circuits involved in motor planning and execution. The mesolimbic pathway is involved in complex target-oriented behavior, including stereotypic motor behaviors in response to internal or environmental stimuli. The dopaminergic innervation of the prefrontal and other association areas of the cerebral

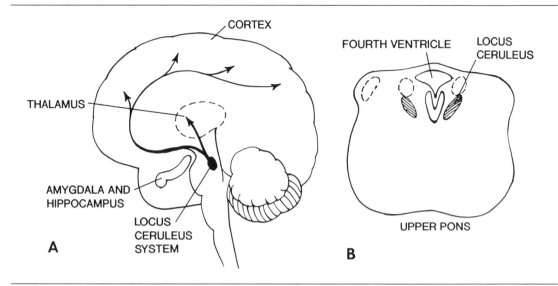

Fig. 12-5. Distribution of cell bodies and projections of locus ceruleus noradrenergic system. A. Sagittal view of main projections to areas involved in sensory, associative, and motor functions in thalamus and cerebral cortex. B. Cross section showing the location of the locus ceruleus in the dorsal pons.

cortex may be important for regulation of high-level sensory and motor processing. The main neuroendocrine effect of dopamine is tonic inhibition of prolactin synthesis and release by the anterior pituitary.

Norepinephrine and Epinephrine

Anatomical Distribution

Norepinephrine and epinephrine are neurochemical mediators in both the central and peripheral nervous systems. In the brain, norepinephrine and epinephrine neurons are restricted to two main areas: the locus ceruleus in the dorsal pons (Fig. 12-5) and the lateral tegmentum of the medulla and pons (Fig. 12-6). The locus ceruleus provides widespread innervation of the brain and spinal cord via extensive axonal collateralization. It innervates regions controlling responses to external stimuli, including sensory and motor nuclei of the brain stem and spinal cord, cerebellum, hippocampus, thalamus, and cerebral cortex.

The lateral tegmental system includes neurons that contain norepinephrine or epinephrine and that are located in the ventrolateral pons and the intermediate reticular zone of the medulla. These lateral tegmental neurons have extensive interconnections with areas involved

in autonomic and neuroendocrine control, such as preganglionic autonomic neurons, the hypothalamus, and the amygdala (see Chapter 9, The Internal Regulation System).

At the peripheral level, norepinephrine is the primary neurotransmitter of postganglionic sympathetic fibers. Epinephrine is released from neuroendocrine cells of the adrenal medulla and circulates in the blood as a neurohormone.

Receptor Mechanisms

Norepinephrine and epinephrine act via three distinct receptor subfamilies: alpha-1, alpha-2, and beta. The alpha-1 receptors are excitatory, whereas alpha-2 receptors mediate presynaptic and postsynaptic inhibition; beta receptors may decrease spontaneous activity but increase neuronal responsiveness. These receptors are differentially distributed in the brain and spinal cord. In the periphery, alpha-1 and beta receptors mediate the effects of norepinephrine at sympathetic neuroeffector junctions.

Functions

Activity in the neurons of the locus ceruleus increases dramatically in response to novel stimuli; thus, these neurons are important in

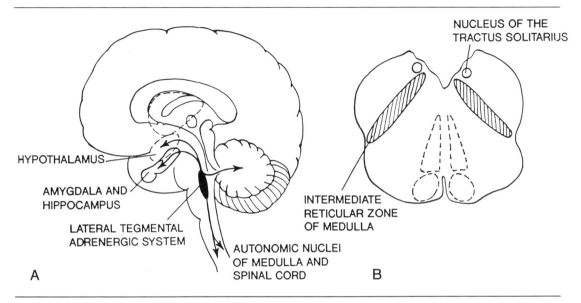

Fig. 12-6. Distribution of cell bodies and projections of the lateral tegmental system of catecholaminergic neurons. A. Sagittal view of projections to hypothalamus, amygdala, and autonomic nuclei of brain stem and spinal cord. B. Cross section showing distribution of norepinephrine and epinephrine neurons in the intermediate reticular zone of the medulla.

the processes of arousal and attention. Neurons in the lateral tegmental system play a crucial role in autonomic and neuroendocrine regulation. The functional interaction between the neurons in the locus ceruleus and the lateral tegmentum in response to challenging external or internal stimuli results in simultaneous increase in alertness (locus ceruleus) and activation of the sympathetic system (the lateral tegmental system). At the peripheral level, norepinephrine and epinephrine act at sympathetic neuroeffector junctions in the heart, blood vessels, and viscera (see Chapter 9, The Internal Regulation System).

Serotonin

Serotonin is an important central neurotransmitter that has a widespread influence.

Biochemistry

Serotonin (5-hydroxytryptamine [5-HT]) is synthesized from the amino acid L-tryptophan by tryptophan hydroxylase. The intermediate product is 5-hydroxytryptophan, which is converted to serotonin by L-amino acid decarboxylase, a nonspecific enzyme.

Similar to catecholamines, the main mechanism of inactivation of serotonin is through reuptake by terminals of serotonergic neurons. Serotonin is then metabolized by monoamine oxidase. The main metabolite of serotonin is 5-hydroxyindoleacetic acid.

Anatomical Distribution

The cell bodies of central serotonergic neurons are located in the raphe nuclei, which are in the midline reticular formation of the brain stem. The group of raphe nuclei include the rostral raphe nuclei located in the upper pons and midbrain and the caudal raphe nuclei in the caudal pons and medulla. Neurons in the rostral nuclei project to the basal ganglia, thalamus, hypothalamus, limbic system, and cerebral cortex, and those in the caudal group to the brain stem and spinal cord (Fig. 12-7).

Receptor Mechanisms

The effects of serotonin are mediated by a large number of receptor subtypes, including 5-HT$_1$-like receptors that are predominantly

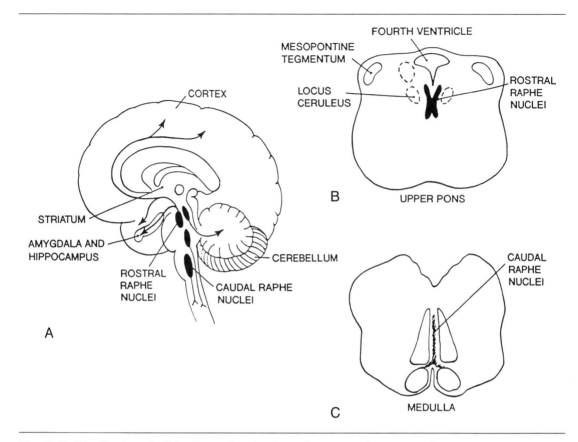

Fig. 12-7. Distribution of cell bodies and projections of serotonergic neurons of raphe nuclei. A. Sagittal view of widespread distribution of cell bodies and pathways throughout the central nervous system. B. Cross section showing location of rostral raphe neurons in rostral pons (project to supratentorial structures). C. Cross section showing caudal raphe neurons of medulla (project to posterior fossa and spinal structures).

inhibitory, 5-HT$_2$ receptors that are predominantly excitatory, and 5-HT$_3$ receptors that are linked directly to a cation channel. The 5-HT$_1$ receptors are also presynaptic inhibitory receptors in serotonergic terminals and terminals containing other neurotransmitters.

Functions

Similar to norepinephrine, serotonin exerts widespread influences throughout the brain and spinal cord via diffuse axonal collateralization. Serotonergic innervation of the cerebral cortex participates in sensory processing and in regulation of the sleep-wake cycle. Serotonergic input to the hypothalamus and brain stem autonomic nuclei is important for homeostasis and neuroendocrine and visceral control. Serotonin mediates central pain-regulation mechanisms

(see Chapter 7, The Sensory System). Cerebral vessels receive abundant serotonergic and noradrenergic innervation, which may be important for regulation of cerebral blood flow.

Histamine

Similar to serotonin, histamine produces widespread effects in both neural and non-neural tissues in the brain.

Biochemistry

Histamine is synthesized from the amino acid L-histidine by the enzyme histidine decarboxylase.

$$\text{L-histidine} \xrightarrow{\text{histidine decarboxylase}} \text{histamine}$$

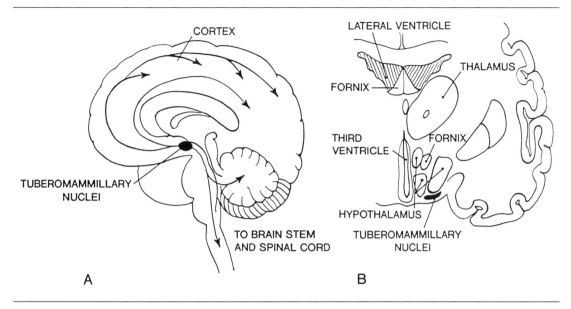

Fig. 12-8. Distribution of cell bodies and projections of histamine neurons of tuberomammillary nuclei. A. Sagittal view of widespread projections to cerebral cortex and rest of central nervous system. B. Cross section showing location of these neurons in lateral hypothalamic region.

Histamine is metabolized by the enzymes histamine-*N*-methyltransferase and monoamine oxidase to its final product methylimidazoleacetic acid. Unlike other monoamines, histamine does not undergo reuptake.

Anatomical Distribution
Histamine neurons are located in the lateral tuberomammillary nucleus of the hypothalamus and provide widely divergent pathways to the cerebral cortex, limbic system, hypothalamus, basal ganglia, brain stem, and spinal cord (Fig. 12-8).

Receptor Mechanisms and Functions
The effects of histamine are mediated via H_1, H_2, and H_3 receptors. The H_1 receptors are important for arousal. Histamine may play an important role in arousal mechanisms, in coupling neuronal activity with cerebral metabolism, and in neuroendocrine control (see Table 12-3).

Neuropeptides

Neuropeptides are abundant in the central and peripheral nervous systems. Many are also present in nonneural tissues, particularly in tissue of the so-called gastroenteropancreatic axis and other endocrine systems.

Biochemistry
Neuropeptides form several families. The neuropeptides of each family have common gene precursors, structural homologies, and functional similarities. Unlike other neurochemicals, neuropeptides are not synthesized in nerve terminals but from messenger RNA in neuronal cell bodies. They are processed and transported to the terminals in large dense-core vesicles via fast anterograde axonal transport. Neuropeptides are synthesized first as a large precursor molecule containing several copies of the same or related peptides. This precursor undergoes cleavage to smaller peptides and post-translational modifications as it traverses the secretory pathway from the endoplasmic reticulum to the Golgi complex and finally to the secretory granule. In many central and peripheral neurons, neuropeptides coexist with other neurotransmitters and are released preferentially during burst firing of the neuron. Unlike monoamines and amino acids, neuropeptides do not undergo presynaptic reuptake. Instead, their action is terminated by hydrolysis by extracellular peptidases.

Anatomical Distribution

Neuropeptides have a widespread but heterogeneous distribution in the central nervous system; the hypothalamus contains the highest concentration. Other neuropeptide-rich areas are the amygdala, autonomic nuclei, pain-modulating circuits of the brain stem and spinal cord, and, to a lesser extent, the basal ganglia and cerebral cortex. Neuropeptides are scarce in the cerebellum and thalamus.

Central peptidergic neurons are organized into two main systems: (1) diffuse projection systems that have cell bodies in the hypothalamus, amygdala, and nucleus of the tractus solitarius and that project diffusely throughout the brain, and (2) local or short projection neurons located throughout the central nervous system. Neuropeptides frequently coexist with other neurotransmitters, including other neuropeptides (hypothalamic neurons), acetylcholine or monoamines (diffuse brain stem systems), or GABA (striatal and cortical neurons).

Receptor Mechanisms

Neuropeptides are potent and active at low concentrations; their synaptic effects have slow onset and long duration. Similar to monoamines, they act via G-protein-coupled receptors, mainly as synaptic modulators. Because neuropeptides frequently coexist with other, primary neurotransmitters, they participate in a complex chemical coding involving presynaptic and postsynaptic modulatory interactions. The prolonged modulatory effects of neuropeptides occur not only at the synaptic level but also at a distance, including neighboring neurons, distal neural targets via volume transmission, or peripheral targets reached via the bloodstream (neuroendocrine effect).

Functions

Neuropeptides exert potent, long-lasting effects on endocrine, autonomic, sensory, motor, and behavioral functions.

Hypothalamic peptidergic neurons exert three types of influence: (1) magnocellular hypothalamic neurons release *vasopressin* and *oxytocin* into the general circulation, (2) hypophysiotropic hypothalamic neurons secrete *releasing factors* (such as corticotropin-releasing factor, gonadotropin-releasing factor, and growth hormone–releasing factor) or *inhib-iting factors* (for example, somatostatin) in the median eminence to control anterior pituitary function, and (3) other neurons project diffusely, especially to autonomic and limbic areas of the brain. Hypothalamic peptides are important in the control of homeostasis, reproduction, and immune function through their effects on endocrine, autonomic, and somatic motor effectors of the internal regulation system.

The amygdala has important peptidergic connections with autonomic areas of the hypothalamus and brain stem, which may be important for modulation of autonomic responses during emotional states.

Brain stem and spinal autonomic regions, including the nucleus of the tractus solitarius, ventrolateral medulla, and preganglionic autonomic nuclei, have an abundance of neuropeptides, which frequently coexist with monoamines. For example, *neuropeptide Y* coexists with catecholamines in pathways that project from the ventrolateral medulla to the hypothalamus and spinal cord. These pathways are important for modulation of visceral reflexes and hypothalamic neuroendocrine function.

At the peripheral level, neuropeptides coexist with the primary neurotransmitters of postganglionic sympathetic and parasympathetic fibers. Postganglionic sympathetic neurons contain neuropeptide Y in addition to norepinephrine. Neuropeptide Y inhibits prejunctional release and potentiates postjunctional effects of norepinephrine. Postganglionic parasympathetic secretomotor neurons contain *vasoactive intestinal polypeptide* in addition to acetylcholine. This peptide is a potent vasodilator and potentiates the secretomotor effect of acetylcholine on exocrine glands. Neuropeptides are also important neurotransmitters in the enteric nervous system (see Chapter 9, The Internal Regulation System).

Neuropeptides are important in central pain-controlling pathways. Primary unmyelinated nociceptive afferents contain various neuropeptides, particularly *substance P* and *calcitonin gene-related peptide*. These peptides not only mediate central transmission of nociceptive information but are also released locally by axon terminals (axon reflex) to produce vasomotor and permeability changes in response to injury, *neurogenic inflammation* (see Chapter 7, The Sensory System). Pain transmission is controlled by opioid peptides, which play a crucial role in spinal and supraspinal analgesia. Opioid peptides include *enkephalins, beta-endorphin*, and *dynorphin*. Enkephalins and dynorphin are contained primarily in local neurons or in short projection neurons, not only in pain-controlling circuits but also in the basal ganglia and autonomic nuclei. Beta-endorphin is produced from a large precursor called *proopiomelanocortin*, which also gives rise to adrenocorticotropin and melanocyte-stimulating hormone. Neurons containing beta-endorphin are restricted to a particular region of the hypothalamus but send diffuse projections throughout the central nervous system. The main effect of opioids is presynaptic and postsynaptic inhibition. Opioids play an important role in supraspinal and spinal analgesia (see Chapter 7, The Sensory System). In addition to central analgesia, opioids have other important effects, including depression of cardiovascular and respiratory functions, pupillary constriction, changes in behavior, regulation of hormone secretion, and body temperature (hypothermia).

In the basal ganglia, neuropeptides are abundant in both local neurons (neuropeptide Y and somatostatin) and in different functional classes of GABAergic projection neurons in the striatum. In the cerebral cortex, vasoactive intestinal polypeptide, neuropeptide Y, cholecystokinin, and somatostatin are localized in intrinsic, or local circuit, GABAergic neurons. They may be important in modulation of cortical neurotransmission and in local regulation of cerebral blood flow. For example, vasoactive intestinal polypeptide is a vasodilator of cerebral blood vessels, and neuropeptide Y is a vasoconstrictor. Thus, these neuropeptides may be important in coupling neuronal activity with local cerebral blood flow (see Chapter 11, The Vascular System).

Functional Organization of Central Neurochemical Systems

On the basis of the anatomical-functional organization, the central neurochemical systems can be divided into three main groups: (1) *relay*, or *direct*, *systems*, (2) *diffuse systems*, and (3) *local circuits*.

Relay, or Direct, Systems

Relay, or direct, systems correspond to the motor and sensory systems that occupy the outer tube of the neuraxis. Information in these systems is phasic, transmitted rapidly via large myelinated fibers that form clearly defined fiber tracts, and processed sequentially in several relay stations located along each pathway. Each relay nucleus contains projection neurons and local circuit neurons. The projection neurons form the interconnecting pathways, transmit signals over long distances, and emit collaterals close to their cell bodies. They are excitatory neurons and use excitatory amino acids, particularly L-glutamate, to provide fast, short-lasting synaptic excitation. Most of the local circuit neurons are inhibitory and use GABA as a neurotransmitter. These neurons are involved in the processes of feedforward or feedback inhibition, which are important for sensory discrimination and for fine motor control. The neurotransmitter of inhibitory interneurons in the spinal cord and brain stem is glycine.

Relay systems provide fast, precise information necessary for sensory and motor function. Interruption of any link in a relay system incapacitates the function of the whole pathway. Virtually all major focal neurologic signs and symptoms are due to interruption of relay pathways.

Diffuse Systems

The diffuse systems include the internal regulation and the consciousness systems, which are located in the inner tube of the neuraxis. Unlike the relay systems, the diffuse systems consist of neurons located in particular nuclei of the brain stem, basal forebrain, and hypothalamus. These systems include (1) brain stem and hypothalamic neuronal groups that contain monoamines (dopamine, norepinephrine, serotonin, histamine), (2) neurons of the basal forebrain and pontomesencephalic tegmentum that contain acetylcholine, and (3) many hypothalamic neurons that contain neuropeptides. Monoamine and neuropeptide transmitters usually coexist in the neurons in the diffuse systems. The neurons have unmyelinated, slow-conducting axons that have a diffuse, multibranched, and divergent pattern. Therefore, a single neuron may simultaneously innervate several functionally different parts of the central nervous system. The axons have varicosities that contain a great number of synaptic vesicles. The neurotransmitter is released in a diffuse manner, so that the cellular targets of these systems are determined by the location of the receptors and not by the site of neurotransmitter release. Projection neurons of the diffuse systems generally have a slow, rhythmic pattern of discharge, which changes dramatically according to the behavioral state (sleep, attention). This activity is influenced by local interneurons and by local feedback mechanisms (generally inhibitory) that involve somatodendritic and presynaptic autoreceptors.

The diffuse systems do not convey topographically specific information but instead are involved in global functions such as regulation of the sleep-wake cycle, attention, emotion, cognition, response to stress, and regulation of visceral, hormonal, sexual, and immune functions.

The functions of the diffuse systems are consistent with the modulatory role of their neurochemical signals, which act via G-protein-linked receptors. These receptors are involved in controlling neuronal excitability and responsiveness rather than rapid excitation or inhibition.

Pathologic alterations or pharmacologic manipulation of the diffuse systems do not produce focal neurologic deficits. Instead, they may cause various clinical manifestations, including marked changes in general motor performance, abnormal responses to pain, altered state of alertness or cognition, abnormal mood and thought processes, and abnormalities in vegetative and endocrine functions.

Local Circuits in Relay and Diffuse Systems

Local circuit neurons, or interneurons, control the flow of information and the pattern of neuronal activity in both relay and diffuse systems. Axons of local circuit neurons have short ramifications that synapse on the cell bodies and dendrites of projection neurons or on terminals of afferent axons in the immediate vicinity. Local circuit neurons may be either excitatory or inhibitory. Most inhibitory interneurons in the central nervous system use GABA. Other interneurons use excitatory amino acids, acetylcholine, or neuropeptides.

Clinical Correlations

The neurochemical systems are involved in the pathophysiology of various neurologic diseases.

Excitatory Amino Acids

Excessive exposure to L-glutamate or other endogenous excitatory amino acids may cause neuronal injury through the mechanism of *excitotoxicity*. Excitotoxicity has been implicated in the pathogenesis of two groups of neurologic diseases: *acute metabolic crises*, such as cerebral hypoxia-ischemia, stroke, hypoglycemia, seizures, and head or spinal injury, and *chronic neurodegenerative disorders*, including those that produce dementia, movement disorders, cerebellar dysfunction, and motor neuron disease. Excessive exposure to L-glutamate may result from increased presynaptic release, impaired energy-dependent reuptake, or both. Excessive activation of AMPA and particularly NMDA receptors causes sodium and calcium ions to accumulate in neurons. Increased concentration of calcium ions in the cytoplasm activates intracellular enzymatic cascades, including proteases and lipases. This generates oxygen free radicals and other intracellular mechanisms that produce neuronal injury or death. Pharmacologic blockade of AMPA or NMDA receptors may have a "neuroprotective" effect.

Inhibitory Amino Acids

GABA is critical in maintaining tonic inhibitory control of most neurons in the central nervous system. Decreased GABA inhibition due to loss of inhibitory interneurons or to blockade of GABA receptors may produce seizures, movement disorders, exaggerated muscle tone, and anxiety. Many drugs used to treat seizures, increased muscle tone, anxiety, or insomnia act by facilitating GABA$_A$ receptor mechanisms. Chronic exposure to drugs acting through these receptor mechanisms, including alcohol, barbiturates, and benzodiazepines, may produce downregulation of GABA$_A$ receptors. Abrupt discontinuation of these drugs results in withdrawal symptoms, including anxiety, tremor, and generalized seizures. Glycine is an important inhibitory amino acid. Impairment of glycinergic transmission by tetanus toxin or strychnine causes autonomic hyperactivity and a severe increase in muscle tone.

Acetylcholine

Alzheimer's disease is a degenerative disorder of the brain that causes dementia. It is associated with loss of the cholinergic neurons that innervate the cerebral cortex. Impairment of cholinergic transmission may explain memory loss in this and other degenerative disorders. Central anticholinergic drugs are used to treat movement disorders due to dysfunction of basal ganglia circuits. Many drugs used to treat neurologic and psychiatric disorders may produce pharmacologic blockade of central muscarinic receptors. This may cause, particularly in elderly persons, confusional state or delirium, characterized by a disorder of alertness, attention, and perception (hallucinations). At the peripheral level, dysfunction of cholinergic mechanisms in skeletal muscle produces defects in neuromuscular transmission. Pharmacologic blockade of nicotinic receptors in the autonomic ganglia produces sympathetic and parasympathetic dysfunction. The blockade of muscarinic receptors abolishes parasympathetic secretomotor and visceral motor functions.

Monoamines

Parkinson's disease is a neurodegenerative disorder characterized by loss of dopaminergic neurons in the substantia nigra. Decreased dopaminergic activity in the striatum produces decreased motor activity, or *akinesia*. Akinesia and other manifestations of Parkinson's disease may also result from the loss of dopaminergic neurons after exposure to toxins such as MPTP (1-methyl-4-phenyl-4-1,2,5,6-tetrahydropyridine) or to blockade of

dopaminergic receptors in the striatum by antipsychotic or antiemetic drugs. Antiparkinsonian drugs include L-dopa (a precursor of dopamine) in combination with carbidopa (an inhibitor of peripheral decarboxylation of L-dopa) and direct dopamine receptor agonists. Products of dopamine oxidation have been implicated in toxic injury of dopaminergic neurons. A relative increase of dopaminergic activity in the striatum causes *hyperkinetic movement disorders* such as chorea.

Abnormal dopaminergic activity in limbic and prefrontal circuits may result in hallucinations. Antipsychotic drugs act via blockade of dopaminergic receptors. Their side effects include symptoms similar to those of Parkinson's disease, with the development of stereotypic movements, referred to as *tardive dyskinesia*.

Activity in the dopaminergic mesolimbic system is part of the basis of drug addiction. Dopaminergic neurons of the hypothalamus exert a tonic inhibitory control on prolactin release. Hypothalamic lesions or pharmacologic blockade that disrupts the inhibitory control causes *hyperprolactinemia*. Dopamine receptor agonists are used to treat prolactin-secreting pituitary tumors. *Neuroleptic malignant syndrome* is characterized by hyperthermia, muscle rigidity, and life-threatening autonomic hyperactivity and may be caused by blockade of dopamine receptors by neuroleptic agents or by the abrupt discontinuation of dopaminergic agonists.

Abnormal function of central noradrenergic and serotonergic circuits has been implicated in disorders of arousal, attention, and affect, including anxiety and depression. Drugs that either increase alpha-2 receptors or block beta receptors in the brain produce somnolence, depression, and hypotension. Drugs that decrease reuptake of norepinephrine or serotonin or that inhibit their metabolism are used to treat depression, panic disorder, narcolepsy, and chronic neurogenic pain. Migraine headache is treated with drugs that act via serotonergic presynaptic receptors in the terminals of trigeminal nerve axons that synapse on blood vessels. They prevent release from the trigeminal terminals of neuropeptides implicated in the pain and vasodilatation that occur with migraine attacks.

Hypothalamic disorders may produce abnormal secretion of circulating neuropeptides, for example, deficient or inappropriate secretion of vasopressin, or abnormal control of pituitary function, producing pituitary hyperfunction or hypofunction. Central stimulation of opioid receptors by morphine or similar drugs produces potent analgesia and marked autonomic, respiratory, endocrine, and behavioral effects. Degenerative diseases of the central nervous system may produce significant alterations in neuropeptide concentration in selected areas of the brain. For example, somatostatin is decreased in the cerebral cortex of patients with dementia but may be relatively increased in such degenerative diseases of the striatum as Huntington's disease.

Objectives

1. Name the different groups of neurochemical transmitters and the main components of each group.
2. Describe the functional and neurochemical characteristics of the relay, diffuse, and local circuit neurochemical systems.
3. Describe the distribution and functions of L-glutamate in the brain. Describe the effects of activation of different glutamate receptor subtypes. Define *long-term potentiation*. List examples of L-glutamate-induced neurotoxicity.
4. Describe the distribution and function of GABA in the brain. Describe the function of astrocytes in GABA metabolism. Explain why GABAergic dysfunction produces seizures.
5. Describe the distribution and list the main functions of acetylcholine in the central and peripheral nervous systems.
6. Describe the biosynthesis and metabolism of catecholamines. Describe the distribution and function of dopaminergic neurons in the brain. Describe the projections and functions of the locus ceruleus and the lateral tegmental systems.
7. Describe the distribution and function of central serotonergic and histaminergic systems.
8. Name the rate-limiting enzymes for the biosynthesis of GABA, acetylcholine, catecholamines, serotonin, and histamine.

Describe the main mechanism of inactivation of amino acids, acetylcholine, catecholamines, serotonin, and neuropeptides.
9. Describe the main mechanism of synthesis, transport, release, and inactivation of neuropeptides. List the brain regions richest in neuropeptides. Give examples of neuropeptides in hypothalamic, autonomic, pain-controlling, striatal, and cortical circuits. Name the neuropeptide cotransmitters in sympathetic and parasympathetic pathways.
10. Name the primary neurotransmitter in the following: corticospinal tract, basal ganglia and cerebellar circuits, basal forebrain, locus ceruleus, substantia nigra pars compacta, raphe nuclei, skeletal neuromuscular junction, autonomic ganglion, postganglionic sympathetic neuron, postganglionic parasympathetic neuron, primary afferent (unmyelinated) nociceptive fibers, and inhibitory interneurons.

Clinical Problems

1. A 55-year-old man had cardiorespiratory arrest. After resuscitation, he remained comatose, and the electroencephalogram showed persistent epileptiform activity.
   a. Where is the lesion?
   b. What is the type of lesion?
   c. What central neurochemical system is most likely to cause this type of neuronal injury?
   d. What are the general mechanisms of injury?
   e. What areas of the brain most likely are affected?
   f. Name possible pharmacologic approaches for neural protection in this and similar cases.
2. A 44-year-old bartender with a history of alcohol abuse had been taking "sleeping pills" to control his anxiety and insomnia. Because of flu-like illness, with vomiting and diarrhea, he abruptly discontinued taking medication and drinking alcohol, and 24 hours later, he had increased anxiety and generalized tremor. Two days later, he had a generalized tonic-clonic seizure.

a. What is the location of the disorder?
b. What is the type of disorder?
c. What neurochemical system most likely is affected by alcohol and sedative agents?
d. What is the mechanism involved that explains the patient's symptoms?

3. A 65-year-old man with a one-year history of memory loss was given a drug for treatment of depression and sleep disturbance. After the dose of medication was increased, there was a relatively rapid onset of disorientation, agitated behavior, and visual hallucinations. On physical examination, dry hot skin, dry mouth, tachycardia, and pupil dilatation were noted. Computerized tomography of the head and cerebrospinal fluid examination did not reveal any abnormality. Generalized slowing was found on electroencephalography.
a. Involvement of what area of the brain explains the memory loss?
b. What type of lesion accounts for the memory loss?
c. Dysfunction of what neurochemical system most likely is responsible for the development of the abrupt change in mental status?
d. In the absence of acute confusional state, what effects would this drug have on memory and other cognitive functions of the patient?

4. A 55-year-old woman in a psychiatric ward received a drug for treatment of her bizarre behavior and auditory hallucinations. After the treatment was initiated, she had decreased facial expression and an absence of arm swing while walking. After 6 months of treatment, stereotyped, repetitive involuntary movements of the tongue, mouth, and face developed. Findings on neurologic examination were otherwise normal except for minimal piano playing-like movements of the fingers. The abnormal movements increased with attempts to discontinue treatment with the drug, and they abated temporarily with an increase in dosage. Results of computerized tomography of the head, electroencephalography, and cerebrospinal fluid examination were unremarkable. She had no family history of dementia or movement disorders.
a. Involvement of what area of the brain

explains the underlying psychiatric disorder?
b. What type of lesion is responsible for the movement disorder?
c. What neurochemical system most likely is involved in this patient?
d. What is the mechanism of the initial effects of the drug?
e. What is the probable mechanism of the stereotypic movements of the face and tongue?
f. What is a potentially dangerous consequence of iatrogenically induced dysfunction of this system?

5. A 25-year-old woman with a history of chronic pain was comatose when examined in the emergency room. Her boyfriend stated that she had been going to different doctors to have her prescription for "pain killers" refilled and had become increasingly depressed. On physical examination, she was unresponsive to noxious stimuli, had shallow respirations, slow pulse, and low blood pressure. Her pupils were markedly constricted but reactive to light.
a. Where is the lesion?
b. What is the type of lesion?
c. What neurochemical system most likely is involved in this patient?
d. What type of drug should be used to treat the coma of this patient?

Additional Reading

Barnes, C. D., and Pompeiano, O. (eds.). *Neurobiology of the Locus Coeruleus (Progress in Brain Research,* Vol. 88). Amsterdam: Elsevier, 1991.

Beal, M. F., and Martin, J. B. Neuropeptides in neurological disease. *Ann. Neurol.* 20:547, 1986.

Cooper, J. R., Bloom, F. E., and Roth, R. H. *The Biochemical Basis of Neuropharmacology* (6th ed.). New York: Oxford University Press, 1991.

DiFiglia, M., and Aronin, N. Amino Acid Transmitters. In G. Paxinos (ed.), *The Human Nervous System*. San Diego: Academic, 1990. Pp. 1115–1132.

Hökfelt, T. Neuropeptides in perspective: The last ten years. *Neuron* 7:867, 1991.

Mesulam, M.-M. Human brain cholinergic pathways. *Prog. Brain Res.* 84:231, 1990.

Pearson, J., Halliday, G., Sakamoto, N., and Michel, J.-P. Catecholaminergic Neurons. In G. Paxinos, (ed.), *The Human Nervous System*. San Diego: Academic, 1990. Pp. 1023–1049.

III

Horizontal Levels

— 13 —

The Peripheral Level

Precise anatomical localization is one of the major goals of neurologic diagnosis. The study of the major longitudinal systems and the manifestations of diseases within each system permit localization of a lesion in one or more systems. In the remaining chapters, the patterns of disease at each of the four major levels are presented. The combination of signs and symptoms resulting from damage to the systems at each major level often allows highly specific localization of the underlying disorder.

The *peripheral* level includes all neuromuscular structures outside the skull and spinal column, including peripheral nerves, sensory receptors, muscles, and the portions of cranial nerves lying outside the cranium. The anatomy, physiology, pathophysiology, and clinical disorders of these structures, which have many common characteristics, are considered in this chapter.

Overview

The peripheral level contains four of the longitudinal systems: motor, sensory, internal regulation, and vascular systems. The peripheral axon of the lower motor neuron, the neuromuscular junction, and the muscle fibers of the motor unit are found at the peripheral level. The distal axon of the primary sensory neuron and the sensory receptors are peripheral. The distal axon of the autonomic preganglionic and postganglionic efferent neurons and the visceral afferent axons are peripheral. Only the distal portions of the neurons of these systems are found in the periphery. The somatic cell bodies and the central processes are located in the spinal canal. The axons of the systems travel together in the periphery, and peripheral lesions typically produce combinations of symptoms and signs from all three of the neural systems. Blood vessels of the vascular system supply all these structures.

Diseases in the periphery may be focal (for example, involving a single nerve) or diffuse (involving all peripheral nerves). A focal lesion may be a mass or a nonmass lesion. Diffuse lesions often involve only one type of structure in the periphery, as in primary disease of muscle. The temporal profile of peripheral diseases may be transient or may be that of one of the major disease types — inflammatory, neoplastic, degenerative-metabolic, vascular, or traumatic.

On the basis of gross anatomical features, the periphery can be divided into nerves and end-organs. Diseases of these subdivisions have different clinical manifestations.

Nerves

Peripheral and Cranial Nerves
These are the gross structures carrying motor, sensory, and visceral axons to the end-organs. (Some nerves contain only internal regulation fibers, for example, the vagus nerve.)

Plexus
A plexus is a complex network of axons traveling peripherally and centrally from the spinal nerves at the spinal level to the peripheral nerves.

End-Organs

Sensory Receptors

The somatic receptors for the sensations of pain, touch, position, vibration, and muscle proprioception have been considered in detail in the chapters on sensory and motor systems and will not be discussed further. Primary disease of these receptors is not of clinical significance. The special sensory receptors of the cranial nerves are considered in Chapters 15 (The Posterior Fossa Level) and 16 (The Supratentorial Level).

Somatic Motor Effectors

Movement is produced by muscle. Within the muscles are the neuromuscular junctions, the muscle fibers, and the contractile elements. Tendons, bones, and joints play an integral part in movement but are not considered further in this text.

Internal Regulation Receptors and Effectors

The widespread and diverse group of visceral structures was considered in Chapter 9 (The Internal Regulation System). Although diseases of these structures are common in general medical practice, they will not be discussed further because they are more properly studied with other organ systems.

Nerve

The major peripheral structures are nerves and muscles. Nerves are a collection of nerve fibers called *axons,* which are bound together by connective tissue. At the peripheral level, nerves form the plexuses and peripheral nerves; at the spinal level, they form the nerve roots entering or leaving the spinal cord and the spinal nerves leaving the spinal column. Nerves, whether peripheral or spinal, are made up of the axons traveling between the central nervous system and the peripheral end-organ. They are similar in their microscopic features, their physiology, and their pathophysiologic alterations with disease. The general features that are common to all types of nerves are considered first and the differences considered subsequently.

Histology

A nerve is composed of thousands of axons ranging in size from less than 1 to 20 μm in diameter. In each nerve trunk, individual fibers are surrounded by a connective tissue sheath, the *endoneurium.* Each of these is grouped with many other axons into bundles of fascicles by the *perineurium.* Groups of fascicles are bound together by an outer covering of connective tissue, the *epineurium* (Fig. 13-1). Nerves have their own blood supply. The nutrient arteries enter at intervals along their length and form anastomotic channels within the connective tissue framework of the nerve. These anastomoses make nerves relatively resistant to vascular disease.

Nerves are made up of afferent and efferent fibers. The axons can be differentiated histologically on the basis of their size and the presence or absence of myelin. The unmyelinated fibers are small and include internal regulation fibers and fibers carrying pain and temperature. Proprioceptive and somatic motor fibers are large (Table 13-1). These characteristics, however, do not permit the identification of the function of an individual axon, because the afferent (carrying information centrally) axons and the efferent (carrying information peripherally) axons have a similar microscopic appearance.

Each nerve fiber consists of an axon embedded in a series of Schwann cells arranged longitudinally along the axon. Each Schwann cell covers 0.5 to 1.0 mm of axon. The junctions between Schwann cells along the axon are seen as constrictions of the nerve fiber and are called the *nodes of Ranvier* (Figs. 13-1 and 13-2). A single Schwann cell surrounds either a number of unmyelinated axons or one myelinated axon. During development, either many unmyelinated axons become embedded in the Schwann cell or the Schwann cell wraps around one axon in concentric circles to form the myelin of the myelinated nerve fiber (Fig. 13-3). Although the fibers in a nerve are adjacent to one another, the electrical activity in each nerve fiber is independent of the activity in all the other fibers in the nerve. The action potentials are isolated from each other by the endoneurium and the myelin.

As the Schwann cell encircles an axon, lay-

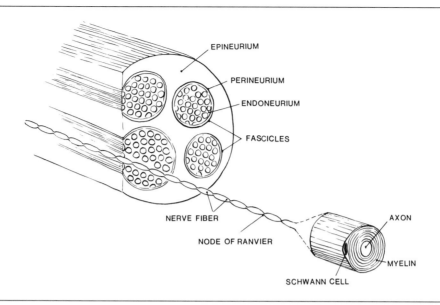

Fig. 13-1. Histologic features of peripheral nerve. Nerve is subdivided into fascicles by perineurium, with multiple motor and sensory nerve fibers intermingled in each fascicle.

Table 13-1. Nerve Fiber Types

Type	Diameter (μm)	Conduction velocity (m/sec)	Function
Muscle nerve afferents			
Ia	12–20	70–120	Afferents from muscle spindle (primary endings — annulospiral)
Ib	12–20	70–120	Afferents from Golgi tendon organs
II	6–12	30–70	Afferents from muscle spindle (secondary endings — flower spray)
III	2–6	4–30	Pressure–pain afferents
IV	<2	0.5–2.0	Pain afferents
Cutaneous nerve afferents			
Aα	12–20	70–120	Joint receptor afferents
Aα	6–12	30–70	Paccinian corpuscle and touch receptor afferents
Aδ	2–6	4–30	Touch, temperature, and pain afferents
C	<2	0.5–2.0	Pain, temperature, and some mechanoreceptors
Visceral nerve afferents			
A	2–12	4–70	Internal regulation receptors
C	<2	0.2–2.0	
Efferents			
Alpha	12–20	70–120	Extrafusal skeletal muscle innervation from alpha motor neurons
Gamma	2–8	10–50	Intrafusal muscle spindle innervation from gamma motor neurons
B	<3	3–30	Preganglionic autonomic efferents
C	<1	0.5–2.0	Postganglionic autonomic efferents

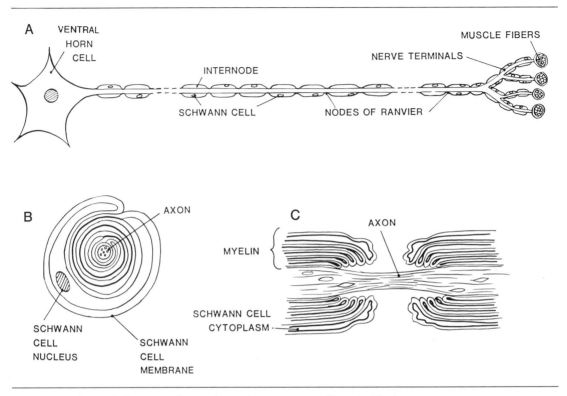

Fig. 13-2. Histologic features of a myelinated motor nerve fiber. A. Single myelinated axon extends from a ventral horn cell to nerve terminals on muscle fibers. B. Cross section of nerve fiber through internode with layers of myelin formed by Schwann cell cytoplasm wrapped around it. C. Longitudinal section of node of Ranvier with Schwann cell and myelin terminations abutting around continuous central axon.

ers of plasma membrane fuse to form myelin (Fig. 13-4). *Myelin* is thus a series of concentric layers of lipids and proteins. The lipids include cerebrosides, sulfatides, proteolipids, sphingomyelin, inositol phosphatides, glycolipids, glycoproteins, and cholesterol. There are three proteins in myelin, a glycoprotein and two basic proteins. The basic proteins in peripheral nerve have similarities to the basic myelin protein in the central nervous system, but they are different proteins.

Although myelin is relatively inert metabolically, it has a significant turnover and responds to various disease states. For instance, myelin may be lost (demyelination) in certain immunologic disorders. When myelin is lost along a peripheral nerve, it is usually lost in the region of a single Schwann cell, which extends from one node of Ranvier to another. This loss is called *segmental demyelination* and alters the function of a nerve fiber. Myelin

also may be formed abnormally or may accumulate myelin metabolites in abnormal quantities. This condition occurs in genetic disorders due to enzyme defects, such as *metachromatic leukodystrophy* in which a deficit of arylsulfatase A results in the accumulation of metachromatic sulfatides in nerve fibers and loss of function in myelinated axons.

The axons of all nerve fibers consist of the axon membrane, or *axolemma,* and the axoplasm. The axoplasm contains mitochondria, microtubules, microfilaments, and neurofilaments. The *mitochondria* mediate the generation of energy needed to establish the concentration gradients across the axolemma. The *microtubules* participate in the transport of proteins, enzymes, and other materials down the axon from the cell body to the periphery. The function of the neurofilaments and microfilaments is related to axoplasmic transport and axon growth.

Fig. 13-3. A, B. Transverse sections of a nerve that contains myelinated and unmyelinated axons of various sizes. (×8,500.) (From K. Sugimura, et al. Interstitial hyperosmolarity may cause axis cylinder shrinkage in streptozotocin diabetic nerve. *J. Neuropathol. Exp. Neurol.* 39:710, 1980. By permission of the American Association of Neuropathologists, Inc.)

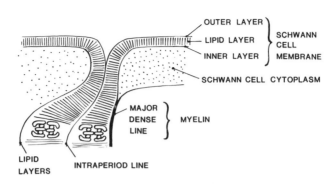

Fig. 13-4. Formation of myelin from layers of Schwann cell membrane. Major dense lines are formed from protein layers of membrane and are separated by the lipid layer, which contains cholesterol, cerebroside, sphingomyelin, and phosphatidylserine.

Axonal Transport

Two transport mechanisms, a slow and a fast, distribute proteins, neurotransmitters, synaptic vessels, mitochondria, and other cellular elements that are formed in the cell body to the distal axons. Slow axoplasmic flow, moving 1 to 3 mm per day, conveys three types of filamentous proteins — neurofilaments, microtubules (formed from two types of tubulin subunits), and microfilaments (which contain neural actin and myosin) — down the axon to the nerve terminal. These filamentous proteins account for 80 percent of the substances transported by axoplasmic flow. The remainder are enzymes and neurotransmitters. The slow transport system furnishes new axoplasm to developing or regenerating neurons and continuously renews the axoplasms of mature neurons.

Fast axonal transport, traveling 400 mm per day, carries particulate matter such as new membrane materials, synaptic vesicles, and precursors of receptor structures from the cell body, where they are synthesized, down the axon to the nerve terminal. Some of this material is deposited along the axon to maintain and replace the axolemma; the rest goes to the nerve terminals to form the synaptic vesicles and receptor structures at the nerve endings. Fast axonal transport moves materials not only away from the cell body but also back from the nerve terminal to the cell body, where they are restored or degraded. The intracellular membranes that are degraded within neuronal lysosomes constitute the major component of the retrograde transport back to the cell body. Retrograde transport is also the mechanism by which neurotropic viruses, such as herpes simplex, rabies, and polio, ascend in the peripheral nerves to reach the central nervous system.

Physiology

The resting potential and action potentials in single axons are described in detail in Chapter 5 (Diagnosis of Neurologic Disorders: Transient Disorders and Neurophysiology). In this chapter, we focus on the physiology of whole nerve trunks. The function of the axons is to carry information in the form of electrical activity from one area to another. A measure of the ability of a nerve to perform this function would be of major clinical value in the identification of disease involving a nerve. However, during normal function, the electrical activities of the fibers in a nerve are asynchronous and cancel each other out. Therefore, physiologic electrical activity from an active nerve trunk cannot be recorded with surface electrodes.

The action potential of a single axon can be recorded experimentally with an intracellular microelectrode that records it as a monophasic wave of depolarization. The electrical activity in a single nerve fiber also can be monitored by placing electrodes in the extracellular

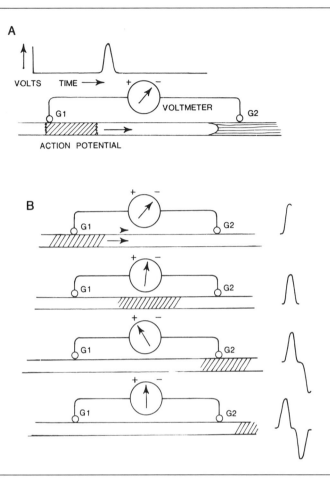

Fig. 13-5. Recording action potentials from nerve trunk with electrodes (G1 and G2). A. With G2 over damaged nerve and G1 over active nerve, a monophasic action potential is recorded as depolarization passes under G1. B. If both electrodes are over active nerve fibers, potentials of opposite polarity are recorded as depolarization passes under G1 and G2, a biphasic action potential. When G1 and G2 are close together, the two potentials fuse to form a smooth biphasic response.

fluid very close to the nerve fiber. This method does not detect transmembrane potential changes; rather, it senses potential changes in the extracellular fluid that result from longitudinal current flow between the depolarized and nondepolarized regions of an axon. The extracellular recording is improved (a bigger voltage change is measured) if the extracellular resistance is artificially increased by recording from the nerve experimentally in air or in oil.

Extracellular recording from single axons is difficult because of their small size; however, it is possible to record from groups of axons or from whole nerve trunks, if all axons discharge synchronously. This recording is obtained experimentally and from patients by applying an electrical shock that activates all axons simultaneously. The potential recorded from a nerve activated in this way is the *compound action potential.* The configuration of the signal obtained from an extracellular recording of the nerve impulse depends on the electrode arrangement. A monophasic potential change is observed from nerve fibers conducting an impulse if only one of the electrodes is placed over an active nerve. A biphasic potential is recorded if both electrodes are placed over the active nerve (Fig. 13-5).

As in the stimulation of a single axon, the

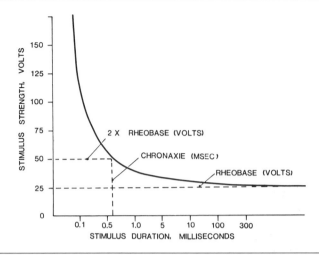

Fig. 13-6. Strength-duration curve. Threshold voltage for each duration is plotted. Rheobase is 25 V, and chronaxie is 0.6 millisecond.

whole nerve trunk is activated by passing a current between the cathode (negative pole) and the anode (positive pole). The cathode depolarizes the underlying axons, and the anode hyperpolarizes them. Depolarization requires current flow inside the axons. Because large axons have lower internal resistance, the threshold for activation is lowest for the larger fibers. The *threshold stimulus* for a nerve trunk is that which just excites the large fibers. Supramaximal stimuli activate all fibers, including the small fibers, and require greater current flow. Excitability, therefore, depends on axon size.

The *excitability* of a nerve can be defined in terms of the two variables of a stimulus: voltage and duration. If the strength of the current (or voltage) is plotted against the duration of a stimulus needed to produce excitation of a nerve, a curve is obtained, which is called a *strength-duration curve*. A shift in the strength-duration curve indicates a change in excitability and is seen in nerve diseases. The strength-duration curve is often characterized in terms of two points. The *rheobase* is the minimal voltage needed to produce excitation with a long stimulus duration (usually 300 msec) and the *chronaxie* is the time required to excite a nerve by a stimulus with a voltage twice as large as the rheobase (Fig. 13-6).

The compound action potential recorded from a nerve trunk after supramaximal stimu-

lation is the summation of action potentials from many axons. Its amplitude can be graded by varying the strength of the stimulus. A threshold stimulation evokes only a small potential resulting from activity in a few large fibers. As the stimulus strength is increased, more fibers are excited, and their activity is added to the compound action potential as each additionally activated fiber produces a small increment in the recorded voltage. When all the fibers are excited, the amplitude of the compound action potential is maximum; it will not increase in amplitude with further increases in the stimulus strength (supramaximal). The compound action potential thus can be graded in amplitude, while action potentials in single axons are not graded but fire in an all-or-nothing fashion.

Variation in axon diameter in a nerve trunk results in different conduction velocities as well as different thresholds for activation. The rate at which an axon conducts is a function of the amount of longitudinal current flow and is greater with larger axons. The *conduction velocity* is calculated by dividing the distance a potential travels by the time it takes to travel that distance. It is approximately five times the axon's diameter in microns — for example, 5 to 100 meters per second for axons of 1 to 20 μm in diameter. If a nerve trunk is stimulated at a distance from the recording electrodes, the compound ac-

Fig. 13-7. Compound action potential recorded directly from a cutaneous nerve, showing peaks generated by different fiber types.

Table 13-2. Fiber Types in a Mixed Nerve

Diameter (μm)	Conduction velocity (m/sec)	Type
12–20	70–120	Ia, Ib, Aα, alpha efferent
6–12	30–70	II, Aα, gamma efferent, visceral afferent
2–6	4–30	III, Aδ, gamma efferent, visceral afferent
<2	0.5–2.0	IV, B, C

tion potential exhibits several components (Fig. 13-7) because of the dispersion of the potentials from fibers of different diameters. The impulses in the large fibers reach the recording site first. The components of the compound action potential thus distinguish activity in groups of fibers whose diameters are within certain size ranges. The afferent fibers in cutaneous nerves (to joints and skin) are subdivided into groups named by letters (Aα, Aδ, and C). The afferent fibers in muscle nerves (nerves to muscle) are subdivided into groups designated by Roman numerals (I, II, III, IV). These are listed in Table 13-1.

Nerves that innervate muscle contain both sensory and motor fibers. The motor fibers arise from the alpha and gamma motor neurons and innervate the extrafusal and intrafusal muscle fibers. The sensory fibers are the group Ia and II fibers from muscle spindles and the group Ib fibers from Golgi tendon organs. Cutaneous nerves innervate joints and skin and are commonly considered sensory nerves, although both they and the muscle nerves contain efferent and afferent fibers of the internal regulation system, the "C" or group IV fibers. Table 13-2 lists by size the components of a mixed nerve.

In addition to transmitting action potentials, axons move proteins along their length. This process is known as *axoplasmic transport* and is important for the production of neurotransmitter in the nerve terminal, for maintaining the integrity of the distal parts of the axon, and for the release of trophic factors from the nerve terminal. The *trophic factors*, released from nerve terminals, are substances necessary for the normal function of the postsynaptic cell. Loss of these trophic factors occurs in some nerve diseases and results in physiologic and histologic abnormalities of the postsynaptic cell.

Pathophysiology

A nerve may be altered in a number of ways by disease processes. These can be classified as diseases of the axolemma, the axoplasm, or the myelin sheath.

Axolemmal Disorders

The axon membrane may undergo physicochemical alterations that block conduction without destruction or histologic alteration of the axon. Such alterations may occur by electrical, pharmacologic, thermal, or mechanical means. The alterations are usually transient and reversible and include the familiar phenomenon of a leg "going to sleep."

Electrical conduction blocks do not occur clinically but can be obtained by the application of steady depolarizing (cathodal block) or hyperpolarizing (anodal block) currents to a nerve fiber or nerve trunk. A depolarizing current may initially evoke an action potential and then block impulse transmission. An anodal block results from a hyperpolarization of

Table 13-3. Sequence of Events of Local Anesthetic Block

Displacement of calcium ions from
nerve receptor site
↓
Binding of local anesthetic to receptor site
↓
Blockade of sodium channel
↓
Decrease in sodium conductance
↓
Decreased depolarization of nerve membrane
↓
Failure to achieve threshold potential level
↓
Lack of development of propagated
action potential
↓
Conduction blockade

---

the axon membrane, which moves the membrane potential away from threshold.

A clinically useful method of producing conduction block is the application of pharmacologic agents (local anesthetics) to a nerve. These include compounds such as procaine hydrochloride (Novocain), benzocaine, cocaine, and other esters of benzoic acid. Local anesthetics interfere with nerve conduction by preventing the membrane permeability changes that occur with depolarization (Table 13-3). The membrane is said to be "stabilized" by local anesthetics. Small, unmyelinated nerve fibers, such as those mediating pain, are more sensitive to local anesthetics than are the larger myelinated fibers and are blocked at low concentrations of the drug that do not appreciably affect large fibers (see Table 13-1).

A transient, reversible conduction block can be obtained by lowering the temperature of nerve fibers. This method of blocking nerve impulse transmission is accomplished by the local application of ice or an ethyl chloride spray and is used clinically to produce superficial anesthesia. Mechanical conduction blocks occur with distortion of a nerve and may be due to alteration of the blood supply or to changes in the configuration of the membrane, with secondary changes in its ionic permeability.

Axoplasmic Disorders

Axons may be affected by acute or chronic disorders of the axoplasm. An acute lesion is one in which the axon is disrupted. This may occur with complete division of the nerve in a laceration or with a severe local crush, traction, or ischemia. In laceration, the connective tissue framework is destroyed; in the other lesions, it remains intact. But in each instance, the continuity of the axons is lost, the distal axon is deprived of axoplasmic flow from the neuron, and it undergoes dissolution in a process called *wallerian degeneration.* Central chromatolysis and peripheral muscle atrophy accompany wallerian degeneration (Fig. 13-8). In most lesions other than laceration, not all axons are destroyed and some function may remain. The smaller fibers are more resistant to such injuries and are more likely to be spared. After acute axonal disruption, recovery occurs only through the growth of new axons.

If a nerve is completely severed, reinnervation is poor because the axonal sprouts have no pathway to follow. Axonal sprouts may grow in the wrong direction and produce spirals or large bulbous tips. These sprouts, with their Schwann cells and connective tissue, may form a *neuroma.* The neuroma may not only prevent proper regrowth of the nerve but may also be painful.

The activity of Schwann cells in the distal nerve stump provides an aid to reinnervation across a gap, as they divide, elongate, and migrate toward the proximal nerve stump. If axonal sprouts manage to reach this Schwann cell outgrowth, they may eventually reinnervate the denervated organs. However, the amount of functional recovery is always less than that seen in a crush injury. One reason for this is that most axonal sprouts will not find their way along the pathway followed originally by their parent fibers and will reinnervate an inappropriate organ. A motor axon that establishes a connection with a sensory receptor organ will not function, and a motor axon that reinnervates a different muscle from the one that it originally supplied cannot take part in the same reflex actions. *Synkinesis* is the result of such aberrant reinnervation, in which attempts to activate one group of muscles produce con-

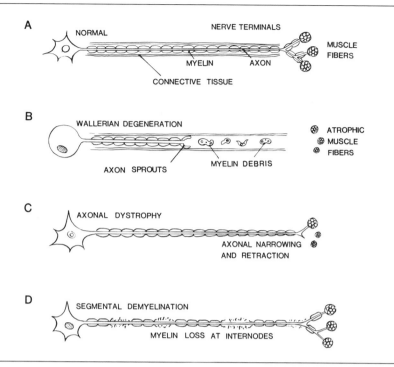

Fig. 13-8. Pathologic changes in peripheral nerve fibers. A. Normal axon. B. Wallerian degeneration occurs distal to local destruction of an axon and is associated with central chromatolysis and muscle fiber atrophy. Regeneration occurs along connective tissue path. C. Axonal dystrophy results in distal narrowing and "dying back" of nerve terminals due to either intrinsic axon or motor neuron disease. D. Segmental demyelination destroys myelin at scattered internodes along axon without axonal damage.

comitant contraction in other muscles innervated by that nerve. The patient can no longer selectively activate a muscle. In injuries to long nerves, the end-organs may atrophy before reinnervation can occur, thus preventing normal recovery.

The rate of nerve regeneration varies with the type of injury. Recovery is quicker with crush injuries than with nerve severance. The delay in recovery depends on axonal growth, reversal of atrophy of the end-organ, reinnervation of the end-organ, and remyelinization and maturation of the axon. In humans, the overall rate of functional recovery under optimal conditions is about 1 to 3 mm per day. The recovery rate in a limb may be quicker proximally than distally.

Axoplasmic disorders may be chronic or slow in evolution and present with different findings than do acute lesions. When the process is complete, the axons degenerate just as

they do in acute lesions; however, there are intermediate stages in which the axons first lose their integrity distally, a so-called dying back. This occurs first in the longest axons and results in loss of function in the most distal parts of the body. The axons also may atrophy or become narrowed in chronic disorders, referred to as axonal *atrophies* or axonal *dystrophies* (see Fig. 13-8). In either situation, there are abnormalities of the axon prior to changes in the myelin. Therefore, unless major narrowing of an axon is present, the conduction of the axons is slowed very little. Chronic axonal disorders occur with many diseases, including genetic, toxic, metabolic, and deficiency states.

The narrow axons seen in some axoplasmic disorders also occur with local compression of a nerve and in regenerating fibers. Moderate narrowing of an axon results in slowing of conduction velocity, but by itself it usually causes little functional impairment. A nerve with slowed conduction velocity can still transmit impulses, though not at as high rates as normal. High-frequency impulses, such as rapid vibrations, the output from muscle spindles, and motor activity in strong muscle contraction, are poorly transmitted so that vibratory sensation and reflexes are lost.

Myelin Disorders

Genetic, immunologic, and toxic disorders can produce primary damage to myelin. In these disorders, myelin is usually lost at internodes, with normal myelin remaining at other internodes. This scattered loss of myelin is segmental demyelination (see Fig. 13-8). The loss of myelin results in slowing of conduction velocity, with mild impairment of vibratory sensation, loss of reflexes, some loss of proprioceptive sensation, and loss of strong muscle contractions. However, with moderate demyelination, the action potential is blocked, producing more severe deficits. Genetic disorders can be associated with a lack of myelin (hypomyelination) or abnormal myelin and can result in functional disturbances similar to those seen with segmental demyelination.

In each of these disorders, there may be varied severity of damage and selective involvement of one or another fiber type. In localized lesions, there is loss of function in the areas supplied by the nerve. In generalized nerve disease, the axons are affected randomly throughout the cross section of a nerve and randomly along the length of the nerve, so that the most likely areas to lose function are the distal regions supplied by the longest nerves. This produces a characteristic distribution of *abnormalities in the distal portions* of the extremities. This distal deficit also occurs in primary neuronal disease in which the neuron is unable to provide sufficient nutrients to the most distal portion of the nerve, with a resultant dying back of the distal portions of the long nerves.

Summary

Because the function of peripheral nerves is to conduct action potentials from one area to another, three general kinds of functional abnormality occur:

1. The excitability of axons may be increased with spontaneous or excessive firing of an axon. This occurs in many disorders, but especially in ischemic or metabolic diseases.
2. The axon may be unable to conduct an action potential, either because of transient metabolic changes or because of structural damage to the axon. If an axon is severed, the distal portion undergoes wallerian degeneration but is able to conduct an impulse in the distal part of the nerve for 3 to 5 days. The proximal portion of the axon continues to function normally.
3. The axon may conduct an impulse slowly or at low rates of firing. This may occur from loss of myelin or be due to narrowing and deformation of the axon. The latter may be seen in the area of compression or in regenerating fibers. Slow conduction results in mild clinical symptoms or signs except for the ability to carry high-frequency information such as vibration, which is severely impaired.

The physiologic alterations seen with diseases of the nerves are associated with two clinically important manifestations. The threshold for activation of some portion of lower motor neurons may be low, and they may discharge spontaneously. If this occurs, all the muscle fibers in the motor unit will contract simultaneously. Such a single, spontaneous contraction of a motor unit is visible as a small twitch under the skin called a *fasciculation*. It is evidence of irritability of the motor unit and occurs in normal persons and in many disorders. Similar irritability in sensory fibers is perceived as paresthesia (tingling) in large fibers or as pain in small fibers.

A second important manifestation is the result of the loss of trophic factors of the nerve acting on muscle. A denervated muscle atrophies and undergoes change in its membrane. This change includes a hypersensitivity to acetylcholine. Normally, most of the acetylcholine receptors are confined to the area immediately adjacent to the end-plate. After denervation, the sensitivity spreads along the surface, until the entire fiber responds to the drug. This is one form of denervation hypersensitivity (Table 13-4). Muscle fibers undergo

Table 13-4. Examples of Denervation Hypersensitivity

Site	Clinical finding	Due to destruction of	Hypersensitivity to
Striated muscle	Fibrillation	Alpha efferents	Acetylcholine
Ventral horn cell	Spasticity, clonus, hyperreflexia	Descending pathway	Local sensory input
Pupil	Miosis	Postganglionic sympathetic	Epinephrine analogs
Pupil	Mydriasis	Postganglionic parasympathetic	Acetylcholine analogs

denervation hypersensitivity and begin to discharge and twitch approximately 2 weeks after losing their innervation. Such spontaneous, regular twitching of single muscle fibers is called *fibrillation.*

Peripheral Nerves

Anatomy

The peripheral nerves are the major nerve trunks in the extremities and are derived from the plexuses. They have the histologic and physiologic features described in the previous section. Each nerve has a well-defined anatomical course in an extremity, supplies a specific area of skin, and provides innervation for specific muscles (Fig. 13-9). The major peripheral nerves and their important areas of innervation are described in Table 13-5. More detailed distributions are shown in Figure 13-10.

Clinical Correlations

The proximity of some nerves to bony structures makes them particularly vulnerable to lesions at those sites. The *median nerve* passes through a tunnel at the wrist (the carpal tunnel) where it is easily and often compressed, producing arm pain, sensory loss of the first three digits, and weakness of the thenar muscles — the carpal tunnel syndrome. The *ulnar nerve* is commonly compressed at the elbow, where it passes around the medial epicondyle in an exposed position (the "funny bone"). Lesions here produce sensory loss in the ring and fifth fingers, with flaccid weakness and atrophy of the intrinsic muscles of the hand. The *radial nerve* is particularly susceptible to injury as it curves around the humerus in the spiral groove in the mid-upper arm. Lesions at this site produce a weakness of wrist and finger

extension. The *peroneal nerve* is in an exposed position over a bony prominence where it curves around the head of the fibula at the knee. Damage at this site produces footdrop and sensory loss of the dorsum of the foot. The deep, protected locations of the sciatic, tibial, and femoral nerves result in fewer injuries. These and all other lesions of the peripheral nerves can be recognized by an analysis of the distribution of the motor, sensory, and reflex changes. The type of lesion may be any of those previously described — with total, irreversible destruction due to wallerian degeneration or with mild, reversible changes due to membrane or myelin alterations. The use of nerve conduction studies to determine the location of slowing or block of conduction is of particular value in identifying the location and severity of such lesions.

Peripheral nerves also may be involved in *diffuse disease* of the myelin or axons. In either instance, the clinical features are similar. There is distal loss of sensation in the upper and lower extremities (more severe in the lower extremities), usually for all modalities, although in some disorders there may be selective involvement of certain fiber types and therefore of certain modalities of sensation. There may be paresthesia, dysesthesia, or hyperalgesia, usually in the same distribution. Reflexes are generally lost. Distal muscles are weak and flaccid and eventually atrophy. Atrophy of distal muscles produces deformities, for example, pes cavus and hammer toes (high arches with cocked-up toes) with loss of intrinsic foot muscles.

Although many peripheral nerve diseases affect both axon and myelin, if the disease process primarily affects the axon, there is more severe atrophy, with loss of innervation and prominent fibrillation in distal muscles. Disorders primarily producing myelin damage are associated with less atrophy, are more

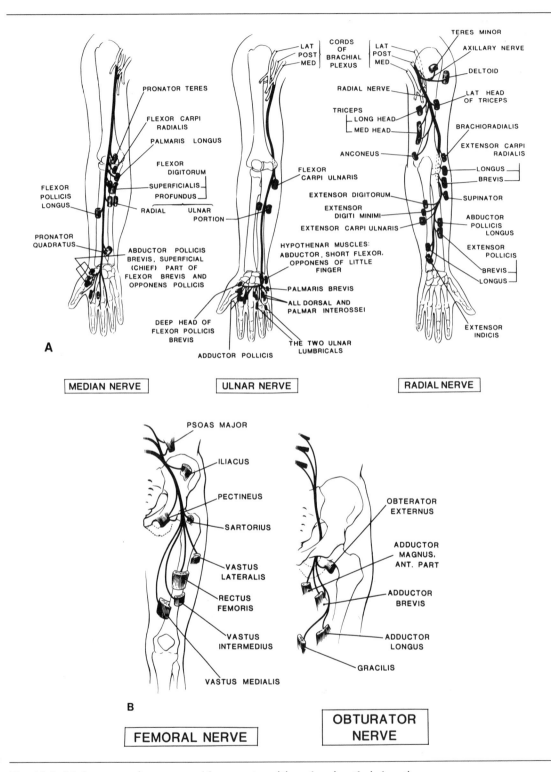

Fig. 13-9. Major nerves in upper and lower extremities, showing their location and muscles that they innervate. A. Arm and hand. B. Thigh and Hip. C. Leg. D. Lower leg and foot. (*ANT* = anterior; *LAT* = lateral; *MED* = medial; *POST* = posterior.) (From W. H. Hollingshead, C. Rosse. *Textbook of Anatomy* [4th ed.]. Philadelphia: Harper & Row, 1985. Pp. 147–164 and 333–347.)

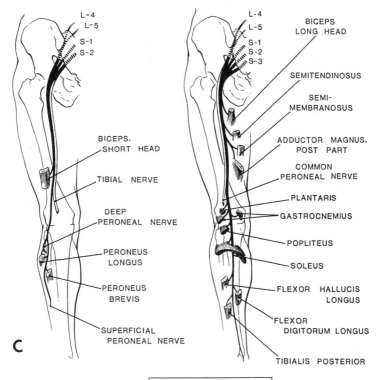

C

SCIATIC NERVE

COMMON PERONEAL
NERVE DIVISION (In black)

TIBIAL NERVE
DIVISION (In black)

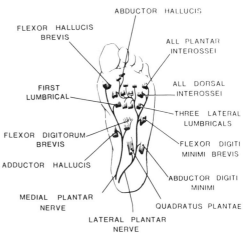

D   COMMON PERONEAL
NERVE

MEDIAL and LATERAL PLANTAR NERVES
(Plantar view of the foot)

readily reversible, and have little or no fibrillation.

Plexus

Anatomy

A *plexus* is a complex recombination of axons as they rearrange themselves in passing from one area to another. There are three major somatic plexuses: the brachial, the lumbar, and the sacral (lumbosacral) plexuses. The *brachial plexus* is derived from spinal nerves C-5 through T-1 and gives rise to the major nerves of the upper extremity. The axons of the spinal nerves are rearranged into trunks, divisions, and cords of the plexus just beneath and behind the clavicle (Fig. 13-11).

The *lumbar plexus,* derived from L-2 through L-4 spinal nerves, and the *sacral plexus,* derived from L-4 through S-3 spinal nerves, give rise to the major nerves of the lower extremity. The femoral and obturator

nerves arise from the lumbar, and the sciatic nerve arises from the sacral plexus. The rearrangements of the axons in the lumbosacral plexus occur in the pelvis, posteriorly, deep to the psoas major muscle (see Fig. 13-11).

Clinical Correlations

Each of these plexuses may undergo the same physiologic or histologic alterations described previously. They are most commonly involved in trauma, tumor, or hemorrhage. The diagnosis of disease in these regions depends on the presence of involvement of proximal muscles innervated by multiple roots, multiple dermatomal involvement, and sparing of the paraspinal muscles. The changes involve motor and sensory fibers and, when severe, result in autonomic disturbances such as loss of sweating, thinning of the skin, and trophic changes in the skin. Reflex loss also occurs.

A number of major plexuses are purely visceral and are a part of the internal regulation system. Although these plexuses may be involved in localized disease processes, this involvement is uncommon and not of clinical significance. The spinal nerves and nerve roots are within the spinal canal and are discussed in the next chapter.

The Neuromuscular Junction

The *neuromuscular junction* is the site at which the motor nerve terminal meets a muscle fiber and where the efferent nerve terminals evoke a contraction of the muscle. This contraction is accomplished through the production of an excitatory synaptic potential called an *end-plate potential.* In the normal skeletal muscle fiber, the end-plate potential always reaches threshold for the production of an action potential, which then propagates along the muscle fiber. The action potential in turn triggers a contraction.

Histology

Each junction consists of a presynaptic portion derived from the nerve terminal and a postsynaptic portion derived from the muscle fiber. As an axon enters a muscle, it branches

Table 13-5. Peripheral Nerve Distributions

Nerve	General innervation	
Median	Sensory:	Palmar surface of thumb and first three fingers
	Motor:	Finger and wrist flexion
Ulnar	Sensory:	Fourth and fifth fingers
	Motor:	Intrinsic hand muscles
Radial	Sensory:	Dorsum of the hand
	Motor:	Forearm, wrist, and hand extension
Femoral	Sensory:	Anterior aspect of thigh and medial part of leg
	Motor:	Hip flexion and knee extension
Sciatic	Sensory:	Posterior aspect of thigh and portion of leg below the knee
	Motor:	Knee flexion and all ankle and foot motion
Peroneal	Sensory:	Lateral aspect of leg and dorsum of foot
	Motor:	Foot and toe dorsiflexion
Tibial	Sensory:	Posterior part of leg and sole of foot
	Motor:	Foot and toe plantar flexion

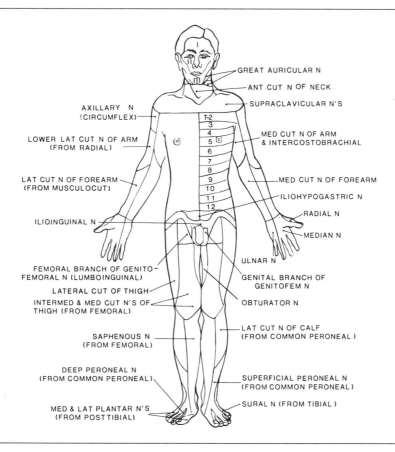

Fig. 13-10. Cutaneous distribution of peripheral nerves. (*ANT* = anterior; *CUT* = cutaneous; *INTERMED* = intermedial; *LAT* = lateral; *MED* = medial; *N* = nerve.) (Redrawn from W. Haymaker and B. Woodhall. *Peripheral Nerve Injuries: Principles of Diagnosis* [2nd ed.]. Philadelphia: Saunders, 1953.)

into many nerve terminals, each of which innervates one muscle fiber. As the terminal approaches the muscle fiber, the axon loses its myelin sheath and comes to lie in a depression in the muscle fiber. The nerve terminal is covered by a Schwann cell, but the inferior portion of the axolemma is directly apposed to the sarcolemma of the muscle fiber, with a synaptic cleft of 500 μm intervening. The postsynaptic portion of the junction consists of complex folds of sarcolemma immediately beneath the nerve terminal. This region can be demonstrated with histochemical techniques that stain acetylcholinesterase (Fig. 13-12). The sarcolemma, with its folds, forms the subneural apparatus. The cytoplasm of the nerve terminal contains a concentration of mitochondria and many synaptic vesicles. Often, the synaptic vesicles seem to be clustered near a region of density of the presynaptic membrane. These specialized areas are located opposite the postsynaptic folds. Acetylcholine is bound to the vesicles in the nerve terminal.

Physiology

Small electrical potentials can be recorded from the region of the neuromuscular junction of skeletal muscle fibers, even in the absence of nerve impulses in the motor fibers. These potentials have all the electrical and pharmacologic properties of end-plate potentials, except that they are small and occur in a random

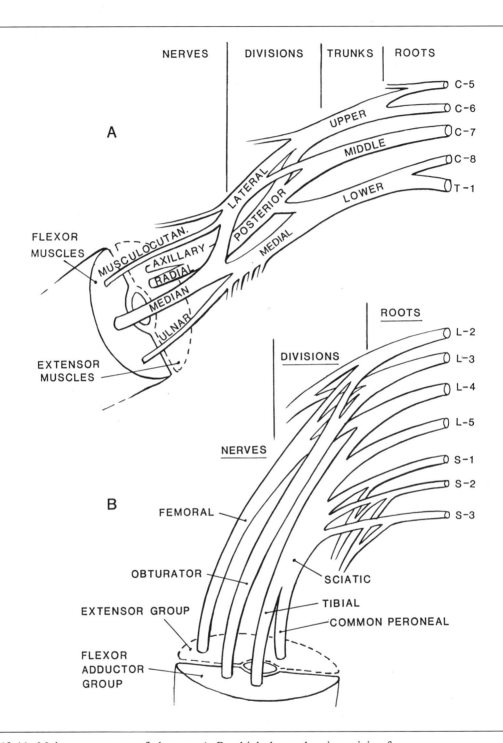

Fig. 13-11. Major components of plexuses. A. Brachial plexus showing origin of the three trunks, three cords, and peripheral nerves. B. Lumbosacral plexus divisions forming nerves of lower extremity. (*MUSCULOCUTAN* = musculocutaneous.)

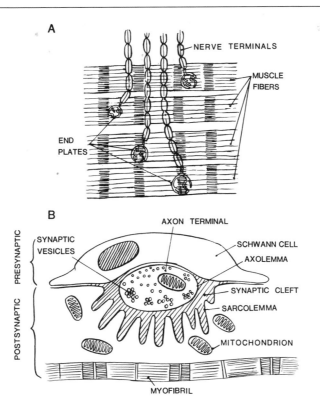

Fig. 13-12. Neuromuscular junction. A. End-plates where single nerve terminals innervate single muscle fibers. B. Cross section of an end-plate. Axon terminal lies in depression on muscle surface covered by Schwann cell. Postsynaptic, sarcolemmal folds contain acetylcholine receptors. Acetylcholine is stored in synaptic vesicles in nerve terminal.

fashion without the need of nerve activity. These have been called *miniature end-plate potentials.*

The miniature end-plate potentials are due to leakage of the neurotransmitter acetylcholine from the presynaptic terminals. The leakage occurs in "quanta" of transmitter; that is, the miniature end-plate potentials are produced by thousands of molecules of acetylcholine released together. The end-plate potential in contrast is produced by the near synchronous release of many quanta triggered by the nerve impulse. The *synaptic vesicles* are the storage sites of quanta of acetylcholine.

When the resting potential of the motor axon terminal at a neuromuscular junction is reduced, the frequency of release of miniature end-plate potentials is increased. The relationship is not a linear one, however. There is a tenfold increase in frequency for every 15 mV of depolarization. The depolarization associated with an action potential in the motor axon terminal results in the release of a burst of several hundred acetylcholine quanta, thus accounting for the end-plate potential. The number (M) of quanta (Q) released by a presynaptic action potential can be calculated by dividing the average end-plate potential amplitude (EPP) by the average miniature end-plate potential amplitude (MEPP):

$$M = \frac{EPP}{MEPP}$$

Acetylcholine increases the permeability of the postsynaptic membrane to both sodium and potassium ions. The membrane potential is thus only partially depolarized; the synaptic

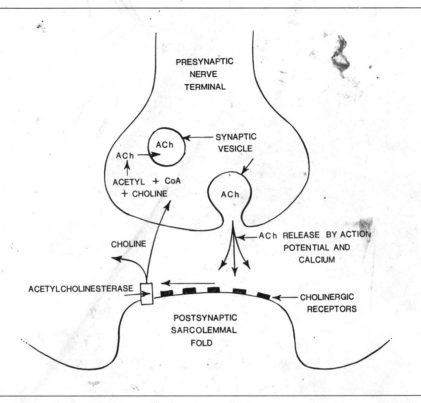

Fig. 13-13. Neurotransmitter action at neuromuscular junction. Acetylcholine (*ACh*) is formed and stored in nerve terminal. It is released by nerve terminal depolarization in the presence of calcium and binds with receptors on postsynaptic membrane. After producing an ionic conductance charge, it is hydrolyzed by acetylcholinesterase. (*CoA* = coenzyme A.)

currents do not flow long enough for the membrane to be depolarized to zero. The end-plate potential is therefore considerably smaller than the action potential; nevertheless, it is well above the threshold for generating a muscle fiber action potential. When the end-plate potential reaches threshold, it triggers the action potential of the muscle. The acetylcholine is rapidly broken down by the enzyme acetylcholinesterase after binding with the postsynaptic membrane and producing the end-plate potential.

Acetylcholine is synthesized by *choline acetyltransferase* from acetyl-CoA and choline in the nerve terminal. It is stored in the vesicles and released by the action potential through calcium binding in the membrane. The acetylcholine diffuses across the synapse and binds with the cholinergic receptor until it is broken down by acetylcholinesterase for partial reuptake into the terminal. A summary of the events occurring at the neuromuscular junction is shown in Figure 13-13.

Pharmacology

A number of important drugs affect neuromuscular transmission. For instance, curare, the poison once used by some South American Indians on the tips of their blowgun arrows, prevents acetylcholine from reacting with the receptor sites of the muscle membrane by competitively binding with the sites and causes paralysis. In contrast to the effect of the acetylcholine, the reaction between the curare molecule and the acetylcholine receptor molecule does not change conductance in the membrane. Curare thus blocks neuromuscular transmission.

Another substance that blocks neuromuscular transmission is botulin, the agent that causes botulism in food contaminated by *Clostridium botulinum*. Botulin blocks the release of acetylcholine from the motor nerve terminals, causes a loss of end-plate potentials, and results in paralysis.

Neuromuscular transmission is enhanced by drugs that block the action of acetylcholinesterase. In the absence of this enzyme, the acetylcholine released by nerve impulses has a greater and more prolonged action. However, if too much acetylcholine accumulates, it may cause a depolarizing block of the muscle membrane. Excess acetylcholine may also desensitize the acetylcholine receptor molecules and reduce the response to acetylcholine. Normally this interaction occurs but is only transient, because the acetylcholine is removed by the esterase. An example of an anticholinesterase used to treat patients clinically is *physostigmine*. Some insecticides and nerve gases are also anticholinesterases. Several drugs can mimic the action of acetylcholine at the neuromuscular junction. One of these is *nicotine*. In low doses, nicotine has an excitatory effect on skeletal muscle, while in high doses, it blocks neuromuscular transmission.

Clinical Correlations

Disorders of neuromuscular transmission theoretically can involve a number of mechanisms, including the synthesis of acetylcholine, packaging of acetylcholine in the vesicles, release of vesicles from the nerve terminal, diffusion of acetylcholine across the synaptic cleft, binding of the acetylcholine with the receptor, response of the receptor to the transmitter, and breakdown of the acetylcholine by acetylcholinesterase. Two of these disorders are well known clinically. Both are manifested as weakness without sensory loss. One of these is *myasthenia gravis,* in which there is partial receptor blockade resulting in weakness that increases after exercise. In the other disorder, *Lambert-Eaton myasthenic syndrome* (LEMS), there is an impairment of release of acetylcholine from the nerve terminal. This also results in weakness; however, it can be partially overcome by continued activity because, with continued activation, changes in

the nerve terminal membrane facilitate acetylcholine release. Thus, patients with this syndrome show increasing strength with a brief period of exercise. In myasthenia gravis, both the end-plate potentials and the miniature end-plate potentials are small. In LEMS, a disorder often associated with carcinoma, the miniature end-plate potentials are normal, but the end-plate potentials are small because of a decrease in the number of quanta released.

Muscle

All body movements are produced by muscles. Through their activity, all the behavior of the organism is affected. The function of muscle is to produce force and movement and to stabilize joints. Striated muscles act through their attachment to tendons and bones, but they depend foremost on their contractile elements. They vary in size and structure, from the very tiny stapedius muscle of the ear to the large, powerful gastrocnemius muscle of the leg. Each is designed to perform specific functions, whether they be finely controlled, rapid, skilled movements, powerful, sudden contractions, or slow, continuous, steady exertion of force. The size, shape (fusiform, unipennate, bipennate, and multipennate), and microscopic anatomy of muscles vary with their function. Muscles requiring sudden, strong, or phasic contractions are made up predominantly of type II, white, or fast-twitch muscle fibers that can function anaerobically; those requiring steady, continuous contractions are made up primarily of type I, red, slow-twitch muscle fibers that depend on aerobic metabolism. The size of motor units, the innervation ratios, and the number of motor units in a muscle also are designed to efficiently perform the appropriate activity. The extraocular muscles, which must perform rapid, quick, very finely controlled movements, have large numbers of motor units — more than a thousand per muscle. Each motor unit has a low innervation ratio, controlling only 5 to 10 muscle fibers. In contrast, the gastrocnemius muscle is a much larger muscle with approximately the same number of motor units. However,

Fig. 13-14. Transverse section of muscle fiber treated with an ATPase stain showing normal random checkerboard pattern of the two types of muscle fibers. Type I fibers are stained lightly; type II fibers are stained darkly. (ATPase stain; ×200.) (Courtesy of Dr. Andrew G. Engel, Mayo Clinic.)

the innervation ratio is much higher, with each lower motor neuron controlling as many as 2,000 muscle fibers.

Muscles have long been classed as "red" or "white" on the basis of their color. More recently, other biochemical and histochemical differences, such as the content of glycogen, mitochondria, and particular enzymes, have been used to identify different types of muscle fiber (Fig. 13-14). Red fibers (type I) contain large amounts of oxidative enzymes (lactic dehydrogenase, succinic dehydrogenase, and cytochrome oxidase), and white fibers (type II) contain little of these enzymes but relatively large amounts of phosphorylase and glycolytic enzymes (ATPase). The fibers in any one motor unit are *uniform;* that is, all muscle fibers innervated by a single anterior horn cell are identical in their histochemical and physiologic properties. These properties are determined by the ventral horn cell. Re-innervation of muscle fibers by other anterior horn cells after denervation changes the muscle fiber type in addition to the size of the muscle fiber. Some of the differences in type I

and type II motor units are shown in Table 13-6.

Structure

Each muscle is made up of large numbers of muscle fibers arranged in parallel with the longitudinal axis of the muscle. The fibers range from 2 to 15 cm in length and from 30 to 60 μm in diameter. Each is attached to the tendon of the muscle via connective tissue attachments. Individual muscle fibers are multinucleated cells containing *myofibrils,* the contractile elements, as well as mitochondria, nuclei, and other cellular constituents. Each muscle fiber has a single end-plate located approximately halfway along its length.

The myofibrils of the muscle are banded and give the muscle fiber a banded appearance. Each muscle contains bundles of myofibrils arranged with their bands in register (Fig. 13-15). The bands are due to the overlapping of the component fibrillar protein of the myofibrils. Each myofibril is approximately 1 μm in diameter and contains two types of fila-

Table 13-6. Characteristics of Motor Units

Tonic	Phasic
Motor neuron (type I)	Motor neuron (type II)
Small alpha motor neuron	Large alpha motor neuron
Small axon	Large axon
Low firing frequency	High firing frequency
Slow-twitch fibers	Fast-twitch fibers
Muscle fibers (red)	Muscle fibers (white)
Aerobic oxidative enzymes (lactic and succinic dehydrogenase, cytochrome oxidase)	Anaerobic glycolytic enzymes and phosphorylase
Small quantities of glycogen	Large quantities of glycogen
Rich in myoglobin	Poor in myoglobin
Lower threshold to stretch	Higher threshold to stretch
Longer contraction time	Shorter contraction time
More mitochondria	Fewer mitochondria
Lower muscle tension	Higher muscle tension
High oxygen consumption	Low oxygen consumption
Constant good blood flow	Rapidly insufficient blood flow
Low fatigability	Pronounced fatigability

Fig. 13-15. Ultrastructure of muscle fiber. Each fiber is made up of many myofibrils containing filaments of actin and myosin organized in bands A, I, and Z. (*NM* = nanometers.)

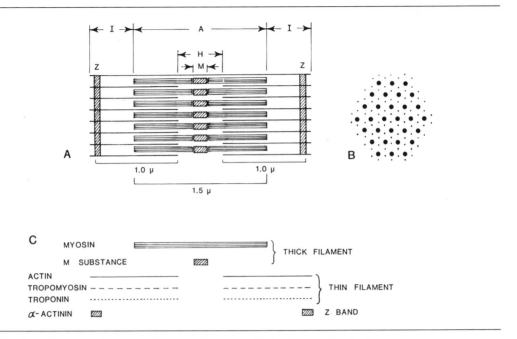

Fig. 13-16. Organization of protein filaments in a myofibril. A. Longitudinal section through one sarcomere (Z disk to Z disk) showing overlap of actin and myosin. B. Cross section through A band, where the thin actin filaments interdigitate with the thick myosin filaments in a hexagonal formation. C. Location of specific proteins in sarcomere.

ments: thin filaments and thick filaments. The thick filament contains *myosin,* a large protein material of approximately 0.1 μm in diameter, with lateral projections of meromyosin. *Actin,* the thin filament, is 0.05 μm in diameter. Actin has two proteins, *troponin* and *tropomyosin,* associated with it; these can prevent the interaction of actin and myosin. The actin and myosin filaments are arranged in a hexagonal formation where they overlap (Fig. 13-16). The area of overlap is darker and is called the *A band.* The area that includes only thin actin filaments is lighter and is called the *I band.* The thin actin filaments are attached to a crystalline structure, which is also dark and is called the *Z disk.* The region including only myosin filaments is the *H zone.* The myosin filaments are bound together at an area of darkness centrally called the *M line* within the H band.

A muscle fiber can be divided longitudinally into areas called *sarcomeres,* which extend from one Z disk to the next. The sarcomere is approximately 2 μm long and consists (in order) of I band, A band, H zone, A band, and I band between two Z disks. Running throughout the muscle and intertwined with the myofibrils is sarcoplasmic reticulum, which forms a longitudinal, anastomotic network of irregular tubular spaces surrounding the myofibrils (Fig. 13-17). At specific locations along the length of the myofibrils, usually at the junction of the A and the I bands, are transverse tubular structures, the *T tubules,* which are near the sarcoplasmic reticulum. The T tubules are hollow structures, continuous with the surface membrane (or sarcolemma), and therefore are open to the extracellular fluid. They run perpendicularly from the surface membrane into the muscle fiber, encircling the myofibrils.

Physiology

The contraction of a muscle is initiated by the action potential. When the end-plate potential reaches threshold, an action potential is initiated in the end-plate region and propagates in both directions down the length of the muscle fiber. As the action potential sweeps down the fiber, the current flow generated by the poten-

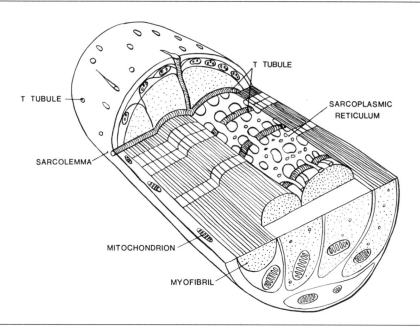

Fig. 13-17. Structure of single muscle fiber cut both horizontally and longitudinally. Individual myofibrils are surrounded and separated by sarcoplasmic reticulum. T tubules are continuous with extracellular fluid and interdigitate with sarcoplasmic reticulum.

tial passes internally into the depths of the fiber via the T-tubule system. These currents cause the release of calcium from the sarcoplasmic reticulum. The calcium binds with troponin, a protein attached to the surface of the actin filaments, and breaks the troponin-tropomyosin linkage. This linkage, which exists at rest, prevents the interaction of the thin and the thick filaments. When calcium eliminates this inhibition, the filaments interact, attach briefly, and move relative to each other, to result in shortening of the sarcomere. The attachments are brief, rapidly broken, and remade with elements further along the filaments as they slide past one another. Thus, contraction is initiated by the inhibition of an inhibition and is accomplished by the sliding of the filaments. The energy required to break the attachments between the actin and myosin is provided by adenosine triphosphate (ATP) acting with magnesium. If a muscle runs out of energy sources, the binding between actin and myosin can no longer be broken, and the muscle becomes rigid (as in rigor mortis). In normal muscle, the reuptake of calcium by the sarcoplasmic reticulum terminates each contraction.

The generation of tension depends on overlap of actin and myosin filaments. If a muscle is stretched too far, there will be only minimal overlap and little opportunity for interaction. The muscle, therefore, has optimal lengths for contraction, as shown on a length-tension diagram (Fig. 13-18).

The rate at which tension develops varies with muscle fiber type. In a slow-twitch muscle in which the twitch lasts 100 msec, repetitive stimulation at 10 per second results in a steady contraction. The same rate of activation in a fast-twitch fiber with a twitch time of 25 msec results in a series of brief distinct twitches with each impulse. The sequence of events leading to the contraction of a muscle is illustrated schematically in Figure 13-19.

Clinical Correlations

A disease may damage a muscle directly, as in a *myopathy,* or indirectly by damaging nerves to cause *neurogenic atrophy.* In either instance, there are weakness and atrophy of the muscle. However, myopathy and neurogenic atrophy are histologically and physiologically

Fig. 13-18. Length-tension diagram of muscle fiber in relation to its sarcomere length. A. Tension generated at different sarcomere lengths. B. Extent of overlap of actin and myosin filaments at different sarcomere lengths.

distinct. If a muscle loses its innervation because of disease of the lower motor neuron, the muscle fibers fibrillate and atrophy. In disorders with incomplete denervation, scattered muscle fibers atrophy. If the process is chronic, viable axons in the muscle reinnervate the denervated fibers, resulting in motor units with a higher innervation ratio and large motor unit potentials. If the large units are lost, the atrophy subsequently appears in large groups of fibers to produce the typical histologic pattern of neurogenic atrophy (Figs. 13-20 and 13-21).

In many myopathies, entire muscle fibers degenerate in a random process, affecting muscle fibers of many motor units, with a loss of fibers from all motor units. With this loss, a smaller force is generated when the motor units are activated. In addition to weakness, the loss of muscle fibers results in smaller motor unit potentials, a feature that can be recognized by needle electromyography. Whereas

many primary muscle diseases or myopathies have specific histologic changes, some features are common to all myopathies: random variation in fiber size, internal migration of nuclei, increased connective tissue, and degenerative changes in the muscle fibers (Fig. 13-22).

Although these abnormalities may affect all muscles in the body, most primary muscle diseases affect the proximal muscles to a greater extent than the distal muscles. Proximal muscle weakness is therefore characteristic of myopathy. It is associated with normal sensation and normal reflexes as long as there is muscle left to contract. The weakness is not associated with an alteration of tone.

Destruction of muscle fibers in their entirety or segmentally along their length is the most common manner for disease processes to affect a muscle. However, two other specific pathophysiologic alterations can occur:

1. Disorder of the sarcolemma, preventing it from generating normal action potentials.
2. Disorder of the excitation-contraction coupling mechanism within the muscle fiber.

Disorders of the Sarcolemma

These result in two types of abnormalities: (1) inability to generate action potentials, as in periodic paralysis in which altered ionic conductance in the membrane causes altered resting potential and loss of action potentials and electrical activity, leaving the muscle contraction weak, and (2) other membrane disorders, such as myotonias, which produce excessive firing or irritability of the membrane, excess muscle contraction, prolonged contraction, or inability to stop contraction.

Disorders of the Contractile Mechanism

In these disorders, muscle fibers generate normal electrical activity but do not generate normal force. In the genetic disorder of phosphorylase deficiency, there is inability to generate sufficient energy. As the muscle runs out of energy, it cramps without electrical activation. Other metabolic and toxic disorders interfere with the excitation-contraction coupling and produce weakness similar in distribution and character to that described with muscle fiber degeneration.

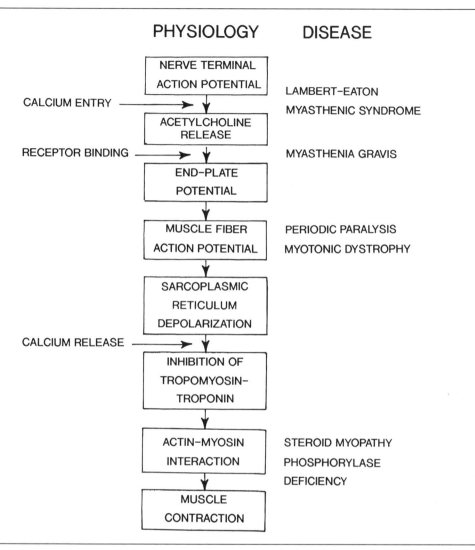

Fig. 13-19. Sequence of events leading to muscle contraction and pathophysiologic correlations.

Clinical Findings with Lesions in the Periphery

Muscle Disease

Patients with primary myopathy have weakness often accompanied by significant atrophy. Voluntary movement is otherwise normal, with no involuntary movements or spasticity. The common types of myopathy, such as muscular dystrophy and polymyositis, involve proximal muscles. There is relative preservation of reflexes because the neural apparatus is intact. Fasciculations (twitching of the muscles), which are indicative of disease of the lower motor neuron, are not present. Patients with disease of muscle show no evidence of damage to the longitudinal systems of the central nervous system. They do not have involvement of mental function, and they do not have sensory symptoms or signs.

Muscular dystrophy is a disease primarily affecting muscle. It is of genetic origin, with one form (Duchenne) due to a defect in the protein, dystrophin, needed to maintain in-

Fig. 13-20. Histologic changes in neurogenic atrophy. Transverse section of muscle fibers showing groups of atrophic fibers and increased connective tissue where many axons have degenerated. (H & E; ×200.) (Courtesy of Dr. Andrew G. Engel, Mayo Clinic.)

Fig. 13-21. Transverse section of reinnervated muscle fiber. Type I fibers are stained lightly and type II darkly. Note the loss of the normal checkerboard pattern; instead there is a grouping of the same type of fibers. (ATPase stain; ×200.) (Courtesy of Dr. Andrew G. Engel, Mayo Clinic.)

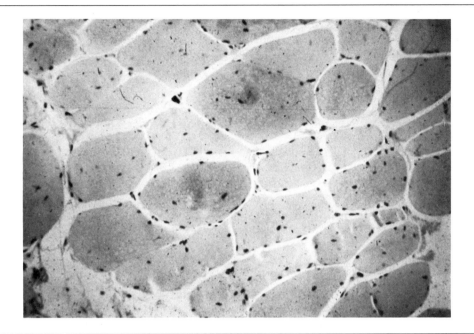

Fig. 13-22. Transverse section of muscle showing general histologic features of myopathy. There is random variation in fiber diameter, with both large and small fibers. Many fibers have internal migration of nuclei, some are splitting or degenerating, and there is an increase in connective tissue. (H & E; ×200.) (Courtesy of Dr. Andrew G. Engel, Mayo Clinic.)

tact sarcolemma. There are a number of forms of muscular dystrophy with different clinical patterns. The three major types are Duchenne, fascioscapulohumeral, and limb-girdle. Each of these shows the histologic alterations typical of a myopathy, with random, patchy degeneration of muscle fibers, central nuclei, and connective tissue proliferation. *Polymyositis,* a connective tissue disease, is an immunologic disorder. It shows pathologic changes similar to those of a dystrophy but with inflammatory cell infiltrates, particularly in and around blood vessels. These changes are more prominent in the peripheral areas of the muscle. Muscular dystrophies have the characteristic temporal profile of degenerative disorders; that is, they are diffuse, chronic, and progressive. Polymyositis, however, has the histologic features of an inflammatory disorder and often shows a subacute temporal profile.

Neuromuscular Junction Disease

The major symptom in patients with defects of neuromuscular transmission is weakness, usually in proximal or cranial muscles. There is no atrophy, and tone is normal. The major features differentiating neuromuscular junction disease from muscle disease are fluctuation of weakness with exertion and the response to drugs acting at the neuromuscular junction, which do not occur in myopathies.

Myasthenia gravis, a disorder affecting the neuromuscular junction, is an autoimmune disease in which antibodies are formed against acetylcholine receptors in the postsynaptic membrane at the motor end-plate. The reduction in the number of receptor sites at the motor end-plate results in a decrease in the response of the muscle fiber to acetylcholine. Clinically, myasthenia gravis is characterized by a fatigable weakness that is induced or increased by exercise and improved by rest or anticholinesterase agents.

Lambert-Eaton myasthenic syndrome (LEMS) is another immune-mediated disorder affecting neuromuscular junctions. In contrast to myasthenia gravis, it affects the presynaptic terminal and blocks the release of acetylcholine quanta. This disorder is usually a paraneoplastic one in which circulating antibodies secreted by small-cell carcinoma of the lung bind with calcium channels in the nerve terminal to prevent calcium entry and quantal release. LEMS is similar to myasthenia gravis in that strength fluctuates with activity, but in contrast to myasthenia gravis, strength may improve with activity because more quanta of acetylcholine are released with continued activation. In the LEMS, the associated findings of muscle weakness and reduced reflexes are due to the neuromuscular junction effects; the dry mouth is due to involvement of parasympathetic junctions.

Peripheral Nerve Disease

Diseases involving the peripheral nerves have a combination of motor, sensory, and autonomic symptoms and signs. There are flaccid weakness and atrophy and sensory loss involving all modalities of sensation in the same distribution as the motor findings. Deep tendon reflexes and superficial reflexes are absent in the distribution of the involved peripheral nerves. Damage to the sympathetic fibers traversing the peripheral nerves may result in alterations in sweating and skin temperature. Other internal regulation disturbances such as hypotension and impotence also may occur.

Diseases of the peripheral nerves are of two types: (1) symmetric polyneuropathies, usually distal and due to a disturbance involving many nerves, and (2) localized mononeuropathies involving a single peripheral nerve, often due to trauma, neoplasm, or compression. In mononeuropathy, or plexus disease, the weakness, pain, sensory deficit, and reflex loss are within the distribution of a specific peripheral nerve, for example, sciatic, radial, median, and ulnar.

Peripheral neuropathy in which there is death or destruction of a portion of the axon results in degeneration of the distal part of the axon in a process called *axonal degeneration* in diffuse disorders and *wallerian degeneration* with focal lesions (see Chapter 4, Diagnosis of Neurologic Disorders: Neurocytology and Pathologic Reactions of the Nervous System). Axonal degeneration occurs in general-

ized disorders of peripheral nerve, such as toxic neuropathies, diabetic neuropathies, and neuropathies due to nutritional deficiencies. In these disorders, the peripheral nerves show loss of axons, fragmentation of axis cylinders, and breakdown of myelin into fragments or myelin ovoids (Fig. 13-23).

Other peripheral neuropathies are characterized primarily by *segmental demyelination.* In the Guillain-Barré syndrome (postinfectious allergic neuritis), there are edema and swelling of myelin and Schwann cell cytoplasm, with cellular infiltration and segmental loss of myelin. If severe, this may be associated with axonal destruction and wallerian degeneration. In the genetic hypertrophic neuropathies, such as Charcot-Marie-Tooth disease, there is repeated demyelination and remyelination of nerve fibers. Each episode leaves a layer of connective tissue forming concentric layers around the axon. Such nerves become very large and firm, and the axons may finally be lost, leaving only the connective tissue stroma.

Peripheral neuropathy may be only one manifestation of a widespread genetic error of metabolism. In metachromatic leukodystrophy, there is a deficit of *arylsulfatase,* an enzyme that is active in the breakdown of myelin products. The absence of the enzyme results in the accumulation of abnormal sulfatides in peripheral nerves and produces the clinical pattern of peripheral neuropathy. There is associated involvement of the white matter of the central nervous system. Pathologically, there is the accumulation of metachromatically staining material along the axons as well as the breakdown of myelin.

Refsum's disease is another genetically determined disease in which the metabolic defect results in an accumulation of phytanic acid, a fatty acid. The disease is characterized by a chronic, sensorimotor polyneuropathy associated with hypertrophic changes and onion-bulb formation of peripheral nerves. The patient also has ichthyosis (dry, rough, scaly skin), retinitis pigmentosa, and deafness. In the past, this was considered an untreatable degenerative neurologic disorder; however, it has now been shown that a diet low in phytanic acid is helpful in treating this condition.

Fig. 13-23. Phase microscopy of a damaged nerve fiber secondary to a crush injury. The upper segment is a transverse section of the nerve showing dilatation, fragmentation, and collapse of the myelin sheaths and an increase in the number of nuclei. The lower segment is a longitudinal section of the nerve showing rows of myelin ovoids indicating a disintegration of the myelin. (From P. J. Dyck. Ultrastructural Alterations in Myelinated Fibers. In J. E. Desmedt [ed.], *New Developments in Electromyography and Clinical Neurophysiology*, Vol. 2. Basel: Karger, 1973.)

Laboratory Studies in the Identification of Lesions in the Periphery

In addition to the clinical features previously listed, a number of laboratory tests are helpful in differentiating diseases involving the peripheral structures. These include biochemical, electrophysiologic, and histologic studies.

General Medical Tests

Peripheral neuromuscular disorders are often found with, or secondary to, systemic disease processes. For example, neuropathies occur with diabetes, nutritional deficiencies, kidney diseases, carcinoma, and poisonings. Myopathies occur with endocrine diseases, connective tissue diseases, metabolic disorders, and neoplasm. Therefore, a general medical assessment is important in the evaluation of peripheral disease.

Muscle Enzymes

Muscle contains a number of enzymes that are important in their metabolism, such as aldolase, serum glutamic-oxaloacetic transaminase (SGOT), and lactic dehydrogenase (LDH). Muscle damage from any disease that results in destruction or degeneration of muscle fibers releases these enzymes into the general circulation. Thus, their levels are commonly elevated in the blood of patients with active primary muscle diseases. However, these enzymes are also found in many other tissues, and their levels can be elevated with other diseases, especially those that damage the heart or liver. *Creatine kinase* (CK) is an enzyme that transfers a phosphate group from creatine phosphate to adenosine diphosphate (ADP) to form creatine and ATP. This enzyme is found mainly in muscle and is therefore a more specific indicator of muscle disease. Creatine kinase levels may be elevated in the serum in patients with early or mild myopathy who have minimal clinical evidence of disease and in persons who are carriers of the abnormal gene in recessively inherited muscle disease.

Nerve Conduction Studies

Often, it is not possible to be certain on the basis of clinical findings whether a patient has a peripheral disorder. To help in this differentiation, the function of peripheral nerves can be evaluated by nerve conduction studies that quantitatively measure their responses to stimulation. Nerve conduction studies are of particular value in localizing disease in peripheral nerves, in assessing the severity of the disease, and in characterizing nerve disease.

The natural activity in individual axons of a peripheral nerve is random and cannot be readily recorded; however, with the application of an electrical stimulus, all the large myelinated fibers can be discharged simultaneously, and the resulting compound action potential can be recorded and measured. If an electrical stimulus (20 to 100 V for 0.1 msec) is applied to a mixed peripheral nerve, action potentials will be initiated that travel in both directions along the nerve. Action potentials traveling centrally will be perceived by the patient as a shock in the distribution of the nerve stimulated. Those traveling peripherally will invade each of the terminal branches of the nerve, where they can be recorded either from cutaneous sensory branches or from muscles innervated by motor branches. Thus, either the motor or the sensory components of the peripheral nerves can be selectively studied.

These two types of potentials, the compound sensory nerve action potential and the compound muscle action potential, are measured on an oscilloscope. The *amplitude* of the potential is a function of the number of axons that can carry activity from the point of stimulation to the recording site. The *latency* is a function of the rate at which the largest fibers in the nerve propagate action potentials down the axon. By measuring the distance traveled and dividing this value by the time, the *conduction velocity* can be determined (Fig. 13-24). Conduction velocity depends on the diameter of the axon and the extent of myelination of the axons. If a nerve is stimulated repetitively at rates of 2 to 40 per second, a normal muscle can respond with the same number of fibers, and the compound action potential with each stimulus will be identical. The presence of peripheral nerve disease is

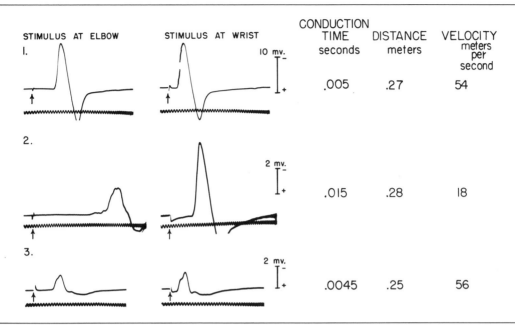

STIMULUS AT ELBOW	STIMULUS AT WRIST	CONDUCTION TIME seconds	DISTANCE meters	VELOCITY meters per second
1.	10 mv.	.005	.27	54
2.	2 mv.	.015	.28	18
3.	2 mv.	.0045	.25	56

Fig. 13-24. Measurement of conduction velocity. *1.* Normal. *2.* Neuropathy: conduction velocity is slowed along entire nerve, and amplitude is reduced with proximal stimulation because of dispersion of the response. *3.* Myopathy: conduction velocity is normal, but amplitude is reduced because of muscle atrophy. (From Department of Neurology, Mayo Clinic and Mayo Foundation. *Clinical Examinations in Neurology* [6th ed.]. St. Louis: Mosby-Year Book, 1991. By permission of Mayo Foundation.)

reflected in the nerve conduction studies. In an axolemmal disorder, the action potential is blocked in the region of the abnormality. Stimulation distal to this point results in normal responses, but proximal stimulation produces either no response or only a reduced amplitude response. Axoplasmic disorders with axonal narrowing result in slowing of conduction, whereas those with axonal degeneration result in a reduced amplitude or absent response to stimulation. In myelin disorders, there is slowing of conduction, with progressive loss of amplitude on more proximal stimulation.

Localized lesions of a peripheral nerve produce a local block or a slowing of conduction in the region of the damage. The block results in a smaller evoked response with proximal rather than with distal stimulation (Fig. 13-25). In generalized disorders of peripheral nerves, there may be a generalized slowing of conduction in segmental demyelinating disorders (Fig. 13-26), a loss of amplitude of re-

sponses, especially distally in axonal dystrophies, or a combination of both.

Disorders of neuromuscular transmission are characterized by progressive loss of amplitude of an evoked motor response with repetitive stimulation, especially at rates of 2 to 5 per second. The evoked responses in primary muscle disease with atrophy are of low amplitude but are without other changes in nerve conduction. In upper motor neuron lesions, results of nerve conduction studies are normal.

Nerve conduction studies are usually performed in conjunction with electromyography because they use similar techniques and complement each other in arriving at diagnoses of peripheral nerve and muscle disease.

Electromyography

Muscle function can be evaluated by measuring the electrical activity by electromyography (EMG or needle examination) (Fig. 13-27).

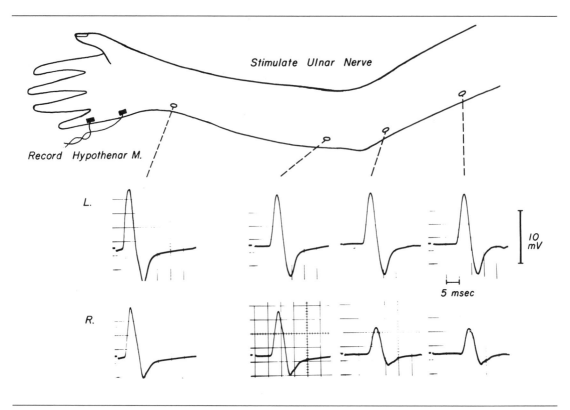

Fig. 13-25. Nerve conduction studies in patient with ulnar neuropathy at the elbow. Normal responses from left arm (*L*); abnormal on right (*R*). There are a localized partial block of conduction (decreased amplitude above the elbow) and localized slowing of conduction velocity at the elbow. (Courtesy of Dr. E. H. Lambert, Mayo Clinic.)

Electromyography provides information about the presence and type of disease involving muscle. Because nerve disorders produce secondary changes in muscle, EMG is valuable not only in diagnosing primary muscle diseases but also in differentiating neurogenic disorders, diseases of neuromuscular transmission, and diseases of the central nervous system.

In EMG, a needle electrode is inserted into a muscle, and the electrical activity is recorded on an oscilloscope and a loudspeaker. The recorded potentials are characterized by their amplitude, duration, and firing patterns (Fig. 13-28). Recordings are made in multiple muscles in three states: at rest, with needle movement, and with voluntary activity.

At rest, there is electrical silence in a normal muscle, except in the region of motor end-plates where end-plate potentials or other small potentials may be recorded (see Fig. 13-

28). If the needle is moved in the muscle, the mechanical stimulation produces a discharge of the muscle fibers in a characteristic brief burst called *insertional activity* (see Fig. 13-28). With voluntary contraction of the muscle, the motor units fire repetitively, in an orderly fashion, with a frequency and number proportional to the effort exerted. The motor unit potentials are measured to determine their amplitude, duration, and firing rate.

If there is a primary myopathy with random degeneration of muscle fibers, each motor unit will have a reduced innervation ratio and the motor unit potential will be of short duration and low amplitude (Fig. 13-29). Because of the reduction in power of each motor unit, many more will fire for any given strength than in a normal muscle. If there is partial destruction of some muscle fibers, the still viable portions may fire spontaneously (fibrillate). In sarcolemmal disorders, there is an overall reduc-

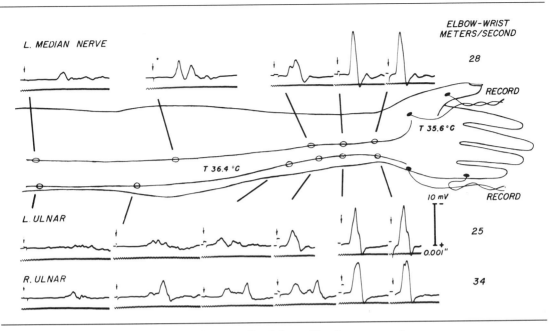

Fig. 13-26. Nerve conduction studies in generalized demyelinating neuropathy. The evoked muscle action potentials with nerve stimulation are shown. Conduction velocity is listed at right. All nerves are affected, with slowing of conduction and dispersion of potentials along their entire length. (L = left; R = right.) (Courtesy of Dr. E. H. Lambert, Mayo Clinic.)

Fig. 13-27. Potentials recorded in electromyography. Motor unit potentials during voluntary contraction in a normal person, muscular dystrophy (myopathy), and amyotrophic lateral sclerosis (lower motor neuron disease). Potentials on left are displayed with a slow time base; on right, with a fast time base.

NORMAL

END-PLATE NOISE

POSITIVE WAVES

MYOTONIA

BIZARRE HIGH-FREQUENCY POTENTIAL

Fig. 13-28. Examples of EMG activity in response to insertion of the needle into the muscle. The top segment shows a normal discharge; the second segment shows biphasic spikes arising in the end-plate region; the third segment shows abnormal positive waves (downward deflections) from denervated muscle; the fourth segment shows a rapid burst of potentials that is characteristic of myotonia; the bottom segment shows a complex repetitive discharge in a chronic neurogenic atrophy.

tion in activity, with small motor unit potentials. In disorders of excitation-contraction coupling, no abnormality is recorded on EMG.

In contrast to the changes in myopathy, a neurogenic disorder produces primarily a loss of a number of motor unit potentials and is seen as poor recruitment with increasing effort and a small number of units firing rapidly with maximal effort. In addition, if there has been a chronic denervation with opportunity for re-innervation and resultant increase in innervation ratio, the motor unit potentials will be of long duration and high amplitude. Any muscle fibers that are denervated because of axonal degeneration will fibrillate. If a motor unit is irritable, single brief twitches or fasciculation of the motor units will occur (see Fig. 13-27).

Diseases of neuromuscular transmission are characterized by variable conduction blocks across individual neuromuscular junctions and result in variations in the amplitude of the motor unit potentials with voluntary contraction. In upper motor neuron disease, the motor units appear normal and recruit normally but fire slowly (poor activation).

By combining the findings from EMG and nerve conduction studies, it is often possible to localize the disease in the periphery and at times to specific sites, to characterize the general type of disorder, and to assist in determining the severity or prognosis in the disorder.

Nerve Biopsy

In some peripheral nerve diseases, the clinical, biochemical, and electrophysiologic studies

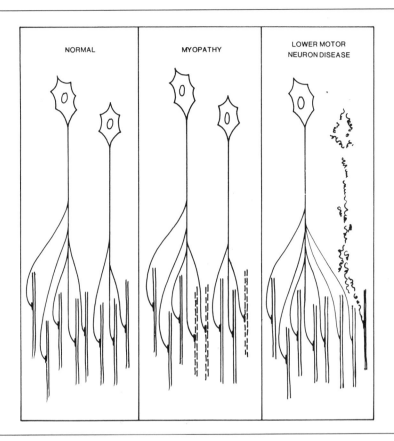

Fig. 13-29. Alteration in innervation patterns in peripheral disease. Myopathy shows random loss of muscle fibers from all motor units. Neurogenic atrophy shows loss of innervation of all fibers in motor unit, with partial reinnervation by surviving axons.

do not reveal the nature of the abnormality. For these patients, a nerve biopsy specimen, usually of a fascicle of the sural nerve, is studied. Nerve biopsy specimens are best studied in three ways: by light microscopy of nerve bundles, teased fiber studies, and cross-sectional fiber counts. For ordinary light microscopy, a piece of nerve is fixed and stained with standard histologic stains and special stains for specific diseases. For instance, in leprosy, the *Mycobacterium leprae* can be stained with acid-fast stains. In metachromatic leukodystrophy or amyloid, other specific stains demonstrate the accumulation of the abnormal materials.

If another portion of the nerve is fixed and stained for myelin, it can be teased or pulled apart into single fibers. These single fibers then can be examined for the presence of segmental demyelination, paranodal loss of myelin, or other characteristic changes such as the presence of linear rows of myelin ovoids after axonal degeneration. In addition, the diameter and the length of the internodes can be measured. Plots of the internodal length compared with the axon diameter can give quantitative estimates of the presence of myelin disorders.

Cross sections of a portion of the nerve also can be stained with myelin stains, and the diameters of the fibers can be measured and plotted as density of fibers. The presence of selective loss of certain fiber types then can be quantitatively determined.

Muscle Biopsy

Although at times the clinical history or pattern of muscle impairment in a patient can permit the diagnosis of a myopathy, often neither the clinical nor the electrophysiologic findings can provide a specific diagnosis. In these situations, muscle biopsy is of clinical diagnostic value. It, like the EMG and nerve conduction studies, can differentiate muscle abnormalities secondary to neurogenic disorders (neurogenic atrophy) from those due to primary myopathy. In the latter case, they can often provide an even more specific diagnosis.

Muscle biopsy specimens are taken from a muscle that shows moderate (but not severe) weakness. In severe weakness, there may be so much replacement of muscle by fat or connective tissue that a diagnosis cannot be made. The specimen is stained with routine stains such as hematoxylin and eosin or trichrome and with various histochemical stains that permit the identification of different fiber types. It is also stained for specific abnormalities, such as glycogen in glycogen-storage diseases or lipid in lipid-storage diseases. Fiber-type grouping provides evidence of neurogenic disease, and the presence of specific materials may allow the diagnosis of a specific myopathy.

Objectives

1. Name the four major systems represented at the peripheral level, and describe the location, histologic features, and function of each.
2. Name the four subdivisions of the peripheral level at which lesions occur, and describe their gross anatomical location and histologic features.
3. List the neurologic deficits that would be associated with damage in each of these subdivisions of the peripheral level, and explain their mechanism of occurrence.
4. Describe the mechanism of muscle contraction.
5. Name the location of, function of, and deficit (motor, sensory, and reflex) resulting from a lesion of each of the following: spinal nerves C-5, C-6, C-7, C-8, L-4, L-5, and S-1; brachial and lumbosacral plexuses; radial, ulnar, median, sciatic, femoral, peroneal, and tibial peripheral nerves.
6. Describe the application of EMG and nerve conduction studies to neurologic diseases.

Clinical Problems

1. A 47-year-old bank manager has had diabetes for 14 years. The diabetes is controlled by insulin. He is seen with a complaint of impotence of 6 months' duration. He has had 2 to 3 years of gradually progressive burning and numbness, first of his feet and recently of his hands. He has occasional dizzy spells on arising. On examination his blood pressure is 115/75 mm Hg supine but decreases to 80/40 mm Hg, with no change in pulse when he arises. He has mild weakness of his toe and foot dorsiflexors but no other weakness. His ankle reflexes are absent. Other reflexes are hypoactive. He has moderate loss of all modalities of sensation in a glove-and-stocking distribution. There is an absence of hair on his legs, and his skin is very dry. On nerve conduction studies, no sensory potentials could be obtained, and motor responses were of low amplitude, with a mild slowing of conduction velocity. The EMG showed fibrillation in distal muscles bilaterally.
   a. What are the localization and type of disease?
   b. What is this disorder called?
   c. What is the significance of low-amplitude evoked potentials?
   d. What is the significance of fibrillation?
   e. How is fibrillation differentiated from fasciculation?
2. A 57-year-old man has been in good health except for a chronic "smoker's cough." During the past 6 months, he has noted gradually increased difficulty in climbing steps and more recently has had trouble in arising from chairs. He has had some dryness of his mouth. Examination revealed no abnormalities other than weakness of proximal muscles and very hypoactive reflexes. Both the strength and the reflexes appear to improve somewhat with exercise. Results of laboratory studies are unremarkable other than for changes in the EMG suggesting the presence of a defect of neuromuscular transmission. On the chest radiograph, there is a mass in the right hilum of the lung. An intercostal muscle biopsy was performed,

and electrophysiologic recordings were made from the muscle. The following data were obtained:

	Patient	Normal
Average resting potential (mV)	75.6	74.7
Average MEPP amplitude (mV)	0.3±0.3	0.3±0.4
Average EPP amplitude (mV)	3.2±0.9	15+
Average single fiber action potential amplitude (mV)	97±3	98±3
Threshold (mV)	60	60

  a. What two factors determine the size of the end-plate potential (EPP)?
  b. Which of these is abnormal in this patient?
  c. What is the quantum content in this patient?
  d. How could this produce weakness?
  e. What is this disorder?
3. A 55-year-old woman developed proximal symmetric weakness during a 2-week period, with mild muscle soreness. On examination, reflexes, sensation, and mentation were normal. All proximal muscles were moderately weak, distal muscles mildly so. There was no fatigue with exercise.
  a. What specific disease is this likely to be?
  b. What are the location and cause of this disorder?
      Results of motor and sensory nerve conduction studies on this patient were normal, except for a borderline low-amplitude compound muscle action potential. A needle electrode (EMG) was inserted in a weak muscle, and recordings were made of the motor unit potentials. Two abnormalities were noted: The potentials were small, and they fired rapidly with minimal contraction.
  c. With disease of the motor unit, if neuromuscular transmission is normal, weakness is due to either of two losses. What are they?
  d. What are the two mechanisms used to increase force of contraction?
  e. In what way will scattered loss of some muscle fibers alter the firing pattern and size of motor unit potentials?
  f. What pattern of histologic change would you expect in this patient?
  g. Would muscle fibers innervated by a single ventral horn cell be grouped together?
  h. In what general situation does fiber type grouping occur?
  i. How could a person with moderately severe motor neuron disease have no weakness?
  j. What do the T tubules, sarcoplasmic reticulum, and calcium have in common?
  k. This patient had an elevation of serum creatine kinase. Why did this occur?

Additional Reading

Brooke, M. H. *A Clinician's View of Neuromuscular Diseases.* Baltimore: Williams & Wilkins, 1977.

Dyck, P. J., et al. (eds.). *Peripheral Neuropathy* (3rd ed.). Philadelphia: Saunders, 1993.

Engel, A. G., and Franzini-Armstrong, C. *Myology* (2nd ed.). New York: McGraw-Hill, in press.

Hubbard, J. I. *The Peripheral Nervous System.* New York: Plenum, 1974.

Waxman, S. G. *Physiology and Pathobiology of Axons* (2nd ed.). New York: Raven, 1984.

— 14 —

The Spinal Level

The spinal level includes the vertebral column and its contents. The spinal canal within the vertebral column is the passage formed by the vertebrae, extending from the foramen magnum of the skull through the sacrum of the spinal column. It contains the spinal cord, nerve roots, spinal nerves, meninges, and the vascular supply of the spinal cord. Five of the major systems are represented in the spinal canal: sensory, motor, internal regulation, vascular, and cerebrospinal fluid systems. The sensory and motor systems constitute the outer tube portion of the spinal cord, and the internal regulation system corresponds to the inner core. The vascular and cerebrospinal fluid structures are the support systems of the spinal cord. Therefore, diseases of the spinal canal involve one or more of these systems to produce patterns of disease distinctive to this level. The anatomical and physiologic characteristics of the spinal cord and spinal nerves that permit identification and localization of diseases in the spinal canal are presented in this chapter.

Overview

Two distinct patterns of abnormality occur with disease of the nervous system: segmental and longitudinal. Damage to segmental structures, as already noted for peripheral lesions, produces signs localized in a single segment of the body. These signs include flaccid weakness, atrophy, loss of reflexes, and loss of all modalities of sensation in a focal distribution. Lesions in the spinal cord usually damage longitudinal systems in addition to segmental

structures. Damage to a longitudinal system produces deficit in that system for all functions below the level of the lesion. It is the combination of these patterns of involvement that permits a precise definition of the location of a disease process.

Localized lesions at the spinal level may produce only segmental signs by damage to the spinal nerves and roots within the spinal column. Segmental signs can occur with spinal level lesions because of the origin and termination of primary sensory neurons and lower motor neurons in the spinal cord. The primary sensory endings in the cord distribute information widely within the cord but in an organized fashion. For example, muscle spindle afferents send excitatory fibers to motor neurons of synergistic muscles and inhibitory fibers to antagonistic muscles. Such connections result in complex reflexes mediated at the spinal cord level. The motor neurons of the somatic and visceral efferent pathways, located in the ventral and intermediolateral gray matter of the spinal cord, are the origin of the peripheral motor axons. These motor neurons integrate information from multiple sources in determining the activity of the peripheral muscles and glands.

Lesions at the spinal level can damage these central components of the primary sensory neurons or lower motor neurons and result in disorders of the peripheral structures manifested as:

1. Atrophy, fasciculation, and weakness, occurring with death or damage of the motor neurons in the ventral horns.
2. Preganglionic sympathetic disturbances

occurring with damage to the neurons in the intermediolateral cell column.

3. Loss of sensation with destruction of the central processes of the primary sensory neurons.

These segmental signs permit the localization of disease along the length of the spinal cord. They are recognized as originating at the spinal level by the associated involvement of ascending or descending tracts, which produces intersegmental signs. The location of a lesion within the spinal canal often can be defined further by the pattern of involvement among the structures in the cross section of the cord. The spinal cord, therefore, is subdivided both along its length and in cross section to aid in the recognition of disease.

Spinal Cord Subdivisions

The segments along the length of the spinal cord are named to correspond to the vertebrae through which the spinal nerves pass.

1. Cervical. The cephalad portion of the spinal cord from which eight pairs of ventral and seven pairs of dorsal roots arise to form the cervical spinal nerves.
2. Thoracic. The middle portion of the spinal cord from which 12 pairs of nerve roots arise to form the thoracic spinal nerves.
3. Lumbar. The upper caudal portion of the spinal cord from which five lumbar nerve roots arise to form the lumbar spinal nerves.
4. Sacral. The caudal end of the cord from which five pairs of sacral nerve roots arise. The conus medullaris is the termination of the cord from which sacral nerve roots arise.

The cross section of the spinal canal is subdivided into major structures from the center to the periphery.

1. Central canal. The central remnant of the ependymal lining of the neural tube.
2. Gray matter. Accumulations of neurons in columns and clusters surrounding the central canal.
3. White matter. Longitudinal fiber tracts in the periphery of the spinal cord.
4. Blood vessels. Vascular supply of the spinal cord located on its external surface.
5. Nerve roots and spinal nerves. The segmental axons of motor and sensory fibers leaving or entering the cord bilaterally along its entire length.
6. Meninges and subarachnoid space. The connective tissue coverings of the spinal cord in the spinal canal and the space they surround.

Spinal Cord Anatomy

External Morphology

The spinal cord lies within the vertebral canal and, in the adult, extends from the foramen magnum to the lower border of the first lumbar vertebra (L-1). The spinal cord is roughly cylindrical, with a slight anteroposterior flattening. It has two wider areas, the *cervical* and *lumbar enlargements,* from which the innervation of the upper and lower extremities arises. The caudal end of the spinal cord tapers to form the *conus medullaris* (Fig. 14-1).

Nerve fibers enter and exit from the spinal cord via the *spinal nerve roots.* These roots form from the union of smaller rootlets and leave the cord dorsolaterally and ventrolaterally. The dorsal and ventral roots join laterally at the intervertebral foramina to form the spinal nerves. Thirty-one pairs of spinal nerves are thus formed and divide the cord into 8 cervical, 12 thoracic, 5 lumbar, and 5 sacral segments and 1 coccygeal segment. Each spinal segment except the first and last has a dorsal (afferent) root and a ventral (efferent) root, which emerge on each side of a spinal segment and become ensheathed by dura as they unite to form the spinal nerve. The dorsal root ganglion, which contains the cell bodies of the nerve fibers in the dorsal root, is an enlargement of the dorsal root at the intervertebral foramen. In the intervertebral foramen, the dura merges with the perineurium of the peripheral nerve.

There are thus four nerve roots arising from each spinal cord segment, a dorsal and ventral root on each side. They are contained entirely within the spinal canal and are bathed in cere-

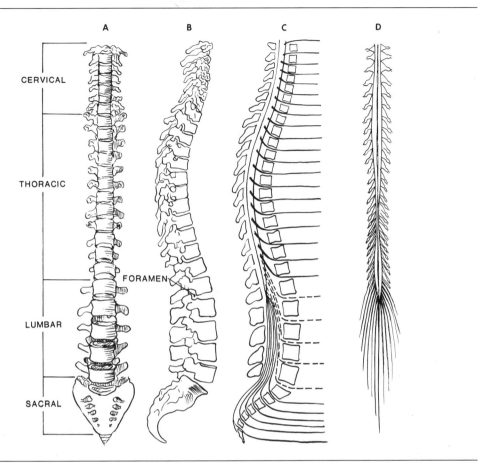

Fig. 14-1. Spinal column and cord showing relationships to each other. A. Ventral view of spine. B. Lateral view of spine. C. Lateral view of spinal cord and roots in spine. D. Dorsal view of spinal cord.

brospinal fluid. They follow a lateral or, in the lower portions of the spinal canal, a descending course to the intervertebral foramen, where the dorsal and ventral roots join to form the spinal nerve (see Fig. 14-1). The ventral roots carry the myelinated axons of the alpha and gamma motor neurons to the somatic musculature and the myelinated axons of the preganglionic neurons of the sympathetic (parasympathetic in the sacral region) nerves to viscera. The dorsal roots carry the sensory input from cutaneous, somatic, muscular, and visceral receptors in myelinated and unmyelinated axons. The cell bodies of these axons are in the dorsal root ganglia.

The spinal nerves are very short nerves in which the motor, sensory, and autonomic components of a single cord segment are united in a single structure as they exit from the spinal canal through the intervertebral foramen (Fig. 14-2). The *foramen* is the bony canal formed by two adjacent vertebrae. Because the nerve is surrounded by this bony structure, it is particularly vulnerable to local compression by a tumor, a herniated nucleus pulposus, or arthritic changes in the bones. Each of the spinal nerves is derived from a segment of the spinal cord, and the names of the nerves correspond to the names of the segments. Because there are only seven cervical vertebrae, the C-1 through C-7 spinal nerves exit *above* the pedicle of the vertebra of the same number, while the C-8 spinal nerves emerge *between* the C-7 and T-1 vertebrae. Caudal to T-1, the spinal nerves all exit below the vertebrae of the same number.

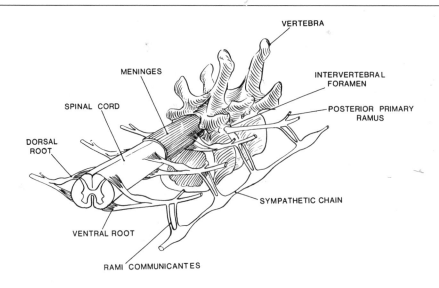

Fig. 14-2. Formation of a spinal nerve as it leaves the spinal canal through the intervertebral foramen.

Each spinal nerve is distributed to a well-defined area of skin called a *dermatome* (Fig. 14-3). Dermatomes of adjacent spinal nerves overlap. This overlap accounts for the variation in sensory loss seen in patients with spinal nerve lesions. The spinal nerves are also distributed to specific groups of muscles called *myotomes* (Table 14-1).

The nerve roots are anchored in the intervertebral foramina at the point where their dural sleeves terminate. Flexion of the spinal cord or traction on a peripheral nerve (such as with a disk herniation or local tumor) can stretch and irritate a spinal nerve and cause pain.

Early in development, the spinal cord segments are at the same level as the corresponding vertebrae. With growth, the vertebral column elongates more than the spinal cord does, and the spinal roots are displaced caudally. The roots of rostral cord segments are displaced less than those of caudal segments. Therefore, the lumbar and sacral nerves have long spinal roots that descend within the dural sac to reach their appropriate vertebral level of exit. These roots are called the *cauda equina* because they have an appearance similar to a horse's tail. Because of the difference in length between the vertebral column and the spinal cord, care must be taken to specify vertebral level or spinal segment level in indicating the

location of a lesion. Generally in a neurologic problem, the affected spinal segment is defined first, and then an attempt is made to correlate that with the appropriate vertebral level. However, in cases of vertebral lesions, the level of the vertebral involvement is often seen on the radiograph, and then the level of a possible spinal injury is determined.

The general guidelines for locating the level of a spinal cord injury with respect to the vertebrae are:

1. Between T-1 and T-10, add two to the number of the vertebral spine to determine the spinal cord segment at the same location.
2. The lumbar segments of the cord are approximately at the level of the spinous processes of T-11 and T-12.
3. Sacral and coccygeal segments are at the level of the L-1 spinous process.
4. There are eight cervical segments and only seven cervical vertebrae, so that the cervical enlargement at C-7 cord segment is centered at the C-7 vertebral level.

The surface of the spinal cord shows several longitudinal furrows. The ventral (anterior) surface is indented by the deep ventral median fissure. The dorsal (posterior) surface contains a shallow dorsal median sulcus. The dorsal

Fig. 14-3. Cutaneous distribution of spinal nerves (dermatomes). (Redrawn from F. R. Ford. *Diseases of the Nervous System: In Infancy, Childhood and Adolescence* [6th ed.]. Springfield, Ill.: Thomas, 1973.)

spinal roots enter each side of the spinal cord along the dorsolateral sulci. Dorsal intermediate sulci extend from the rostral cervical to the midthoracic spinal cord, between the dorsal root entry zone and the midline.

Meninges

The spinal cord is ensheathed by three membranous coverings, the *meninges* (Fig. 14-4). The outer membrane is the *dura mater.* The inner two membranes, or *leptomeninges,* are the *arachnoid* and the *pia mater.* The arachnoid is a nonvascular membrane separated from the pia mater by the *subarachnoid space* containing cerebrospinal fluid.

The spinal cord is anchored to the inner surface of the dura mater by a series of lateral collagenous bands called *denticulate ligaments,* derived from the pia mater. From 18 to 24 of these ligaments firmly attach the pia mater midway between the dorsal and ventral

roots to the arachnoid and the dura mater on each side of the spinal cord. The dural sheath terminates at the level of the second sacral vertebra. A pial extension, the *filum terminale,* arises from the caudal tip of the conus medullaris and pierces the end of the dural sac. It continues as connective tissue, the *coccygeal ligament,* to attach to the periosteum of the coccyx.

Blood Supply

One anterior and two posterolateral arteries run the length of the spinal cord and form an irregular plexus around the spinal cord. The *spinal arteries* receive their supply from the *vertebral arteries* and from the intercostal, lumbar, and sacral arteries through six to eight *radicular arteries* (see Fig. 11-8), the largest usually entering at the lower thoracic or upper lumbar region of the cord (Fig. 14-5). The spinal arteries are interconnected by anastomo-

Table 14-1. Myotomes Listed by Spinal Nerve and Muscle

Spinal nerve	Muscles
C-5	Biceps, deltoid, infraspinatus
C-6	Biceps, deltoid, infraspinatus, wrist flexors, wrist extensors, forearm pronators
C-7	Wrist extensors, wrist flexors, finger flexors, finger extensors, triceps
C-8	Intrinsic hand muscles
L-4	Iliopsoas, quadriceps, anterior tibial
L-5	Anterior tibial, toe dorsiflexors, hamstrings, posterior tibial
S-1	Gluteus maximus, hamstring, gastrocnemius, intrinsic foot muscles

Muscles	Spinal nerves*
Neck flexors	C-1 to C-6
Neck extensors	C-1 to C-6
Shoulder external rotator	C-5, C-6
Deltoid	C-5, C-6
Biceps brachii	C-5, C-6
Triceps	C-6, <u>C-7</u>, C-8
Wrist extensors	C-6, C-7, C-8
Wrist flexors	C-6, C-7, C-8, T-1
Digit extensors	<u>C-7</u>, C-8
Digit flexors	C-7, C-8, T-1
Thenar	C-8, T-1
Hypothenar	C-8, T-1
Interossei	C-8, T-1
Abdomen	T-6 to L-1
Rectal sphincter	S-3, S-4
Iliopsoas	<u>L-3</u>, L-4
Thigh adductor	L-2, L-3, L-4
Quadriceps	L-2, L-3, L-4
Thigh abductor	L-4, <u>L-5</u>, S-1
Gluteus maximus	<u>S-1</u>, S-2
Hamstrings	L-4, <u>L-5</u>, <u>S-1</u>
Anterior tibial	L-4, L-5
Toe extensors	L-4, <u>L-5</u>, S-1
Peronei	<u>L-5</u>, S-1
Posterior tibial	<u>L-5</u>, S-1
Toe flexors	L-5, S-1
Gastrocnemius	L-5, <u>S-1</u>, S-2

*Spinal nerves underlined provide the major innervation for that muscle.

ses circling the surface of the cord and sending short branches inside the cord. *Sulcal* branches from the anterior spinal artery in the anterior median fissure go alternately right and left. The *posterior spinal arteries* provide the blood supply for the posterior columns. The remainder of the cord is supplied by the *anterior spinal artery.*

The venous plexus is irregular, and there may be six or seven longitudinal veins at the surface of the cord. This plexus communicates with the occipital and marginal sinuses and with the basal plexus of veins above the level of the foramen magnum.

Internal Morphology

A cross section of the spinal cord reveals a central H-shaped gray area surrounded by white matter.

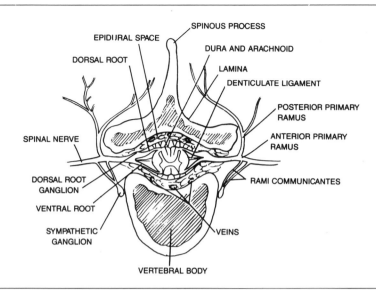

Fig. 14-4. Cross section of spinal canal showing spinal cord, its meningeal coverings, and manner of exit of spinal nerves.

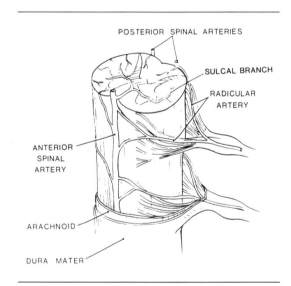

Fig. 14-5. The arterial supply of a spinal cord segment enters via the radicular arteries.

The spinal cord is organized into four concentric zones: two zones constitute the gray matter, and two zones constitute the white matter. The gray matter occupies the central region and is divided into the *intermediate zone*, containing interneurons and propriospinal neurons, and the *dorsal* and *ventral horns*, containing sensory and motor neurons, respectively. White matter surrounds the gray matter and is divided into two zones: the *pericentral zone* consisting of intersegmental (propriospinal) fibers and the *peripheral zone* consisting of suprasegmental projectional fibers (Fig. 14-6).

White Matter

The white matter is composed of longitudinally arranged myelinated and unmyelinated nerve fibers, with an abundance of myelin that gives it a glistening white appearance. The white matter is also divided into longitudinal columns. The large bundle of fibers between the dorsal gray horns is divided into two posterior funiculi, or dorsal columns, by the *dorsal median septum*. This septum is composed of glial elements and pia and extends from the dorsal median sulcus to the dorsal gray commissure. From the first cervical spinal segment (C-1) to about the sixth thoracic segment (T-6), each dorsal white column, or dorsal funiculus, is divided into a laterally located fasciculus cuneatus and a medially located fasciculus gracilis by the dorsal intermediate septum. The remainder of the white matter constitutes the ventral and lateral funiculi. The ventral white commissure consists of a band of transversely oriented nerve fibers located between the ventral gray commissure and the ventral median fissure. The locations

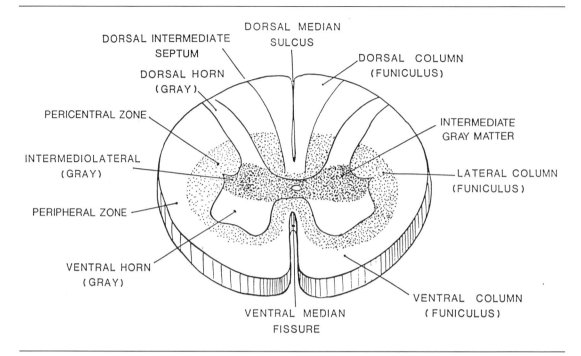

Fig. 14-6. Major horizontal subdivisions of the spinal cord.

and functions of the major ascending and descending fiber tracts in the white matter are discussed with the longitudinal systems. Their location in the spinal cord and lamination are illustrated in Figure 14-7.

Gray Matter

The gray matter consists of a longitudinally continuous matrix of neuronal cell bodies, dendrites, myelinated and unmyelinated axons, and glial cells. The gray matter is divided into *dorsal horns, intermediate gray,* and *ventral horns.* The interconnecting gray in the midline is separated into a *dorsal gray commissure* and a *ventral gray commissure* by the central canal. A lateral projection of the intermediate gray, the *lateral horn,* is present in the first thoracic (T-1) through the second lumbar (L-2) spinal cord segments.

The two main types of neurons in the gray matter are projectional neurons and interneurons (Table 14-2). The projectional neurons are divided into sensory projectional neurons, which send axons to supraspinal centers, and motor projection neurons, which send axons out of the central nervous system via the ventral spinal roots to muscles. Sensory projec-

tional neurons consist of nociceptive (pain)-specific neurons, nonnociceptive (low-threshold mechanoreceptive) neurons, and wide dynamic range (multireceptive) neurons. They are located in the dorsal horn. The motor projectional neurons consist of alpha and gamma motor neurons; they are located in the ventral horn. The interneurons have axonal projections that remain in the spinal cord. These neurons are located throughout the spinal cord, particularly in the intermediate gray matter, and constitute the bulk of spinal neurons.

Many interneurons have axonal terminations within the cord segment where they originate. Others have axonal projections that course in a rostral or caudal direction for several spinal segments before terminating. Intersegmental axonal projections may course along several segments in the surrounding white matter before reentering the gray matter to terminate. These are termed *propriospinal* fibers and form the *fasciculi proprii,* which surround the spinal gray matter. The dorsolateral fasciculus (Lissauer's tract) is located at the apex of the dorsal horn (Fig. 14-8) and contains many propriospinal fibers. The axons

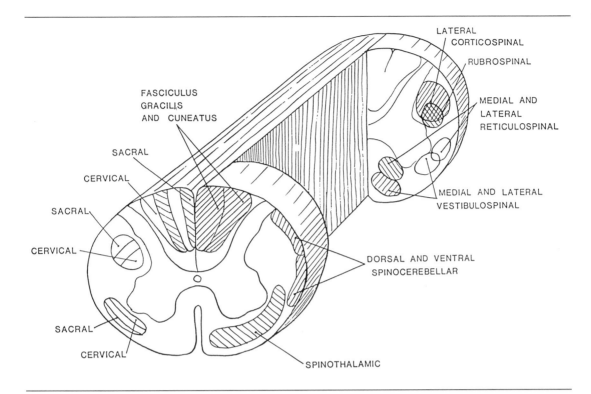

Fig. 14-7. Principal tracts of the spinal cord. Lamination in the dorsal columns and corticospinal and spinothalamic tracts is shown in the left half of the diagram. The location of the sensory pathways is shown at the same level on the right, and the location of the motor pathways is shown at another level on the far right.

Table 14-2. Cell Types in the Spinal Cord

Cell type	Location	Neurotransmitter
Sensory projectional neurons		
Nociceptive, nonnociceptive, wide dynamic range	Dorsal horn	Glutamate
Motor projectional neurons		
Alpha motor neurons and gamma motor neurons	Ventral horn	Acetylcholine
Interneurons		
Inhibitory	Diffuse	GABA
Renshaw cell	Ventral horn	Glycine
Excitatory	Diffuse	Glutamate
Autonomic		
Sympathetic preganglionic	Intermediolateral cell column (T-1 to L-2)	Acetylcholine
Parasympathetic preganglionic	Ventral horn (S-2 to S-4)	Acetylcholine

GABA = gamma-aminobutyric acid.

may remain on the same side of the cord (ipsilateral) or cross the midline to terminate in the contralateral gray matter. Interneurons that send projections across the midline are termed *commissural neurons.* Such cells are found in abundance in the medial portion of the ventral horn. An interneuron is not restricted to a single pattern of axonal projection; instead, it may have several collaterals with different areas of termination. For example, a commissural neuron also may have an axon collateral that terminates ipsilaterally.

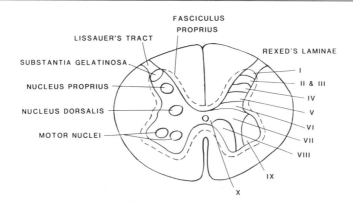

Fig. 14-8. Groups of nuclei in the spinal cord (*left*) and laminae of the spinal cord (*right*).

Thus, spinal cord interneurons integrate segmental and intersegmental activity, both ipsilaterally and contralaterally.

The distribution of neurons in the spinal gray matter is not random. Scattered throughout the gray matter are clusters of neurons that extend longitudinally for varied distances along the spinal cord as cell columns (see Fig. 14-8). Conspicuous groups of cells are found in the ventral horns. The axons of these cells emerge from the spinal cord to innervate skeletal muscle fibers. These cells are called *alpha motor neurons,* and the cell columns in which they reside are *somatic motor (efferent) nuclei.* Alpha motor neurons innervate the extrafusal muscle fibers, and the small *gamma motor neurons,* scattered nearby, innervate the intrafusal muscle fibers of muscle spindles. Alpha motor neurons are up to 80 μm in diameter and are among the largest neurons in the nervous system.

Another class of efferent fibers, exiting from the cord via the ventral root, arises from a distinct column of cells located in the lateral aspect of the intermediate gray matter (lateral horn). These cells form the *intermediolateral cell column,* which extends from the first thoracic spinal segment (T-1) to the second lumbar spinal segment (L-2). The axons of these neurons synapse with ganglion cells of the sympathetic (thoracolumbar) division of the visceral nervous system. Therefore, the intermediolateral cell column is termed a *visceral efferent nucleus.* The parasympathetic motor

(efferent) neurons are in the sacral cord. However, they do not form a well-defined cell group but are located throughout the ventral horn of S-2 to S-4. The reflex center for micturition is in this area of the cord.

The *nucleus dorsalis (Clarke's column)* is a distinct group of cells located in the medial portion of the base of the dorsal horn. This nucleus extends from the eighth cervical (C-8) to the second lumbar (L-2) spinal segment. The cells of the nucleus dorsalis are tract cells that send axons to the cerebellum via the dorsal spinocerebellar tracts.

The *substantia gelatinosa* forms the prominent caplike portion of the dorsal horn. It consists of small cells (6 to 20 μm) with axonal projections that remain in the substantia gelatinosa. This column of cells processes sensory information entering via dorsal root fibers (see Fig. 14-8).

The cell bodies of primary afferent fibers are located in the dorsal root ganglia. These cells have a distal axon segment that terminates in a sensory receptor and a central axon segment that enters the spinal cord via the dorsal root. The central or proximal axon segment may take several courses on entering the spinal cord. It may turn rostrally and join the dorsal columns to ascend to supraspinal centers, or it may divide into ascending and descending collaterals, which course over several segments in the white matter while sending collateral branches into the gray matter. The collateral branches of the different types of

Table 14-3. Projections to and from
Rexed's laminae

Projections	Lamina
To lamina	
Nociceptors	I, II, V
Mechanoreceptors	III–VI
Group Ia (primary endings in muscle spindles)	VI, VII, IX
Group II (secondary endings in muscle spindles)	IV–VII, IX
Group Ib (Golgi tendon organs)	V–VII
Unmyelinated C fibers	II
Corticospinal tract	III–VII
Reticulospinal tract	I, II, V–VIII
From lamina	
Ventrospinocerebellar	V–VII
Spinothalamic	I, IV–VI
Postsynaptic dorsal column neurons	III–V

receptors in turn synapse with cells in specific areas of the gray matter of the spinal cord, predominantly with the projectional cells in the dorsal horn. These in turn send projections to supraspinal structures. The nociceptive-specific cells that mediate pain send projections via the spinothalamic and spinoreticular tracts; the low-threshold non-nociceptive mechanoreceptors that mediate touch send projections via the dorsal columns, the dorsolateral quadrant, and spinothalamic tract; and the wide dynamic range neurons that mediate both pain and touch send projections via the spinothalamic tract, the dorsal columns, and the spinoreticular pathways (Table 14-3).

The spinal cord is organized into 10 cell layers, or laminae (Rexed's laminae), based on neuronal size, cell density, and staining characteristics. Laminae I through V are located in the dorsal horn and subserve sensory functions; laminae VI through VIII are located in the intermediate gray matter and are involved with reflex activity; lamina IX is in the ventral horn and is involved with motor function; and lamina X surrounds the central canal (see Fig. 14-8).

Lamina I, the most dorsal layer, receives input from propriospinal neurons and nociceptors. It contains marginal cells, impor-

tant cells of the dorsal horn that project to the other segments of the spinal cord, the cervical area, the nuclei of the dorsal columns, the reticular formation, and the thalamus (forming part of the spinothalamic tracts).

Lamina II is the substantia gelatinosa. It contains interneurons and receives input from unmyelinated nociceptive C fibers.

Lamina III represents the dorsal part of the nucleus proprius and receives input from mechanoreceptors.

Lamina IV represents the ventral part of the nucleus proprius. It contains a number of types of sensory cells. It receives input from mechanoreceptors and group II fibers from muscle spindles and gives rise to spinothalamic tract fibers.

Lamina V forms the base of the dorsal horn, is continuous with the reticular formation, and receives input from the reticulospinal tract, lamina IV, mechanoreceptors, nociceptors, group II fibers, and group Ib fibers from Golgi tendon organs.

Lamina VI contains exteroceptive and proprioceptive sensory cells with a large receptive field.

Lamina VII contains Clarke's column. The lateral horn is a lateral extension of this lamina. It receives input from the corticospinal tract, the reticulospinal tract, and afferents from muscle spindles and Golgi tendon organs.

Lamina VIII contains cells with projections mainly to the contralateral ventral horn and the ventral funiculus.

Lamina IX contains the motor neurons.

Lamina X surrounds the central canal and consists of the dorsal and ventral gray commissures.

The gray matter thus consists of multiple interacting cell groups that process inputs from the periphery, spinal cord, and descending pathways from the brain; mediate reflexes; and give rise to ascending spinal tracts.

The variations in the configuration of the gray and white matter at different segments of the spinal cord help in identifying the level of a section of the cord (Fig. 14-9 and Table 14-4). The nerve roots and spinal nerves are made up of myelinated and unmyelinated axons

Fig. 14-9. Cross sections of spinal cord with myelin stain showing relative proportions of white matter (*dark areas*) and gray matter (*light areas*) at various levels. A. Cervical; B. Thoracic; C. Lumbar; D. Sacral.

with the same histologic and physiologic characteristics as the peripheral axons described in Chapter 13 (The Peripheral Level). The pathophysiologic alterations of nerve roots are, therefore, also the same.

Spinal Cord Physiology

The major functions of the spinal cord are the transmission of activity via the longitudinal pathways and the mediation of local reflexes. The reflex activity of the spinal cord depends on the neuronal activity of the cells in the gray matter of the cord.

A neuron does not merely relay information; rather it processes information by the integration of its total synaptic input. The excitability of a neuron changes from moment to moment, depending on the relative effectiveness of the excitatory and inhibitory input in altering the state of polarization of the postsynaptic membrane. However, once the membrane is depolarized to threshold, the neuron responds in an all-or-none fashion, with the generation of an action potential.

Table 14-4. Configurational Characteristics of the Spinal Cord

Shape of cord	Oval at cervical segments, nearly circular at lumbar segments, and almost quadrangular at sacral segments
Proportion of white to gray matter	Progressively increasing from below up
Size of anterior horn	Enlargement at cervical and lumbar segments
Posterior intermediate sulcus	Present in cervical and upper thoracic segments
Lateral horn	Well marked at thoracic segments
Nerve roots	Many present around cord at lumbar and sacral segments

The amount of transmitter released from a presynaptic ending when an action potential is conducted into the nerve terminal is dependent on the absolute potential change produced across the nerve terminal membrane. A subthreshold depolarization of the terminal membrane reduces the amplitude of an impulse being conducted into the terminal; hence, the amount of transmitter substance released is reduced. Such a subthreshold depolarization is produced in presynaptic endings by activity in axoaxonal synapses. In *axoaxonal synapses,* an axon terminal ends on another axonal ending, which is presynaptic to the dendrite of a neuron. The reduction in the effectiveness of synaptic transmission produced by this mechanism is termed *presynaptic inhibition* (Fig. 14-10). Presynaptic inhibition that occurs on afferent nerve fibers is termed *primary afferent depolarization.* It reduces the input of sensory information to the central nervous system.

The motor neurons in the autonomic and somatic efferent pathways of the spinal cord have similar physiologic characteristics. Both act as integrators of information, summating the excitatory postsynaptic potentials (EPSPs) and inhibitory postsynaptic potentials (IPSPs) from multiple sources and firing only when the membrane potential reaches threshold. The firing pattern in both is similar. These neurons do not normally produce single discharges but fire repetitively at a rate that is a function of the level of depolarization of the cell. Firing is initiated at low frequencies of four to eight per second and gradually increases in frequency as more and more excitation occurs. The neurons innervating the same muscle lie together in groups, are influenced by similar inputs, and therefore tend to fire at the same time. However, differences in size of neurons result in differences in threshold of firing and different firing rates. The number of cells firing in a given motor neuron pool, therefore, is a function of the amount of inhibitory and excitatory input coming to the entire pool of neurons.

Disorders of motor neurons can alter response to input so that the neurons fire spontaneously or with minimal input, as occurs in tetanus or in strychnine poisoning. Disorders may also result in single, spontaneous discharges, such as fasciculations, or in reduced response to input, as in the weakness seen in motor neuron disease. If the neuron degenerates, it no longer provides the neurotrophic factors needed for normal function of the end organ, which then atrophies. A denervated end organ also undergoes denervation hypersensitivity, becoming more sensitive to the transmitter.

Spinal Cord Functions

Spinal cord structures are responsible for (1) processing and modulating sensory input, (2) integrating the activities of the spinal cord, (3) mediating spinal reflexes and other motor functions, and (4) mediating autonomic functions.

Sensory Functions

Processing of sensory information occurs mainly in the dorsal horn, which contains various circuits that permit not only transmission of sensory input but a high degree of sensory processing. Important aspects of this sensory processing are plasticity and central modulation of transmission of pain information. The two classes of spinothalamic neurons, the nociceptive-specific and wide dynamic range neurons, may change their activity and responsiveness to afferent nociceptive input in

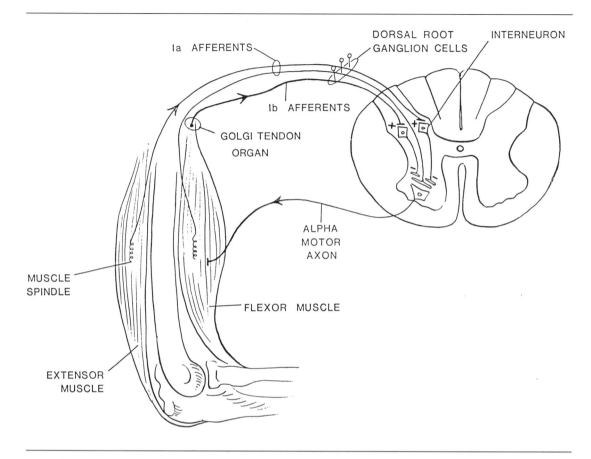

Fig. 14-10. Mechanism of presynaptic inhibition. Type Ia afferents from flexors are inhibited by Golgi tendon organ and antagonistic spindle afferents.

response to segmental or suprasegmental influences. These regulatory circuits involve primary afferents, descending pathways, and local interneurons.

Interneurons in the dorsal horn are located primarily in the substantia gelatinosa. They may be excitatory or inhibitory. Inhibitory interneurons contain gamma-aminobutyric acid (GABA), enkephalins, or other neuropeptides and are important for local processing and modulation of pain transmission. They receive segmental primary afferent fiber input as well as descending supraspinal input.

There are two important segmental mechanisms for modulation of pain transmission. The first mechanism involves inhibition of pain transmission by activation of large-diameter afferents: stimulation of low-threshold, highly myelinated mechanoreceptive afferents *inhibits* pain transmission in the dorsal horn, probably by activation of local inhibitory interneurons. This is the basis for the *gate control theory of pain modulation.* The second mechanism involves the increased activity and responsiveness of spinothalamic tract neurons after nerve injury or repetitive activation of small nociceptive fibers. Repetitive firing of nociceptive fibers causes increased activity in dorsal horn nociceptive neurons. This involves plastic changes in neurotransmission in the dorsal horn, including activation of *N*-methyl-D-aspartate (NMDA) receptors of spinothalamic neurons by L-glutamate released by primary nociceptive afferents. These excitatory effects are potentiated by substance P and other neuropeptides released from C-afferent fibers.

In addition to segmental mechanisms, suprasegmental influences modulate nociceptive transmission in the dorsal horn. This effect is mediated mainly by descending serotonergic and norepinephrine pathways from the ventral medulla, which inhibit spinothalamic neurons either directly or via interneurons. The interruption of these pathways may explain some forms of pain that occur with spinal cord lesions.

Thus, the segmental input from primary sensory afferents and interneurons and the suprasegmental influences from the sensory cortex and brain stem modulate the perception of pain, sensory discrimination, and the affective nature of sensory stimuli.

Motor Functions

The segmental motor apparatus of the spinal cord is involved in two types of activity: reflex activity, including phasic and tonic stretch reflexes, and complex motor synergies, such as locomotion. The segmental motor apparatus includes (1) topographically organized groups of motor neurons in the ventral horn, (2) local interneurons, (3) propriospinal neurons, (4) peripheral afferents, and (5) descending motor control pathways. At the segmental level, there is a high degree of sensorimotor integration, largely via the interneurons that receive multiple segmental and supersegmental inputs.

Motor neurons are somatotopically arranged into functionally distinct groups in lamina IX — those innervating axial musculature are located ventromedially, those innervating intrinsic muscles of the limbs are located dorsolaterally, and those innervating girdle muscles occupy an intermediate position. Motor neurons that innervate extensor muscles are called *extensor motor neurons*, and those innervating flexor muscles are *flexor motor neurons*. Muscles that functionally aid one another are called *synergists*, and those that functionally act in opposition are *antagonists*. For example, both the gastrocnemius and soleus muscles are responsible for plantar flexion of the foot; therefore, they are synergists. The anterior tibial muscle is responsible for dorsiflexion of the foot and so is an antagonist of the gastrocnemius and soleus muscles.

The motor functions are mediated by the motor projection neurons in the ventral horn: the alpha motor neurons and the gamma motor neurons.

Alpha motor neurons are large, innervate the extrafusal muscle fibers, and constitute the final common pathway for motor control. They integrate multiple central and peripheral influences — including inputs from primary afferents, interneurons, and descending pathways — into an output that precisely controls muscle contraction and produces coordinated motor patterns. The size of the alpha motor neuron relates to its firing pattern. Smaller cells have a lower threshold for firing and fire at lower frequencies; larger cells have a high threshold and fire at faster frequencies. During voluntary or reflex muscle contraction, motor neurons fire in order of increasing size. This is the *size principle*: small motor neurons are recruited first and the larger ones later. The size principle is important in determining the increments of force that develop at various levels of muscle contraction.

The motor unit consists of the alpha motor neuron, its axon, and the muscle fibers it innervates. On the basis of size and firing characteristics of alpha motor neurons, motor units can be divided into two types: slow-twitch motor unit and fast-twitch motor unit. The slow-twitch motor unit is supplied by the smaller alpha motor neurons with smaller diameter axons that innervate type I muscle fibers, which are slow to contract, produce smaller amounts of force, and are resistant to fatigue. The fast-twitch motor unit is supplied by the larger alpha motor neurons with larger and more rapidly conducting axons that innervate type II muscle fibers, which contract rapidly, develop large twitch tensions, and fatigue easily (Table 14-5). During muscle contraction, the smaller motor units are recruited first, whereas stronger levels of contraction require activation of the larger units. Thus, the force generated by muscle contraction depends on the number and type of motor neurons recruited and their discharge rate.

Gamma motor neurons are smaller than alpha motor neurons and innervate the intrafusal muscle fibers of the muscle spindle. The muscle spindle is a complex proprioceptive stretch receptor that responds selectively to changes in muscle length. The two functional types of muscle spindle are static spindles, which respond to stretching of the muscle, and dynamic spindles, which respond to the rate of change of muscle stretch.

Table 14-5. Comparison of Small and Large Motor Units

	Motor unit	
	Small	Large
Twitch contraction time	Slow	Fast
Axon diameter	Small	Large
Conduction speed	Slow	Fast
Threshold	Low	High
Recruitment	Early	Late
Fatigability	Low	High
Muscle type	I	II

Integrated Functions

Interneurons are responsible for the integrated functions of the spinal cord. Most of the input from the sensory afferents, descending pathways, and local segmental structures synapse on the interneurons. Through their many connections, interneurons process, modify, modulate, and integrate the activities of the motor, sensory, and visceral structures of the spinal cord.

Spinal Reflexes

The simplest level of motor control is a reflex, in which a specific sensory input induces a specific motor response. Such reflex responses can either promote movement (phasic muscle contractions promote reposition of limbs) or maintain posture (tonic muscle contractions counteract gravity and maintain the body in an upright position). The segmental circuits mediating movement reflexes primarily involve excitation of flexor motor neurons, whereas those mediating posture involve excitation of extensor and axial motor neurons. Spinal reflex patterns are subjected to increasing amounts of control from supraspinal levels during the course of development. The magnitude of this reflex subordination in adults is indicated by the complete areflexia and flaccidity that follow spinal cord transection.

A reflex arc consists of the receptor, an effector, and the interconnecting neural elements. The simplest reflex, a *monosynaptic reflex*, involves only two neural elements: an afferent neuron and a motor neuron in synaptic contact with each other. *Polysynaptic reflexes* involve one or more interneurons interposed between the afferent and efferent neurons (Fig. 14-11).

Spinal reflexes are not stereotyped but depend on complex interactions among primary afferents and descending inputs converging on the same sets of interneurons and motor neurons. The four main types of segmental inputs to motor neurons are (1) primary spindle endings with group Ia afferents, (2) secondary spindle endings with group II afferents, (3) Golgi tendon organs with group Ib afferents, and (4) groups III and IV muscle afferents and cutaneous receptor afferents, which together with group II spindle afferents constitute the so-called flexion reflex afferent system. The different classes of afferents converge on the same interneuronal pools; excitability of these interneurons provides flexibility of reflex responses in the spinal cord.

Many types of reflex activity are mediated at the spinal cord level (Table 14-6). They are illustrated by the stretch reflex, clasp-knife phenomenon, flexion reflex, and long-latency reflex.

Stretch Reflex

The response initiated by an afferent discharge from the muscle spindles is a *stretch reflex*. This reflex continuously activates extensor and axial muscles and results in stabilization of the trunk and limbs to counteract the downward force of gravity and maintain upright posture. This reflex is not clearly functional in humans until approximately the seventeenth week of gestation. Subsequently, it becomes integrated with other postural influences that descend from pontomedullary levels. The stretch reflex is of two types: phasic and tonic.

The *phasic stretch reflex* is elicited by muscle stretch sufficient to discharge the primary spindle afferents (group Ia). These large, myelinated, primary afferent fibers enter the dorsomedial portion of the spinal cord dorsal horn and project directly onto homonymous motor neurons (neurons innervating the muscle from which the spindle discharge originated) to produce contraction of the homonymous muscle; concurrent monosynaptic reflex activation of the synergistic muscles results in stabilization of the joint across which the synergists attach. Even though the motor neurons

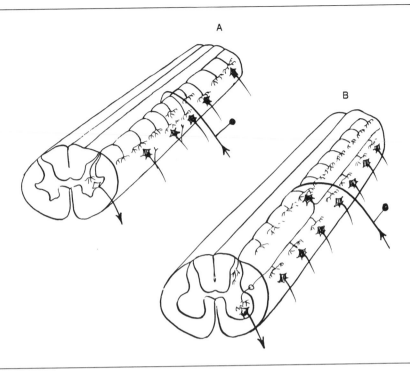

Fig. 14-11. Reflex connections of primary afferents. A. Monosynaptic (no interneurons). B. Polysynaptic (one or more interneurons). Note longitudinal spread of connections in both types of reflex.

Table 14-6. Summary of Spinal Reflexes

Reflex	Receptor	Afferent fiber	Responses
Phasic stretch reflex	Muscle spindle (primary endings)	Group Ia (large, myelinated)	Brisk, transient contraction of muscle from which the Ia activity arises
Tonic stretch reflex	Muscle spindle (secondary endings)	Group II (intermediate, myelinated)	Sustained contraction of muscle from which the II activity arises
Flexion reflex (withdrawal from noxious stimulus)	Nociceptors (free nerve endings) and other receptors	Small myelinated and unmyelinated cutaneous afferents (Aδ, C) and muscle afferents (group III, C)	Withdrawal of stimulated limb and extension of contralateral limb (crossed extension)
Tension feedback	Golgi tendon organs	Group Ib (large, myelinated)	Adjusts contraction in response to tension changes

supplying synergistic muscles receive excitatory input, they normally are not depolarized to threshold. They are said to be in the *subliminal fringe.*

The Ia afferent reflex provides a length-feedback mechanism. Group Ia afferents from spindle primary endings are stimulated by a rapid rate of change in the length of the muscle and have an overall excitatory effect on the motor neuron pools of the homonymous muscle and synergistic muscles and an overall inhibitory effect on the motor neuron pools of the antagonistic muscles. The excitatory effect includes a burst of excitatory monosynaptic inputs to motor neurons (the Ia monosynaptic pathway) as well as multisynaptic excitation.

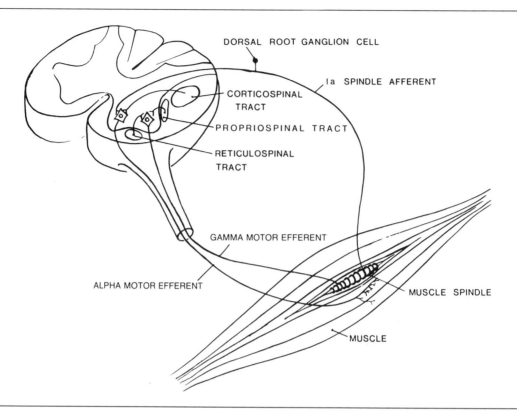

Fig. 14-12. Pathways for monosynaptic reflex and gamma loop. Group Ia afferent fibers from muscle spindle make monosynaptic contact with alpha motor neuron supplying that muscle. Gamma motor neuron sends efferent fiber, via ventral root, to innervate intrafusal muscle fibers of muscle spindle. Input to gamma motor neuron is from both segmental and supraspinal sources (corticospinal, reticulospinal, propriospinal tracts).

The stretch reflex mediated by Ia fibers elicits a *dynamic*, or *phasic*, response initiated by a rapid rate of change in muscle length and produces a burst of excitatory synaptic input to alpha motor neurons supplying the muscle and its synergists. If the change in muscle length is sufficiently sudden, a brisk contraction of the muscle occurs.

The gain of the Ia monosynaptic reflex is controlled by *fusimotor activity of gamma motor neurons* innervating the corresponding muscle and by *presynaptic inhibition* of neurotransmitter release from the Ia afferent.

Gamma motor neurons receive the same inputs as alpha motor neurons, except that primary spindle afferents do not project to gamma motor neurons. In general, gamma and alpha neurons innervating the same muscle are activated in the same way by an incoming stimulus. However, compared with alpha motor neurons, gamma motor neurons respond at lower thresholds to segmental influences and descending activity, especially that from indirect pathways.

Contraction of the whole muscle would cause the length of muscle spindles to shorten and stop firing, unless a mechanism were available to regulate the length of the muscle spindle. Regulation is achieved by the gamma motor neurons that innervate the muscle spindles (Fig. 14-12). The muscle spindle consists of sensory receptors on the center of specialized muscle fibers, the *intrafusal fibers*. Gamma motor neurons activate the intrafusal fibers, causing contraction and shortening of the intrafusal fibers on either side of the central noncontractile region. Contraction of the ends of the intrafusal fibers stretches the central region and activates the sensory receptors and the afferent nerve terminals. Thus, an afferent spindle discharge may occur as a direct effect of gamma motor neuron excitation of the intrafusal fibers. When the gamma motor neurons are active during muscle contraction, the resultant intrafusal fiber contractions are sufficient to overcome the slack in the spindle that would result from the whole muscle contraction. This allows the spindle to maintain a high degree of sensitivity over a wide range of different lengths during voluntary and reflex movements.

Gamma motor neurons innervate both primary (dynamic) receptors with Ia afferents and secondary (static) receptors with group II afferents. There are two types of gamma motor neurons: dynamic and static. Dynamic fusimotor fibers enhance the responsiveness of primary spindle endings to small, rapid changes in muscle length; static fibers rapidly shorten the intrafusal muscle fibers and maintain sensitivity of the muscle spindle during unloading of the spindle as a result of the contraction of extrafusal fibers. In relaxed muscles, spindles have little background fusimotor activity and, therefore, do not contribute significantly to muscle tone.

Presynaptic inhibition involves local GABAergic neurons and is critical for modulation of the excitability of the Ia monosynaptic excitatory pathway. Presynaptic inhibitory neurons make axoaxonal synapses with primary afferents and produce primary afferent depolarization. Primary afferent depolarization reduces the influx of calcium ions responsible for the release of excitatory neurotransmitter from the Ia afferent, thus reducing the gain of the Ia monosynaptic pathway. Afferents to presynaptic inhibitory neurons include segmental afferents and supraspinal pathways.

In addition to producing monosynaptic excitatory postsynaptic potentials in homonymous and synergistic alpha motor neurons, group Ia afferents have collaterals that simultaneously inhibit motor neurons innervating antagonistic muscles. This process is called *reciprocal inhibition* (Fig. 14-13). The reciprocal group Ia inhibition of the antagonistic muscles is a disynaptic pathway that involves an *Ia inhibitory interneuron*. These inhibitory inter-

neurons not only mediate disynaptic inhibition of antagonistic muscles but are an important integrating center for various inputs. The Ia inhibitory neurons receive convergent excitatory input from other afferents and from descending pathways and are inhibited by collaterals of homonymous Renshaw cells.

Renshaw cells control the output of motor neurons, and hence the efferent arm of spinal reflexes, via *recurrent inhibition*. Renshaw cells are inhibitory interneurons that contain glycine or GABA and are excited by recurrent collaterals of alpha motor neuron axons (Fig. 14-14). Axons of Renshaw cells, after a short course in the white matter, produce inhibitory synapses on homonymous alpha motor neurons and on synergistic motor neurons located in their proximity. They also inhibit gamma motor neurons, Ia inhibitory interneurons, and other Renshaw cells. In addition to excitatory input from alpha motor neurons, Renshaw cells receive complex afferent and descending inputs. The negative feedback circuit of the alpha motor neuron–Renshaw cell–alpha motor neuron pathway stabilizes discharge of the alpha motor neuron; however, Renshaw cells may also have a role in integrating motor neuron discharge with the firing of gamma motor neurons and Ia inhibitory interneurons.

A second type of response to muscle stretch is the *static*, or *tonic*, response, initiated by a change in the length of the muscle. It provides a continuous background of excitatory input to alpha motor neurons via group II and Ia spindle afferents. This activity is responsible for clinical muscle tone and is described as the *tonic stretch reflex*.

During a voluntary contraction, the muscle shortens and the muscle spindles tend to go slack. As a result, the intrafusal fibers are stretched less and the spindle afferent discharge decreases. If the muscle is passively stretched, the intrafusal fibers are also stretched, and the spindle sensory discharge increases. The excitation of motor units in a muscle in response to muscle stretching provides a normal level of resistance to passive movement of a joint, which is called *muscle tone*. Muscle tone is defined clinically as the resistance to passive movements of the limbs when the patient is in a state of voluntary re-

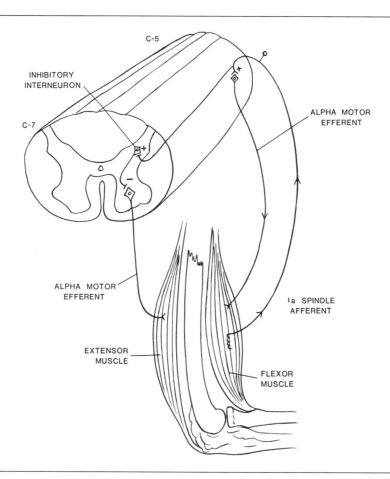

Fig. 14-13. Pathways for monosynaptic reflex and reciprocal innervation. A flexor Ia afferent is shown making monosynaptic contact with a flexor motor neuron and an inhibitory interneuron. Interneuron sends axonal projections to extensor motor neuron, providing the pathway for reciprocal inhibition.

laxation. It is defined physiologically as a state of tension or steady contraction of the muscle. Muscle tone depends not only on monosynaptic spindle reflex pathways but also on various other mechanisms, including (1) mechanical properties of the muscle, (2) short-latency spinal reflexes mediated by muscle spindle pathways, (3) feedback reflexes mediated by Golgi tendon organ pathways, (4) long-latency reflexes, and (5) voluntary influences.

Golgi tendon organs, innervated by group Ib afferents, provide a tension-feedback mechanism during muscle contraction. These receptor organs are in series with the extrafusal fibers and are located in muscle aponeurosis at the site of tendon insertions. Thus, they are well positioned for monitoring tension gener-

ated by muscle contraction. They are silent in relaxed muscles but are very sensitive to increases in tension produced by contraction of their in-series motor units. Therefore, Golgi tendon organs are tension receptors that respond selectively to active tension produced by contraction of the extrafusal fibers that insert in the tendon bearing the receptor. The large Ib afferents from Golgi tendon organs located in muscles that act at the same and at different joints converge onto single interneurons, called *Ib inhibitory interneurons.* These inhibitory interneurons, in turn, form widespread inhibitory synapses with alpha motor neurons.

The motor neuron output of a spinal segment is determined by the balance between

Fig. 14-14. Pathways for recurrent inhibition. Recurrent collateral of the axon of an alpha motor neuron making excitatory synaptic contact with a Renshaw cell. Excitation of Renshaw cell produces inhibition of alpha motor neuron.

afferents from the length and tension receptors. Together, muscle spindles and Golgi tendon organs, which have opposite effects on the motor neuron pool, provide the central nervous system with the types of information required to control muscle length, tone, force, and movement. Their functions are complementary in the programming and reflex control of movement. In the absence of muscle tone, there is no resistance to passive movement, and the muscle is *flaccid.*

During complete relaxation, fusimotor activity is low or absent, and there is little contribution of the muscle spindle reflexes to muscle tone in most normal persons. Dorsal rhizotomy (section of the dorsal roots) interrupts the afferent limb of the tonic stretch reflex, producing a dramatic reduction in muscle tone. This procedure also abolishes the phasic stretch reflex.

Clinically, the monosynaptic reflex is elicited by tapping on a tendon to produce a sudden stretch of a muscle. A commonly observed monosynaptic reflex is that involving the contraction of the quadriceps muscle (knee jerk), elicited by tapping on the patellar tendon. A number of such monosynaptic reflexes are routinely tested in the neurologic examination of a patient. The monosynaptic reflex has been given many names (*myotatic reflex*, stretch reflex, tendon-jerk reflex, and deep tendon reflex). The last term, *deep tendon reflex*, is used

extensively and may be misleading. It implies that the receptors for the reflex reside in the tendon, which they do not. The tap on the tendon stretches the muscle and produces a phasic, synchronous discharge of primary spindle afferents, which triggers the monosynaptic stretch reflex. Hyperactive tendon jerks (hyperactive stretch reflexes) on one side of the body are indicative of upper motor neuron damage. The increased resistance to passive movement caused by increased tonic stretch reflexes is termed *spasticity.* Rapid movement is an adequate stimulus for demonstrating spasticity. In a patient with spasticity, if a constant stretch is applied to the muscle and a tendon tap or sudden additional stretch is superimposed, not one but a series of tendon-jerk reflexes results. This repetitive jerking is called *clonus* and reflects the highly sensitive state of the alpha motor neurons to synchronous afferent volleys. Spasticity is due to lack of presynaptic inhibition of Ia afferent inputs caused by interruption of descending input to presynaptic inhibitory interneurons.

Clasp-Knife Phenomenon
Patients with lesions of the internal capsule and other upper motor neuron lesions typically have spasticity with increased resistance to passive stretch of the muscle. However, if a spastic muscle is stretched beyond a given length, there is an abrupt decrease in the resistance of stretching. This is known as the *clasp-knife phenomenon.* A clasp knife has an initial resistance to being closed, and then at a certain point, the knife suddenly snaps shut. In the clasp-knife phenomenon, an initial resistance (increased tone) at the beginning of the stretch of a flexor or extensor muscle persists up to a certain point and is then followed by sudden loss of muscle tone.

The genesis of the clasp-knife phenomenon is complex. The buildup of reflex resistance is a consequence of the velocity-dependent stretch reflex and can occur in any muscle, particularly in the quadriceps and hamstring muscles. The clasp-knife phenomenon may reflect disinhibition of local spinal cord interneurons mediated by secondary muscle spindles (group II); group II, III, and IV muscle afferents; and joint mechanoreceptors. Together with cutaneous afferents, these afferents predominantly initiate flexion responses and are called *flexion reflex afferents*. These afferents are subject to supraspinal control by a number of pathways but particularly by the reticulospinal pathway that inhibits the first-order interneuron of the flexion reflex afferent pathway. Interruption of this descending input disinhibits interneurons of the flexion reflex afferent pathway.

Flexion Reflex

The term *flexion reflex* is a general one encompassing various polysynaptic reflexes. These can range from reflex withdrawal of a portion of the body from a noxious stimulus to flexion of the lower extremities during walking. The flexion reflex afferents include secondary group II muscle spindle afferents, small-diameter muscle afferents (groups III and IV), and joint, touch, pressure, and nociceptive afferents. These afferents have access to motor neurons through various interneurons that receive convergent proprioceptive and descending supraspinal control.

The flexion reflex response is thus known by a number of terms, including withdrawal reflex, nociceptive reflex, and cutaneous reflex. This reflex results in limb movement mediated by flexor muscle contraction away from the source of stimulation. Both ontogenetically and phylogenetically, the flexion reflex is one of the most primitive reflexes of the central nervous system. It is found in all the vertebrates, and in humans it is present by the seventh to eighth week of gestation. In the adult, the circuit underlying this reflex is incorporated into the more complex volitional movements of cortical initiation.

Stimuli that evoke the flexion reflex cause a discharge of cutaneous receptors, which in turn triggers action potential discharges along unmyelinated and finely myelinated fibers that enter the dorsolateral portion of the dorsal horn of the spinal cord. This input is then transmitted through short, multisynaptic relays to the ventral motor neuronal pool (Fig. 14-15).

During flexion reflex activation, there is ipsilateral flexor motor neuron excitation and extensor inhibition (reciprocal innervation). Contralateral to the side of stimulation, there is flexor motor neuron inhibition and extensor excitation (double reciprocal innervation).

This *crossed extension reflex* stabilizes the body as the ipsilateral limb is flexed. Even though flexion reflex afferents initially were thought to selectively inhibit extensor motor neurons and facilitate flexor motor neurons (hence, their name), they may also excite ipsilateral extensor motor neurons.

Because the flexion reflex is polysynaptic, there is afterdischarge in the interneuronal relays, and the motor response outlasts the stimulus. Activation of the flexor motor neurons is typically widespread so that flexor muscles at the ankle, knee, and hip contract to withdraw the whole limb.

The flexion reflex circuits receive important supraspinal control, including inhibition by descending monoaminergic and dorsal reticulospinal pathways and facilitation by corticospinal and rubrospinal pathways. A function of the corticospinal tract may be to choose the synaptic actions of the flexion reflex afferents appropriate to a particular task.

In upper motor neuron syndrome and spasticity, damage to the inhibitory dorsal reticulospinal and corticospinal tract may explain symptoms and findings. After spinal cord transection and after the acute phase of spinal shock and areflexia, flexion reflexes are disinhibited and patients may develop *flexor spasms*. Although flexor spasms may occur after brain stem injury, they are rare in more rostral lesions that spare the inhibitory dorsal reticulospinal pathways arising in the pontomedullary reticular formation. In general, patients with complete spinal cord transection pass through a phase of alternating flexor and extensor spasms into a final phase of predominantly extensor spasms. Extensor spasms may be precipitated by either cutaneous stimulation or body movements, and reflex extension of a limb commonly accompanies the withdrawal of the opposite limb.

Interruption of descending inhibitory reticulospinal pathways that control the interneurons of the flexion reflex afferent pathways may underlie the clasp-knife phenomenon observed in spasticity.

Most cutaneous reflex responses activate underlying muscles (local sign), so that, for example, cutaneous stimulation over an extensor muscle results in extensor contraction to move the muscle away. However, painful cutaneous

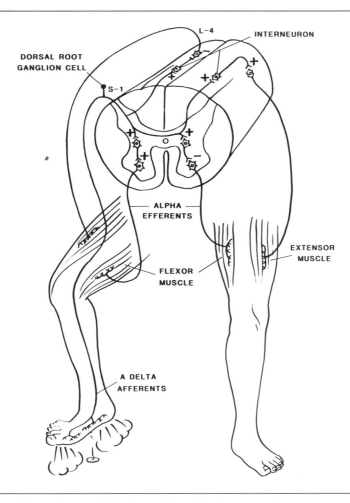

Fig. 14-15. Flexion reflex pathway. Afferent supply and interneuronal connections for flexion reflex in lower extremity are illustrated in spinal cord section. Noxious stimulus applied to lower extremity results in ipsilateral flexion (withdrawal) and, provided that stimulus strength is sufficiently high, extension of contralateral limb (crossed extension reflex).

stimulation in the distal portions of the limb induces reflex withdrawal, or flexion, and thus represents the common usage of the term *flexion reflex* for cutaneous reflex activation.

A number of cutaneous, or superficial, reflexes are included in neurologic examinations. In general, these reflexes are mediated by polysynaptic segmental circuits similar to those of the cutaneous flexion reflex. Abnormalities in specific superficial reflexes can be diagnostic of central nervous system lesions. For example, in the normal person, plantar flexion of the toes occurs with noxious stimulation of the sole of the foot. In the presence of corticospinal tract disease, however, these lo-

cal cord reflexes are altered and a more primitive form of flexion reflex occurs — *Babinski's sign*, in which the great toe responds to plantar stimulation with dorsiflexion. The abdominal contractions normally induced by cutaneous stimulation of the abdomen and the cremasteric contractions normally induced by cutaneous stimulation along the inner side of the thigh (both forms of flexion reflex) are no longer elicitable after a corticospinal tract (direct activation pathway) lesion.

Long-Latency Reflexes
Reflex responses to disturbance of voluntary movement or to electrical stimulation have

been found in the human arm at approximately 60 milliseconds. These long-latency reflexes involve supraspinal pathways and areas and reflect higher levels of control of motor function.

Long-latency reflexes are transcortical reflexes. Input from muscle spindles is relayed via the dorsal column–lemniscal system to sensorimotor cortex, and corticospinal output to spinal motor neurons results in generation of the late responses of muscle. These responses, also called *long-loop reflexes*, supplement segmental monosynaptic stretch reflexes in their ability to compensate for changes in the mechanical load imposed on a muscle and may be altered by voluntary control.

Interneurons and Propriospinal Neurons

The two intrinsic neuronal populations that control the motor output of the spinal cord are the local interneurons and propriospinal neurons. They occupy the intermediate gray matter (laminae V–VIII). *Interneurons*, including the Ia, Ib, and presynaptic inhibitory interneurons and the Renshaw cells, are interposed between incoming (afferent) and outgoing (efferent) fibers in the spinal cord. Interneurons receive input from the periphery, local spinal segments, and descending pathways from higher centers; they form multisynaptic, divergent, or convergent connections with motor neurons, afferent neurons, and other neuronal groups in the spinal cord. This convergence of input and divergence of output allow individual interneurons to receive input from multiple sources and to influence the activity of multiple neurons. The interneurons thus serve as links among the peripheral nervous system, descending pathways from the brain, local neuronal groups, and motor neurons. The interneurons (1) regulate voluntary and reflex motor acts, (2) coordinate the activity in muscle groups with the appropriate degree of contraction and relaxation of agonists and antagonists, (3) transmit information from the periphery and higher centers to motor neurons, (4) modulate afferent impulses by allowing or preventing transmission of afferent impulses from the periphery and local spinal circuits, and (5) provide a background of spontaneous activity and readiness to respond.

The interneurons at the spinal level serve as the basis for regulating voluntary movements, local control of motor behavior, automatic movements, and other integrated activities.

Propriospinal neurons are intrinsic spinal cord neurons that are not interposed between afferent and efferent pathways but are involved in intrasegmental and intersegmental connections with different motor neuron pools necessary for coordinated motor activity. These neurons are concentrated in laminae V through VIII, and their axons travel in the white matter adjacent to the gray matter, the *fasciculi proprii*. Long-projecting propriospinal neurons are concentrated in the ventromedial part of the gray matter and innervate motor neurons controlling axial and girdle muscles. These propriospinal pathways are mainly bilateral and coordinate intersegmental postural reflexes. Short-projecting propriospinal neurons are located in the dorsolateral part of the gray matter and coordinate the activity of motor neurons involved in controlling movements of the distal extremities, particularly the hand.

The interneuronal and propriospinal networks in the lumbar spinal cord are critical for locomotion. The neural substrate for coordinated locomotion is thought to exist in the lumbar spinal cord, the *central (spinal) pattern generator for locomotion*. Lumbar interneurons and propriospinal neurons coordinate the alternating pattern of muscle contraction for step and stance during locomotion via sequential activation of alpha motor neurons that supply the different flexor and extensor muscle groups, respectively. The spinal pattern generator for locomotion is modulated by (1) peripheral feedback from muscle, joint, and cutaneous receptors, (2) local spinal circuits, and (3) descending pathways. Activity in the spinal generator may involve excitatory amino acid mechanisms mediated via both non-NMDA and NMDA receptors, reciprocal local inhibitory interactions mediated by glycine and GABA, and modulatory (facilitation) influences from descending monoaminergic pathways.

Autonomic Function

Preganglionic sympathetic neurons are organized into different sympathetic functional units in the intermediolateral cell column of the spinal cord. These include skin vasomotor, muscle vasomotor, visceromotor, pilomotor, and sudomotor units. These neurons do not discharge massively but instead control specific targets. Thus, there is not a generalized sympathetic "tone" but coordinated activity of specific subsets of sympathetic neurons.

In humans, sympathetic nerve activity in skeletal muscles is finely regulated by baroreflex activity, whereas in the skin it is regulated mainly by environmental temperature and emotional state. Several parallel pathways descending from the hypothalamus and brain stem and containing various neurotransmitters differentially modulate preganglionic neurons; this is critical for their coordinated action. Preganglionic neurons are the effectors of segmental somatosympathetic and viscerosympathetic reflexes triggered by skin, muscle, or visceral afferents in the dorsal root. In general, these afferents stimulate preganglionic neurons via local interneurons. The segmental reflexes are controlled by suprasegmental inputs. For example, innocuous stimulation of the skin or bladder distention produces minimal change in preganglionic activity. Patients with cervical cord lesions that interrupt descending pathways cannot maintain arterial pressure when they are tilted and do not have thermoregulatory responses below the level of the lesion. Also, bladder distention or innocuous skin stimulation in these patients may trigger massive sympathetic excitation, including intense sweating, muscle and skin vasoconstriction, tachycardia, and hypertension. This phenomenon is known as *autonomic dysreflexia*.

Micturition

Preganglionic parasympathetic neurons are restricted to segments S-2 to S-4 and innervate the colon, bladder, and organs of reproduction. Their function involves reciprocal interactions with sacral somatic motor neurons innervating the sphincters and pelvic floor muscles. Parasympathetic neurons are *excited*, whereas somatic sphincter motor neurons are *inhibited* during micturition and defecation; the opposite occurs during storage of

urine and feces. Sacral parasympathetic inputs to the bladder are carried in the pelvic nerve; sacral somatic inputs to external sphincter muscles are carried in the pudendal nerve.

As the bladder fills, a constant low intravesical pressure is maintained because of the inherent properties of the smooth muscle. Urine is retained in the bladder by both the changes in configuration of the internal urethral sphincter and the contraction of the external urethral sphincters. This "continence system" involves lumbar sympathetic and sacral sphincter motor neurons activated by afferents from the bladder and pelvic floor; these neurons favor urine storage by producing relaxation of the bladder detrusor and contraction of the external sphincter. With increased stretch of the smooth muscle of the bladder, proprioceptive information, which gives rise to the feeling of bladder fullness, is carried to pontine micturition centers and to sacral reflex centers.

Normally, the coordinated activity of the bladder detrusor and external sphincter during micturition depends on supraspinal input from pontine micturition centers. Activity in these centers causes excitation of the sacral parasympathetic neurons innervating the bladder detrusor and inhibition of the sacral motor neurons innervating the external sphincter. This coordination of bladder detrusor contraction and external sphincter relaxation allows complete bladder emptying. Interruption of descending pathways from the pontine centers leads to reflex but incoordinated activity of the sacral preganglionic and sphincter motor neurons, a condition called *detrusor-sphincter dysynergia* (see Fig. 9-22).

Clinical Correlations

Diseases at the spinal level, like those at other levels, can be classified as focal or diffuse. *Focal disease* at the spinal level may be *segmental* with symptoms and signs at only one level, as in lesions of the spinal nerve in the intervertebral foramen. Or focal disease at the spinal level may present with a combination of *segmental* and *longitudinal* symptoms and signs, if there is involvement of the ascending or descending pathways in the spinal cord along with the segmental structures.

Diffuse disease in the spinal level may involve only a *single system* such as the motor system in motor neuron disease or the ventriculosubarachnoid system in meningitis. Or it may involve *multiple systems,* as in some degenerative and inflammatory disorders.

Focal Disorders at the Spinal Level

Focal lesions at the spinal level are characterized by segmental signs or symptoms specific for a particular level of the spinal canal. These may be due to damage to a spinal nerve, a dorsal or ventral nerve root, a single vertebra, or a spinal cord function found only at a single level.

Segmental Localization

Lesions of the spinal nerves are often due to (or related to) disease of the vertebral column and are at the spinal level. However, many of their clinical features are similar to those of peripheral nerve lesions. Lesions of the spinal nerves are recognized by their pattern of distribution. They are associated with motor, sensory, autonomic, and reflex changes.

1. *Motor involvement.* These are the findings of lower motor neuron damage, that is, lesions affecting the final common pathway (Table 14-7). There is flaccid weakness in a myotomal distribution. When present for sufficient duration, there is associated atrophy. There also may be fasciculation and fibrillation in muscles in the appropriate myotome. Because the lesion is proximal to the origin of the posterior primary ramus of the spinal nerve, the paraspinal muscles are involved as well as other proximal muscles (see Table 14-1). This involvement is in contrast to lesions that involve the peripheral nerve.
2. *Sensory involvement.* There is sensory loss in a dermatomal distribution, a loss usually best recognized in regard to pain, temperature, or touch. There may be paresthesia from spontaneous firing of the larger axons or dysesthesia from abnormal firing of large and small axons. Spontaneous pain in a dermatomal distribution is common and

Table 14-7. Summary of Findings in Upper and Lower Motor Neuron Lesions

Finding	Upper motor neuron[a]	Lower motor neuron[b]
Strength	Decreased	Decreased
Tone	Increased	Decreased
Deep tendon reflexes	Increased	Decreased
Superficial reflexes	Decreased	Decreased
Babinski's sign	Present	Absent
Clonus	Present	Absent
Fasciculations	Absent	Present
Atrophy	Absent	Present

[a]Involves direct and indirect activation pathways.
[b]Involves final common pathway.

is probably due to local swelling, edema, and ionic changes in the spinal nerve, with spontaneous firing of small pain fibers. The pain is often perceived beyond the distribution of the spinal nerve because of intraspinal spread of electrical activity (referred pain). Irritable spinal nerves are more sensitive to stretch, and pain is produced when the extremities are put in certain positions, as for example, when a leg is put through a straight leg raising test.

3. *Autonomic involvement.* Autonomic fibers also are involved, but because of their more extensive overlapping, autonomic disturbances do not occur with lesions of single spinal nerves. Bilateral sacral spinal nerve or cauda equina damage, however, may result in abnormalities of bladder function.
4. *Reflex involvement.* Peripheral reflexes may be lost if either the motor or the sensory component of the reflex arc is damaged. They are, therefore, an important sign of spinal nerve disease (Table 14-8).

The term *radiculopathy* refers specifically to disease of the nerve root that is located within the vertebral column and spinal canal. Localized nerve root disease produces purely motor or purely sensory deficits, depending on whether the ventral or dorsal root is affected. However, the nerve roots have the same segmental derivation as the spinal nerves, and it is common usage to refer to disease of the spinal nerve (in which the dorsal and ventral roots have joined) as radiculopathy.

Table 14-8. Deep Tendon Reflexes

Reflex	Spinal nerves*	Plexus	Peripheral nerves
Biceps jerk	C-5, C-6	Brachial	Musculocutaneous
Triceps jerk	C-7, C-8	Brachial	Radial
Knee jerk	L-3, L-4	Lumbar	Femoral
Ankle jerk	L-5, S-1	Sacral	Sciatic, tibial

*Spinal nerves underlined provide the major innervation.

Localization to a specific spinal level may be on the basis of:

1. Local anterior root or anterior horn signs such as segmental atrophy, flaccid weakness, hypotonia, or some combination of these.
2. Local sensory abnormalities such as segmental (radicular) loss of all modalities of sensation.
3. Local segmental loss or depression of deep tendon reflexes due to interruption of the stretch reflex arc. This may occur because of damage to efferent or afferent limbs of the reflex arc.
4. Segmental signs of vertebral column involvement. Occasionally, this may be seen as localized pain and tenderness of a vertebra, but more commonly it depends on radiographic visualization of a structural abnormality at one level.
5. Segmental signs of bladder involvement, such as evidence of a nuclear lesion in the conus of the spinal cord or an infranuclear lesion in the cauda equina with an autonomous (nonreflex) bladder, loss of voluntary control, loss of anal reflex, and large residual urine.

In the absence of specific signs of spinal cord involvement, it may be difficult to distinguish a purely segmental lesion at the spinal level from a more peripheral disorder. However, if the lesion is in the distribution of a single spinal nerve, it can be assumed to be at the spinal level or within the vertebral column (see Chapter 13, The Peripheral Level). Other clues to a lesion at this level are the presence of bilateral abnormalities, the presence of proximal involvement such as in the paraspinal muscles, and signs of meningeal or subarachnoid involvement such as Brudzinski's sign (in which neck flexion with leg extension produces pain).

Intersegmental Localization
The most convincing evidence of a focal lesion at the spinal level is the combined presence of segmental signs of the type previously described in association with *intersegmental signs* due to involvement of the long ascending or descending pathways of the spinal cord. There are three major types of intersegmental signs that appear with focal diseases in the spinal canal:

1. A long tract motor level. These findings are those of an upper motor neuron lesion that involves the direct and indirect pathways (see Table 14-7). They are spastic paralysis, increased deep tendon reflexes, and Babinski's sign below the level of the lesion. Other abnormal reflexes due to damage of the direct and indirect activation pathways also may be seen, such as loss of the abdominal reflexes, flexion reflexes, and crossed extension reflexes.
2. A long tract sensory level. This level is indicated by posterior column or lateral spinothalamic tract deficits on the appropriate side below the level of the lesion.
3. Autonomic disturbances below the level of the lesion. The most striking is reflex (upper motor neuron or automatic) neurogenic bladder dysfunction, with incontinence due to contractions of a spastic bladder (Table 14-9). There also may be other evidence of autonomic disturbances, such as loss of blood pressure control, abnormalities of sweating, and loss of rectal control.

Combinations of segmental and long tract signs permit the identification of the site of

Table 14-9. Neurogenic Bladder

	Type	
	Reflex (upper motor neuron or automatic)	Nonreflex (lower motor neuron or autonomous)
Anal and bulbocavernous reflexes	Present	Absent
Clinical features		
Urgency	Yes	No
Incontinence	Yes	Yes
Retention	Yes	Yes
Detrusor sphincter dysynergia	Yes	No
Urodynamics		
Tone	Spastic	Flaccid
Uninhibited contractions	Yes	No
Capacity	Decreased	Increased
Denervation supersensitivity	No	Yes
Examples of lesions	Spinal cord lesion	Conus medullaris or cauda equina lesion

cord disease with some accuracy. Some characteristic patterns of abnormality are:

1. Upper cervical. This pattern includes long tract signs in the upper and lower extremities for motor and sensory modalities and a reflex bladder dysfunction.
2. Middle and lower cervical. Segmental signs of motor and sensory dysfunction appear in the upper extremities, along with long tract signs in the lower extremities and reflex bladder dysfunction.
3. Thoracic. Long tract signs in the lower extremities appear with a segmental sensory finding (level of sensation) in the trunk and a reflex bladder dysfunction.
4. Lumbar and upper sacral. This pattern includes segmental motor and sensory signs in the lower extremities with a reflex bladder dysfunction.
5. Conus medullaris. Segmental signs appear in the lower extremities with a nonreflex (lower motor neuron or autonomous) bladder disturbance.
6. Cauda equina. There is pain and asymmetric motor and sensory involvement of multiple roots with or without a nonreflex bladder.

Spinal Shock

Focal lesions may be acute, subacute, or chronic. An acute lesion of the spinal cord may be accompanied by *spinal shock,* which may mask some of the signs previously outlined. Spinal shock occurs when the spinal cord is suddenly severely damaged or there is an acute transection of the spinal cord, after which all cord functions and reflexes below the level of the transection become depressed or lost. The normal activity of spinal cord neurons depends to a great extent on continual tonic discharges from higher centers, particularly discharges transmitted through the vestibulospinal tract and the excitatory portion of the reticulospinal tracts. The acute loss of this input results in loss of neuronal activity.

After a few days to a few weeks, the spinal neurons gradually regain their excitability. This is characteristic of neurons in the nervous system — that is, after loss of facilitatory impulses, they increase in excitability. In most nonprimates, the excitability of the cord centers returns to normal within a few hours to a few weeks, but in humans, the return often may be delayed for several months and occasionally is never complete. However, in some patients, the recovery of excitability is excessive, with hyperexcitability of reflexes.

Some major functions are affected by spinal shock. The arterial blood pressure rapidly decreases, sometimes to as low as 40 mm Hg, with loss of sympathetic activity. The pressure ordinarily returns to normal within a few days. All muscle reflexes are blocked during

Table 14-10. Effects of Lesions at Spinal Cord Segments

Segment	Deficit	Independence	Aids required
C-4, C-5	Quadriplegia Impaired respiration Reflex bladder	None	Wheelchair Constant care
C-6, C-7	Quadriplegia	Minimal	Wheelchair Hand splints
C-8, T-1	Impaired respiration Reflex bladder Paraplegia Hand weakness	Personal care Drives car	Wheelchair Special braces
T-2, T-3	Impaired respiration Reflex bladder Paraplegia	Complete	Wheelchair Leg braces
T-12, L-1	Paraplegia Reflex bladder	Complete	Wheelchair Leg braces
L-4, L-5	Paraplegia Reflex bladder	Complete	Foot braces
S-2, S-3	Nonreflex bladder	Complete	Catheter

the initial stages of shock. Some reflexes eventually become hyperexcitable, particularly if a few facilitatory pathways remain intact between the brain and the cord. The sacral reflexes for control of bladder and colon evacuation are suppressed in humans for the first few weeks after cord transection, but eventually they return.

The first reflexes to reappear are flexion reflexes, especially in response to stimulation of the plantar surface of the foot (Babinski's sign). After 3 to 4 weeks, flexion reflexes can be triggered from a broader area and are more generalized. After several months, hyperexcitability has developed to the point that plantar stimulation may induce flexion responses on both sides of the body as well as profuse autonomic discharge (for example, sweating, contractions of bladder and rectum). Such mass reflexes may occur even with no obvious source of stimulation. Even after flexion reflexes reappear, the limbs remain flaccid in the absence of tonic stretch reflex activation. After several months, a return of muscle tone and tendon reflexes may occur.

After recovery from spinal shock, a patient who has suffered a major spinal cord injury is left with major deficits that are a function of the level of the lesion. The primary task of the physician, after localizing a lesion and minimizing the damage, is to enable the patient to achieve maximal use of whatever residual function remains. Some of the effects of spinal cord lesions are listed in Table 14-10.

Transverse lesions of the spinal cord can be further localized in a cord cross section. In chronic or subacute lesions, it is often necessary to localize a lesion in this manner in order to identify the most likely type of lesion. It is of particular importance to determine if a lesion is *extrinsic* (extramedullary) or *intrinsic* (intramedullary). Extrinsic lesions arise outside the substance of the spinal cord and compress it. These are more common than intrinsic lesions and often can be removed surgically, with recovery of some or all functions.

Extrinsic lesions commonly damage the dorsal or ventral roots and are therefore usually associated with radicular pain. Because the dorsal root ganglion contains the cell bodies that maintain the axons traveling both peripherally and centrally in the sensory system, the destruction of it can result in wallerian degeneration in both the peripheral nerves and the central pathways. In contrast, a lesion that destroys the dorsal root proximal to the ganglion produces sensory loss and reflex loss, with degeneration in the central processes but not in the peripheral nerve. Destruction of the root distal to the ganglion produces the same clinical symptoms and signs but is associated with peripheral but not central wallerian degeneration. The presence or absence of peripheral wallerian degeneration often can be determined by electrical studies of patients. Ventral root damage produces degeneration of the peripheral nerves, with associated reflex loss, atrophy, and weakness.

Intrinsic lesions arise within the substance of the spinal cord and often spare the more peripheral pathways of the spinal cord. Although sensory symptoms are prominent, they are often painless. A review of Figure 14-7 shows that the pathways of the lumbar and sacral segments in the spinothalamic and corticospinal tracts are more superficial. Intrinsic lesions preferentially damage the pathways from higher levels and may manifest sacral sparing, in which the long tract signs spare the most caudal segments, because they are more laterally placed in the cord. A syrinx or tumor in the cervical cord gray matter may produce sacral sparing.

Localization is aided by knowledge of the decussations of the pathways. Because the spinothalamic pathways cross to the opposite side within two or three segments of their entry, a lesion of one side of the spinal cord produces dissociation of the sensations of pain and temperature (lost contralaterally below the lesion), from position and vibration (lost ipsilaterally below the lesion). Similarly, a lesion in the region of the central canal destroys the spinothalamic fibers decussating in the anterior commissure and gives segmental loss of pain and temperature, with segmental signs of motor neuron destruction if the lesion extends into the ventral horns, but sparing of other modalities of sensation.

Focal disorders of the spinal cord may be either mass or nonmass in type. The same criteria applied at other levels can be used to differentiate a mass from a nonmass. In the clinical history, progression favors a mass, as does the presence of distortion, destruction of tissue, or obstruction of the subarachnoid spaces on special studies (myelography). The pathologic changes can be identified by the temporal profile and may include vascular lesions (infarct of the cord, arteriovenous malformations, hematomas) (Fig. 14-16), neo-

Fig. 14-16. Magnetic resonance image (lateral view) of spinal cord showing a tumor (*arrow*) (hemangioblastoma of the thoracic cord).

plastic diseases (tumors of the nerve roots, intramedullary or extramedullary cord tumors), inflammatory disease (poliomyelitis, abscess, arachnoiditis), and traumatic lesions (cord transection, ruptured intervertebral disks) (Fig. 14-17). Focal lesions are typically single. However, in multiple sclerosis, there are multifocal lesions that can produce complex findings.

Multiple Sclerosis
This is a disorder associated with localized areas of demyelination in the white matter of the central nervous system (Fig. 14-18). Although spinal cord involvement is common, the lesions also may appear in the white matter of the brain stem, cerebellum, and cerebrum. The focal lesions develop over a few days, and the symptoms may resolve over a few days to weeks or leave a persistent deficit. They occur in scattered areas to produce a *multifocal* disorder. The disease is of unknown cause, but its subacute course, some of the histologic features, and laboratory findings suggest that it may be an autoimmune disorder with inflammatory features. The areas of demyelination vary in size from a few millimeters to several centimeters in diameter

Fig. 14-17. Magnetic resonance image of thoracic cord showing a traumatic transection of the cord (*arrow*).

Fig. 14-18. Sections of spinal cord showing multifocal areas of demyelination in a patient with multiple sclerosis.

and show myelin breakdown, with preservation of the axis cylinders (see Fig. 4-22). In the acute lesions, there may be perivascular infiltrations of lymphocytes. Later during the course of a lesion, there are predominantly macrophages phagocytosing the myelin products. As the lesion resolves, it becomes gliotic. Severe lesions may be associated with axonal destruction, and the disorder may clinically appear to be degenerative late in the course as remissions no longer occur. The clinical history of multiple sclerosis is one of recurrent episodes of deficit in widespread areas, corresponding to the intermittent occurrence of such lesions in disseminated areas. Any single such lesion in the spinal cord could be associated with segmental signs at the level of the lesion, or with longitudinal tract deficits below the level, or with both.

Diffuse Disorders at the Spinal Level

Diffuse disorders of the spinal canal are generally chronic and progressive, thus suggesting a degenerative cause. These may involve a single system or multiple systems. Motor neuron diseases (amyotrophic lateral sclerosis or progressive muscular atrophy) are examples of diffuse single system disorders in the spinal cord. In motor neuron disease, there is a progressive destruction of the motor neurons in the anterior horn of the spinal cord, with or without degeneration of neurons in the direct and indirect activation pathways (see Chapter 8, The Motor System).

However, not all diffuse, progressive system diseases of the spinal level (or elsewhere) are degenerative. *Combined system disease* is a motor and sensory system degeneration affecting the posterior and lateral columns that is due to vitamin B_{12} deficiency (Fig. 14-19). The major pathologic change is that of demyelination of these regions. If the metabolic defect persists, the process becomes more severe, with axonal destruction and necrosis but little gliosis initially. In patients with long-duration, progressive disease who are

Fig. 14-19. Section of thoracic spinal cord showing demyelination of posterior columns secondary to pernicious anemia.

not treated, gliosis also develops. There is often peripheral nerve and cerebral involvement as well. These lesions result in the clinical pattern of a slowly progressive sensory ataxia, with upper motor neuron signs, some lower motor neuron signs (depressed ankle reflexes), paresthesia, and occasionally dementia. The disorder is also often associated with macrocytic anemia (pernicious anemia) that is also due to vitamin B_{12} deficiency. The reclassification of this degenerative disease as a metabolic disorder due to a nutritional deficiency was a major medical advance. It can be hoped that other degenerative disorders seen in a neurologic practice will soon have their causes determined in the same way, to permit appropriate treatment.

Spinal nerve lesions as described thus far have been lesions of single spinal nerves. There also may be diffuse involvement of spinal nerves in *polyradiculopathy*. Although polyradiculopathy may be difficult to recognize clinically, demonstrating the involvement of paraspinal muscles at multiple levels by EMG is strong evidence of it. Proximal weakness, which is more commonly seen in muscle disease, may also occur in polyradiculopathy, but usually there are additional abnormalities such as reflex and sensory loss. One form of polyradiculopathy is the Guillain-Barré syndrome, a subacute, inflammatory disorder that produces segmental demyelination predominantly in nerve roots.

Objectives

1. Name and identify the four major longitudinal subdivisions and the six major horizontal subdivisions at the spinal level.
2. Describe the differences in the horizontal components at the four longitudinal subdivisions.
3. Describe the relationship of cord segment to spinal nerve and vertebrae.
4. Name the longitudinal systems found at the spinal level, and describe the location of each.
5. Describe the different types of cells in the spinal cord, their distribution, and their function.
6. Describe reciprocal inhibition, recurrent inhibition, presynaptic inhibition, and spinal shock.
7. Describe with examples the stretch reflexes and flexion reflexes.
8. List the symptoms and signs associated with lesions of the spinal cord at C-6, T-6, L-5, and S-2.
9. List the features that differentiate an extramedullary lesion from an intramedullary lesion.
10. List the major clinicopathologic features of multiple sclerosis and pernicious anemia.
11. List the spinal nerves and cord segments that mediate the biceps, triceps, knee, and ankle reflexes.

Clinical Problems

1. A 55-year-old man underwent surgery for carcinoma of the prostate 1 year ago. Six days ago, while watching TV after a big meal, he found that he was unable to walk when he tried to arise from the couch. There was no pain or trauma.

    On examination, the mental status, cranial nerves, and upper extremities were normal. There was a severe flaccid paralysis, with hypotonia of the lower abdominal muscles, hip flexors, hip adductors, and knee extensors. There was a moderate weakness of other muscles of the lower extremities but with some increase in tone (spastic). Reflexes were normal in the arms, absent at the abdomen and knees, and hyperactive at the ankles. He had Babinski's sign bilaterally and loss of sensation for pain and temperature over both lower extremities. Position, vibration, and two-point discrimination were normal. All findings were symmetric.

a. What is the level, side, and type of lesion?

b. What is the longitudinal and horizontal location of the lesion?

c. Is the conus medullaris involved in the lesion?

d. What type of bladder dysfunction would occur with lesions of the lumbar cord and sacral cord?

e. What is the most likely cause?

2. A 60-year-old woman first noted numbness of all fingers of the right hand 2½ years ago. Clumsiness of the right hand developed shortly thereafter. Defective appreciation of temperature with the right hand had been noted 1½ years ago; and 7 months before her admission, a similar numbness of all fingers of the left hand developed. At the same time, a stiffness of both lower extremities was noted, accompanied by an unsteadiness on rapid turning.

On neurologic examination, the mental status and cranial nerves were intact. Fasciculations and a minor degree of atrophy were present in muscles of both shoulders. Fasciculations were not present in the lower extremities. Strength was decreased bilaterally as follows: moderate weakness in shoulder abductors and elbow flexors and extensors. There was a marked weakness of intrinsic hand muscles. The lower extremities had minimal weakness. Spasticity was noted on passive motion in the lower extremities and her gait was spastic. The triceps, quadriceps, and Achilles reflexes were increased bilaterally. Plantar responses were extensor bilaterally. Abdominal reflexes were absent. Pain and temperature were decreased at the C-4 to T-1 segments bilaterally, with total loss in her right hand and lower arm. In these segments, touch sensation was intact.

a. What is the level and type of lesion?

b. Which systems and which subdivisions of each are involved?

c. Which cord segments are involved and in what horizontal location?

d. What is the most likely cause?

3. A 52-year-old woman is hospitalized because of ataxia and mental symptoms. She is unable to give a history, but her husband relates that for the past 3 years she has complained of a "pins and needles" sensation in her feet and hands that gradually spread to her knees and elbows. For the past 18 months, she has had a progressive gait ataxia and weakness of the legs. For about the same length of time, she has had mental symptoms. At first, she was irritable and uncooperative. At present, she has impaired memory, thinks her husband is trying to poison her, and is confused at night. She is also incontinent of urine and stool.

On examination, she is demented and is ataxic when she walks. The Romberg sign is positive. Both legs are moderately and symmetrically weak. Tendon reflexes are normal in the arms and absent in the legs. Babinski's sign is present bilaterally. Position sense is impaired in her toes. Vibration sense is absent in her legs. Touch, pain, and temperature sensations are not significantly impaired. She has a bladder catheter in place.

a. What is the location and type of lesion?

b. Which sensory pathways are involved?

c. Why are tendon reflexes absent and Babinski's sign present?

d. What is one identifiable cause for certain neurologic disorders previously classified as "degenerative" diseases?

4. A 30-year-old man had an acute onset of severe back and right leg pain after falling while carrying a sack of bagels. His symptoms have worsened over the 4 weeks since onset. On examination, there is a slight hypalgesia on the lateral aspect of his leg. Reflexes are normal. There is mild weakness of hip abductors, hamstrings, ankle dorsiflexors, and toe extensors on the right. He experiences severe pain when he coughs or when his leg is elevated.

a. What is the site and type of lesion?

b. What neural structure is involved?

c. In a patient with footdrop, at what sites could the lesion be located?

d. What produces pain on straight leg raising?

Additional Reading

Adams, R. D., and Victor, M. (eds.). *Principles of Neurology* (4th ed.). New York: McGraw-Hill, 1989.

Brookhart, J. M., et al. (eds). *Handbook of Physiology.* Section 1: The Nervous System. Vol. II: Motor Control. Part 1. Bethesda, MD: American Physiological Society, 1981.

Burke, D. Spasticity as an adaptation to pyramidal tract injury. *Adv. Neurol.* 47:401, 1988.

Davidoff, R. A. Skeletal muscle tone and the misunderstood stretch reflex. *Neurology* 42:951, 1992.

Kandel, E. R., Schwartz, J. H., and Jessell, T. M. *Principles of Neural Science* (3rd ed.). New York: Elsevier, 1991.

Woolsey, R. M., and Young R. R. (eds.). Disorders of the spinal cord. *Neurol. Clin.* 9 (3), 1991.

— 15 —

The Posterior Fossa Level

The posterior fossa level contains all the structures located within the skull below the tentorium cerebelli and above the foramen magnum (Fig. 15-1). These structures are derivatives of the embryonic mesencephalon, metencephalon, and myelencephalon and include portions of all the systems discussed earlier. The major structures of this level are the brain stem (medulla, pons, and midbrain), the cerebellum, and segments of cranial nerves III through XII, before their emergence from the skull. The brain stem, the central core of the posterior fossa level, is a specialized rostral extension of the embryonic neural tube that preserves, even in the mature state, many of the longitudinal or intersegmental features found in the spinal cord and also provides for the segmental functions of the head.

This chapter describes the general features of each major longitudinal system as they relate to the posterior fossa level and discusses in further detail the cranial nerves and internal anatomy of the medulla, pons, midbrain, and cerebellum. Three additional systems (oculomotor, auditory, and vestibular), which are located primarily at this level, are introduced and described.

Overview

The brain stem contains ascending and descending pathways traveling to the thalamus, hypothalamus, cerebral cortex, cerebellum, cranial nerve nuclei, and spinal cord. The main sensory pathways include those that originate in the spinal cord (the spinothalamic tracts, medial lemniscus, and the spinocer- ebellar pathways), as well as those that arise from the cranial nerve nuclei (the descending tract of the trigeminal nerve, the trigeminal-thalamic tract, and the lateral lemniscus). The main motor pathways include the direct activation pathways (the corticospinal and corticobulbar pathways) and the indirect activation pathways (reticulospinal, rubrospinal, and vestibulospinal pathways). Additional important intersegmental pathways found at this level include the medial longitudinal fasciculus, the ascending and descending fibers of the consciousness and internal regulation systems, and many of the structures of the oculomotor, auditory, and vestibular systems.

It is traditional to subdivide the brain stem into three parts: the medulla (derived from myelencephalon), which contains the motor neurons for swallowing, tongue movement, talking, and certain visceral motor functions; the pons (derived from metencephalon), which contains the nuclei associated with motor, sensory, and parasympathetic innervation of the face and abduction of the eye; and the midbrain (derived from mesencephalon), which contains the nuclei of the ascending reticular activating system, the nuclei that govern eye movements (except abduction), and the fibers involved in pupillary constriction and accommodation.

Although the tubular configuration of the central nervous system is greatly altered in the brain stem, the general relationships described above between systems developing in the inner tube region (primitive, indirect, diffuse) and the outer tube region (newer, direct, discrete) can still be discerned. The anatomical structure that typifies the former is the reticular forma-

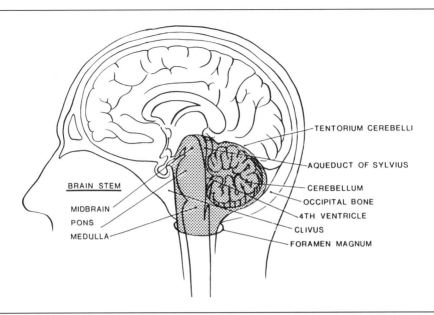

Fig. 15-1. Posterior fossa (*stippled area*) is bordered by foramen magnum, tentorium cerebelli, clivus, and occipital bones.

tion, a complex group of nuclei and interconnections that extends throughout the core of the brain stem. In each of the three major subdivisions of the brain stem, the reticular formation is divided into medial, intermediate, and lateral zones. The relative importance of these zones and the functions they subserve differs at each level. The major functional components of the reticular formation are discussed in the following sections that deal with each of the subdivisions of the brain stem.

The brain stem has 10 pairs of cranial nerves (Fig. 15-2), which perform segmental functions comparable to the functions of the spinal nerves. The portions of these nerves contained within the cranium are considered part of the posterior fossa level, and the segments distal to the bones of the skull are considered part of the peripheral level. The location and general function of the cranial nerves at the posterior fossa level are summarized in Table 15-1.

The *cerebellum* (a derivative of metencephalon) lies dorsal to the pons and medulla and consists of a midline vermis and two lateral hemispheres. The cerebellum is functionally and anatomically divided into three lobes: the flocculonodular lobe, responsible for equilibration and balance; the anterior lobe, responsible for gait and posture; and the large

posterior lobe, responsible for coordinated movements of the extremities.

The cerebrospinal fluid system is represented at the posterior fossa level by the aqueduct of Sylvius, the fourth ventricle, the meninges, the extraventricular subarachnoid cisterns, and the cerebrospinal fluid itself. The entire blood supply to the posterior fossa level is derived from the vertebrobasilar arterial system supplying paramedian, short, and long circumferential arteries to the brain stem and cerebellum. The major long circumferential arteries are the posterior inferior cerebellar arteries at the medullary level, the anterior inferior cerebellar arteries at the pontine level, and the superior cerebellar artery at the level of the midbrain.

The major components of three additional systems are also found at this level. The oculomotor system is represented by cranial nerve nuclei III, IV, and VI; their axons traveling toward the extraocular muscles; the medial longitudinal fasciculus; and the fibers for supranuclear control of eye movement descending from the cortex. The auditory system is represented by the auditory nerves, cochlear nuclei, trapezoid bodies, and multiple bilateral pathways that ascend to the inferior colliculi en route to the thalamus and temporal

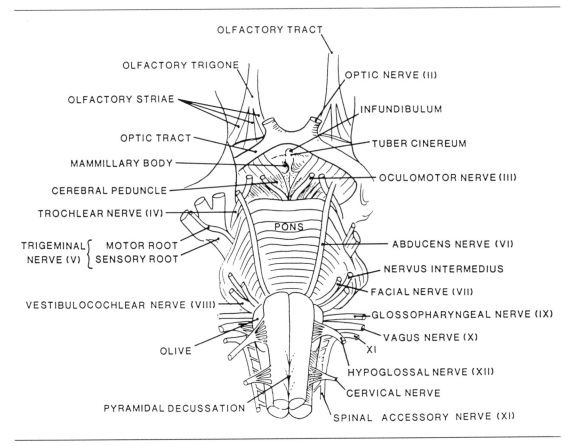

Fig. 15-2. Ventral (anterior) view of brain stem showing the cranial nerves. (Only cranial nerves III through XII are at the posterior fossa level.)

Table 15-1. The Location and General Function of Cranial Nerves at the Posterior Fossa Level

Level	Cranial nerve	General function
Medulla	XII Hypoglossal	Motor to muscles of tongue
	XI Spinal accessory	Motor to sternocleidomastoid and trapezius muscles
	X Vagus	Motor to muscles of soft palate, pharynx, and larynx; parasympathetic fibers to thoracic and abdominal viscera; sensory fibers from pharynx and external auditory meatus; visceral sensory fibers from thoracic and abdominal cavities
	IX Glossopharyngeal	Motor to stylopharyngeus muscle; sensory from pharynx and tongue; taste from posterior tongue
Pons	VIII Vestibulocochlear	Hearing and equilibration
	VII Facial	Motor to muscles of facial expression; parasympathetic to salivary glands; taste from anterior tongue
	VI Abducens	Motor to lateral rectus muscle of eye
	V Trigeminal	Sensory from face; motor to muscles of mastication
Midbrain	IV Trochlear	Motor to superior oblique muscle of eye
	III Oculomotor	Motor to medial, superior, and inferior recti, and inferior oblique muscles of eye, and levator palpebrae of eyelid; parasympathetic to constrictors of pupil

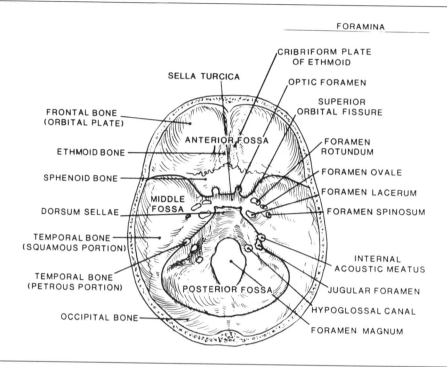

FORAMINA

CRIBRIFORM PLATE
OF ETHMOID

OPTIC FORAMEN

SELLA TURCICA

SUPERIOR
ORBITAL FISSURE

FRONTAL BONE
(ORBITAL PLATE)

ANTERIOR FOSSA

FORAMEN
ROTUNDUM

ETHMOID BONE

FORAMEN OVALE

SPHENOID BONE

FORAMEN LACERUM

MIDDLE
FOSSA

FORAMEN SPINOSUM

DORSUM SELLAE

TEMPORAL BONE
(SQUAMOUS PORTION)

INTERNAL
ACOUSTIC MEATUS

TEMPORAL BONE
(PETROUS PORTION)

POSTERIOR FOSSA

JUGULAR FORAMEN

HYPOGLOSSAL CANAL

OCCIPITAL BONE

FORAMEN MAGNUM

Fig. 15-3. Base of skull with major bones and foramina.

cortex. The vestibular system is represented by the vestibular nerves, vestibular nuclei, and their multiple connections with the cerebellum, spinal cord, medial longitudinal fasciculus, and structures at the supratentorial level.

Lesions can be precisely localized at the posterior fossa level when there is a combination of intersegmental and segmental involvement. Lesions at the posterior fossa level are unique in that unilateral brain stem lesions may produce involvement of the ipsilateral side of the face and the contralateral side of the body. Other types of neurologic dysfunction that help localize a lesion at the posterior fossa level are disturbances of cerebellar function or involvement of the intracranial portions of cranial nerves III through XII.

General Anatomy of the Posterior Fossa Level

Posterior Cranial Fossa and Tentorium

The posterior cranial fossa is formed by the occipital bones at the base of the skull and the temporal bones anteriorly and laterally (Fig.

15-3). The inferior limit of the posterior fossa is the foramen magnum, where the cervical cord merges with the medulla. The rostral limit of the posterior fossa is the tentorium cerebelli, which lies between the cerebellum and the occipital lobe. The tentorium is attached posteriorly and posterolaterally to the transverse sinus and anterolaterally to the petrous ridge. The anterior border is not attached to bone but forms the tentorial notch, through which the midbrain passes to merge with the diencephalon.

Systems Contained in the Posterior Fossa Level

The neural structures of the posterior fossa level consist of cranial nerves III through XII, the midbrain, pons, medulla, and cerebellum. Each of the previously studied systems is represented at the posterior fossa level.

The Cerebrospinal Fluid System

Cerebrospinal fluid flows into the posterior fossa in the *aqueduct of Sylvius,* a narrow canal in the midbrain between the third and fourth ventricles. The fourth ventricle is located at the level of the medulla and pons, which form the ventricular floor. The roof of the fourth ventricle is the ventral midline portion of the cerebellum. Cerebrospinal fluid leaves the fourth ventricle through the foramen of Magendie (at the caudal end of the ventricle) and through the two foramina of Luschka (at each lateral angle of the ventricle) to enter the subarachnoid space, where it circulates through the cisterna magna, cerebellopontine, prepontine, interpeduncular, and ambient cisterns.

The Sensory System
The brain stem contains ascending pathways mediating (1) pain and temperature (spinothalamic); (2) conscious proprioception and discriminative sensation (dorsal column–lemniscal); (3) unconscious proprioception (ventral and dorsal spinocerebellar); and (4) touch (spinothalamic and dorsal column–lemniscal). In addition, sensory input from the face and head enters at this level.

The Consciousness System
The central core of the brain stem contains the reticular formation and its ascending projectional pathways. The brain stem, along with other areas of the nervous system, thus serves the important function of mediating consciousness, attention, and sleeping and waking cycles.

The Motor System
All subdivisions of the motor system are represented at the posterior fossa level. The lower motor neurons of several of the cranial nerves contain the final common pathway to muscles of the head and neck. The direct activation pathways are represented by the corticospinal tracts, which descend through the brain stem and decussate in the lower medulla en route to the spinal cord, and the corticobulbar pathways, which provide supranuclear innervation to brain stem motor nuclei. The indirect activation pathways in the brain stem consist of short multineuronal descending pathways of the reticulospinal, rubrospinal, and vestibulospinal tracts arising in the brain stem. Much of the cerebellar control circuit is located at this level, and portions of the basal

ganglia control circuit (substantia nigra and red nucleus) are present in the midbrain.

Internal Regulation System
The posterior fossa contains visceral sensory relay nuclei (particularly the nucleus of the tractus solitarius), the reticular formation, and preganglionic parasympathetic neurons. The intermediate zone of the medullary reticular formation contains interneurons and neurons that project to preganglionic sympathetic neurons and to spinal motor neurons controlling respiration. The lateral zone contains the central pattern generator, which integrates complex motor patterns involving multiple cranial nerves to produce such actions as swallowing and vomiting. In addition to the reticular formation and the ascending and descending pathways that regulate visceral function, the posterior fossa level contains the preganglionic parasympathetic fibers carried in cranial nerves III, VII, IX, and X.

The Vascular System
The structures in the posterior fossa receive their blood supply from the vertebrobasilar arterial system (Fig. 15-4). The vertebral arteries enter the cranial cavity through the foramen magnum and then course rostrally along the ventrolateral surface of the medulla, where they give off branches to form the anterior spinal artery, which descends on the ventral aspect of the lower medulla to the cervical spinal cord. At the level of the pons, the two vertebral arteries merge to form the basilar artery, which continues rostrally to the upper midbrain level, where it branches to form the posterior cerebral arteries.

Branches of the vertebral and basilar arteries are subdivided into three groups that supply each level of the brain stem and the cerebellum. The paramedian zone on either side of the midline is supplied by paramedian branches, the *intermediate zone* is supplied by short circumferential branches, and the lateral zone is supplied by long circumferential branches (Fig. 15-5). The *paramedian* and *lateral zones* are often involved by vascular lesions, with significant clinical deficit. The paramedian area of the medulla is supplied by paramedian branches of the anterior spinal artery, while the intermediate zone is supplied

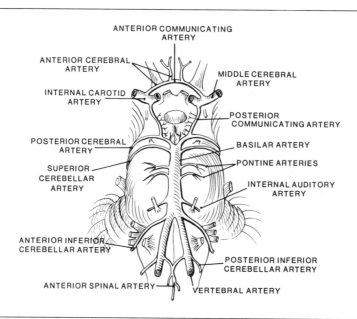

Fig. 15-4. Blood supply of posterior fossa structures from the vertebral and basilar arteries.

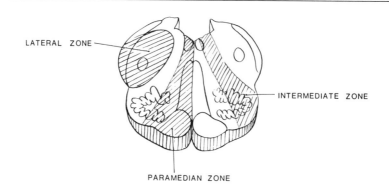

Fig. 15-5. Blood supply of the medulla. Lateral zone is from the posterior inferior cerebellar artery, paramedian zone from the anterior spinal artery, and intermediate zone from the vertebral artery.

by the vertebral arteries. The paramedian areas of the pons and midbrain are supplied by the paramedian branches of the basilar artery. The lateral areas of the brain stem are supplied by three pairs of long circumferential arteries: the *posterior inferior cerebellar artery* arising from the vertebral arteries and supplying the lateral area of the medulla and posterior inferior aspect of the cerebellum; the *anterior inferior cerebellar artery,* a branch of the basilar artery that supplies the lateral area of

the pons and the anterior inferior aspect of the cerebellum; and the *superior cerebellar artery,* a branch of the basilar artery that supplies the lateral area of the midbrain and superior surface of the cerebellum.

Three additional special systems are found primarily at the posterior fossa level: (1) the oculomotor system, which mediates eye movement; (2) the auditory system, which mediates hearing; and (3) the vestibular system, which mediates balance and equilibrium.

Fig. 15-6. Alar and basal plates of brain stem at the level of the medulla in 5-week (*left*) and 10-week (*right*) embryo (see Table 15-2).

Table 15-2. Components of the Cranial Nerves

Component	Function	Cranial nerve
Efferent	Motor	
General somatic efferent (GSE)	Somatic striated muscles	III, IV, VI, XII
General visceral efferent (GVE)	Parasympathetic glands and smooth muscles	III, VII, IX, X
Special visceral efferent (SVE)	Branchial arch muscles	V, VII, IX, X, XI
Afferent	Sensory	
General somatic afferent (GSA)	Somesthetic senses	V, IX, X
Special somatic afferent (SSA)	Hearing and balance, vision	II, VIII
General visceral afferent (GVA)	Pharynx and viscera	IX, X
Special visceral afferent (SVA)	Smell, taste	I, VII, IX, X

Embryologic Organization of the Brain Stem

The primitive neural tube displays an anatomical organization similar to that of the spinal cord, with functional areas for sensation (alar plate) and motor activity (basal plate) separated by the sulcus limitans. Within these sensory and motor areas, the brain stem is divided further into somatic and visceral regions (Fig. 15-6). This organizational framework is grafted onto the concepts developed above that relate older, more diffuse pathways to the inner tube of the brain stem and newer, more direct, and discrete pathways to the outer tube of the brain stem.

These functional divisions exist as rostrocaudal cell columns from which the cranial nerve nuclei are derived. Some cranial nerves contain components from more than one of these columns. The appearance of new structures in the brain stem and the enlargement of the embryonic neural canal into the fourth ventricle displace some of these nuclear columns from their embryonic position. The location of the cell columns in the adult brain stem and the cranial nerves arising from each is shown in Figure 15-7. These functionally oriented cell columns provide an important framework for learning the intrinsic anatomy of each of the major subdivisions of the posterior fossa. The components of each of these cell columns, found in each of the cranial nerves, are shown in Table 15-2.

The Medulla

The medulla oblongata is that portion of the brain stem extending from the level of the foramen magnum to the caudal border of the base of the pons. Many of the features of the medulla are similar to those of the spinal cord (Fig. 15-8). The major ascending and descending pathways present in the spinal cord are also present in this area; however,

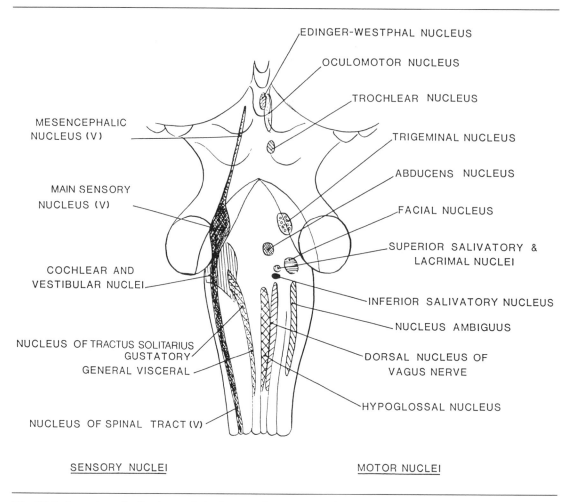

EDINGER-WESTPHAL NUCLEUS

OCULOMOTOR NUCLEUS

TROCHLEAR NUCLEUS

MESENCEPHALIC
NUCLEUS (V)

TRIGEMINAL NUCLEUS

ABDUCENS NUCLEUS

MAIN SENSORY
NUCLEUS (V)

FACIAL NUCLEUS

SUPERIOR SALIVATORY &
LACRIMAL NUCLEI

COCHLEAR AND
VESTIBULAR NUCLEI

INFERIOR SALIVATORY NUCLEUS

NUCLEUS AMBIGUUS

NUCLEUS OF TRACTUS SOLITARIUS
GUSTATORY
GENERAL VISCERAL

DORSAL NUCLEUS OF
VAGUS NERVE

HYPOGLOSSAL NUCLEUS

NUCLEUS OF SPINAL TRACT (V)

SENSORY NUCLEI   MOTOR NUCLEI

Fig. 15-7. Location of cell columns in brain stem. Sensory nuclei are shown on left
and motor nuclei on right.

there are several important changes that occur in this region, including (1) the location of the corticospinal tracts in the medial-ventral portion of the medulla (the medullary pyramids), (2) the termination of the fasciculus gracilis and cuneatus in their respective nuclei and the subsequent course of the second-order neurons in the *medial lemniscus,* (3) the replacement of the zone of Lissauer by the *descending tract of the trigeminal nerve,* (4) the replacement of the central gray portion of the spinal cord by the reticular formation, (5) the entrance of the dorsal spinocerebellar tracts into the inferior cerebellar peduncle, and (6) the replacement of the central canal of the spinal cord by the fourth ventricle.

Further important anatomical features of the medulla include the following.

Decussation of the Pyramids
At the lower end of the medulla, most of the fibers in the descending corticospinal pathways cross to the opposite side of the brain stem before descending in the spinal cord as the lateral corticospinal tracts (see Fig. 15-8).

Decussation of the Medial Lemniscus
In the caudal medulla rostral to the pyramidal decussation, second-order axons originating from the nucleus gracilis and cuneatus sweep ventromedially around the central gray matter as the *internal arcuate fibers.* These fibers then cross the midline to the

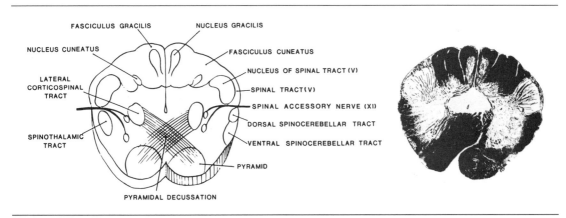

Fig. 15-8. Cross section of low medulla at the decussation of pyramids. Myelin-stained section on right.

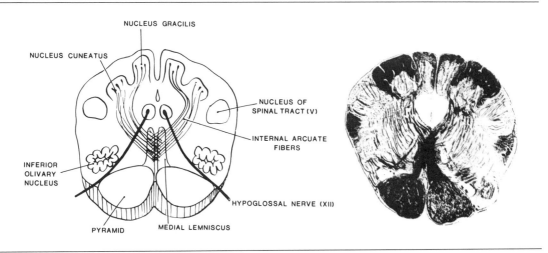

Fig. 15-9. Cross section of low medulla at the decussation of medial lemnisci. Myelin-stained section on right.

opposite side and continue rostrally as the medial lemniscus (Fig. 15-9).

Inferior Olivary Nuclei
The convoluted bands of cells located in the ventrolateral portion of the medulla are the inferior olivary nuclei, which receive fibers from the dentate nucleus of the cerebellum, red nuclei, basal ganglia, and cerebral cortex. Axons from the inferior olivary nuclei form the olivocerebellar tract, which travels through the inferior cerebellar peduncle to the opposite cerebellar hemisphere. The inferior olive is a major relay station in the cerebellar pathways. It provides tonic cerebellar support

for reflex movements and triggers phasic motor programs in the cerebellum.

Medial Longitudinal Fasciculus
This fiber tract is located in the paramedian regions of the brain stem dorsal to the medial lemniscus (Fig. 15-10). The medial longitudinal fasciculus extends rostrally from the cervical cord to the upper midbrain level and transmits information for the coordination of head and eye movements.

Inferior Cerebellar Peduncle (Restiform Body)
One of the three major connections between the cerebellum and brain stem, this pathway is

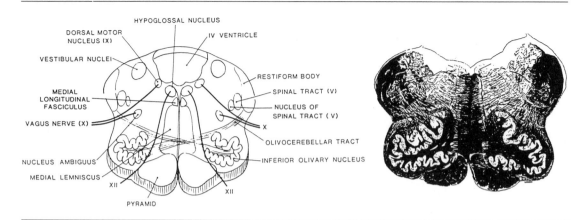

Fig. 15-10. Midportion of medulla at origin of hypoglossal and vagus nerves. Myelin-stained section on right.

Table 15-3. Structure and Function of the Hypoglossal Nerve

Component	Function	Nucleus of origin or termination	Ganglion	Foramen	Signs of dysfunction
GSE	Motor innervation of the tongue	Hypoglossal		Hypoglossal	Weakness of tongue movement

located in the dorsolateral portion of the medulla and contains dorsal spinocerebellar, olivocerebellar, vestibulocerebellar, and reticulocerebellar fibers, as well as cerebellovestibular fibers (see Fig. 15-10).

Hypoglossal Nerve (Cranial Nerve XII)

Function
The hypoglossal nerve supplies motor innervation to the intrinsic muscles of the tongue. It is a motor nerve whose nuclei are part of the general somatic efferent (GSE) group of cranial nerve nuclei.

Anatomy
The hypoglossal nucleus is located in the paramedian area of the caudal medulla in the floor of the fourth ventricle (see Figs. 15-9 and 15-10). The fibers course ventrally and exit from the ventral aspect of the medulla, between the medullary pyramids and the olive. After exit from the brain stem, these fibers pass through the hypoglossal canal in the occipital condyle and innervate the striated musculature of the tongue (Fig. 15-11).

Pathophysiology
Diseases involving the hypoglossal nucleus or cranial nerve XII are associated with atrophy, paresis, and fasciculations of tongue muscles. Unilateral weakness causes the tongue to deviate toward the side of the weakness on protrusion of the tongue. Involvement of upper motor neuron pathways innervating the hypoglossal nuclei produces slowing of alternating movements of the tongue and weakness, without atrophy. The structure and function of the hypoglossal nerve are summarized in Table 15-3.

Spinal Accessory Nerve (Cranial Nerve XI)

Function
The spinal accessory nerve is a motor nerve that innervates the sternocleidomastoid and trapezius muscles. It is a special visceral efferent (SVE) nerve innervating striated muscles derived from the branchial arches.

Anatomy
Cranial nerve XI arises mainly from cell bodies in the ventral gray horn of the upper five cervical cord segments (Fig. 15-12). The nerve

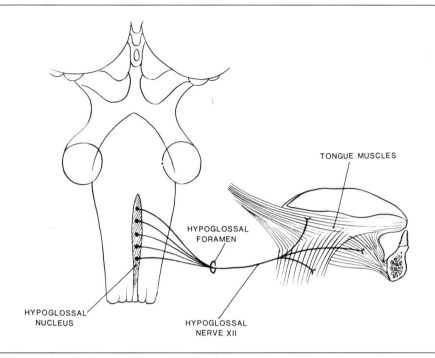

Fig. 15-11. Origin, course, and distribution of hypoglossal nerve.

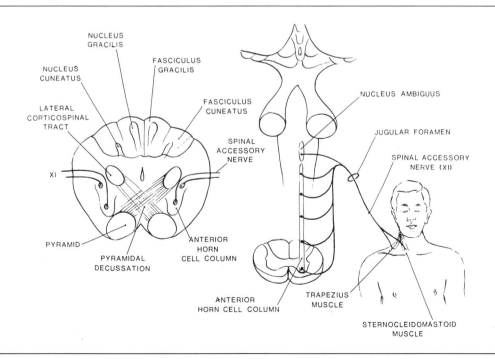

Fig. 15-12. Spinal accessory nerve. Origin of axons in the upper cervical cord and their course to trapezius and sternocleidomastoid muscles are shown on right. Nuclei of origin in the medulla are shown in the cross section on the left.

Table 15-4. Structure and Function of the Spinal Accessory Nerve

Component	Function	Nucleus of origin or termination	Ganglion	Foramen	Signs of dysfunction
SVE					
Spinal	Motor to sternocleido-mastoid and trapezius muscles	Anterior horn cells of cervi-cal cord		Jugular	Weakness of head rotation and shoulder elevation
Bulbar	Motor to pharyngeal and laryngeal muscles	Nucleus ambiguus		Jugular	Joins vagus below jugular foramen (see Table 15-5)

ascends in the spinal canal lateral to the spinal cord, enters the skull through the foramen magnum, where it is joined by the minor accessory component that originates in the nucleus ambiguus, and leaves the cranial cavity via the jugular foramen to innervate the sternocleidomastoid and trapezius muscles. The accessory component passes to the vagus nerve below the jugular foramen and ultimately innervates the larynx and pharynx.

Pathophysiology

The spinal accessory nerve may be compressed by lesions in the region of the foramen magnum (where the nerve enters the skull) or in the region of the jugular foramen as it exits from the skull. Signs of dysfunction of cranial nerve XI include weakness of head rotation (sternocleidomastoid muscle) and inability to elevate or shrug the shoulder (trapezius muscle) on the side of the lesion. The sternocleidomastoid muscle rotates the face to the opposite side so that damage to the spinal accessory nerve results in weakness in turning the head toward the side contralateral to the lesion. The structure and function of the spinal accessory nerve are summarized in Table 15-4.

Vagus Nerve (Cranial Nerve X)

Function

The vagus nerve is a mixed nerve with SVE, general visceral efferent (GVE), general somatic afferent (GSA), general visceral afferent (GVA), and special visceral afferent (SVA) functions. The functions of cranial nerve X are innervation of the striated muscles of the soft palate, pharynx, and larynx derived from branchial arches (SVE); parasympathetic

innervation to the thoracic and abdominal viscera (GVE); sensory innervation of the external auditory meatus (GSA); sensory innervation of the pharynx, larynx, and thoracic and abdominal viscera (GVA); and innervation of taste receptors on the posterior pharynx (SVA).

Anatomy

The SVE fibers of the vagus nerve innervating the striated muscles of the soft palate, pharynx, and larynx arise from the *nucleus ambiguus* located in the lateral medullary region dorsal to the inferior olive (Fig. 15-13). The GVE components of the vagus nerve contain preganglionic parasympathetic fibers arising in the *dorsal motor nucleus* to supply the thoracic and abdominal viscera. Preganglionic vagal neurons innervating the heart are located in the area of the nucleus ambiguus. These preganglionic fibers synapse with postganglionic neurons in the cardiac, pulmonary, esophageal, or celiac plexuses or within the visceral organs themselves.

The afferent fibers carried in the vagus nerve arise from three different sources: (1) GSA fibers carrying general sensation from the external auditory meatus have their cell bodies in the *superior (jugular) ganglion,* and central processes from this ganglion enter the medulla with the vagus and terminate in the spinal nucleus of the trigeminal nerve; (2) GVA fibers carrying information from abdominal and thoracic viscera have their cell bodies in the *inferior (nodose) ganglion,* and the central processes terminate in the *nucleus of the tractus solitarius;* and (3) SVA fibers in the vagus nerve carrying taste from the posterior pharynx also have their cell bodies located in

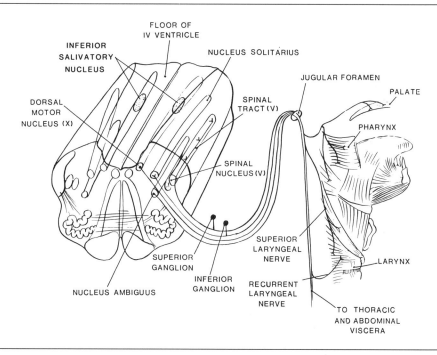

Fig. 15-13. Motor and sensory nuclei of the vagus nerve in the medulla and the course and distribution of some of its SVE fibers.

the *inferior (nodose) ganglion,* and central processes terminate in the nucleus of the tractus solitarius.

The vagus nerve emerges from the lateral aspect of the medulla, dorsal to the olives, and leaves the skull through the jugular foramen. The superior and inferior ganglia of the vagus nerve are located in (or just below) the jugular foramen. The vagus nerve then passes down the neck near the carotid artery and the jugular vein. At the base of the neck, the vagus nerve passes in front of the subclavian artery. At this point on the right side, the right vagus nerve gives off the *right recurrent laryngeal nerve,* which loops below and behind the subclavian artery and runs upward to the larynx to innervate most of the laryngeal muscles on the right side. On the left side, the vagus nerve descends in front of the arch of the aorta and gives off the *left recurrent laryngeal nerve,* which loops under the arch of the aorta and then runs upward to the larynx to provide innervation of most of the laryngeal muscles on the left side. The vagus nerve, after giving off the recurrent laryngeal nerves, descends into the thoracic and abdominal cavities to supply

the esophagus, heart, lungs, and abdominal viscera.

Pathophysiology

Because of the dual innervation of many viscera and their ability to function within certain limits independently of innervation, unilateral disease processes that involve this nerve do not produce symptoms involving the viscera. Instead, the neurologic signs usually consist of weakness of the striated muscles of the larynx and pharynx and difficulty in swallowing and speaking. Injury to the recurrent laryngeal nerves results in vocal cord paresis and a hoarse voice. The structure and function of cranial nerve X are summarized in Table 15-5.

Glossopharyngeal Nerve (Cranial Nerve IX)

Function

The glossopharyngeal nerve is also a mixed nerve with SVE, GVE, GSA, GVA, and SVA components. The functions of cranial nerve IX are innervation of the stylopharyngeus muscle of the pharynx (SVE); parasympa-

Table 15-5. Structure and Function of the Vagus Nerve

Component	Function	Nucleus of origin or termination	Ganglion	Foramen	Signs of dysfunction
SVE	Motor to muscles of soft palate, pharynx, and larynx	Nucleus ambiguus		Jugular	Hoarseness, dysphagia, decreased gag reflex
GVE	Parasympathetic to thoracic and abdominal viscera	Dorsal motor nucleus of nerve X		Jugular	Visceral disturbance, tachycardia
GSA	Sensation: external auditory meatus	Spinal nucleus of nerve V	Superior (jugular)	Jugular	Decreased sensation: external auditory meatus
GVA	Sensation: pharynx, larynx, and thoracic and abdominal viscera	Nucleus of tractus solitarius	Inferior (nodose)	Jugular	Decreased sensation: pharynx
SVA	Taste: posterior pharynx	Nucleus of tractus solitarius	Inferior (nodose)	Jugular	Not clinically significant

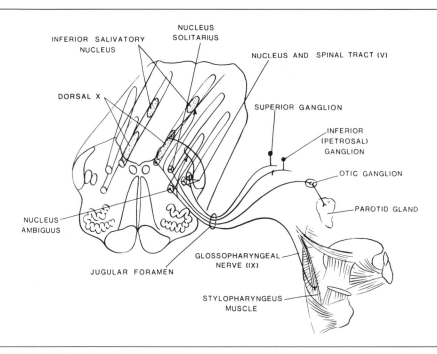

Fig. 15-14. Motor and sensory nuclei of the glossopharyngeal nerve in the medulla and the course and distribution of SVE fibers to the stylopharyngeus muscle and GVE fibers to the parotid gland.

thetic innervation to the parotid gland (GVE); sensory innervation to the back of the ear (GSA); sensory innervation to the pharynx, tongue, eustachian tube, carotid body, and carotid sinus (GVA); and innervation of taste receptors from the posterior one-third of the tongue (SVA).

Anatomy

The SVE fibers to the stylopharyngeus muscle originate in the nucleus ambiguus. (Fig. 15-14). The GVE components of the glossopharyngeal nerve carry preganglionic parasympathetic fibers that arise in the inferior salivatory nucleus and terminate in the otic ganglion.

Table 15-6. Structure and Function of the Glossopharyngeal Nerve

Component	Function	Nucleus of origin or termination	Ganglion	Foramen	Signs of dysfunction
SVE	Motor to stylopharyngeus muscle	Nucleus ambiguus		Jugular	Not clinically significant
GVE	Parasympathetic to parotid gland	Inferior salivatory nucleus	Otic	Jugular	Decreased salivation
GSA	Sensation: back of ear	Spinal nucleus of nerve V	Superior	Jugular	Decreased sensation: back of ear
GVA	Sensation: pharynx, tongue, carotid receptors	Nucleus of tractus solitarius	Inferior (petrosal)	Jugular	Decreased gag reflex
SVA	Taste: posterior one-third of tongue	Nucleus of tractus solitarius	Inferior (petrosal)	Jugular	Decreased taste

Postganglionic fibers from this ganglion supply the parotid salivary glands; stimulation increases salivary flow.

The afferent fibers carried in the glossopharyngeal nerve arise from three sources: (1) GSA fibers, carrying general sensation from behind the ear, have their cell bodies in the superior ganglion; their central processes terminate in the spinal nucleus of the trigeminal nerve; (2) GVA fibers carrying sensation from the pharynx; and (3) SVA fibers carrying taste sensation from the posterior tongue. The latter two arise from cell bodies contained in the inferior (petrosal) ganglion and have central processes that terminate in the nucleus of the tractus solitarius. Within the medulla there are segmental reflex connections between the pharyngeal sensory fibers and the motor neurons supplying the muscles of the pharynx to mediate the gag reflex.

The glossopharyngeal nerve emerges from the medulla, dorsal to the inferior olivary nuclei, and passes through the jugular foramen (which is also the location of its ganglia) to innervate peripheral structures. The components and structure of the glossopharyngeal nerve are thus similar to those of the vagus (Table 15-6).

Pathophysiology
Isolated lesions of the glossopharyngeal nerve are rare but, with or without vagus damage, result in loss of pharyngeal sensation and of the gag reflex. Occasionally, lesions give rise to a paroxysmal pain syndrome of unknown cause (*glossopharyngeal neuralgia*). In this disorder, the patient experiences brief attacks of severe pain that usually begin in the throat and radiate down the side of the neck in front of the ear and to the back of the lower jaw. On occasion, the pain may begin deep in the ear. Attacks of discomfort may be precipitated by swallowing or protrusion of the tongue.

Reticular Formation
The reticular formation of the medulla occupies much of the core area, in which it is dispersed among the tracts and nuclei described above. This location reflects its primitive, indirect, diffuse organization as opposed to the phylogenetically newer direct, discrete motor and sensory pathways occupying the ventral and lateral surfaces of the medulla. In transverse (transaxial) sections, the medullary reticular formation can be divided into three zones: medial, intermediate, and lateral. The medial zone projects to spinal motor neurons, predominantly via the ipsilateral lateral reticulospinal tract (an indirect activation pathway). The intermediate zone projects to preganglionic sympathetic neurons in the spinal cord to influence vasomotor tone. It also projects to spinal motor neurons supplying respiratory muscles and is one of several brain stem "centers" involved in control of respiration. The lateral zone contains the central pattern generator concerned with coordination of complex reflexes involving multiple cranial nerves important in swallowing and vomiting.

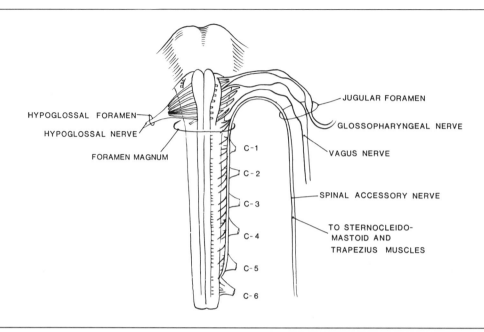

Fig. 15-15. Ventral view of medulla and cranial nerves IX, X, and XI exiting together through the jugular foramen. Dorsal roots of C-1 through C-6 in the upper cervical spinal cord are also shown.

Clinical Correlations: Medulla and Lower Cranial Nerves

Jugular Foramen Syndrome

Cranial nerves IX, X, and XI leave the skull with the jugular vein through the jugular foramen (Fig. 15-15). A lesion (usually a mass lesion) in or adjacent to the jugular foramen may affect all three cranial nerves and cause ipsilateral weakness of the pharyngeal and laryngeal muscles (nerve X), decreased sensation of the ipsilateral pharynx (nerve IX), and weakness of the ipsilateral trapezius and sternocleidomastoid muscles (nerve XI). One cause of this syndrome is a chemodectoma arising in chemoreceptors along the jugular vein.

Bulbar and Pseudobulbar Palsy

Dysfunction of the motor components of the cranial nerves of the lower portion of the brain stem (particularly the medulla, or "bulb") occurs with either upper or lower motor neuron lesions. Lesions affecting lower motor neurons (final common pathway) produce *bulbar palsy,* which is manifested as flaccid weakness of the muscles associated with talking, chew-

ing, swallowing, and movement of the tongue and lips. Supranuclear lesions, involving cortical or subcortical components of the direct or indirect activation pathways, produce upper motor neuron dysfunction of the bulbar musculature, manifested as slow movements and a harsh, strained speech pattern. Because most bulbar motor nuclei receive bilateral cortical innervation, unilateral supranuclear lesions do not usually produce significant bulbar dysfunction. However, bilateral supranuclear lesions result in severe paresis of bulbar muscles characterized by spastic weakness with dysarthria, dysphagia, and reduced mouth and tongue movements. This involvement of bulbar function by bilateral supranuclear lesions is called *pseudobulbar palsy.*

The Pons

The pons is that portion of the brain stem bounded ventrally by the rostral and caudal borders of the basis pontis (see Fig. 15-2). In transaxial sections, it is divided into two general areas. The ventral area is called the *basis pontis,* formed by transversely oriented cross-

Fig. 15-16. Cross section of lower pons at level of cranial nerves VI and VII. Myelin-stained section on right.

ing (pontocerebellar) fibers of the middle cerebellar peduncle and bundles of rostrocaudally running fibers of the corticospinal, corticobulbar, and corticopontine tracts. Small collections of neurons, the *pontine nuclei,* are dispersed in the basis pontis and are the origin of the axons that make up the *pontocerebellar fibers* that congregate laterally as the *middle cerebellar peduncle.*

The area of the pons dorsal to the basis pontis and ventral to the floor of the fourth ventricle is the *tegmentum,* within which are the spinothalamic tracts, medial lemnisci, and the medial longitudinal fasciculi. The reticular formation and the pathways related to the consciousness and internal regulation systems are concentrated in the core of the pontine tegmentum. The tegmentum also contains structures related to the following cranial nerves: acoustic and vestibular divisions of nerve VIII, facial (nerve VII), abducens (nerve VI), and trigeminal (nerve V). The location of many of these structures is shown in Figure 15-16.

Auditory Nerve (Cranial Nerve VIII)

Cranial nerve VIII (also called the auditory, vestibulocochlear, or statoacoustic nerve) is made up of two divisions: one mediates hearing, and the other mediates vestibular input. Because they are grossly inseparable in their course from the brain stem to the *internal auditory meatus,* they traditionally are considered a single nerve (Fig. 15-17). However, these two divisions represent the peripheral connections of two functionally distinct subsystems of the sensory system and have separate peripheral receptors and central connections and pathways. Therefore, the two divisions are discussed separately.

Acoustic Division of Cranial Nerve VIII

Function
The acoustic division of cranial nerve VIII is an afferent nerve that conducts impulses from the inner ear structures related to hearing. Hearing is a special somatic afferent (SSA) function.

Anatomy
Fibers in this division of cranial nerve VIII arise from cell bodies in the *spiral ganglion* of the cochlea in the inner ear (see Fig. 15-17). The nerve, composed of the central axons of these first-order neurons, enters the dorsolateral medulla at the pontomedullary junction. The axons bifurcate on entering the brain stem and synapse in both the *dorsal* and *ventral cochlear nuclei* located at that level. The subarachnoid space from the internal auditory meatus to the dorsolateral medulla, through which cranial nerve VIII courses, is bordered by the base of the pons and the ventral surface of the cerebellar hemisphere and is

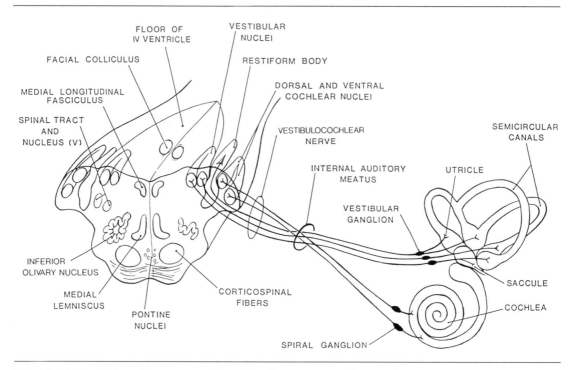

FLOOR OF
IV VENTRICLE

VESTIBULAR
NUCLEI

FACIAL COLLICULUS

RESTIFORM BODY

MEDIAL LONGITUDINAL
FASCICULUS

DORSAL AND VENTRAL
COCHLEAR NUCLEI

SPINAL TRACT
AND
NUCLEUS (V)

VESTIBULOCOCHLEAR
NERVE

SEMICIRCULAR
CANALS

INTERNAL AUDITORY
MEATUS

UTRICLE

VESTIBULAR
GANGLION

INFERIOR
OLIVARY NUCLEUS

SACCULE

MEDIAL
LEMNISCUS

CORTICOSPINAL
FIBERS

COCHLEA

PONTINE
NUCLEI

SPIRAL GANGLION

Fig. 15-17. Vestibulocochlear nerve. The cell bodies are located in ganglia near the cochlea and semicircular canals, with primary afferent terminations in the lateral pons.

Table 15-7. Structure and Function of the Acoustic Division of Cranial Nerve VIII

Component	Function	Nucleus of origin or termination	Ganglion	Foramen	Signs of dysfunction
SSA	Hearing	Dorsal and ventral cochlear nuclei	Spiral	Internal auditory meatus	Decreased hearing

SSA = special somatic afferent.

called the *cerebellopontine angle cistern.* Pathways arising from the cochlear nuclei relay auditory information through the brain stem to the medial geniculate body of the thalamus bilaterally and from there to the auditory cortex of the temporal lobes. These pathways are discussed under The Auditory System.

Pathophysiology
Lesions of the acoustic division of cranial nerve VIII produce unilateral loss of hearing. The physiology and pathophysiology of hearing are discussed under The Auditory System. The structure and function of the auditory division of cranial nerve VIII are summarized in Table 15-7.

Vestibular Division of Cranial Nerve VIII

Function
The vestibular division of cranial nerve VIII is an afferent nerve that conducts gravitational and rotational information from the inner ear. This information is necessary for maintaining proper balance and equilibrium, which are SSA functions.

Anatomy
Fibers in this division of cranial nerve VIII arise from bipolar cells in the *vestibular (Scarpa's) ganglion* located in the internal auditory canal. The peripheral axons of these ganglion cells innervate sensory receptors lo-

Table 15-8. Structure and Function of the Vestibular Division of Cranial Nerve VIII

Component	Function	Nucleus of origin or termination	Ganglion	Foramen	Signs of dysfunction
SSA	Balance and equilibrium	Vestibular nuclei	Vestibular	Internal auditory meatus	Disequilibrium vertigo

SSA = special somatic afferent.

cated in the organs of balance (utricle, saccule, and semicircular canals) in the inner ear. Their central axons travel to the brain stem with the auditory division of nerve VIII and synapse in the vestibular nuclei located beneath the floor of the fourth ventricle in the upper medulla and caudal pons (see Fig. 15-17). Pathways arising from the vestibular nuclei conduct information to the cerebellum, spinal cord, reticular formation, and, via the medial longitudinal fasciculus, to the nuclei of cranial nerves III, IV, and VI. They are discussed under The Vestibular System.

Pathophysiology
Lesions of the vestibular division of cranial nerve VIII cause the sensation of vertigo (hallucination of rotatory movement) or disequilibrium. The physiology and pathophysiology of equilibrium are discussed under The Vestibular System. The structure and function of the vestibular division of cranial nerve VIII are summarized in Table 15-8.

Facial Nerve (Cranial Nerve VII)

Function
The facial nerve innervates the muscles of facial expression, which are derived from branchial arch mesoderm. This is the SVE component of the nerve. The facial nerve also has a GVE component, consisting of parasympathetic fibers to the lacrimal, submaxillary, and submandibular glands, and an SVA component that innervates taste receptors on the anterior two-thirds of the tongue.

Anatomy
The SVE fibers innervating the striated muscles of the face arise in the *facial nucleus* located in the lateral tegmentum of the pons (see Figs. 15-16 and 15-18). Axons from this nucleus first course medially and then arch dorsally, forming a loop, or genu, around the ab-

ducens nucleus before proceeding to the lateral surface of the caudal pons where they emerge medial to nerve VIII. The looping of the facial nerve fibers around the abducens nucleus causes a slight bulge, called the *facial colliculus,* on each side of the midline in the floor of the fourth ventricle.

As the facial nerve leaves the pons, two separate nerve roots are apparent: the larger division carries the SVE component supplying the facial muscles, and the smaller division, the *nervus intermedius,* carries the GVE and SVA components. The parasympathetic (GVE) fibers of the facial nerve originate in the superior salivatory nucleus and, after joining the SVE fibers, emerge from the pons to innervate the lacrimal, sublingual, and submandibular glands (Fig. 15-19).

The SVA component of the facial nerve mediates taste from the anterior two-thirds of the tongue. The cell bodies of the first-order neurons of this component are located in the *geniculate ganglion,* a name derived from its position at a bend in the facial canal. The central axons from this ganglion enter the pons as part of the nervus intermedius. In the pons, these axons turn caudally to synapse, along with other taste fibers, in the *nucleus of the tractus solitarius.*

Both divisions pass through the cerebellopontine angle cistern and leave the cranial cavity through the internal auditory meatus and enter the facial canal of the temporal bone. The SVE fibers to the face continue through the horizontal and then vertical parts of the canal, exiting at the stylomastoid foramen below the ear (see Fig. 15-19). In addition to innervating the muscles of facial expression, a small branch is given off to the stapedius, a tiny striated muscle in the middle ear. The nervus intermedius does not traverse the entire facial canal. In the region of the geniculate ganglion, it splits into two branches: the

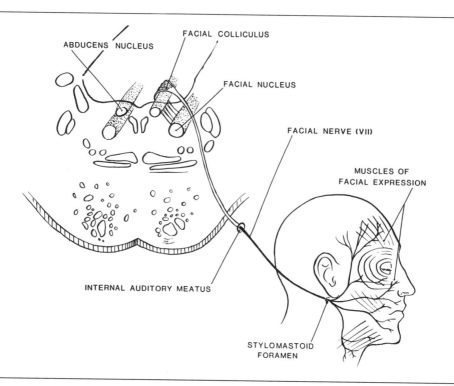

Fig. 15-18. Facial nerve nucleus in pons and course and distribution of motor axons. The loop of the facial nerve over the abducens nucleus forms the facial colliculus in the floor of the fourth ventricle.

greater superficial petrosal nerve (GVE fibers for the lacrimal gland) and the *chorda tympani* (GVE fibers for the salivary glands and SVA fibers for taste).

Preganglionic parasympathetic fibers carried in the greater superficial petrosal nerve synapse in the *sphenopalatine ganglion.* Postganglionic cholinergic fibers from this ganglion proceed to the lacrimal gland. The chorda tympani nerve leaves the facial canal in its vertical segment, enters the middle ear cavity, arches over the tympanic membrane, and emerges from the petrous bone to join the lingual branch of cranial nerve V on its way to the tongue. The preganglionic parasympathetic fibers leave the lingual nerve and synapse in the *submandibular ganglion.* Postganglionic cholinergic fibers supply the sublingual and submandibular salivary glands.

Pathophysiology

The most conspicuous result of disorders of the facial nerve is weakness of the muscles of facial expression. Loss of taste on the anterior two-thirds of the tongue may also occur. Facial weakness, however, may also result from lesions involving the direct activation pathway descending from the cerebral cortex to the facial nucleus. It is clinically important to distinguish between *upper motor neuron (central) facial weakness* involving the lower half of the face and *lower motor neuron (peripheral) facial weakness* involving both the upper and lower halves of the face.

Bell's palsy is a relatively common disorder that produces peripheral facial weakness. Although the cause is usually unproved, it is thought to result from inflammation of the facial nerve in the facial canal. Patients with this condition exhibit weakness of both upper and lower facial muscles, including weakness of eye closure, a feature not seen in upper motor neuron facial weakness. Also, depending on the site of involvement of the nerve in the facial canal, patients may have decreased lacrimation and salivation, decreased taste sensation, and hyperacusis (increased sensitivity to noise due to weakness of the stapedius muscle).

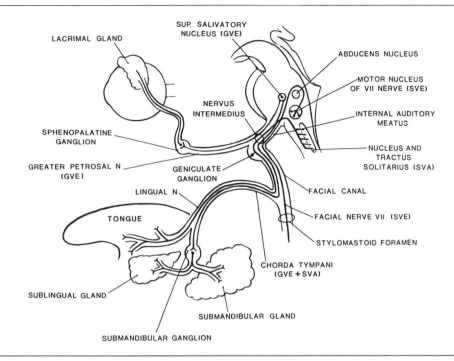

Fig. 15-19. Course of visceral efferent and afferent divisions of the facial nerve. (*N* = nerve; *SUP* = superior.) (Redrawn from R. C. Truex and M. B. Carpenter, *Strong and Elwyn's Human Neuroanatomy* [5th ed.]. Baltimore: Williams & Wilkins, 1964.)

Table 15-9. Structure and Function of the Facial Nerve

Component	Function	Nucleus of origin or termination	Ganglion	Foramen	Signs of dysfunction
SVE	Motor to muscles of facial expression	Facial nucleus		Internal auditory meatus, stylomastoid	Facial weakness, hyperacusis
GVE	Parasympathetic Lacrimal gland	Superior salivatory nucleus	Sphenopalatine	Internal auditory meatus	Decreased tearing
	Salivary glands		Submandibular		Decreased salivation
SVA	Taste: anterior two-thirds of tongue	Nucleus of tractus solitarius	Geniculate	Internal auditory meatus	Decreased taste

The structure and function of the facial nerve are summarized in Table 15-9.

Abducens Nerve (Cranial Nerve VI)

Function

The abducens nerve is a GSE nerve that innervates the *lateral rectus muscle* of the eye. Con-traction of this muscle produces lateral movement (abduction) of the eyeball.

Anatomy

The abducens nuclei are located in the GSE cell column at the midpontine level, beneath the floor of the fourth ventricle and near the midline (see Fig. 15-16). Axons take a ventral

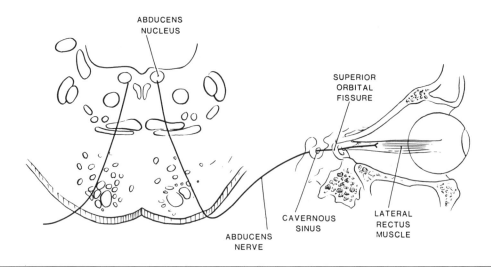

Fig. 15-20. The abducens nerve arises from nucleus in pons and has a long intracranial course to the lateral rectus muscle via cavernous sinus and superior orbital fissure.

Table 15-10. Structure and Function of the Abducens Nerve

Component	Function	Nucleus of origin or termination	Ganglion	Foramen	Signs of dysfunction
GSE	Motor to lateral rectus muscle	Abducens		Superior orbital fissure	Diplopia, medial deviation of eye

and slightly caudal course through the tegmentum and basis pontis to emerge on the ventral surface near the pontomedullary junction. The nerve then ascends ventral to the base of the pons, traverses the lateral wall of the cavernous sinus (along with cranial nerves III, IV, and the first division of V), and leaves the cranial cavity through the superior orbital fissure to supply the lateral rectus muscle of the eye (Fig. 15-20).

Pathophysiology

Lesions affecting the abducens nerve produce weakness of the lateral rectus muscle, with inability to abduct the eye, causing double vision (diplopia) (discussed under The Oculomotor System). Because the intracranial course of cranial nerve VI is unusually long, the nerve may be affected by many pathologic processes involving the pons, the base of the skull (clivus), the cavernous sinus, the superior orbital fissure, or the orbit. The structure and function of the abducens nerve are summarized in Table 15-10.

Trigeminal Nerve (Cranial Nerve V)

Function

The trigeminal nerve is the sensory nerve to the face. It is a mixed nerve containing GSA and SVE components. In addition to carrying touch, pain, temperature, and proprioceptive information (GSA) from the face, cranial nerve V provides motor innervation (SVE) to the muscles of mastication, which are derived from branchial arches.

Anatomy

The GSA fibers mediating touch, pain, and temperature sense arise from cell bodies in the trigeminal (gasserian, semilunar) ganglion that lies in a dural fold called *Meckel's cave* on the medial petrous ridge (Fig. 15-21). Axons travel centrally from the ganglion to enter the lateral aspect of the pons. Fibers mediating touch synapse directly on the *main (chief) sensory nucleus of V* located in the dorsolateral tegmentum of the pons. Second-order neurons from this nucleus ascend via both crossed and

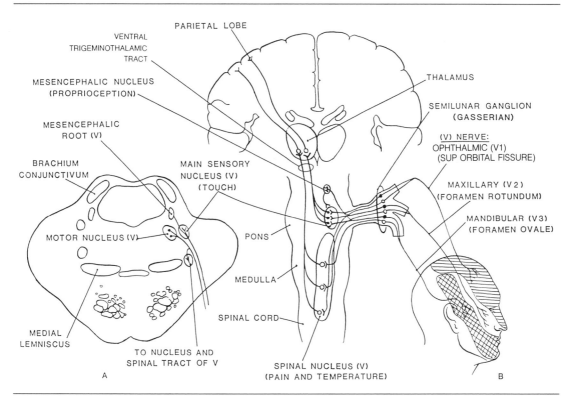

Fig. 15-21. Trigeminal nerve. A. Midpontine cross section. B. Horizontal section with course and distribution of sensory axons. (*SUP* = superior.)

uncrossed pathways, the trigeminothalamic tracts, to synapse in the ventral posteromedial nucleus of the thalamus.

Pain and temperature fibers do not synapse in the main sensory nucleus but turn caudally to descend through the dorsolateral medulla and upper three or four segments of the cervical spinal cord as the *spinal (descending) tract of the trigeminal nerve* (see Fig. 15-21). Axons in this tract synapse on cell bodies of second-order neurons in the underlying *nucleus of the spinal (descending) tract of the trigeminal nerve.* The GSA components carried in cranial nerves IX and X, from the skin of the external ear, join the spinal tract of V where they enter the medulla. The topography of the spinal tract of the trigeminal nerve is such that the fibers from the mandibular division are most dorsal and those from the ophthalmic division are most ventral as the tract descends through the caudal pons and medulla. The pattern of termination of these axons in the spinal nucleus is controversial, although some authors

suggest a concentric pattern in which fibers representing the central (perioral) region of the face terminate in the most rostral part of the spinal nucleus and those representing the most peripheral areas of the face (bordering dermatomes C-2 and C-3) terminate caudally. Second-order fibers from the spinal nucleus of V cross to the opposite side of the medulla and ascend to the thalamus as the *ventral trigeminothalamic tract,* which is near the medial lemniscus. These fibers synapse in the ventral posteromedial nucleus of the thalamus, where third-order neurons send axons to the parietal lobe.

Proprioceptive fibers in the trigeminal nerve, unlike all other first-order sensory neurons, arise from cell bodies *located in the central nervous system.* These cell bodies form the mesencephalic nucleus of the trigeminal nerve and lie along the lateral border of the rostral fourth ventricle and aqueduct of Sylvius (see Fig. 15-21). The peripheral axons of these unique first-order neurons innervate receptors

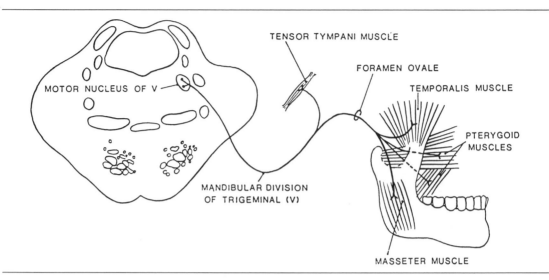

TENSOR TYMPANI MUSCLE

FORAMEN OVALE

TEMPORALIS MUSCLE

MOTOR NUCLEUS OF V

PTERYGOID MUSCLES

MANDIBULAR DIVISION OF TRIGEMINAL (V)

MASSETER MUSCLE

Fig. 15-22. Motor division of trigeminal nerve with nucleus in pons and course of axons to muscles of mastication.

in the muscles of mastication (and perhaps other muscles) and travel without synapse through the trigeminal ganglion to enter the lateral pons along with the rest of the nerve. Central axons from the mesencephalic nucleus synapse directly in the motor nucleus of V to mediate the monosynaptic jaw reflex.

The SVE fibers that innervate the muscles of mastication arise from cell bodies in the motor nucleus of V, located medial to the main sensory nucleus (Fig. 15-22). Axons course ventrolaterally and exit from the lateral surface of the pons as the motor root, medial to the sensory root. These fibers run along the ventral aspect of the trigeminal ganglion and join the mandibular (third) division of the trigeminal nerve to exit the skull through the foramen ovale. They innervate the temporalis, masseter, medial and lateral pterygoid, and tensor tympani muscles. The temporalis, masseter, and medial pterygoid muscles close the jaw, the lateral pterygoid muscles open and facilitate lateral movement of the jaw, and the tensor tympani, a small muscle in the middle ear, dampens vibration of the eardrum.

From the trigeminal ganglion, sensory fibers of nerve V course peripherally via three major divisions: the ophthalmic division (V_1) passes through the superior orbital fissure to innervate the upper face; the maxillary division (V_2) exits the skull via the foramen rotundum to innervate the midface; and the mandibular division

(V_3), joined by the motor root, exits via the foramen ovale to innervate the lower face.

Pathophysiology

Lesions involving nerve V produce loss of facial sensation and, if the motor fibers are involved, weakness of the masticatory muscles, which causes the jaw to deviate to the side of the weakened muscles when the jaw is opened.

Trigeminal neuralgia (tic douloureux) is a disorder characterized by transient, brief, repetitive paroxysms of pain in the distribution of one or more branches of nerve V. The pain is severe and either occurs spontaneously or is triggered by relatively minor sensory stimulation of the face. Although various pathologic changes have been noted in the trigeminal ganglion, nerve, or root entry zone in the pons, the cause of the syndrome is unknown.

Two reflexes tested as part of the neurologic examination involve cranial nerve V. The *jaw jerk* is the only muscle stretch reflex that can be elicited in the head. It is mediated entirely by the mandibular branch of nerve V. Tapping the jaw briefly stretches the muscles of mastication. Proprioceptive impulses travel centrally, synapse in the motor nucleus of V, and activate reflex contraction of the jaw muscles. The clinical usefulness of this reflex in detecting lesions affecting the reflex arc is limited by the frequent difficulty in eliciting it in healthy persons. Therefore, it is regarded as abnormal

Table 15-11. Structure and Function of the Trigeminal Nerve

Division of trigeminal nerve V	Component	Function	Nucleus of origin or termination	Ganglion	Foramen	Signs of dysfunction
Ophthalmic (V$_1$)	GSA	Sensation: forehead pain	Spinal nucleus of nerve V	Gasserian (semilunar)	Superior orbital fissure	Decreased forehead pain Decreased corneal reflex
		Touch: forehead	Main sensory nucleus of nerve V	Gasserian (semilunar)	Superior orbital fissure	Decreased forehead touch Decreased corneal reflex
Maxillary (V$_2$)	GSA	Sensation: cheek pain	Spinal nucleus of nerve V	Gasserian (semilunar)	Rotundum	Decreased cheek pain
		Touch: cheek	Main sensory nucleus of nerve V	Gasserian (semilunar)	Rotundum	Decreased cheek touch
Mandibular (V$_3$)	GSA	Sensation: jaw pain	Spinal nucleus of nerve V	Gasserian (semilunar)	Ovale	Decreased jaw pain
		Touch: jaw	Main sensory nucleus of nerve V	Gasserian (semilunar)	Ovale	Decreased jaw touch
		Proprioception	Mesencephalic nucleus		Ovale	Decreased jaw jerk
	SVE	Motor to muscles of mastication	Motor nucleus of nerve V		Ovale	Weakness of muscles of mastication, decreased jaw jerk

only when it is hyperactive, which occurs with bilateral upper motor neuron lesions affecting the direct and indirect activation pathways to the motor nucleus of V.

The *corneal reflex* is elicited by touching the cornea of one eye with a piece of cotton. The afferent limb of this reflex is the ophthalmic division of nerve V. The observed result of this maneuver is an apparently simultaneous blink of both eyes, both the side stimulated (direct reflex) and the side not stimulated (consensual reflex). This response implies bilateral activation of facial nucleus neurons related to the orbicularis oculi muscles through complex central connections. Lesions involving the ophthalmic division of nerve V, the tegmentum of the pons, or the facial nerve alter this reflex. The structure and function of the trigeminal nerve are summarized in Table 15-11.

Reticular Formation

The pontine reticular formation, located in the core of the tegmentum, is continuous with the reticular formation of the medulla caudally and of the midbrain rostrally. As in the medullary reticular formation, different functional zones can be distinguished in transverse section. The medial zone at this level is primarily concerned with the oculomotor system and the reticulospinal system. The role of the paramedian pontine reticular formation and the coordination of eye movements are discussed below. The lateral pontine reticular formation contains neurons of the internal regulation system, including those that modulate the micturition reflex. The pontine reticular formation also contains several neuronal groups of the consciousness system, including the raphe nuclei and the locus ceruleus.

The Midbrain

The midbrain is that portion of the brain stem located between the pons and the diencephalon. The major external anatomical features that mark its boundaries are the cerebral pe-

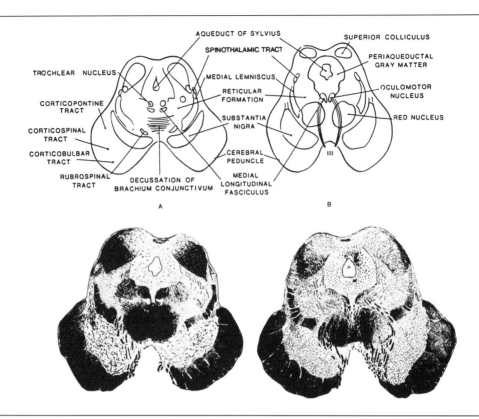

Fig. 15-23. Cross section of midbrain. A. Lower midbrain (level of inferior colliculus). B. Upper midbrain (level of superior colliculus). Myelin-stained sections are shown below.

duncles ventrally and the quadrigeminal plate, featuring the paired inferior and superior colliculi, dorsally. In transverse section, the midbrain is divided dorsoventrally into three main regions: the *tectum* (dorsal), the *tegmentum,* and the *base* (ventral) (Fig. 15-23). Its derivation from the primitive neural tube is most clearly highlighted by its tubular cavity, the aqueduct of Sylvius.

The *tectum,* or roof, of the midbrain lies above the transverse plane of the aqueduct of Sylvius. The tectum is made up of two paired structures, the *inferior* and *superior colliculi,* collectively called the *corpora quadrigemina.* The inferior colliculi act as a relay station for auditory fibers that pass to the thalamus via the brachium of the inferior colliculus. The superior colliculi are associated with oculomotor control. The aqueduct of Sylvius, a remnant of the neural canal, is surrounded by a zone of periaqueductal gray matter.

The *tegmentum* is the area lying ventral to

the aqueduct and dorsal to the substantia nigra. The major longitudinal pathways in the tegmentum of the midbrain are the lateral lemniscus, spinothalamic tract, medial lemniscus, medial longitudinal fasciculus, indirect activation pathways of the motor system, descending pathways of the internal regulation system, and projection pathways of the reticular formation. In addition, it contains the nuclei of cranial nerves III and IV and their axons, the red nuclei, and the decussation of the superior cerebellar peduncles (see Fig. 15-23A).

At the midbrain level, perhaps more clearly than at other brain stem levels, the primitive concentric organization of the neural tube can be recognized. The phylogenetically older multisynaptic pathways concerned with internal regulation, consciousness, and other primitive functions occupy the inner regions close to the aqueduct; the newer, more direct and functionally discrete pathways concerned with somatic motor and sensory functions lie more peripherally.

The Superior Cerebellar Peduncle (Brachium Conjunctivum)

Efferent fibers from the dentate nucleus of the cerebellum pass rostrally, and near the dorsal surface of the midbrain, just caudal to the inferior colliculi, they can be identified grossly as the *superior cerebellar peduncles*. From this point, they pass ventrally into the tegmentum of the midbrain. In caudal midbrain (level of the inferior colliculus), they cross to the opposite side, forming the *decussation of the brachium conjunctivum* (see Fig. 15-23A). The fibers then proceed to the red nucleus and the thalamus.

The Red Nucleus

The red nucleus is a large oval mass of gray matter in the central portion of the tegmentum on each side at the level of the superior colliculus (see Fig. 15-23B).When viewed in a freshly cut brain, this nucleus is slightly red because of its density of capillaries and high iron content. The red nuclei receive fibers from the cerebellum and the cerebral cortex and give rise to (1) descending fibers that synapse in the ipsilateral inferior olivary nucleus, from which fibers project to the contralateral cerebellar cortex, and (2) the rubrospinal tract, which crosses in the ventral tegmental decussation caudal to the red nucleus and descends to the spinal cord.

The Basis Pedunculi

The base of the midbrain, also called the *basis pedunculi,* consists of the cerebral peduncles (containing the corticospinal, corticobulbar, and corticopontine tracts) and the substantia nigra, which is dorsal to each cerebral peduncle (see Fig. 15-23). The substantia nigra is dark because of its melanin-containing neurons. It is functionally related to the basal ganglia as part of the indirect activation pathway of the motor system.

Trochlear Nerve (Cranial Nerve IV)

Function

The trochlear nerve is a GSE nerve that innervates the superior oblique muscle of the eye.

Contraction of this muscle causes downward movement of the eye when it is in the adducted position.

Anatomy

The trochlear nucleus lies at the level of the inferior colliculus just ventral to the periaqueductal gray matter and dorsal to the medial longitudinal fasciculus. Its axons pass dorsolaterally and caudally around the periaqueductal gray matter. They cross caudal to the tectum and emerge from the dorsal aspect of the midbrain on the side contralateral to their origin. This is the only completely crossed cranial nerve and the only cranial nerve to emerge from the dorsal surface of the brain stem (Fig. 15-24). The nerve then passes around the midbrain to enter the lateral wall of the cavernous sinus. It enters the orbit through the superior orbital fissure to innervate the superior oblique muscle.

Pathophysiology

Lesions of the trochlear nerve cause weakness of the superior oblique muscle, causing diplopia on downward and inward gaze. The patient may compensate for the torsional imbalance caused by the unopposed action of the inferior oblique muscle by tilting the head to the opposite side. Isolated injury to the trochlear nerve may occur where it runs along the edge of the tentorium toward the cavernous sinus. This often results from head trauma. Otherwise, the nerve is usually involved along with nerves III, V, and VI by lesions of the cavernous sinus, superior orbital fissure, or orbit. The structure and function of the trochlear nerve are summarized in Table 15-12.

Oculomotor Nerve (Cranial Nerve III)

Function

The oculomotor nerve is a mixed motor nerve that provides GSE innervation to the following muscles of the eye: superior rectus, inferior rectus, medial rectus, inferior oblique, and levator palpebrae superioris. Cranial nerve III also supplies GVE, parasympathetic fibers to the pupil and to the ciliary muscle controlling the lens of the eye.

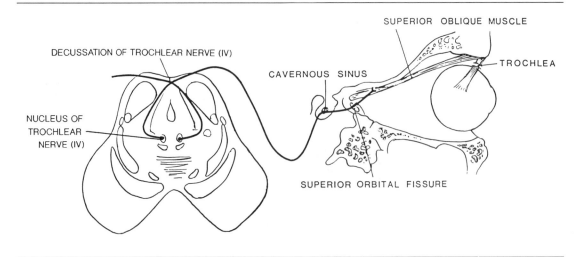

Fig. 15-24. Trochlear nerve. Cross section of lower midbrain showing trochlear nucleus and course and distribution of axons to the superior oblique muscle of the opposite eye.

Table 15-12. Structure and Function of the Trochlear Nerve

Component	Function	Nucleus of origin or termination	Ganglion	Foramen	Signs of dysfunction
GSE	Motor to superior oblique muscle	Trochlear nucleus on opposite side		Superior orbital fissure	Diplopia

Anatomy

The GSE fibers of nerve III arise from the oculomotor nucleus, which is ventral to the aqueduct at the level of the superior colliculus (Fig. 15-25). The nucleus is composed of subnuclei for each of the muscles innervated. All the projections are ipsilateral except for those to the superior rectus muscle (which are crossed) and those to the levator palpebrae superioris muscle (which are crossed and uncrossed). The crossing occurs in the nucleus itself. Axons pass ventrally through the tegmentum and base of the midbrain and emerge in the interpeduncular fossa.

The GVE fibers that provide preganglionic parasympathetic innervation to the pupil arise in a small subnucleus, the *Edinger-Westphal nucleus,* at the rostral end of each oculomotor nucleus. These GVE fibers join the GSE fibers and, after en.erging from the interpeduncular fossa, pass through the lateral wall of the cavernous sinus and superior orbital fissure to enter the orbit (see Fig. 15-25).

GSE fibers continue directly to the extraocular muscles and innervate them, and the GVE fibers synapse in the ciliary ganglion. Postganglionic fibers from this ganglion proceed to the pupilloconstrictor muscle of the iris and to the ciliary body.

Pathophysiology

Lesions involving the GSE component of nerve III produce weakness of all voluntary eye muscles, except the lateral rectus and superior oblique, and cause diplopia. The eye tends to deviate downward and outward because of the unopposed action of the lateral rectus and superior oblique muscles, and ptosis is often present because of weakness of the levator palpebrae superioris muscle. In rare cases in which the nucleus itself is the site of the lesion, there is weakness of the contralateral superior rectus and bilateral ptosis.

Ptosis caused by weakness of the levator palpebrae superioris must be distinguished from ptosis due to lesions affecting the sympa-

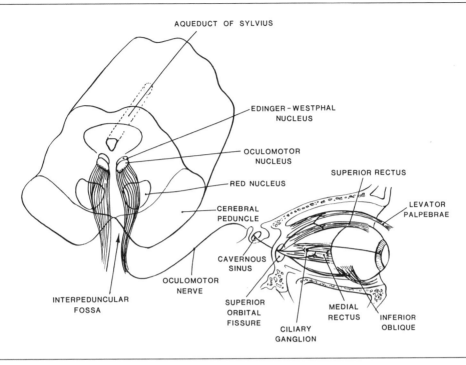

Fig. 15-25. Oculomotor nerve. Cross section of upper midbrain with oculomotor nucleus and course and distribution of axons to the eye.

thetic innervation of the eye. These postganglionic sympathetic fibers are from the superior cervical sympathetic ganglion, ascend into the cranial cavity along the internal carotid artery, and join nerve III in the cavernous sinus. Damage to these sympathetic fibers causes mild ptosis because of loss of innervation of the smooth muscle in the upper lid (Müller's muscle); the damage also causes *miosis* (pupillary constriction). In contrast, lesions of the GVE component of nerve III cause loss of the parasympathetic innervation of the eye and produce *mydriasis* (pupillary dilatation).

Observation of pupillary size and testing of the pupillary light reflex are an integral part of the neurologic examination. The size of the pupil is influenced by many factors, primarily by the intensity of light falling on the retina. The afferent pathway of the pupillary light reflex is conducted by the optic nerve (cranial nerve II). The fibers from each retina partially decussate in the optic chiasm and proceed via the optic tracts and brachium of the superior colliculus to the *pretectal area* (Fig. 15-26),

from which fibers pass to the *Edinger-Westphal nucleus* on both sides. From the Edinger-Westphal nucleus, the efferent limb of the pupillary light reflex continues in the oculomotor nerve.

The normal pupil constricts briskly when light is shown on the ipsilateral retina. This is the *direct light reflex.* Because of the partial decussation of the optic pathway in the optic chiasm and again in the pretectal area, the contralateral pupil also constricts; this is the *consensual light reflex.* Unilateral lesions of the optic nerve do not produce anisocoria (unequal pupils) but diminish both the direct and the consensual light reflex when the involved eye is tested. However, moving the light source rapidly from the normal eye (with a strong direct and consensual light reflex) to the involved eye (with a diminished reflex) can make it appear as if the pupils actually dilate in response to light. Of course, they are only moving to a less constricted state due to decreased detection of light in the involved eye. Both pupils will again constrict briskly when the light source is moved back to the normal

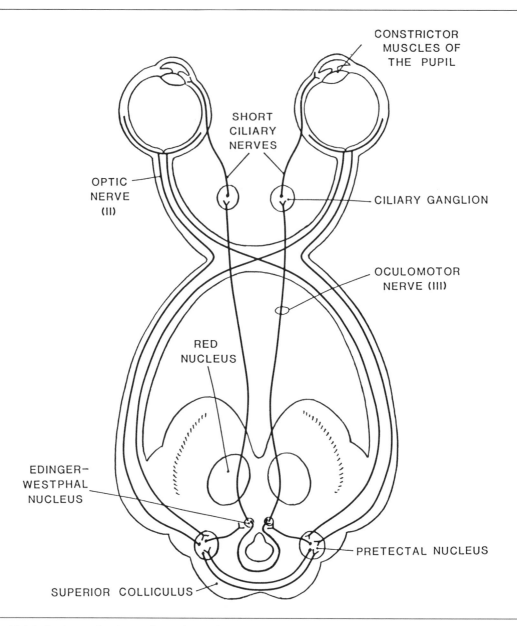

CONSTRICTOR
MUSCLES OF
THE PUPIL

SHORT
CILIARY
NERVES

OPTIC
NERVE
(II)

CILIARY GANGLION

OCULOMOTOR
NERVE (III)

RED
NUCLEUS

EDINGER–
WESTPHAL
NUCLEUS

PRETECTAL NUCLEUS

SUPERIOR COLLICULUS

Fig. 15-26. Pathways for the pupillary light reflex with the afferent arc in the optic nerve and efferent arc in the oculomotor nerve.

eye. This phenomenon can be demonstrated repeatedly by moving the light source back and forth from the involved to the uninvolved eye. This response identifies the so-called *afferent pupillary defect,* which is due to a decreased conduction in the afferent limb of the pupillary light reflex.

Lesions that involve the parasympathetic innervation of the eye cause ipsilateral mydriasis and loss of the direct pupillary light reflex with preservation of the consensual reflex on testing the involved eye (and the reverse on testing the uninvolved eye). Anisocoria also occurs with lesions involving the sympathetic innervation of the pupil, resulting in ipsilateral miosis with normal pupillary light reflexes. This pupillary abnormality is usually accompanied by other features of Horner's syndrome, including mild ptosis due to denervation of Müller's muscle (see

Table 15-13. Structure and Function of the Oculomotor Nerve

Component	Function	Nucleus of origin or termination	Ganglion	Foramen	Signs of dysfunction
GSE	Motor to medial rectus, superior rectus, inferior rectus, inferior oblique, and levator palpebrae	Oculomotor		Superior orbital fissure	Diplopia, ptosis
GVE	Parasympathetic pupilloconstrictor muscles, ciliary muscle	Edinger-Westphal	Ciliary	Superior orbital fissure	Mydriasis, loss of direct pupillary reflex, loss of lens accommodation

above) and decreased sweating on the ipsilateral face due to loss of sympathetic innervation of sweat glands. The structure and function of the oculomotor nerve are summarized in Table 15-13.

Reticular Formation

Perhaps more clearly than at other levels of the brain stem, the reticular formation in the midbrain is concentrated around the inner tube, which surrounds the neural canal derivative, the aqueduct of Sylvius. Its most conspicuous component is the periaqueductal gray matter, which is concerned predominantly with the central modulation and control of pain and with integrating responses to stress. The rostral interstitial nucleus of the medial longitudinal fasciculus (important in the coordination of vertical eye movements), the raphe nuclei and mesopontine cholinergic nuclei (important in the consciousness system), and other specific nuclei in the midbrain reticular formation are discussed in connection with the systems in which they perform important functions.

The Cerebellum

The cerebellum is the largest structure in the posterior fossa. It lies dorsal to the pons and medulla and forms the roof of the fourth ventricle. The cerebellum is an embryonic derivative of the metencephalon, and although it is derived from the alar plate (rhombic lip) and is important in the integration of unconscious proprioception, it is closely related functionally to the motor system and is the central

structure in the cerebellar control circuit (see Chapter 8, The Motor System).

Gross Anatomy

The cerebellum is composed of two lateral lobes, the *cerebellar hemispheres,* and a midline portion called the *vermis* (Fig. 15-27). The cerebellum is also divided transversely into three lobes, with each one containing a portion of the vermis and the adjacent hemisphere.

1. The *anterior lobe* consists of the vermis and cerebellar hemispheres anterior to the primary fissure.
2. The *flocculonodular lobe* consists of the most caudal lobule of the vermis, the nodulus (in the roof of the fourth ventricle), and the flocculus.
3. The *posterior lobe* consists of the rest of the cerebellum and includes the cerebellar tonsils, which are apparent on the inferomedial aspect of the cerebellar hemispheres just above the foramen magnum.

Functional Anatomy

Clinically, it is convenient to discuss the cerebellum in terms of its functional anatomy. The vermis of the anterior and posterior lobes forms the *midline cerebellar zone,* which receives the spinocerebellar afferents and is concerned mainly with the muscle synergies involved in walking. The terms *paleocerebellum,* reflecting its phylogenetic origin, and *spinocerebellum,* reflecting its major functional connections, roughly correspond to this zone. The *lateral zone* corresponds to most of the cerebellar hemisphere including the major

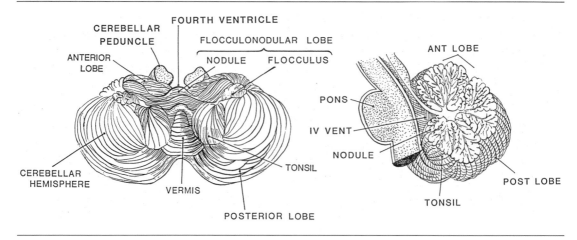

Fig. 15-27. Lobes of the cerebellum from the inferior surface. (*ANT* = anterior; *POST* = posterior; *VENT* = ventricle.)

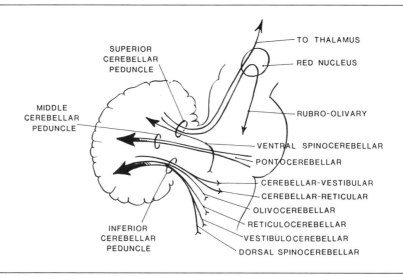

Fig. 15-28. Afferent and efferent fibers in the cerebellar peduncles.

part of the posterior lobe. It receives the corticopontocerebellar afferents and is also referred to as the *neocerebellum* or *corticocerebellum*. The lateral zone is involved in the coordination of ipsilateral limb movement. Between the midline zone and the lateral zone of each hemisphere, anatomists recognize an "intermediate zone," which projects via the globose and emboliform nuclei to the nuclei of the indirect activation pathways; the clinical relevance of this region in humans is unknown. The *flocculonodular lobe* receives input from the vestibular system and is also referred to as the *archicerebellum* or *vestibulocerebellum*. It is concerned primarily with coordination of head and eye movements and the maintenance of equilibrium.

The Cerebellar Peduncles

The cerebellum is connected to the brain stem by three pairs of peduncles that carry cerebellar afferents and efferents (Fig. 15-28).

The *inferior cerebellar peduncle* (restiform body) contains both afferent and efferent fibers. It carries most of the information the

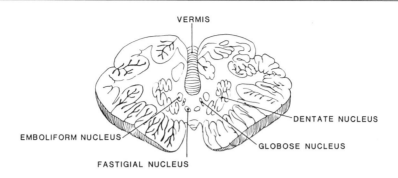

Fig. 15-29. Cerebellar nuclei in horizontal section.

cerebellum receives from the spinal cord and medulla. The most important afferent pathways reaching the cerebellum through this peduncle are the dorsal spinocerebellar and cuneocerebellar tracts (carrying proprioceptive input that does not reach consciousness) and the vestibulocerebellar, reticulocerebellar, and olivocerebellar pathways. The main efferent fibers are the cerebellovestibular and cerebelloreticular pathways.

The *middle cerebellar peduncle* (brachium pontis) contains only afferent fibers, which originate in the contralateral pontine nuclei. The pontine nuclei receive afferents from the ipsilateral cerebral cortex via the corticopontine tract. The corticopontocerebellar connections establish a pathway whereby each cerebellar hemisphere is influenced by the contralateral cerebral hemisphere.

The *superior cerebellar peduncle* (brachium conjunctivum) contains both afferent and efferent fibers and is the main outflow pathway from the cerebellum. The only afferent component in this peduncle is the ventral spinocerebellar tract. Efferent fibers originating in the dentate nucleus constitute the bulk of the superior cerebellar peduncle. In caudal midbrain, these fibers cross as the decussation of the brachium conjunctivum and proceed to the contralateral red nucleus, thalamus, and inferior olivary nucleus. The fibers descending to the inferior olivary nucleus are in the central tegmental tract. As a result of the connections described above, two loops are established: the cortico-ponto-cerebello-dentato-thalamo-cortical pathway and the cerebello-dentato-rubro-olivo-cerebellar

pathway. Their roles in monitoring and modulating the activity of the motor system are not completely understood.

Internal Anatomy

The cerebellar cortex is a highly convoluted structure. The individual convolutions are referred to as *folia* rather than gyri. Deep to the cerebellar cortex is white matter that is made up of the fiber tracts entering and leaving the cortex. Four paired nuclei lie within the deep cerebellar white matter: the dentate, emboliform, globose, and fastigial nuclei. They are relay stations for efferent fibers from the cerebellar cortex and are the origin of most of the efferent pathways from the cerebellum (Fig. 15-29). The dentate nucleus is the largest and most lateral of these nuclei and receives fibers mainly from the posterior lobe. The emboliform and globose nuclei receive fibers from the anterior lobe and paravermian zone. The fastigial nucleus, the most medial of the group, receives fibers from the flocculonodular lobe.

Histologically, the cerebellar cortex consists of three layers named the *molecular layer,* the *Purkinje cell layer,* and the *granule cell layer* (Fig. 15-30). The outermost is the molecular layer; it consists mainly of axons and dendrites, among which are a small number of neurons called *basket cells* and *stellate cells.* The middle layer consists of a single layer of large goblet-shaped neurons called *Purkinje cells.* The innermost (granular cell) layer is composed of densely packed small neurons called *granule cells* and scattered larger neurons called *Golgi cells.*

Afferent fibers entering the cerebellar cortex

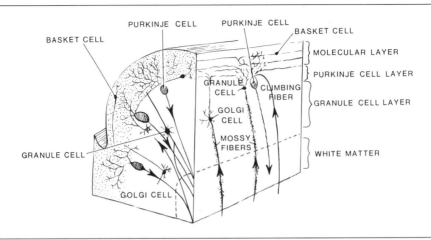

Fig. 15-30. Cell layers and connections of the cerebellar cortex.

terminate as either *mossy fibers* or *climbing fibers.* The mossy fibers represent the cerebellar afferent fibers from all sources except the inferior olivary nucleus. They synapse on the dendrites of granule cells and Golgi cells. Axons of the granule cells, in turn, enter the molecular layer and synapse on Purkinje cell dendrites. Purkinje cell dendrites arborize in a fan-like fashion perpendicular to the long axis of the folium. Granule cell axons enter the molecular layer and bifurcate to run, as *parallel fibers,* 2 to 3 mm in each direction in the long axis of the folium. Thus, each parallel fiber can synapse with the dendrites of up to 500 Purkinje cells as well as with dendrites of basket cells and stellate cells. The Golgi cell dendrites also ramify in the molecular layer and are excited by the parallel fibers of the granule cells. Golgi cell axons end in the granule cell layer and form inhibitory synapses on granule cells. Activation of a single incoming mossy fiber can produce excitation of a small, rectangular array of Purkinje cells, because the mossy fiber contacts multiple granule cells whose parallel fibers contact multiple Purkinje cells. The mossy fiber synapses and parallel fiber synapses are excitatory. All the other neurons activated by parallel fibers (Golgi, basket, and stellate cells) are inhibitory to Purkinje cells. Because of the spatial organization of the cerebellar cortex, these inhibitory neurons create a simultaneous intense inhibition of Purkinje cells surrounding the activated zone. The mossy fiber system con-

stantly modulates cerebellar activity during voluntary movement.

Climbing fibers are the axons of the olivocerebellar pathway; they synapse directly on Purkinje cells via an array of terminal axon branches that wind around and "climb" the Purkinje cell body and dendritic tree. The climbing fiber input to Purkinje cells, like the granule cell input, is excitatory. The climbing fiber system signals errors in motor performance and adapts Purkinje cell firing to the new circumstance. It is important in motor learning.

All output from the cerebellar cortex is via the axons of the Purkinje cells, which project to the deep cerebellar nuclei and form inhibitory synapses. A few Purkinje cell axons go directly to the vestibular nuclei.

Pathophysiology

As described in Chapter 8 (The Motor System), disturbances of cerebellar function are manifested as loss of balance and equilibrium or as a disorder in the modulation of the range, force, rate, and direction of movement. The flocculonodular lobe is primarily responsible for balance and equilibrium, and lesions in this region of the cerebellum result in an inability to sit or stand without swaying or falling (*truncal ataxia*). The anterior lobe is primarily responsible for posture and coordination of gait. Lesions involving this region result in an unsteady, staggering gait (*gait ataxia*). The posterior lobe is primarily responsible for coordination of ipsilateral voluntary movements of the extremities. Lesions of this region result in loss of motor coordination of the extremities, dysmetria, and, if the dentate nucleus or its outflow pathway (the brachium conjunctivum) is involved, intention tremor (*limb ataxia*).

New Systems at the Posterior Fossa Level

In addition to the major longitudinal systems discussed in other chapters, three additional special systems — oculomotor, auditory, and vestibular — are found at the posterior fossa level.

The Oculomotor System

The oculomotor system controls eye movements and is part of the motor system. Its major components, particularly the final common pathway (lower motor neurons), are located at the posterior fossa level, although, as in other parts of the motor system, the pathways for supranuclear control originate at the supratentorial level. Vision itself is exclusively a supratentorial function. The anatomy and physiology of the visual system are discussed with that level (see Chapter 16, The Supratentorial Level).

Eye movement is accomplished through the action of the extraocular muscles, which are activated by cranial nerves III, IV, and VI. Most of the input to the nuclei of these cranial nerves is through the paramedian reticular formation of the brain stem, which determines the activity of lower motor neurons for both reflex and voluntary eye movements. Input to the reticular formation for voluntary and pursuit movements comes via descending supranuclear pathways from the frontal eye fields and parietooccipital visual cortex, respectively. Reflex movements are mediated by input from the vestibular nuclei in the medulla to the abducens nucleus (nerve VI) and then via the medial longitudinal fasciculus to the trochlear (nerve IV) and oculomotor (nerve III) nuclei. Input from the retina travels to the superior colliculus and the pretectal region and then to the brain stem reticular formation.

Lesions at the supratentorial, posterior fossa, or peripheral levels can produce oculomotor disorders such as paresis of one or more extraocular muscles, with diplopia, gaze paresis, or nystagmus.

Physiology

Different neutral mechanisms are used for eye movements that subserve different functions. Saccadic eye movements are rapid reflex movements that bring a visual image to the fovea. Smooth pursuit movements keep the fovea focused on a moving target. Vergence movements maintain the visual image on the fovea when objects move toward the eyes (convergence) or away from them (divergence). Vestibuloocular reflexes hold images steady on the retina during brief head rotations. Optokinetic movements hold stable images on the retina as long as possible when object-filled space is moving past the eyes and then quickly refixates on the next available target.

Each of these eye movements is mediated via the nuclei of cranial nerves III, IV, and VI and coordinated through neurons in the brain stem paramedian reticular formation. The different pathways acting on the reticular formation to produce these movements have not been fully clarified, but some of the anatomical features of the various control systems are well defined.

Anatomy

The five major areas of oculomotor control are (1) the nuclei of cranial nerves III, IV, and VI, described above; (2) the brain stem paramedian reticular formation; (3) the superior colliculus and pretectal region; (4) vestibular connections via the abducens nucleus and the medial longitudinal fasciculus; and (5) the cortical eye fields.

The anatomy of the oculomotor, trochlear, and abducens nuclei and nerves forming the final common pathway of the oculomotor system is described above. The medial and lateral recti muscles turn the eye inward and outward. The superior and inferior recti muscles move the eye up and down when it is turned outward, and the inferior and superior oblique muscles move the eye up and down

Table 15-14. Functions of the Ocular Nerves

Nerve	Muscles	Function (deviation of the eye)	Signs of dysfunction
III	Medial rectus Superior rectus Inferior rectus Inferior oblique	Medially Up and out Down and out Up and in	Eye is deviated down and out with complete paralysis of nerve III (usually associated with ptosis and mydriasis)
IV	Superior oblique	Down and in	Limitation of downward gaze when eye is looking medially, extorsion of eye
VI	Lateral rectus	Laterally	Eye is deviated medially

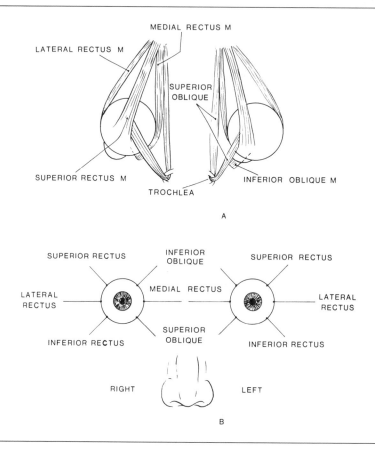

Fig. 15-31. A. Attachment of eye muscles. B. Eye movement produced by each muscle. (*M* = muscle.) (Redrawn from A. B. Baker. *Clinical Neurology* [2nd ed.], Vol. 1. Hagerstown, MD: Harper & Row, 1962.)

when it is turned inward (Table 15-14). The muscles that turn the two eyeballs are yoked in pairs so that the eyes move conjugately in exactly the same direction with exactly the same velocity and force. This principle of equal innervation of yoked pairs of extraocular muscles is known as *Hering's law.* For example, the left medial rectus and right lateral rectus muscles are the yoked pair for right lateral gaze, and when looking to the right, the right superior rectus and left inferior oblique are the yoked pair for upward gaze. When the eye is turned outward, the oblique muscles produce more torsion than up and down movement. Similarly, when the eye is turned inward, the action of the superior and inferior recti becomes primarily torsional (Fig. 15-31A). Ocular movements are tested by asking

Table 15-15. Location of Control Cells for Horizontal and Vertical Conjugate Eye Movements

	Location		
Movement	Burst cells	Tonic cells	Pause cells
Horizontal	Pontine paramedian reticular formation	Nucleus prepositus hypoglossi (medulla)	Raphe nucleus
Vertical	Rostral interstitial nucleus of the medial longitudinal fasciculus (midbrain)	Nucleus prepositus hypoglossi (medulla)	Raphe nucleus

the patient to look in the six cardinal directions of gaze, as depicted in Figure 15-31B.

The brain stem paramedian reticular formation is located along the midline and paramedian core of the brain stem from the midbrain to the medulla and receives input from all prenuclear areas concerned with eye movements, including the vestibular nuclei, superior colliculi, pretectal region, cerebellum, and cortical eye fields. This region is made up of small scattered nuclei that show different firing patterns with different types of eye movement. On the basis of their effect on the firing pattern of the neurons of cranial nerve nuclei III, IV, and VI, the neurons in these cell groups are classified as *pause cells, burst cells,* and *tonic cells* (Table 15-15). When the eyes are still, pause cells located in the raphe nuclei fire tonically and inhibit the burst cells. When the eyes make a rapid movement, or saccade, the pause cells are inhibited. Burst cells then fire briefly, driving the eyes to their new position. Tonic cells also begin to fire and their discharge frequency is just enough to hold the eye at the new desired position. Pause cells are distributed along the midline area of the reticular formation. The burst neurons for horizontal saccades are located in the pontine paramedian reticular formation (PPRF) near the abducens nucleus, and the burst neurons for vertical eye movements are located in the rostral interstitial nucleus of the medial longitudinal fasciculus. The pulse created by the burst neuron firing and the step created by the firing of tonic neurons drive the eye to the new position and hold it there. The burst and tonic neurons must have their firing integrated, such that the eye goes to the new position and stays there without drifting off the target. This is accomplished by an area referred to as the *neural integrator*; it probably is located with the

tonic neurons for both horizontal and vertical eye movements in the *nucleus prepositus hypoglossi* in the upper medulla. Slow eye movements take place without a burst and simply with cessation of pause cell firing and introduction of tonic cell firing to drive the eyes to the new position and to hold them there.

The vestibular and optokinetic systems control compensatory eye movements to head rotation and movement of the visual environment. When the semicircular canals are stimulated by head movement, signals are sent to the paramedian reticular formation and from there to the appropriate combination of cranial nerves III, IV, and VI for compensatory eye movement in the opposite direction. If one looks at a target and shakes the head from side to side, the eyes can be maintained on the target through this mechanism. It does not require any cortical input and, in fact, can be seen in comatose patients. The pathway from the vestibular nuclei to cranial nerves III, IV, and VI is largely through the medial longitudinal fasciculus (Fig. 15-32).

The superior colliculus and the pretectal region receive input from the retina, the cortical eye fields, and the inferior colliculus, which is a relay station in the auditory pathway. Fibers from these regions connect with the reticular formation and mediate eye movements in response to targets picked up in peripheral vision and in response to sound. The superior colliculi map the visual and auditory environment, which helps in the localization of objects and sounds in space.

Eye movements usually have to be conjugate to maintain a visual image on the fovea of both eyes; however, if the object moves closer to the observer, the eyes converge to maintain the image on the fovea. When the object moves away, the eyes diverge. The anatomy

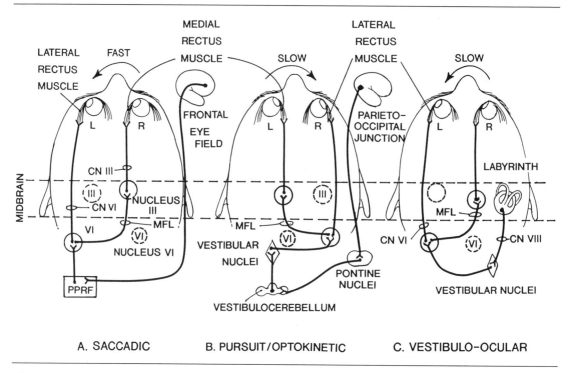

Fig. 15-32. Three systems for lateral gaze. (*CN* = cranial nerve; *MLF* = medial longitudinal fasciculus; *PPRF* = pontine paramedian reticular formation.)

and physiology of convergence movements are not well understood. They are slow and seem to be mediated by pontine and medullary structures but *not* by the medial longitudinal fasciculus.

Two other reflexes normally accompany convergence: accommodation and miosis. Both are mediated by the Edinger-Westphal nucleus, the origin of the parasympathetic fibers of the oculomotor nerve. These fibers travel with nerve III to the ciliary ganglion, where they synapse with postganglionic cells that innervate the ciliary muscle. This muscle relaxes the tension on the lens, allowing it to round up and shorten its focal distance. Parasympathetic activity also causes contraction of the circular muscle of the iris, causing constriction of the pupil.

The two cortical eye fields are the frontal and parietooccipital fields (Fig. 15-33). The frontal eye field is in the posterior portion of the middle frontal gyrus, Brodmann's area 8, and is responsible for the voluntary control of conjugate saccades (see Fig. 15-32). Fibers from this region project to the pontine reticular forma-

tion and the superior colliculus. Stimulation of the frontal eye field produces conjugate deviation of the eyes to the opposite side and acute destruction results in conjugate deviation of the eyes toward the side of the lesion.

The parietooccipital eye field is located at the parietooccipital junction of each hemisphere (Brodmann's area 19). This eye field is responsible for involuntary smooth pursuit movements in which the eyes are fixated on an object and maintain visual fixation as the object moves (see Fig. 15-32). Fibers from area 19 project to nuclei in the pretectal region and to the superior colliculus and from there to the reticular formation. Voluntary fixation on a visual target is broken when the target reaches the limit of the visual field. The eyes then make a quick movement in the opposite direction to fixate on a new target. This movement is called *optokinetic nystagmus* and depends on an intact parietooccipital eye field.

Pathophysiology

Disturbances of ocular movements are important localizing signs in neurologic diagnosis.

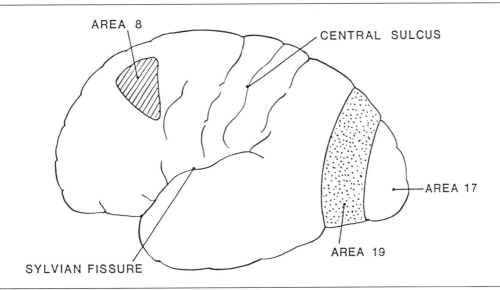

Fig. 15-33. Cortical eye fields. Area 17 is primary visual cortex. Cortical gaze centers are in areas 8 and 19.

Lesions of the final common pathway occur at either the posterior fossa level (nucleus or nerve) or the peripheral level (nerve, neuromuscular junction, or muscle) and produce diplopia. Supranuclear or prenuclear control over the final common pathway is affected by lesions of the brain stem, vestibular system, cerebellum, or cortical eye fields.

Diplopia, or double vision, occurs when an image no longer falls on exactly corresponding areas of the two retinas. The brain interprets this as seeing two images instead of one (Fig. 15-34). Diplopia usually occurs secondary to a lesion affecting one or more of the ocular nerves or extraocular muscles. The affected eye shows restricted movement in the field of the weak muscle, and the patient reports maximum separation of the images in the direction of gaze of the weak muscle.

Prenuclear brain stem lesions can produce various gaze disorders. Lesions of the paramedian pontine reticular formation interrupt horizontal conjugate eye movements toward the side of the lesion. This occurs because the PPRF sends fibers to the ipsilateral abducens nucleus and from there via the medial longitudinal fasciculus to the contralateral oculomotor nucleus, specifically to the neurons innervating the medial rectus muscle. Lesions in the rostral interstitial nu-

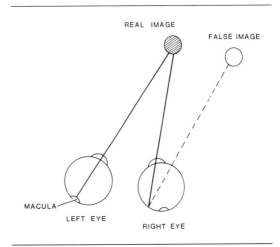

Fig. 15-34. Diplopia occurs when the images of one object fall on different parts of the two retinas. The brain interprets this as seeing two images. In this example, the right lateral rectus muscle is paretic, and the patient cannot rotate the right eye to the right. The image of the object falls on the nasal aspect of the retina of the right eye, and the brain interprets this as a second image (false image) to the right of the real image.

cleus of the medial longitudinal fasciculus affect both upward and downward vertical gaze. The fibers from this nucleus that mediate upward gaze pass dorsally through the posterior commissure to the oculomotor nucleus, so that a lesion here may affect only upward gaze.

In addition to lower motor neurons, the abducens nucleus contains *internuclear neurons* that send axons through the contralateral medial longitudinal fasciculus to the oculomotor nucleus. Therefore, a lesion in the medial longitudinal fasciculus prevents adduction of the eye on the side of the lesion when the patient attempts to gaze toward the opposite side. This clinical syndrome is called *internuclear ophthalmoplegia.* A lesion in the abducens nucleus itself, on the other hand, will produce an ipsilateral conjugate gaze palsy similar to that caused by a lesion of the pontine paramedian reticular formation. However, the paralysis of the ipsilateral lateral rectus muscle will be disproportionately severe.

The connection between the vestibular and oculomotor systems is most evident clinically in a phenomenon called *nystagmus.* Nystagmus is a combination of slow eye movements in one direction followed by quick saccades in the opposite direction. It occurs normally with stimulation of the vestibular system, for example, when a person is rotated rapidly in a circle and then stopped. Optokinetic nystagmus is also a normal response to a moving visual environment, for example, when a person watches a train passing in front of him or her. The eyes make a following movement along with the train and then a quick saccade back to the primary position. Nystagmus can also be a sign of disease in the vestibular end organ or in the vestibulocerebellar pathways in the brain stem.

The most important clinical feature of cortical oculomotor control is the tonic influence of the frontal eye field on the contralateral pontine paramedian reticular formation, causing the eyes to tend to deviate toward the opposite side (see Fig. 15-32). Normally, the influence from the two sides is balanced. Supratentorial lesions involving the frontal eye fields produce loss of voluntary conjugate gaze to the opposite side. When the lesion is acute, the eyes may be forcefully, conjugately deviated toward the side of the lesion. An irritative lesion, that is, a focal seizure, can cause tonic deviation of the eyes to the opposite side. When lesions affect the parietooccipital eye field, the optokinetic response toward the side of the lesion is abolished. This is demonstrated by moving a striped tape or rotating a striped drum in front of the patient's eyes. When the stripes move toward the normal side, the eyes follow and then jerk back to pick up the next stripe. When the stripes move toward the abnormal side, the eyes do not move.

The Auditory System

The auditory system is represented at the posterior fossa and supratentorial levels. The auditory structures transform mechanical energy (sound) into action potentials and relay them to the brain stem and cerebral cortex. Auditory information is used for communication.

Sound waves are transformed into electrical signals by the structures in the inner ear. Afferent impulses pass centrally via the acoustic division of cranial nerve VIII and, after synapse in the cochlear nuclei, ascend bilaterally through a multisynaptic brain stem pathway to the superior temporal gyrus of the temporal lobe. Relay nuclei in the brain stem include the superior olivary nuclei, nucleus of the lateral lemniscus, inferior colliculus, and medial geniculate body. Although lesions central to the cochlear nuclei result in some alteration of auditory function, unilateral loss of hearing is found only with lesions of cranial nerve VIII or the peripheral receptors.

The Ear

The receptors for the auditory system are in the ear, which is subdivided into three major regions (Fig. 15-35): (1) the *external ear* consists of the pinna, which collects and directs sounds through the external auditory canal; (2) the *middle ear,* or tympanic cavity, contains the tympanic membrane (eardrum) and the auditory ossicles, which convert sound waves into waves in a fluid-filled chamber; and (3) the *inner ear,* or labyrinth, which is a series of fluid-filled membranous channels in the petrous portion of the temporal bone. The membranous labyrinth duplicates the shape of the bony labyrinth and is divided into two channels, one containing endolymph and the other containing perilymph. The ionic composition of these two fluids is different. Perilymph is similar to spinal fluid, whereas endo-

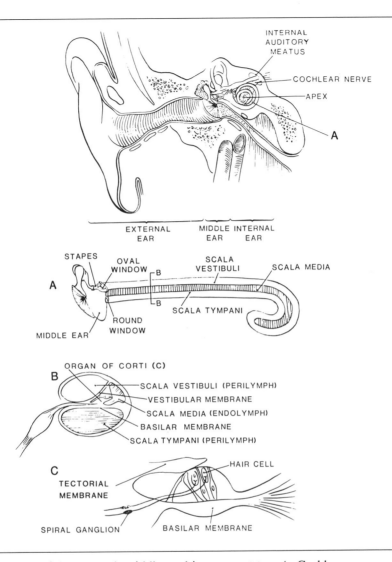

Fig. 15-35. Structures of the external, middle, and inner ear at top. A. Cochlea uncoiled and showing the three chambers. B. Cross section of cochlea (*B–B* in Fig. 15-35A) showing three chambers and basilar membrane. C. Close-up view of organ of Corti.

lymph has a high potassium and low sodium content. The labyrinth is further divided into the cochlea and the vestibule, which consists of the utricle, the saccule, and the three semicircular canals. The cochlea contains the receptors for sound, and the vestibule contains the receptors of the vestibular apparatus.

Anatomy

The cochlea contains three parallel chambers and is shaped like a snail, coiled 2¾ turns from its base to its apex (see Fig. 15-35). The two outer chambers, the *scala vestibuli* and *scala*

tympani, contain perilymph and are in continuity at the apex of the coil. The middle chamber, the *scala media* (also called the *cochlear duct*), contains endolymph.

The scala vestibuli and scala media are separated by the vestibular (Reissner's) membrane, and the scala tympani and scala media are separated by the basilar membrane. At the base of the cochlea, the scala vestibuli ends at the oval window, and the scala tympani ends at the round window. The *organ of Corti* lies on the surface of the basilar membrane and contains mechanically sensitive *hair cells,* the

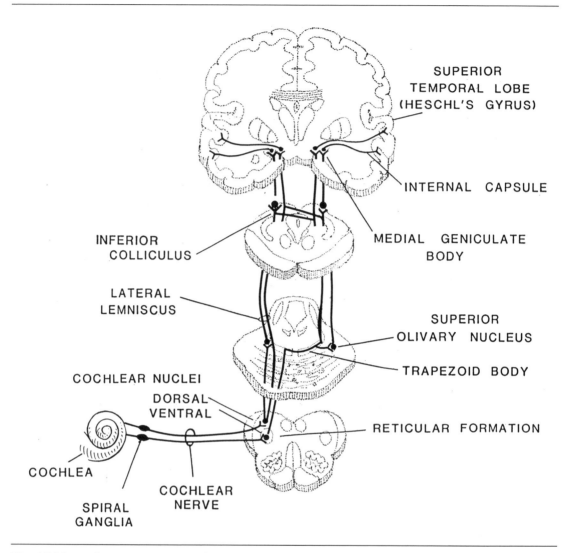

SUPERIOR TEMPORAL LOBE (HESCHL'S GYRUS)

INTERNAL CAPSULE

INFERIOR COLLICULUS

MEDIAL GENICULATE BODY

LATERAL LEMNISCUS

SUPERIOR OLIVARY NUCLEUS

TRAPEZOID BODY

COCHLEAR NUCLEI

DORSAL

VENTRAL

RETICULAR FORMATION

COCHLEA

COCHLEAR NERVE

SPIRAL GANGLIA

Fig. 15-36. Auditory pathways. Auditory impulses can ascend directly in the ipsilateral lateral lemniscus or synapse in the trapezoid body or superior olivary nucleus. They also may cross to the opposite side and ascend in the contralateral lateral lemniscus. Fibers thus ascend bilaterally to the inferior colliculus, medial geniculate bodies, and auditory cortex.

auditory receptors. These cells generate electrotonic potentials in response to movement of the basilar membrane produced by sound waves. The base of the hair cell is enmeshed in a network of nerve endings of the cochlear nerve. The cochlear nerve fibers emerge from the coils of the cochlea in the central axis of the coil and join together to form the acoustic division of nerve VIII. The cell bodies of these first-order neurons for hearing are located in the spiral ganglion in the axis of the helix.

Fibers pass centrally, enter the brain stem, and synapse in the dorsal and ventral cochlear nuclei (Fig. 15-36).

From the cochlear nuclei, second-order neurons travel via several pathways to the thalamus. Some fibers enter the reticular formation and participate in the alerting functions of the consciousness system. Some fibers ascend directly in the ipsilateral lateral lemniscus, whereas others synapse in the nuclei of the trapezoid body or the superior

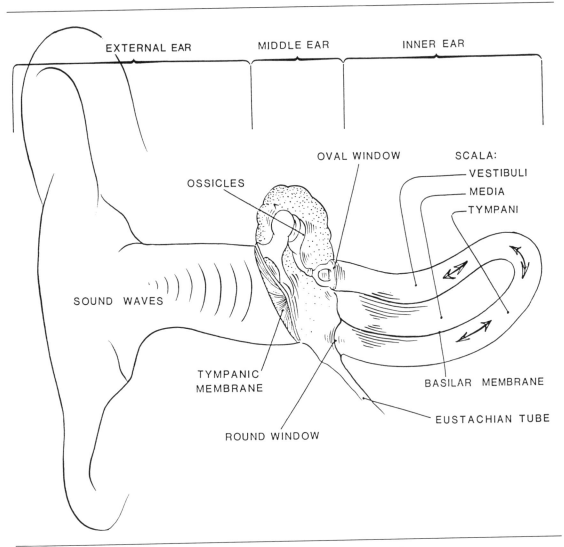

Fig. 15-37. Conversion of sound waves to movements of the basilar membrane.

olivary nuclei in the ventral tegmentum of the pons (see Fig. 15-36). Many but not all these fibers cross to the opposite side in the trapezoid body before passing rostrally. Thus, in each lateral lemniscus, there are auditory fibers that conduct information from both ears. Some of the fibers synapse in the nucleus of the lateral lemniscus en route to the inferior colliculus. At the inferior colliculus, some fibers again synapse, and a few may pass to the opposite side. Fibers traveling via the brachium of the inferior colliculus end in the medial geniculate body of the thalamus, which gives rise to axons that pass through the sublenticular portion of the in-

ternal capsule to go to the auditory cortex of the superior temporal gyrus (*Heschl's gyrus*) (see Fig. 15-36). Because of the partial decussation of auditory fibers, sound entering each ear is transmitted to both cerebral hemispheres.

Physiology

The ear converts sound waves in the external environment into action potentials in the auditory nerves. Sound waves entering the external auditory canal move the tympanic membrane (Fig. 15-37). This movement is transmitted to the ossicles (malleus, incus, and stapes) of the middle ear, which amplify

Table 15-16. The Weber and Rinne Tests for Unilateral Deafness

Test	Method	Normal response	Conduction deafness	Sensorineural deafness
Weber	Base of vibrating tuning fork placed on vertex of skull	Heard equally in both ears (or center of the head)	Sound louder in abnormal ear	Sound louder in normal ear
Rinne	Each ear is tested separately — base of vibrating tuning fork is placed on the mastoid region until subject no longer hears sound (bone conduction), then held in air next to the ear (air conduction)	Air conduction is better than bone conduction	Bone conduction is better than air conduction in involved ear	Air conduction is better than bone conduction in involved ear

and transform the movements of the eardrum into smaller and more forceful movements of the footplate of the stapes, which rests against the oval window of the inner ear. The movement of the stapes against the oval window produces traveling pressure waves in the perilymph of the scala vestibuli. At the apex of the cochlea, these waves pass into the scala tympani and are dissipated by movement of the round window. As the sound waves enter the perilymph of the scala vestibuli, they are transmitted through the vestibular membrane to the endolymph of the scala media. This causes displacement of the basilar membrane, which in turn stimulates the *hair cells* in the organ of Corti. The movement of the hair cells generates electrotonic potentials that are converted into action potentials in the auditory nerve fibers.

From the base to the apex, the basilar membrane gradually decreases in width and increases in tension. Because of this, different portions of the basilar membrane respond to different frequencies. Thus, the cochlea mechanically separates the activation of different hair cells by different frequencies.

Pathophysiology

Patients with disease of the auditory division of cranial nerve VIII or its receptors complain of tinnitus (buzzing or ringing sensation in the ear) or loss of hearing. These can be important symptoms and signs in localizing a pathologic process to the posterior fossa level. Lesions within the central nervous system seldom produce a significant alteration in hearing. Therefore, unilateral

hearing loss commonly indicates disease in the ipsilateral ear or in cranial nerve VIII. It is important to distinguish between the types of hearing deficit found in ear disease and in neural disease. *Conduction deafness* is due to disease of the external or middle ear that prevents sound waves being transmitted to the cochlea. *Sensorineural deafness* is due to disease of the cochlea or the auditory nerve or its nuclei. The distinction can often be made with a tuning fork, by performing the Weber and Rinne tests, as outlined in Table 15-16. Audiometric testing identifies the frequencies most impaired. Middle ear disease is associated with low-frequency loss, and nerve damage is associated with high-frequency loss.

Patients with lesions central to the cochlear nuclei do not complain of hearing loss. Although bilateral lesions of the inferior colliculi, medial geniculate bodies, or superior temporal gyri do produce hearing loss, examples of these are so rare as to be of no practical clinical importance. Unilateral lesions in the region of the auditory receptive areas of the cerebral cortex do not cause hearing loss, but they produce a deficit in sound localization or discrimination. Focal seizures involving the cortical auditory receptive area in the temporal lobe produce hallucinations of sound. Electrical potentials evoked by click stimulation, called *brain stem auditory evoked potentials,* can be recorded on the scalp from the structures along the auditory pathway (Fig. 15-38). Abnormalities in these potentials can identify and localize lesions in the auditory system.

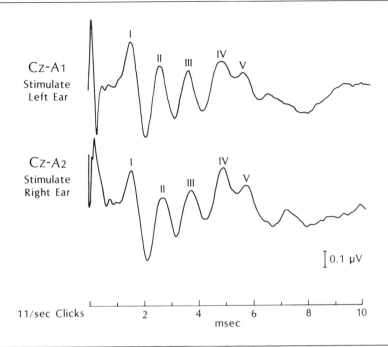

Fig. 15-38. Normal brain stem auditory evoked potentials (*I–V*) in a 26-year-old man. Top segment represents the response of the left ear; bottom segment, response of the right ear. (The responses represent an average of 2,048 samples with summation of two superimposed responses.) (*CZ* = central vertex area; *A1* = left ear; *A2* = right ear.)

The Vestibular System

The vestibular structures provide the nervous system with information about gravity, rotation, and acceleration that is necessary for maintenance of balance and equilibrium. These structures are located primarily in the posterior fossa.

Receptors that detect gravitational pull, rotational movements, and acceleration are located in the utricle, saccule, and semicircular canals of the inner ear. They transmit information to the central nervous system via the vestibular division of cranial nerve VIII. Numerous connections exist between the vestibular nuclei and the cerebellum, spinal cord, reticular formation, medial longitudinal fasciculus, and cerebral cortex to allow integration of vestibular impulses with other sensory information for normal balance and equilibrium. Lesions affecting the vestibular structures cause a sense of imbalance (disequilibrium). *Vertigo* is a highly specific symptom of vestibular system dysfunction. Nystagmus

also occurs with lesions of the vestibular system or its connections.

Anatomy and Physiology

The receptors for the vestibular system are enclosed in the vestibular portion of the labyrinth in the utricle, the saccule, and the three semicircular canals (Fig. 15-39). The receptors are *hair cells* that respond to mechanical movement and initiate impulses that are transmitted via the vestibular division of cranial nerve VIII to the vestibular nuclei in the medulla and pons (see Fig. 15-17). The cell bodies of the first-order neurons are in the vestibular ganglion located in the internal auditory meatus. Movement of the hair cells produces local generator potentials that increase or decrease the frequency of action potentials in the nerve. The hair cells in the utricle and saccule respond to positional and gravitational change, and those in the semicircular canals respond to rotational or angular acceleration.

The utricle and saccule contain endolymph. Specialized areas of epithelium called *macu-*

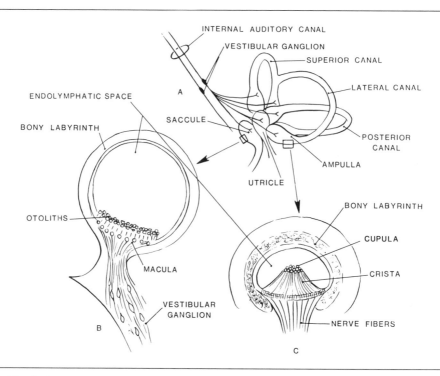

Fig. 15-39. Vestibular receptors. A. Nerve supply to vestibular receptors (utricle, saccule, and semicircular canals). B. Macula of utricle and saccule. C. Ampulla of semicircular canals.

lae are present in their walls (see Fig. 15-39). Each macula is a tuft of ciliated columnar epithelial cells embedded in a gelatinous matrix containing small calcified particles (*otoliths*). When the head is tilted from the vertical position, gravitational pull on the otoliths distorts the hair cells and initiates an action potential in the vestibular nerve. The three semicircular canals monitor acceleration in any plane. At one end of each canal is an enlargement called the *ampulla* (see Fig. 15-39). The ampulla contains a specialized region of epithelium, the *crista,* similar to the maculae in the saccule and utricle. The crista is on a transverse ridge that projects into the lumen of the semicircular canal (see Fig. 15-39). During rotational movement, the endolymph in the semicircular canal moves and distorts the crista, thus stimulating the hair cells and initiating action potentials. Each semicircular canal lies in a different plane so that each one is sensitive to rotation about a different axis.

Fibers of the vestibular division of cranial nerve VIII synapse in the superior, medial, lateral, and inferior vestibular nuclei located in the floor of the fourth ventricle. These nuclei have connections with several areas of the central nervous system. Some fibers of the vestibular nerve pass directly to the cerebellum via the inferior cerebellar peduncle. Others synapse in the inferior and medial vestibular nuclei before entering the cerebellum and terminating in the flocculonodular lobe. The flocculonodular lobe, in turn, sends fibers via the fastigial nucleus to the lateral vestibular nucleus, the origin of the lateral vestibulospinal tracts and a portion of the medial vestibulospinal tract, to regulate muscle tone in response to changing position. All the vestibular nuclei send fibers to the reticular formation, which can modify activity in the internal regulation and conciousness systems. The medial longitudinal fasciculus receives fibers from the vestibular nuclei for coordination of head and eye movements (see Fig. 15-32). Pathways ascending to the cerebral cortex are not clearly defined. However, vestibular function is represented in the temporal lobes.

Pathophysiology

Input from the vestibular apparatus on each side is continuous and balanced. When receptor activity is altered by motion, the pattern of afferent impulses changes and a subjective sensation of motion is produced. When sensations of motion are in harmony with other sensory input, they are perceived as a correct response to a changing environment. When a lesion renders a portion of the vestibular system either hypoactive or hyperactive, the centrally integrated afferent impulses are not in accord with other sensory stimuli, and disequilibrium is experienced. Dizziness, lightheadedness, giddiness, and wooziness are common but nonspecific examples of disequilibrium and frequently are not associated with disease of the vestibular system. However, vertigo, the hallucination of rotatory movement, is a highly specific form of disequilibrium and is suggestive of disease of the vestibular system. Rarely, vertigo is a manifestation of focal seizures involving the temporal lobe; it is more often a manifestation of disease of the peripheral receptors, vestibular nerve, or brain stem. Thus, vertigo is an important neurologic symptom of disease at the posterior fossa level or in the ear. Vertigo caused by disorders of the vestibular system is often accompanied by nausea, vomiting, ataxia, and nystagmus, because of the resulting dysfunction of the reticular, cerebellar, and oculomotor connections of the vestibular system described above.

Vestibular system function is evaluated by caloric stimulation and by testing the oculocephalic reflexes. In caloric testing, the external canal of each ear is irrigated with either warm or cold water. The temperature gradient of the water causes convection currents and movement of the endolymph in the semicircular canals. If the labyrinth, vestibular nerves, medial longitudinal fasciculus, and oculomotor system in the brain stem are intact, nystagmus occurs. Quantitative electrical measurement of the direction and amplitude of the eye movements produced in caloric testing is used in electronystagmography to help define the location and severity of vestibular lesions. The oculocephalic (doll's eye) reflexes are tested by rapidly turning the head from side to side or up and down. This movement stimulates the semicircular canals and causes the eyes to move conjugately in the opposite direction. Clinical caloric testing and doll's eye movements are commonly used to test the integrity of brain stem pathways in patients with altered states of consciousness. Abnormal results are helpful in localizing the responsible lesion to the posterior fossa level.

Clinical Correlations

Lesions that involve the posterior fossa level are associated with abnormalities in cranial nerve, cerebellar, or brain stem function. Because components of each of the major longitudinal systems are found at this level, dysfunction in any of these systems may be present. Lesions in all etiologic categories are found at this level, and the pathologic nature of these lesions can be determined, as at other levels, by applying the general principles of neurologic diagnosis outlined in Chapter 4 (Diagnosis of Neurologic Disorders: Neurocytology and Pathologic Reactions of the Nervous System). In this section, the clinical correlates of ischemic lesions and certain types of neoplasms, which are relatively common at this level, are discussed, as well as the effects of expanding supratentorial mass lesions that may secondarily involve the posterior fossa level (herniations of the brain).

Ischemic Lesions of the Brain Stem

The blood supply of the brain stem is derived from the vertebrobasilar arterial system. The pattern of supply to each level is relatively constant, with the midline region being supplied by small penetrating paramedian branches of the vertebral and basilar arteries and the lateral area being supplied by larger circumferential branches: the posterior inferior cerebellar artery at the level of the medulla, the anterior inferior cerebellar artery at the level of the pons, and the superior cerebellar artery at the level of the midbrain. Ischemic lesions involving the brain stem usually occur either in the paramedian region or in the lateral region. Infarction of the paramedian region involves the descending motor pathways, medial lemniscus, and the nuclei of cranial nerves III, IV, VI, and XII. Infarction of the lateral region involves

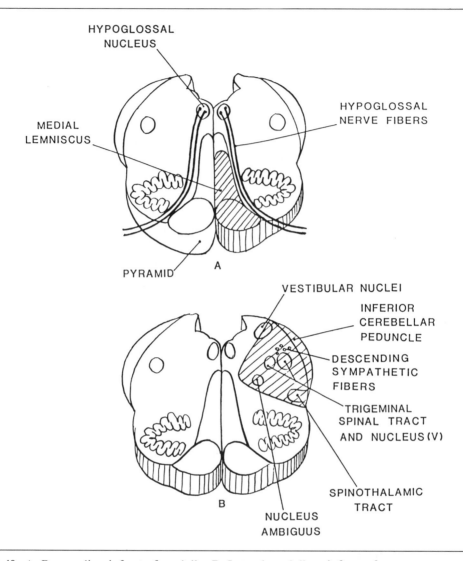

Fig. 15-40. A. Paramedian infarct of medulla. B. Lateral medullary infarct of medulla (Wallenberg's syndrome).

the cerebellum, cerebellar pathways, descending sympathetic pathways, the lateral spinothalamic tract, and the nuclei of cranial nerves V, VII, VIII, IX, or X.

Vascular Lesions of the Medulla

The paramedian region of the medulla is supplied by vessels from the anterior spinal and vertebral arteries. An infarction in the paramedian medulla involves the medullary pyramids, medial lemniscus, and cranial nerve XII, resulting in contralateral hemiparesis, impaired conscious proprioceptive sensation, and ipsilateral tongue weakness (Fig. 15-40).

The lateral regions of the medulla and portions of the cerebellum are supplied by the posterior inferior cerebellar artery. Occlusion or thrombosis of this artery (or its parent vertebral artery) produces infarction of the lateral medulla and results in a constellation of signs and symptoms referred to as *Wallenberg's syndrome* (Fig. 15-40). This syndrome includes dysarthria and dysphagia due to involvement of the nucleus ambiguus; ipsilateral impairment of pain and temperature on the face due to involvement of the descending nucleus and tract of nerve V; contralateral loss of pain and temperature in the trunk and extremities due

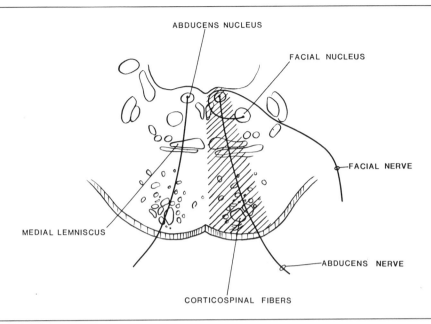

Fig. 15-41. Paramedian infarct of pons (*shaded area*) with involvement of VI nerve nucleus, facial nerve, medial lemniscus, and corticospinal tract.

to involvement of the spinothalamic tract; an ipsilateral Horner's syndrome due to involvement of the descending sympathetic fibers in the lateral part of the brain stem; ipsilateral limb ataxia due to involvement of the inferior cerebellar peduncle; and vertigo, which is due to involvement of the vestibular nuclei or vestibulocerebellar fibers in the tegmentum of the medulla.

Vascular Lesions of the Pons

An infarct of the paramedian area of the pons results in ipsilateral sixth nerve palsy due to involvement of the nucleus of nerve VI, ipsilateral facial weakness secondary to involvement of the facial nerve as it passes around the abducens nucleus, contralateral hemiparesis due to involvement of the corticospinal tracts in the basis pontis, and contralateral impairment of conscious proprioception due to involvement of the medial lemniscus (Fig. 15-41).

An infarct of the lateral portion of the pons causes ipsilateral facial paralysis due to involvement of the facial nucleus; impairment of touch, pain, and temperature on the same side of the face due to involvement of the main sensory nucleus and tract of cranial nerve V; loss of pain and temperature on the

contralateral side of the body due to involvement of the spinothalamic tract; ipsilateral deafness due to involvement of the nuclei of nerve VIII; ipsilateral Horner's syndrome due to involvement of the descending sympathetic fibers; and ipsilateral cerebellar signs due to involvement of the middle cerebellar peduncle.

Vascular Lesions of the Midbrain

Infarction of the lateral midbrain is uncommon; however, ischemic lesions involving the paramedian region (Fig. 15-42) are seen occasionally and produce diplopia, ptosis, and mydriasis due to involvement of cranial nerve III and contralateral hemiparesis due to involvement of the cerebral peduncle. This constellation of symptoms is called *Weber's syndrome.*

Neoplasms of the Posterior Fossa

Certain tumors of the posterior fossa are more commonly encountered in children and young adults. Ependymomas and medulloblastomas frequently arise in the region of the fourth ventricle and are associated with ataxia, nausea, and vomiting. As these lesions increase in size, they obstruct the outflow of cerebrospinal fluid from the ventricular system and

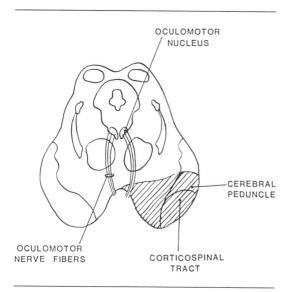

OCULOMOTOR
NUCLEUS

CEREBRAL
PEDUNCLE

OCULOMOTOR
NERVE FIBERS

CORTICOSPINAL
TRACT

Fig. 15-42. Paramedian infarct of midbrain — Weber's syndrome (*shaded area*), with involvement of nerve III and cerebral peduncle.

cause a noncommunicating hydrocephalus and signs of increased intracranial pressure. Astrocytomas of the cerebellum also are common in childhood; they arise in the cerebellar hemisphere (resulting in ipsilateral limb ataxia). These tumors, which are frequently cystic in structure, display a unique biologic behavior; the early diagnosis and surgical removal of cerebellar astrocytomas, in contrast to astrocytomas of other locations, are associated with a good prognosis.

Astrocytomas also arise from glial cells located within the substance of the brain stem to result in a brain stem or pontine glioma (Fig. 15-43). These tumors involve either the base or the tegmentum and are usually associated with progressive (often bilateral) symptoms of cranial nerve, motor, and sensory dysfunction. If the reticular formation is affected, consciousness is altered.

Certain tumors arise outside the parenchyma of the brain stem (extra-axial tumors), often from the meninges (meningiomas) or from the supporting cells in the cranial nerves. Extra-axial tumors initially produce alteration in cranial nerve function and secondarily affect brain stem function by compression or direct invasion. The most common tumor in this group is the vestibular schwannoma. Although it is commonly referred to as "acoustic neuroma," the tumor arises from Schwann cells in the vestibular division of cranial nerve VIII in virtually all

Fig. 15-43. Gross specimen of brain stem glioma. Transverse section showing diffuse asymmetric enlargement.

Fig. 15-44. Vestibular schwannoma. A. Gross specimen with posterior fossa and contents viewed from above with tumor (*arrow*) of cranial nerve VIII. (Note normal cranial nerves VII and VIII on the opposite side.) B. Computerized tomographic scan of posterior fossa at the level of the pons showing tumor (*arrow*) in cerebellopontine angle compressing pons.

cases (Fig. 15-44). The tumors are frequently bilateral in "central," or type II, neurofibromatosis. Early signs of a vestibular schwannoma are unilateral tinnitus, decreased hearing, and disequilibrium. As the tumor enlarges, ipsilateral facial paresis, loss of corneal reflex, and ipsilateral limb ataxia occur. With further increase in size, there may be additional signs of

brain stem compression and increased intracranial pressure. These tumors are usually seen with computerized tomographic scanning and, even when very small, with magnetic resonance imaging scanning.

Herniations of the Brain

Expanding supratentorial mass lesions may secondarily affect the structures located in the posterior fossa. The cranial cavity is a closed space and cannot accommodate to changes in intracranial volume. In the presence of a supratentorial or posterior fossa mass, intracranial pressure increases, and with further expansion, the brain adjusts to the increased volume by alteration in shape and slight shifts in position. With further compression and shift, the function in areas of the nervous system remote from the expanding mass is also compromised, and further deterioration in the clinical condition occurs. The changes in shape and position that occur secondary to intracranial mass lesions are called *herniations of the brain.*

Uncal Herniation

Uncal herniation characteristically occurs when unilateral, expanding supratentorial lesions, especially in the middle fossa, shift the mediobasal edge of the uncus of the hippocampal gyrus toward the midline and over the free edge of the tentorium, compressing the adjacent midbrain (Fig. 15-45A and Table 15-17). Cranial nerve III and sometimes the posterior cerebral artery on the side of the herniating temporal lobe are compressed by the overhanging swollen uncus. The clinical sign resulting from compression of cranial nerve III is an ipsilateral third-nerve paresis, usually beginning with dilatation of the pupil. Compression of the contralateral cerebral peduncle against the free edge of the tentorium can cause hemiparesis ipsilateral to the expanding lesion. Midbrain compression also affects the ascending reticular activating system, and there is progressive loss of consciousness. If the posterior cerebral artery is compressed, infarction of the occipital lobe occurs, producing homonymous hemianopia.

Central or Transtentorial Herniation

This type of herniation occurs as a further progression of uncal herniation and in association

Fig. 15-45. Herniations of the brain. A. Uncal herniation. B. Central (transtentorial) herniation. C. Tonsillar (foramen magnum) herniation. (Redrawn from F. Plum and J. B. Posner. *The Diagnosis of Stupor and Coma* [2nd ed.]. Philadelphia: Davis, 1972.)

Table 15-17. Herniations of the Brain

Type	Location	Cause	Anatomical structures involved	Clinical effects
Uncal	Tentorial notch, midbrain	Mass lesion in temporal lobe or middle fossa	Parahippocampal gyrus and uncus	
			Oculomotor nerve	Paresis of nerve III
			Cerebral peduncle	Hemiparesis
			Midbrain ascending reticular activating system	Coma
			Posterior cerebral artery	Homonymous hemianopia
Central (transtentorial)	Tentorial notch, midbrain	Mass lesion in frontal, parietal, or occipital lobe	Midbrain and pons	Decerebrate rigidity
		Progression of uncal herniation	Ascending reticular activating system	Coma
Tonsillar (foramen magnum)	Foramen magnum, medulla	Mass lesion in posterior fossa	Cerebellar tonsils	Neck pain and stiffness
		Progression of uncal or transtentorial herniation	Indirect activation pathways	Flaccidity
			Ascending reticular activating system	Coma
			Vasomotor centers	Alteration of pulse, respiration, blood pressure

with parasagittal or bilateral supratentorial masses. It consists of a caudal displacement of the diencephalon, midbrain, and pons (see Fig. 15-45B and Table 15-17). Caudal displacement of the basilar artery (which is attached to the circle of Willis via the posterior cerebral arteries) does not occur to the same degree, resulting in stretching and shearing of paramedian perforating vessels, with secondary infarction and hemorrhage in the brain stem. This type of herniation blocks the flow of cerebrospinal fluid through the aqueduct of Sylvius, thus further increasing the volume of the supratentorial contents. The clinical signs of central herniation are oculomotor paresis, progressive alteration of consciousness, and decerebrate rigidity. Because mass lesions rarely are directly in the midline, some degree of lateral shift and uncal herniation nearly always accompanies transtentorial herniation.

Tonsillar or Foramen Magnum Herniation

As a result of an expanding mass in the posterior fossa or further progression of uncal or transtentorial herniation, herniation of the cerebellar tonsils through the foramen magnum occurs, with compression of the medulla (see Fig. 15-45C and Table 15-17). Signs of tonsillar herniation include neck pain and stiffness, the result of stretching and irritation of the lower cranial nerves supplying the neck muscles; progressive loss of consciousness secondary to involvement of the ascending reticular activating system; generalized flaccidity; alteration of vital signs, with slowing of the pulse and vasomotor instability; and periodic or irregular respiration, the result of involvement of visceral centers in the medulla.

The three types of herniation of the brain are summarized in Figure 15-45 and Table 15-17.

Neurologic Examination of the Posterior Fossa Level

The integrity of the posterior fossa is examined by testing the function of each of the major longitudinal systems found at this level (see Chapters 6 through 11) and the functions associated with the oculomotor, auditory, and vestibular systems and cranial nerves III through XII.

The Oculomotor System and Cranial Nerves III, IV, and VI

Neurologic examination of the eyes begins with observing the size and bilateral symmetry of the palpebral fissures, especially looking for ptosis. The size, shape, and symmetry of the pupils are noted. The pupillary light reflex is tested by shining a light into each eye while observing the direct and consensual pupillary responses. The near reflex is tested by bringing a target toward the patient's nose and by observing pupillary constriction and eye convergence.

The position, alignment, and stability of the eyes when the patient attempts to gaze straight ahead (primary position) are observed. Abnormalities include inability to maintain the primary position because of conjugate deviation, misalignment of the eyes because of monocular deviation, and spontaneous nystagmus. Eye movement is tested in the six cardinal directions, first with both eyes fixing on the target and then testing each eye with the other covered. Subtle muscle weakness can be demonstrated by placing a red glass in front of one eye while the patient follows a white light. This inhibits the reflex tendency of the brain to fuse identical images if possible and allows clearer identification of the field of gaze in which the image separation (diplopia) is greatest, thus identifying the weak muscle. Nystagmus is also looked for in each direction of gaze.

Cranial Nerve V

Sensory function is examined by testing the patient's ability to perceive pinprick and light touch applied to the skin supplied by the three divisions of the trigeminal nerve. The corneal reflex (which also involves cranial nerve VII) is tested by asking the patient to look to one side while the cornea is gently touched with a wisp of cotton, brought toward the cornea from the opposite direction. The normal response is prompt, bilateral blinking.

Motor function is tested by having the patient open the jaw. In the presence of unilateral pterygoid weakness, the jaw deviates to the weak side. The patient is also asked to bite firmly while the examiner palpates the masseter and temporalis muscles on each side. Jaw jerk is tested by placing the examiner's forefinger on the relaxed jaw and by striking the finger with a reflex hammer.

Cranial Nerve VII

Examination of the facial nerve begins with observing the patient's facial expressions. As the patient talks and smiles, facial asymmetry or reduced contraction becomes apparent. Specific muscle groups are then examined. The frontalis muscles are tested by asking the patient to wrinkle the forehead; strength can be assessed by attempting to smooth the wrinkles on each side. The orbicularis oculi can be tested by asking the patient to tightly close the eyes and then to try opening them. The lower facial muscles are tested by asking the patient to smile or show the teeth. Taste is not examined unless a peripheral facial nerve lesion is suspected. It is tested by having the patient protrude the tongue and then asking him or her to identify sugar, salt, or other substances applied to the side of the tongue.

The Auditory and Vestibular Systems and Cranial Nerve VIII

Audiometry provides the best means of examining hearing, but a rough estimate of the functioning of the acoustic system can be made by determining if the patient can hear the sound of a watch or the sound produced by rubbing the forefinger and thumb together in front of the ear. Auditory acuity of one side is compared with that of the other. The Weber and Rinne tests should be performed (see Table 15-16).

Vestibular function ordinarily is not examined unless disease of cranial nerve VIII, sensory ataxia, or brain stem disease is suspected. Caloric testing (irrigating the outer ear canal with cold water and observing for nystagmus, conjugate deviation of the eyes, or subjective vertigo) is a convenient means of testing vestibular function but usually is reserved for comatose patients.

Cranial Nerves IX and X

The glossopharyngeal and vagus nerves are often tested together by listening to the patient talk and inquiring about difficulty in speaking or swallowing. A soft, breathy voice associated with nasal escape of air is suggestive of weakness in the oropharynx, whereas a hoarse or husky voice suggests a lesion of the nerve supply to the larynx. The patient is also asked to open the mouth and say "ah." Normally, the palate rises in the midline; unilateral palatal weakness causes the uvula to deviate toward the intact side. The gag reflex is examined by touching the back of the throat with a tongue blade and noting the contraction of the pharyngeal muscles.

Cranial Nerve XI

The sternocleidomastoid muscle is tested by asking the patient to turn the head to the side, against resistance applied by the examiner to the patient's jaw. The contracting muscle (on the side opposite the turn of the head) can be observed and palpated. The trapezius muscle is examined by having the patient elevate the shoulders against resistance applied by the examiner.

Cranial Nerve XII

The patient is asked to protrude the tongue in the midline and then to wiggle it from side to side. With upper motor neuron lesions, there is slowing of the alternate motion rate of the tongue. With unilateral lower motor neuron weakness, there are ipsilateral atrophy and fasciculations, and the protruded tongue deviates toward the side of the lesion.

Speech

Verbal communication includes both cognitive and motor skills. The cognitive aspects of verbal communication are considered language and are described in Chapter 16 (The Supratentorial Level). Some motor speech disorders may result from disease of the brain stem and cranial nerves (flaccid dysarthria) or cerebellum (ataxic dysarthria). Spastic, hypokinetic, and hyperkinetic dysarthrias result from disease at the supratentorial level.

Tests for disorders of speech, the dysarthrias, are commonly administered at the same time as the testing of cranial nerve function. Speech can be evaluated by listening to spontaneous speech or by having the patient repeat the syllables *pa-pa-pa* (facial muscle and nerve function), *ta-ta-ta* (tongue and hypoglossal nerve function), and *ka-ka-ka* (pharyngeal muscle and ninth and tenth nerve function). The syllables *pa-ta-ka-pa-ta-ka* test cranial muscle coordination (cerebellar function).

Objectives

1. Name and identify the nuclei and peripheral portions of cranial nerves III through XII. Describe their functions, clinical ex-

amination, and the signs and symptoms that indicate their dysfunction.

2. Identify the major anatomical features of the medulla, pons, midbrain, and cerebellum as described in the text, and state their function.

3. Outline the physiologic and anatomical features of the auditory and vestibular systems, and identify the signs and symptoms of their dysfunction.

4. Describe the actions of the ocular muscles, the significance of diplopia, the anatomy of the pupillary light reflex, and the significance of nystagmus, the oculocephalic reflex (doll's eye phenomenon), and ptosis.

5. List the major herniations of the brain, and briefly describe their mechanisms of symptom production.

Clinical Problems

1. A 68-year-old woman, previously in good health, suddenly became extremely nauseated and dizzy — as if the room were spinning around her. She remained conscious and could describe her symptoms to a companion, who noted that her voice was hoarse. Examination in the emergency room several hours later revealed the following abnormalities: The patient could not sit or stand because of vertigo. She was anxious and perspiring, except on the left side of her face. Her left pupil was small, and her left eyelid drooped slightly. There was horizontal and rotatory nystagmus. The left palate was drooping, and the left gag reflex was absent. There was loss of pain and temperature sensation on the left side of her face. Touch was preserved. Muscle strength and stretch reflexes were normal in the extremities. There was moderate incoordination of her left arm and leg. Sensory examination revealed loss of pain and temperature sensation in her right arm, trunk, and leg.
   a. What is the location and type of the abnormality?
   b. Specifically, what is the site of the lesion?
   c. What artery supplies the involved area?

d. What anatomical structures are responsible for the loss of pain and temperature sensation on the left side of the face and on the right side of the trunk?
   e. What is the cause of the ptosis, miosis, and anhidrosis on the left?

2. A 50-year-old man was well until 6 months ago when he noted some difficulty in swallowing. Food seemed to "stick" in the right side of his throat, and liquids occasionally entered the right side of his nose. In the past 3 months, he had noted a progressive hoarseness of his voice and difficulty in reaching overhead with his right arm. Examination revealed that the soft palate sagged on the right side. When the left posterior pharynx was stimulated, the soft palate pulled upward and to the left. When the right side was similarly stimulated, nothing happened and the patient said he could barely feel the touch. Indirect laryngoscopy revealed that the right vocal cord did not move with phonation. Muscle testing revealed weakness and atrophy of the right trapezius and sternocleidomastoid muscles. Results of the rest of the examination were normal.
   a. What is the location and type of lesion?
   b. What neural structures are involved?
   c. Through what foramen do these structures leave the skull?
   d. What other structure also passes through this foramen?
   e. Name one lesion that can produce the above syndrome.

3. A 70-year-old woman had sudden onset of weakness of her right arm and leg and difficulty in moving her tongue. When seen in the emergency room a few hours later, she had weakness of her right arm and leg and decreased ability to perceive proprioceptive and tactile stimuli on the right. When her tongue was protruded, it deviated to the left.
   a. What is the location and type of lesion?
   b. What structures are involved?
   c. What is the pathologic nature of the lesion?

4. A 25-year-old man awoke one morning and noted that the left side of his face seemed weak. On looking into a mirror, he noted that he could not retract the left corner of his mouth as well as the right. He also noted that he could no longer close his left eye completely or smile with the left side of his face. Neurologic examination revealed no abnormality except for the following: At rest, the left side of his face drooped, and the left palpebral fissure was wider than the right. The left side of his forehead did not wrinkle when he tried raising his eyebrows. He could not close his left eye completely. When he attempted to show his teeth, his mouth pulled to the right. Results of testing for sensations of pain, temperature, and touch of the face were normal. Taste was absent on the left side of his tongue. Strips of filter paper were placed in the conjunctival sacs; the one on the right became moist within a few minutes, and the left side remained dry.

   a. What is the location and type of lesion?
   b. Why was taste involved?
   c. Why was there decreased lacrimation?
   d. What is the name of this clinical entity?

5. A 60-year-old woman had ringing (tinnitus) in her right ear for the past year, as well as intermittent episodes of feeling that the room was spinning around her. In the past 6 months, she began staggering to the right and had difficulty with coordination of her right hand. Three weeks ago, she noted that the right side of her face was weak. Examination revealed a loss of hearing and an absent caloric response on the right. She could not wrinkle her forehead or retract the right side of her face when asked to smile. She had trouble with coordination in her right hand and had an intention tremor on finger-to-nose and heel-to-shin testing of the right upper and lower extremities.

   a. What is the location and type of lesion?
   b. What specific anatomical structures are involved?
   c. What is the general anatomical term used to describe the region of involvement?
   d. Name one pathologic lesion that can produce this syndrome.
   e. What diagnostic studies might be useful in defining the location of this lesion?

6. A 60-year-old woman had a myocardial infarction. Several days later, however, she complained to the nurse that she had an abrupt onset of seeing double whenever she looked to the left and that she was having some difficulty in using her right arm. Testing of cranial nerves revealed a paralysis of the left lateral rectus muscle. Her speech was slightly slurred, and the left nasolabial fold was flattened. She could not tightly close her left eye, and she could not raise her eyebrow on the left as high as on the right. Facial sensation and taste were normal. Testing of the extremities revealed weakness of the right arm and leg, with hyperactive reflexes and Babinski's sign on the right. There was loss of joint position and vibration sense in the right arm and leg.

   a. What is the location and type of lesion?
   b. What anatomical structures are involved?
   c. What is the pathologic nature of the lesion?

7. A 73-year-old diabetic woman entered the hospital because of abrupt onset of double vision and left-sided weakness. Examination several hours later revealed that her right pupil was 4 mm and her left was 3 mm. The direct and consensual light response of the right pupil was less brisk than the left. There was slight ptosis of the eyelid on the right. On following a light with her eyes, she reported seeing two images when the light was moved directly to her left and to her right and upward. A red glass was placed over her right eye. When the light was moved to the left, the red image was seen to the left of the white image. When the light was moved to her right and upward, the red image was above the white image. In each instance, the separation increased as the light was moved further. The only other abnormali-

ties on neurologic examination were slight drooping of the left corner of her mouth and slight weakness of her left arm and leg, with hyperactive deep tendon reflexes, reduced abdominal reflexes, and Babinski's sign on the left.

a. What is the location and type of lesion?

b. What anatomical structures are involved?

c. Diplopia testing indicated weakness of which muscles?

d. Why was the pupillary light reflex altered?

e. What is the pathologic nature of the lesion?

8. A 10-year-old boy was seen because of trouble with coordination of his left side. He had been well until 3 months ago, when he experienced severe headaches. Two months ago, he began to note that his left hand shook when he reached for an object. One month before admission, he noted increasing clumsiness of his left leg. Because of the headaches, nausea and vomiting, and increased clumsiness of the left arm and leg, he was examined. Examination showed that his optic nerve heads were swollen and that he took frequent missteps with his left leg and had an intention tremor on finger-to-nose and heel-to-shin testing. His muscle tone was slightly decreased on the left, but strength and sensation were intact.

a. What is the location and type of lesion?

b. What specific area of the neuraxis seems to be involved?

c. What signs and symptoms suggest the presence of increased intracranial pressure?

d. Name the most common lesion occurring in children that can produce this syndrome.

9. A 55-year-old man had noted progressive difficulty in swallowing and talking during the past year; liquids had tended to go down his "windpipe" or out his nose, and he had felt that his trouble with speech was due to his "tongue not working right." Examination revealed fasciculations and atrophy of the tongue bilater-

ally. He had trouble protruding his tongue and moving it from side to side. When he was asked to say "ah," his palate showed only minimal elevation. When asked to say "ka, ka, ka," he had nasal emission of speech. When asked to show his teeth, he was noted to have bilateral facial weakness, left greater than right, and he could not whistle. Slight distal extremity weakness and fasciculations also were seen. Deep tendon reflexes were reduced, but Babinski's sign was present bilaterally. Results of the rest of the examination were normal.

a. What is the location and site of the lesion?

b. What system(s) is involved?

c. What component(s) of the system(s) is involved?

d. Name one disorder that can produce this syndrome.

10. A 13-year-old girl awoke one morning complaining of a left earache and a dull generalized headache. Her temperature was 102°F (38.7°C) orally. She did not improve with aspirin and bed rest and that evening she was taken to her family physician, who diagnosed acute otitis media and gave her an injection of penicillin. For the next several days, she continued to have some ear drainage and mild left-sided ear pain and headache. During the next week, she had increasingly severe headaches, with nausea and vomiting. One day before admission, she experienced progressive weakness of the right face, arm, and leg and difficulty in speaking. She also seemed to have difficulty in thinking of what word she wanted to say, and she had difficulty in understanding what people were saying to her.

a. At this point, what is the suspected location and type of lesion?

When seen at the local hospital, she was stuporous but could be aroused by strong stimuli. Her left pupil was dilated and reacted poorly to light. The right pupillary reflex was intact. The left eye was deviated down and out, and she had ptosis of the left eyelid. During the examination, her right hemiparesis became much worse.

b. What is the reason for her change in level of consciousness?

c. How do you explain the eye findings?

d. Why was there worsening of her hemiparesis?

e. What is the term used to describe the above process?

It was decided to send the patient to the nearest neurosurgical facility, which was several hours away. On arrival at the second hospital, she was deeply comatose. Respirations were deep and rapid. Her temperature was 105°F (40.3°C). Her pupils were slightly dilated and did not react to light. Her jaw was tightly clenched. Her spine was extended and arched posteriorly. Her arms were stiffly extended and the fists clenched. Her legs were also stiffly extended.

f. The findings present at this point suggest involvement at what level of the neuraxis?

g. What term describes her body position and tone?

h. What term describes the process producing this clinical picture?

Additional Reading

Baloh, R. W., and Honrubia, V. *Clinical Neurophysiology of the Vestibular System* (2nd ed.). Philadelphia: Davis, 1990.

Department of Neurology, Mayo Clinic and Mayo Foundation. *Clinical Examinations in Neurology* (6th ed.). St. Louis: Mosby, 1991.

Hudspeth, A. J. The cellular basis of hearing: The biophysics of hair cells. *Science* 230:745, 1985.

Ito, M. *The Cerebellum and Neural Control.* New York: Raven, 1984.

Leigh, R. J., and Zee, D. S. *The Neurology of Eye Movements* (2nd ed.). Philadelphia: Davis, 1991.

Miller, N. R. *Walsh and Hoyt's Clinical Neuro-Ophthalmology* (4th ed.), Vol. 2. Baltimore: Williams & Wilkins, 1988.

Schubert, E. D. *Hearing: Its Function and Dysfunction.* New York: Springer-Verlag, 1980.

Wilson-Pauwels, L., Akesson, E. J., and Stewart, P. A. *Cranial Nerves: Anatomy and Clinical Comments.* Toronto: Decker, 1988.

— 16 —

The Supratentorial Level

The supratentorial level consists of two main anatomical regions: the diencephalon and the telencephalon. As with other levels, the structures of the supratentorial level include "inner tube" and "outer tube" components of the nervous system. The phylogenetically older inner tube components include the limbic lobe, amygdala, basal forebrain, olfactory structures, hypothalamus, and the thalamic nuclei that interconnect these regions. These structures are involved with the functions of the internal regulation and consciousness systems, emotion, and motivation. The phylogenetically newer outer tube structures include the neocortex of the cerebral hemispheres, the basal ganglia, and the thalamic nuclei that connect these regions. These structures are involved with higher cognitive functions, language, programming of motor function, fine motor control, and processing of sensory information (visual, somatosensory, auditory). Memory is a complex function that involves structures of both the inner and the outer tubes.

This chapter discusses the anatomy, physiology, and clinical correlates of the anatomical areas and systems at the supratentorial level.

Overview

The supratentorial level includes all structures located within the skull and above the tentorium cerebelli. These structures have evolved from the embryonic prosencephalon and, therefore, include derivatives of the diencephalon and telencephalon (Table 16-1 and Fig. 16-1). The diencephalon consists of the structures between the midbrain and the cerebral hemispheres that surround the third ventricle.

The diencephalon includes the thalamus, hypothalamus, and surrounding regions. The *thalamus* is the largest structure in the diencephalon and consists of nuclei that act as relay and integrating stations for sensory input to the cerebral cortex and corticosubcortical circuits for motor control and higher cognitive functions.

The *hypothalamus* is anterior and inferior to the thalamus and contains nuclei involved with the endocrine and autonomic functions important in homeostasis and reproduction. The inferior aspect of the hypothalamus (the ventral surface of the brain) consists of the tuber cinereum and mammillary bodies. The pituitary gland is not part of the hypothalamus but is attached to the tuber cinereum by the pituitary stalk. The hypothalamus regulates visceral and endocrine functions, body temperature, blood osmolality, food intake, and sleep.

The diencephalon includes two other regions: the *epithalamus*, containing the pineal gland, and the *subthalamus*, a poorly defined region that contains the ventral thalamus and the subthalamic nucleus, which is part of the basal ganglia circuits.

The telencephalon consists of the cerebral hemispheres and the basal forebrain. The *cerebral hemispheres* are subdivided into three anatomical regions: basal ganglia, subcortical white matter, and cerebral cortex. The *basal ganglia* — including the striatum and globus pallidus and their connections with the cerebral cortex, thalamus, and brain stem — form one of the motor control systems.

Table 16-1. Structures at the Supratentorial Level

	Inner tube structures	Outer tube structures
Diencephalon		
Thalamus	Intralaminar, midline, dorsomedial, and anterior nuclei	Ventral, geniculate, dorsomedial, and pulvinar nuclei
Hypothalamus	All hypothalamic nuclei	—
Epithalamus	Pineal gland	—
Telencephalon		
Basal ganglia	Ventral striatum (nucleus accumbens)	Dorsal striatum (caudate, putamen)
Basal forebrain	Amygdala, septal region, nucleus basalis	—
Cerebral cortex	Archicortex/paleocortex (limbic/paralimbic cortex, hippocampus, insula, and cingulate and orbitofrontal gyri)	Neocortex (dorsal prefrontal, lateral frontal, primary motor and sensory, and association cortices)

Fig. 16-1. The supratentorial level (*stippled area*) includes the diencephalon and telencephalon.

The *subcortical white matter* is composed of dense fiber tracts connecting cortical and subcortical structures. Projectional fibers connect the cortex with the thalamus, hypothalamus, basal ganglia, cerebellum, and other subcortical structures. Commissural fibers connect homologous areas between the two hemispheres, and association fibers connect areas within one hemisphere.

The *cerebral cortex* is a relatively thin mantle of gray matter covering the outer surface of the cerebral hemispheres; it forms the gyri of the brain. The two main sulci that divide the hemisphere into different lobes are the *central sulcus* and the *sylvian fissure*. Each cerebral hemisphere is divided into five lobes: frontal, parietal, occipital, temporal, and limbic. The frontal lobe, anterior to the central sulcus, has effector (motor) functions. The parietal, occipital, and temporal lobes are posterior to the central sulcus and have receptive and perceptive functions. The sylvian fissure separates the temporal lobe from the frontal and parietal lobes. The right and left hemispheres have

Table 16-2. Functions of the Supratentorial Level

Inner tube	Outer tube
High-level autonomic control	Motor programming
Homeostasis and reproduction	Fine motor control
Motivated behavior	Sensory discrimination
Behavioral arousal	Visuospatial orientation
Emotion	Vision
Learning	Higher cognitive functions
Memory	Attention
Olfaction	Judgment
	Memory storage and retrieval
	Language

specialized functions. The left hemisphere is involved with language and calculation, and the right hemisphere is involved with visuospatial functions.

The *frontal lobe* includes the prefrontal region and the premotor and motor areas. The prefrontal area is involved with motor planning, attention, concentration, and control of affective behavior. The premotor and motor areas are involved with the programming and execution of motor function, oculomotor control, and speech production. The *parietal lobe* is concerned with somatosensory function; the primary somatosensory area is in the postcentral gyrus. Parietal association areas integrate sensory input from several sources. The *occipital lobe* contains the visual areas. The *temporal lobe* consists of a lateral portion, which is the primary sensory area for auditory and vestibular information, and a medial portion, which is involved with memory and is part of the limbic system. The *limbic lobe* is on the medial surface of the hemisphere and includes the orbitofrontal region, cingulate gyrus, and medial portions of the temporal lobe, especially the hippocampus and amygdala. The limbic lobe has an integral role in memory and in visceral and emotional activity.

The *basal forebrain* is an anatomically complex structure that includes the ventral part of the basal ganglia, the amygdala, and the cholinergic neurons of the nucleus basalis.

As is true of other levels, structures at the supratentorial level can be subdivided into inner tube and outer tube components (see Table 16-1). The inner tube structures of this level include what is termed the *limbic system*.

The limbic system contains diencephalic and telencephalic structures and consists of the hypothalamus, septal region, basal forebrain, limbic cortex (hippocampus and cingulate), and the thalamic nuclei interconnecting these areas. These structures are involved in high-order autonomic control, neuroendocrine function, homeostasis, emotion, behavioral arousal, motivated behavior, memory, and learning (Table 16-2). The sensory system associated with the limbic system is the olfactory system.

The outer tube components include the lateral surface of the cerebral hemispheres, the basal ganglia, and the thalamic regions interconnecting these areas. The functions of the outer tube structures include attention, control of behavior, motor programming and execution, sensory processing, perception, language, memory, and visuospatial orientation (see Table 16-2).

Disorders at the supratentorial level may alter motor and sensory functions contralaterally. Disorders involving the diencephalon impair the relay of information to and from the cerebral hemispheres or impair visceral, endocrine, or emotional functions. Disorders involving the cerebral hemispheres may cause general intellectual deterioration (dementia), amnesia, aphasia, agnosia (inability to perceive the meaning of sensory input), apraxia (inability to perform complex motor activities voluntarily), or seizures. In general, lesions of the left hemisphere affect language-related functions and lesions of the right hemisphere affect visuospatial-related functions.

An important sensory system of the outer

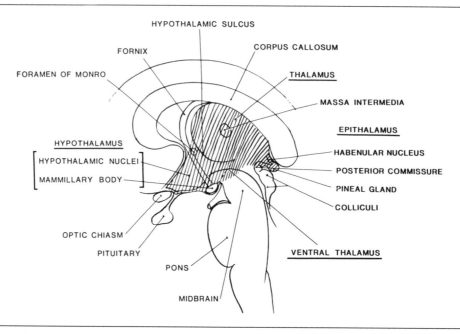

HYPOTHALAMIC SULCUS

FORNIX

CORPUS CALLOSUM

FORAMEN OF MONRO

THALAMUS

MASSA INTERMEDIA

EPITHALAMUS

HYPOTHALAMUS

HABENULAR NUCLEUS

HYPOTHALAMIC NUCLEI

POSTERIOR COMMISSURE

MAMMILLARY BODY

PINEAL GLAND

COLLICULI

OPTIC CHIASM

PITUITARY

VENTRAL THALAMUS

PONS

MIDBRAIN

Fig. 16-2. Diencephalon (*shaded area*) and its four subdivisions: thalamus, ventral thalamus, epithalamus, and hypothalamus.

tube is the visual system. The structures of the visual system — the eye, retina, visual pathway, and occipital cortex — are found at the peripheral, diencephalic, and telencephalic levels.

Diencephalon

The diencephalon is rostral to the brain stem and includes the structures surrounding the third ventricle: thalamus, ventral thalamus, epithalamus, and hypothalamus. The diencephalon is bounded superiorly by the floor of the lateral ventricles, corpus callosum, and fornix and laterally by the internal capsule. Anteriorly, it extends to the region of the foramen of Monro, and caudally, it merges with the tegmentum of the midbrain (Fig. 16-2).

The thalamus is the largest structure in the diencephalon and contains a number of thalamic nuclei. The thalamic relay nuclei constitute the dorsal thalamus. The thalamic reticular nucleus is derived from the ventral thalamus. The hypothalamus lies inferior and anterior to the thalamus and is separated from the thalamus by the hypothalamic sulcus — a groove in the wall of the third ventricle from

the foramen of Monro to the aqueduct of Sylvius. The ventral thalamic region lies ventral and posterior to the thalamus and merges with the midbrain. The epithalamus forms part of the roof of the diencephalon and lies superior to the ventral thalamus and posterior to the thalamus.

Thalamus

The thalamus consists of a group of nuclei in the wall of the third ventricle. The thalami sometimes fuse in the midline and form the interthalamic adhesion (or massa intermedia). The anterior end of the thalamus, containing the anterior nucleus, is narrow, and the posterior end, containing the pulvinar and geniculate bodies, is broad. The Y-shaped internal medullary lamina divides the thalamus into anterior, medial, and lateral areas (Fig. 16-3).

The anterior nuclear group is in the anterior area, and the dorsomedial and midline nuclei are in the medial area. The lateral nuclei are arranged in two tiers: a dorsal tier and a ventral tier (Table 16-3). The nuclei in the dorsal tier, from anterior to posterior, are the dorsolateral nucleus, the lateral posterior nucleus,

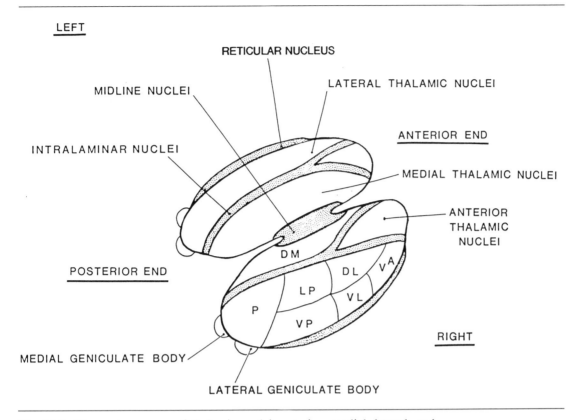

Fig. 16-3. The major groups of thalamic nuclei: anterior, medial, lateral, and intralaminar. The medial group includes the midline and dorsomedial (DM) nuclei. The lateral group includes dorsolateral (DL), lateral posterior (LP), pulvinar (P), medial and lateral geniculate bodies, ventral anterior (VA), ventral lateral (VL), and ventral posterior (VP) nuclei. (Redrawn from F. H. Netter. *The Ciba Collection of Medical Illustrations.* Volume I: The Nervous System. Summit, N.J.: Ciba Pharmaceutical Products, 1962. P. 48.)

and the pulvinar. The medial geniculate and lateral geniculate bodies extend posteriorly from the ventral surface of the pulvinar. In the ventral tier, from anterior to posterior, are the ventral anterior, ventral lateral, and ventral posterior nuclei (see Fig. 16-3). Between and surrounding these well-defined nuclear groups are layers of cells forming sheetlike nuclei: the intralaminar nuclei in the Y-shaped border between the major groups, the reticular nuclei around the outside, and the midline nuclei.

The *thalamic nuclei* integrate and relay information for the sensory, motor, consciousness, and limbic systems. The ventral posterior (posterolateral and posteromedial) nuclei relay somatic sensory system information to the cerebral cortex. The ventral posterolateral nucleus is the site of termination of the spinothalamic and medial lemniscal pathways from the trunk

and limbs. Similarly, axons of the trigeminal thalamic pathways from the head terminate in the ventral posteromedial nucleus. Axons from the ventral posterior nuclei project in the posterior limb of the internal capsule to the primary somatosensory cortex in the postcentral gyrus of the parietal lobe.

The ventral lateral nucleus receives input from the cerebellar nuclei and projects to primary motor cortex. The ventral anterior nucleus receives input from the globus pallidus and substantia nigra and projects to the supplementary motor and premotor cortical areas.

The medial geniculate body receives auditory afferent fibers from the inferior colliculus via the brachium of the inferior colliculus and sends efferent fibers through the auditory radiations in the sublenticular portion of the posterior limb of the internal capsule to the audi-

Table 16-3. Summary of Thalamic Nuclei

Anterior area ————————————————————————	Anterior nucleus
Medial area ————————————————————————	⌐Midline
	└Dorsomedial
Intralaminar area ————————————————————	Intralaminar nuclei
	⌐Dorsolateral
	Lateral posterior
Dorsal tier ———————————	Pulvinar
	Medial geniculate
Lateral area ———————————	└Lateral geniculate
	⌐Ventral anterior
Ventral tier ———————————	Ventral lateral
	└Ventral posterior
	⌐Reticular

tory cortex of the temporal lobe. The lateral geniculate body relays visual impulses from the optic tract via the retrolenticular portion of the posterior limb of the internal capsule to the calcarine cortex of the occipital lobe and is part of the visual system.

The pulvinar receives visual information and projects to the posterior parietal cortex and is important for the process of directed visual attention.

The dorsomedial nucleus of the thalamus relays information to the prefrontal cortex. The dorsomedial and midline thalamic nuclei are part of the circuits of the amygdala, hippocampus, and other parts of the internal regulation system. The intralaminar nuclei are components of the indirect pathway of the sensory system and the consciousness system and have important connections with the basal ganglia. The anterior nuclei, via connections with the hippocampus, mammillary bodies, and cingulate gyrus, are involved with learning and memory.

The reticular nucleus of the thalamus is derived from the ventral thalamus. This nucleus projects to other thalamic nuclei. It is critical in regulating thalamic nuclei that relay information to the cortex, particularly in regard to the sleep-wake cycle. All thalamic nuclei receive projections from the areas of the cerebral cortex to which they project (reciprocal thalamocortical connections).

Ventral Thalamus

The ventral thalamus, or subthalamus, gives rise to the reticular thalamic nucleus. The ven-

tral thalamus is a poorly defined area at the mesencephalodiencephalic junction; it includes the subthalamic nucleus, which is part of the basal ganglia circuits. A lesion of the subthalamic nucleus causes *hemiballismus*, a movement disorder in which rapid flailing movements occur in one extremity or on one side of the body.

Epithalamus

The epithalamus lies in the dorsal wall of the posterior part of the third ventricle beneath the splenium of the corpus callosum.

The main structure of the epithalamus is the *pineal gland*, which is formed from an evagination of the roof of the diencephalon. The cavity of the evagination is the pineal recess of the third ventricle. Other structures located in the region include the habenular nuclei, which lie in the walls of the epithalamus, and the posterior commissure, which crosses the midline ventral to the pineal gland (see Fig. 16-2).

The pineal gland is part of the circuit for controlling circadian rhythms, which originate in the suprachiasmatic nucleus of the hypothalamus. The circuits are affected by the light cycle. The pineal gland produces melatonin, a hormone that mediates circadian changes, including the sleep-wake cycle.

The blood supply to the posterior thalamus is via branches of the vertebrobasilar circulation. Discrete lesions that destroy the ventral posterior nucleus of the thalamus produce a contralateral hemianesthesia, with loss of all sensory modalities in the trunk, limbs, and face. This is often the result of an infarction due to hypertensive vascular disease or thrombosis of one of the branches of the posterior cerebral artery. The initial stage of contralateral hemianesthesia after a thalamic infarct may in turn be followed by a partial return of sensation associated with a very unpleasant burning sensation; this is referred to as the *thalamic syndrome*. Motor function can be altered by lesions of the motor relay nuclei of the thalamus. Discrete neurosurgical lesions in the ventral anterior thalamic nucleus disrupt connections between the basal ganglia and the cerebral cortex and thereby decrease the tremor and rigidity in some patients with Parkinson's disease. Lesions of the medial part of the thalamus can produce somnolence and problems with memory.

Hypothalamus

The hypothalamus is the main control area of the visceral system. It integrates activity for the limbic, consciousness, internal regulation, and endocrine systems. The hypothalamus includes those structures in the diencephalon anterior and inferior to the thalamus that are separated from it by the hypothalamic sulcus. The hypothalamus consists of the hypothalamic nuclei in the walls of the third ventricle and the tuber cinereum and mammillary bodies in the floor of the third ventricle (Fig. 16-4).

The hypothalamus extends from the region of the optic chiasm to the caudal border of the mammillary body. The region located in front of the optic chiasm is known as the *preoptic region*, a telencephalic derivative. The preoptic region and hypothalamus form an anatomical-functional unit.

The hypophysis, or pituitary gland, is functionally related to the hypothalamus and is attached to it at the tuber cinereum by the infundibulum, or pituitary stalk. Other closely related structures not part of the hypothalamus are the optic chiasm, located immediately below the anterior hypothalamus; the internal carotid arteries in the cavernous sinus, located just lateral to the pituitary gland; and cranial nerves III, IV, V, and VI, which lie adjacent to the pituitary gland in the cavernous sinus (Fig. 16-5). The hypothalamus has fiber connections with all areas of the brain stem and cerebral hemispheres but particularly with the basal frontal and medial cortical areas and with the reticular formation. The most prominent fiber tracts are the fornix, which ends in the mammillary bodies, and the mammillothalamic tract, which terminates in the anterior nuclei of the thalamus. These tracts and the hypothalamic nuclei are part of the limbic system.

The hypothalamic nuclei can be grouped into three functional zones: the periventricular zone, the medial zone, and the lateral hypothalamic zone (Table 16-4; see Chapter 9, The Internal Regulation System, and Fig. 9-7).

The nuclei in the periventricular zone are involved in biologic rhythms, neuroendocrine control, and complex autonomic responses. The medial zone contains nuclei involved in homeostasis and reproduction. The lateral zone contains the tuberomammillary nuclei and the medial forebrain bundle, which are involved with arousal mechanisms and motivated behavior. The hypothalamic nuclei and tracts have functional interactions with the limbic system, reticular formation, autonomic centers, and anterior pituitary lobe.

The hypothalamus has the following functions (see Table 16-4):

1. *Neuroendocrine control.* The neuroendocrine functions of the hypothalamus are mediated by two systems: the magnocellular and the parvocellular neurosecretory systems. The magnocellular system consists of the supraoptic and paraventricular nuclei; they secrete vasopressin, or antidiuretic hormone, which controls water metabolism, and oxytocin, which controls uterine contractions. The parvocellular system includes neurons in the paraventricular and arcuate nuclei and the medial preoptic area that secrete releasing or inhibitory hormones controlling anterior pituitary function. The hormones that control anterior pituitary secretion are called *hypothalamic regulatory hormones*, because they regulate the secretions and release of hormones by the anterior pituitary gland. Interruption of hypothalamopituitary connections may cause decreased secretion of all pituitary hormones except prolactin, which is increased. Failure of secretion of antidiuretic hormone produces

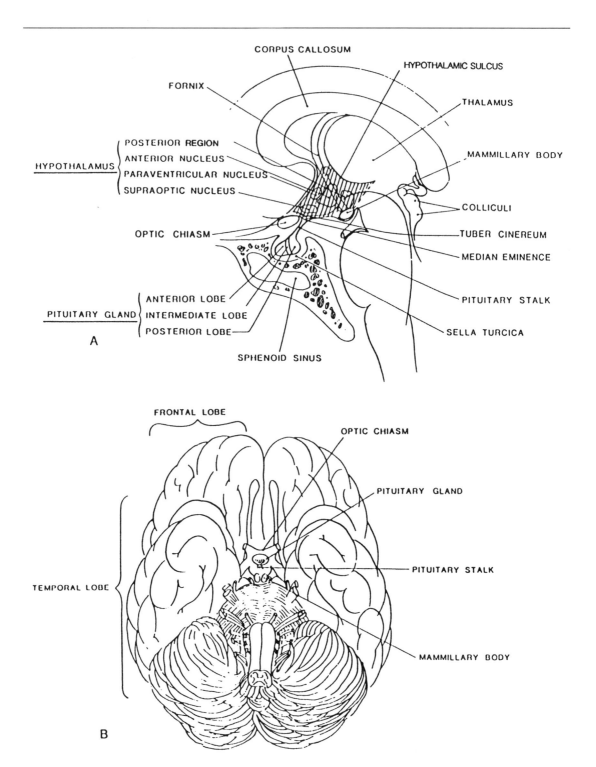

Fig. 16-4. The hypothalamus. A. Midline section of the hypothalamic nuclei (*shaded area*), the pituitary gland in the sella turcica, and the mammillary bodies. B. Base of the brain with the optic chiasm, pituitary stalk, and mammillary bodies.

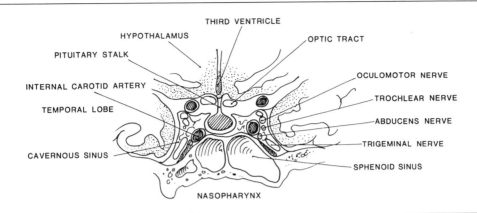

Fig. 16-5. Coronal section of the base of the brain. The structures adjacent to the pituitary gland are in the cavernous sinus located on either side of the pituitary gland: cranial nerves III, IV, V, and VI and the internal carotid arteries. The optic tracts are adjacent to the pituitary stalk.

Table 16-4. Hypothalamic Functions and Dysfunction

Nucleus	Function	Dysfunction
Periventricular zone		
Suprachiasmatic	Circadian rhythms	Disruption of circadian rhythms
Supraoptic and paraventricular	Antidiuretic hormone (ADH) and oxytocin	Diabetes insipidus, inappropriate secretion of ADH
Tuberoinfundibular	Releasing factors (regulatory hormone)	Hypopituitarism, Cushing's disease, acromegaly, sexual precocity, amenorrhea, hyperprolactinemia
Medial zone		
Medial preoptic	Thermoregulation	Hyperthermia/hypothermia
Anterior	Osmoregulation, sleep induction	Hypernatremia, thirst disorders, salt wasting syndrome, insomnia
Ventromedial	Food intake	Obesity
Lateral zone	Cortical arousal, motivated behavior	Hypersomnia, aphagia, adipsia

diabetes insipidus, in which excessive quantities of dilute urine are excreted. Inappropriate secretion of antidiuretic hormone causes retention of water and can produce hyponatremia.

2. *Autonomic control.* The paraventricular nucleus, nuclei in the medial zone, and the lateral hypothalamus contain a mixed population of neurons that innervate sympathetic and parasympathetic regions of the brain stem and spinal cord. Autonomic manifestations of hypothalamic disease include the diencephalic syndrome of autonomic hyperactivity with hyperthermia, hypertension, tachycardia, and sweating.

3. *Thermoregulation.* The preoptic-anterior hypothalamic region contains thermosensitive neurons, including "warm sensitive neurons" that initiate heat loss responses (skin vasodilatation and sweating) and "cold sensitive neurons" that initiate heat gain responses (skin vasoconstriction and shivering). Hypothalamic lesions may cause hypothermia or hyperthermia.

4. *Water metabolism (osmoregulation).* The circuit controlling water metabolism includes the subfornical organ and other osmosensitive circumventricular organs in the anterior wall of the third ventricle, the preoptic region, and the magnocellular supraoptic and paraventricular nuclei. These regions exert a major role in water metabolism via two mechanisms: thirst and secretion of antidiuretic hormone. Destruction of the anterior hypothalamic region produces disorders of thirst with hypernatremia, or syndrome of salt wasting.

5. *Food intake.* Several hypothalamic regions contain glucosensitive neurons that also respond to various peptides; these neurons control autonomic output to the endocrine pancreas and adrenal gland, which are important for regulation of energy metabolism. These hypothalamic regions include the paraventricular and the ventromedial nuclei and the lateral hypothalamic area; they are involved in the control of food intake. Lesions of the medial hypothalamus, including the paraventricular nucleus, produce increased appetite and obesity. Lesions of the lateral hypothalamus produce a decrease in the urge to eat or drink.

6. *Reproductive function.* The hypothalamus affects sexual function and reproduction via control of secretion of gonadotropin-releasing hormones and prolactin and control of specific sexual behaviors. Important regions include the medial preoptic area, which contains a sexually dimorphic nucleus, and the ventromedial nucleus. These regions contain an abundance of receptors for sex steroids (estrogens and androgens). Hypothalamic disorders may produce precocious puberty, amenorrhea, and other disorders of sexual function.

7. *Sleep-wake cycle.* Two hypothalamic areas control the sleep-wake cycle: the medial preoptic region can initiate slow wave sleep as a part of a thermoregulatory heat loss mechanism, and the lateral hypothalamic area is the rostral part of the reticular activating system and is involved in cortical arousal.

Pituitary Gland

The pituitary gland (hypophysis) lies within a bony-walled cavity, the *sella turcica* ("Turk's saddle"), in the sphenoid bone at the base of the brain (see Fig. 16-4A). It is connected to the hypothalamus by the *pituitary stalk*, which arises from the median eminence — a midline, ventral projection from the tuber cinereum. The pituitary stalk is located between the optic chiasm and the mammillary bodies. Its relationship with the optic chiasm is clinically important because enlargement of the pituitary gland may compress the visual pathways in the optic chiasm.

The pituitary gland consists of three divisions: the anterior lobe, or adenohypophysis; the posterior lobe, or neurohypophysis; and the intermediate lobe. Although each lobe is part of a single gland, each has a different embryologic origin. The anterior lobe arises from a neuroectodermal ridge in the oral region, and the posterior lobe arises from a downward evagination of the embryonic diencephalon (see Fig. 2-11). The posterior lobe and the pituitary stalk are formed from this evaginated neural process, which serves as the neural connection with the diencephalon in the adult. The anterior lobe, which fuses with the posterior lobe, has no known neural connections with the brain and receives its hypothalamic control through a system of portal vessels. The release of hormones from the pituitary gland is regulated by a vascular mechanism in the case of the anterior lobe (Fig. 16-6A) and by a neural mechanism in the case of the posterior lobe (Fig. 16-6B).

The portal circulation connecting the hypothalamus and anterior lobe consists of hypophyseal arteries located in the median eminence that give rise to capillaries that drain into a series of parallel veins coursing down the pituitary stalk (see Fig. 16-6A). On reaching the anterior lobe, the veins form a capillary plexus that supplies blood to the anterior lobe. The release of the anterior pituitary hormones is under the control of neurohumoral substances secreted by the hypothalamus. These substances, the regulatory hormones, are released from nerve endings in the median eminence. They enter the capillaries of the portal circulation, travel down the pituitary stalk through the portal veins, and then empty into the capillary plexus of the anterior pituitary gland, where they stimulate the anterior pituitary cells to release specific hormones.

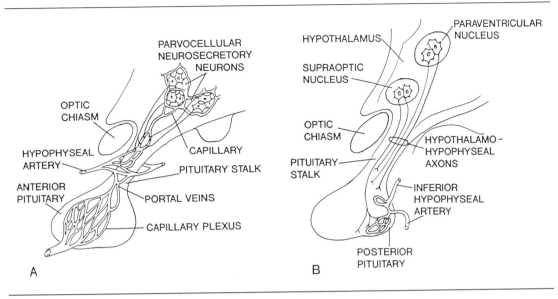

Fig. 16-6. A. Portal circulation carries releasing factors from hypothalamus to anterior pituitary lobe. B. Axons carry hormones from hypothalamic nuclei to posterior pituitary lobe.

The posterior pituitary hormones, vasopressin and oxytocin, are synthesized in the cells in the hypothalamus and are transported by axons in the pituitary stalk to the nerve terminals in the posterior lobe for storage or release (see Fig. 16-6B). Vasopressin regulates water metabolism and blood osmolality, whereas oxytocin enhances contractility of uterine musculature during and after delivery and of the myoepithelial cells of the breast ducts in lactating women. This facilitates milk ejection.

As defined by immunostaining and electron microscopy, the anterior lobe of the pituitary gland contains at least five cell types. These cells and their hormones, functions, and hypothalamic regulatory hormones are outlined in Table 16-5.

Clinical Correlations

Lesions affecting the hypothalamus and surrounding structures can be seen in any type of medical practice because they cause derangements of visceral, endocrine, visual, or homeostatic functions. Lesions of the hypothalamic nuclei result in a disturbance of visceral and homeostatic functions, such as sleep, appetite, temperature regulation, and water metabolism, whereas lesions of the pituitary gland cause endocrine disorders owing to increased or decreased secretion of pituitary hormones. Examples of endocrine disorders include the following:

1. *Growth hormone.* Increased secretion causes gigantism in children and acromegaly (enlargement of the face, hands, and feet) in adults. Decreased secretion during childhood results in dwarfism.
2. *Thyroid-stimulating hormone.* Decreased secretion results in hypothyroidism with loss of hair, dry skin, slow pulse, loss of energy, mental apathy, decreased cold tolerance, and slow relaxation of deep tendon reflexes.
3. *Adrenocorticotropic hormone (ACTH).* Increased secretion results in signs of hyperadrenalism with hirsutism, vascular striae, obesity, and hypertension. Decreased secretion results in hypoadrenalism with generalized weakness, hypotension, and decreased tolerance to stress.
4. *Gonadotropic hormone.* Decreased secretion results in amenorrhea and decreased libido.
5. *Thyroid-stimulating hormone.* Increased secretion of thyroid-stimulating hormone can cause goiter and hyperthyroidism.

Table 16-5. Anterior Pituitary Hormones

Cell type	Hormones	Hypothalamic regulatory hormone	Function
Somatotroph	Growth hormone (GH)	Growth hormone-releasing hormone	Linear growth
		Somatostatin (inhibits release)	Intermediary metabolism
Lactotroph	Prolactin (PRL)	Vasoactive intestinal peptide (stimulates release)	Lactogenesis
		Dopamine (inhibits release)	Breast growth and development
Corticotroph	Corticotropin (ACTH), beta-lipotropin (LPH), beta-endorphin (END)	Corticotropin-releasing hormone (CRH)	Functional integrity and steroidogenic function of adrenal cortex
Gonadotroph	Luteinizing hormone (LH), follicle-stimulating hormone (FSH)	Gonadotropin-releasing hormone (GnRH)	Gonadal function, sexual maturation, reproductive function, gametogenesis, sex steroid production
Thyrotroph	Thyrotropin (TSH)	Thyrotropin-releasing hormone (TRH)	Integrity and function of thyroid gland, secretion of thyroxine and triiodothyronine
		Somatostatin (inhibits release)	

6. *Prolactin.* Prolactin excess causes amenorrhea-galactorrhea syndrome in women and hypogonadism and impotence in men. Lack of prolactin is manifested in postpartum women as inability to lactate.

The visual deficits resulting from involvement of structures adjacent to the hypothalamus serve as additional localizing signs of lesions in this area. A mass lesion in the area of the sella turcica can press on the optic chiasm and cause a characteristic visual field defect, bitemporal hemianopia. A lesion involving the carotid artery or cranial nerves in the cavernous sinus can cause diplopia and loss of sensation over the forehead and cheek. A mass lesion in or near the sella can cause enlargement of the sella or erosion of the bony margins of the sella, which can be seen on radiographs of the skull.

The three most common mass lesions encountered in this region are pituitary adenoma, craniopharyngioma, and aneurysm of the internal carotid artery. A *pituitary adenoma* is a tumor arising from the cells of the anterior pituitary gland. As the tumor expands, it produces enlargement of the sella and compression of the optic chiasm.

Pituitary adenomas were previously classified according to their staining characteristics with acid and basic dyes (acidophilic, basophilic, and chromophobe adenomas). However, with this scheme, correlation with the hormonal activity of the tumor is imprecise. The demonstration of specific secretory granules by electron microscopy and of hormone content by immunostaining (immunoperoxidase, immunofluorescence) permits a more meaningful classification of these biologically active tumors.

Tumors that are acidophilic on routine stains are most often associated with either somatotropin secretion (which causes acromegaly in adults or gigantism in children) or prolactin secretion (which causes amenorrhea and galactorrhea in women). Tumors that produce corticotropin (ACTH) are usually basophilic and associated with Cushing's syndrome.

Although all the tumors mentioned contain densely granulated cells, similar hormonal activity may occur in much less densely granulated tumors, classed as chromophobe adenomas on routine staining. Many other chromophobe adenomas, while containing identifiable hormone granules, do not result in clinical evidence of trophic hormone excess. These tumors may grow to enormous size and

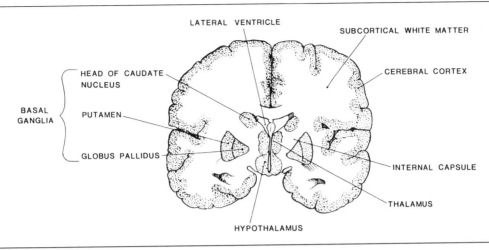

Fig. 16-7. Coronal section through cerebral hemispheres. The basal ganglia (caudate nucleus, putamen, globus pallidus) are nuclei deep in the cerebral hemispheres.

produce clinical effects by compression of the normal pituitary gland and adjacent structures. Pituitary tumors with no identifiable hormone production, called *oncocytomas*, are rare.

A *craniopharyngioma* is a tumor that arises from an embryonic remnant of Rathke's pouch and is usually located in the region of the pituitary stalk or sella, near the hypothalamus and pituitary gland. It can cause endocrine disturbances, visual symptoms, and erosion of the sella. An *aneurysm* of the internal carotid artery in the region of the sella frequently causes disturbances in extraocular muscle function but rarely disturbs pituitary function.

Telencephalon

The lateral evaginations of the most rostral portion of the embryologic neural tube form the telencephalon, from which the cerebral hemispheres arise. The two cerebral hemispheres fill most of the cranial cavity above the tentorium cerebelli and are separated by the falx cerebri. Each cerebral hemisphere contains three layers of tissue surrounding the ventricular cavities deep within the hemispheres (Fig. 16-7). Immediately adjacent to the ventricles, near the thalamus, are the basal ganglia. Surrounding these deep gray nuclei is

the *white matter*, a dense intermingling of axons that connect areas within the cerebral hemispheres with each other and with other areas of the nervous system. The outermost layer, the cerebral cortex, contains neurons that have migrated to this location during fetal development. This outer layer of gray matter is referred to as *cortical*, whereas the white matter and deep gray matter are referred to as *subcortical*.

The ventral portion of the telencephalon constitutes the *basal forebrain*; the medial region between the two hemispheres is known as the *septal area*.

The telencephalon can be divided *anatomically* into the basal ganglia, subcortical white matter, and cortex.

Basal Ganglia

Basal ganglia is a collective term used to refer to several areas of subcortical gray matter, including the caudate nucleus, putamen, and globus pallidus (see Fig. 16-7). The subthalamic nucleus and substantia nigra are also considered part of the basal ganglia circuits. The caudate nucleus and putamen constitute the *corpus striatum*, or *striatum*, so named because of the striated appearance of these structures. The striatum consists of the dorsal striatum (caudate and putamen) and the ventral striatum (nucleus accumbens). The striatum is the primary afferent structure of the basal ganglia and receives input from the cerebral cortex, limbic system, thalamus, and substantia nigra. The cortical input is excitatory (L-glutamate is the neurotransmitter) and includes projections from the sensory and motor cortex to the putamen, from prefrontal cortex to the caudate, and from limbic cortex and amygdala to the ventral striatum. The thalamic input is from the intralaminar nuclei, and the dopaminergic input is from dopaminergic neurons in the substantia nigra. The globus pallidus and the nondopaminergic part of the substantia nigra are the efferent structures of the basal ganglia. They tonically inhibit the thalamus, superior colliculus, and other targets.

The tonic inhibitory output of the basal ganglia is transiently interrupted by cortical input acting through the striatum. This results in disinhibition of the thalamus and other target areas. The inhibitory activity in the basal ganglia is mediated by gamma-aminobutyric acid (GABA). The subthalamic nucleus provides excitatory projections to the globus pallidus and substantia nigra.

The basal ganglia, thalamus, and cortex have parallel pathways, including a motor circuit via the putamen, other circuits via the caudate, and a limbic circuit via the ventral striatum. These circuits control motor, oculomotor, cognitive, and limbic functions.

Two of the pathways from the striatum have opposite effects. The direct pathway described above results in inhibition of the globus pallidus and, consequently, disinhibition of the thalamus, superior colliculus, and other targets. An indirect pathway, including the subthalamic nucleus, results in excitation of the output neurons of the globus pallidus, thus increasing inhibition of their target organs. The activity of the basal ganglia circuits is modulated by the dopaminergic neurons in the substantia nigra. Dopamine has an excitatory effect on the striatal neurons of the direct pathway and an inhibitory effect on those of the indirect pathway. The net effect of dopamine is to decrease the tonic inhibitory activity of the globus pallidus and substantia nigra on the thalamus, superior colliculus, and other targets.

The basal ganglia are involved with motor control and the automatic performance of learned motor acts by facilitating the use of motor plans. The basal ganglia do not initiate motor acts, but they modulate motor patterns initiated at cortical levels.

The alteration in balance between the activity of the direct and indirect pathways and the excitatory and inhibitory functions of the motor control circuits of the basal ganglia underlie the various types of hypokinetic and hyperkinetic movement disorders, such as Parkinson's disease, Huntington's disease, and hemiballismus.

Subcortical White Matter

A large proportion of the cerebral hemispheres between the ventricles and the cortex is composed of myelinated axons that connect multiple areas in the cerebral hemispheres. These fibers carry action potentials from one area to another without synapse or modification. These fibers are named on the basis of the areas that they connect. *Projectional fibers* travel between the cerebral cortex and the subcortical nuclear structures; *commissural fibers* connect homologous areas in the two hemispheres; and *association fibers* connect cortical areas within one hemisphere.

Projectional Fibers

As the axons that connect subcortical and cortical areas pass between the subcortical nuclei, they are collected into a compact structure, the *internal capsule*. The internal capsule is a broad band flanked medially by the thalamus and laterally by the globus pallidus and putamen (Fig. 16-8). In horizontal section, it is a V-shaped structure pointed medially, with an anterior limb, a posterior limb, and a junction called the genu. The caudate is medial to the anterior limb, the thalamus is medial to the posterior limb, and the globus pallidus and putamen are lateral to the genu. The axons of the projectional fibers carry action potentials either toward the cerebral cortex (afferent) or away from the cerebral cortex (efferent). As the axons of the internal capsule spread out from the internal capsule to reach all areas of cortex, they are known as the *corona radiata*.

The afferent projectional fibers arise largely from the thalamus and are called *thalamic radi-*

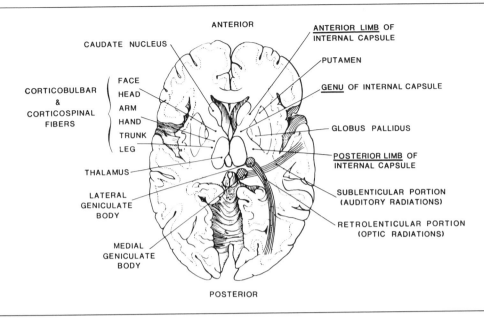

Fig. 16-8. Internal capsule. The anterior limb carries fibers from the frontal lobe, the genu from the motor areas, and the posterior limb to the sensory areas. The retrolenticular portion of the internal capsule contains the optic radiations; the sublenticular portion contains the auditory radiations.

ations. Fibers traveling to the frontal lobe from the anterior and medial thalamic nuclei, carrying visceral and other information, are located in the anterior limb of the internal capsule. Fibers from the ventral anterior and ventral lateral nuclei of the thalamus, projecting to the motor and premotor areas of the frontal lobe, are in the genu and posterior limb of the internal capsule. Fibers from the ventral posterolateral and medial thalamic nuclei, carrying sensory information to the parietal cortex, travel in the posterior limb of the capsule. Optic radiations, carrying visual information from the lateral geniculate body and pulvinar to the occipital and parietal cortex, are in the posterior limb behind the globus pallidus and putamen (retrolenticular portion of the internal capsule). Auditory information is carried from the medial geniculate body to the temporal lobe via the fibers in the posterior limb beneath the globus pallidus and the putamen (sublenticular portion of the internal capsule).

The efferent projectional fibers have several destinations, including the basal ganglia, hypothalamus, red nucleus, and brain stem reticular formation. The largest groups of fibers, however, constitute the direct activation pathway projecting from the precentral gyrus via the posterior limb of the internal capsule to the motor nuclei in the brain stem (corticobulbar) and the spinal cord (corticospinal). A second large efferent projection contains fibers primarily from the frontal lobe traveling via the internal capsule and cerebral peduncles to the pontine nuclei of the brain stem, which relay information to the cerebellum. All these fibers are involved in the initiation of voluntary movements, integration of motor function, modification of reflex activity, modulation of sensory input, regulation of visceral function, and regulation of states of consciousness and attention.

Commissural Fibers

Commissural fibers connect homologous areas in the two hemispheres to integrate the activity on the two sides (Fig. 16-9A). Most of the connections pass through the corpus callosum, which is a large flat bundle of fibers forming the roof of the lateral ventricles. Two smaller bundles connect areas in the temporal lobes. The *anterior commissure* anterior to the third ventricle interconnects anterior temporal areas, whereas the *hippocampal commis-*

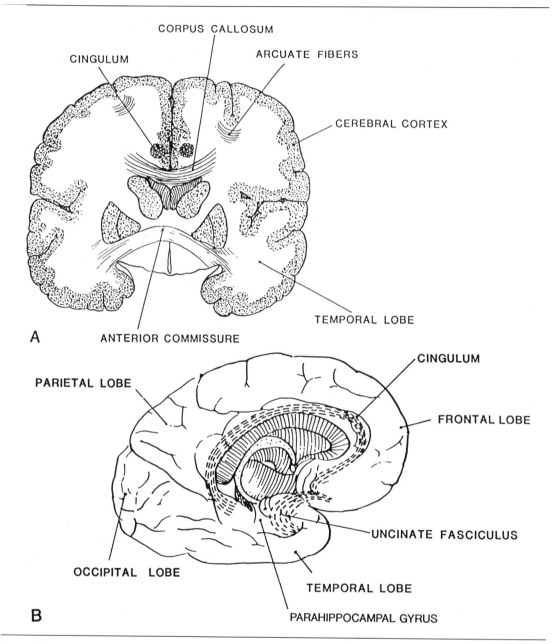

Fig. 16-9. A. Coronal section of the cerebral hemispheres. Commissural fibers (corpus callosum and anterior commissure) connect the two hemispheres. The arcuate fibers (short association fibers) connect gyri. B. Medial view of cerebral hemisphere. The long association fibers are the cingulum and the uncinate fasciculus.

sure interconnects the hippocampal formation on the two sides.

Association Fibers

A number of fiber tracts known as association pathways run longitudinally within a single hemisphere to correlate activities in different lobes (Fig. 16-9B). Two of the long association tracts are the uncinate fasciculus, which joins the temporal and frontal lobes, and the cingulum, which interconnects the medial surfaces of the frontal, parietal, and temporal lobes.

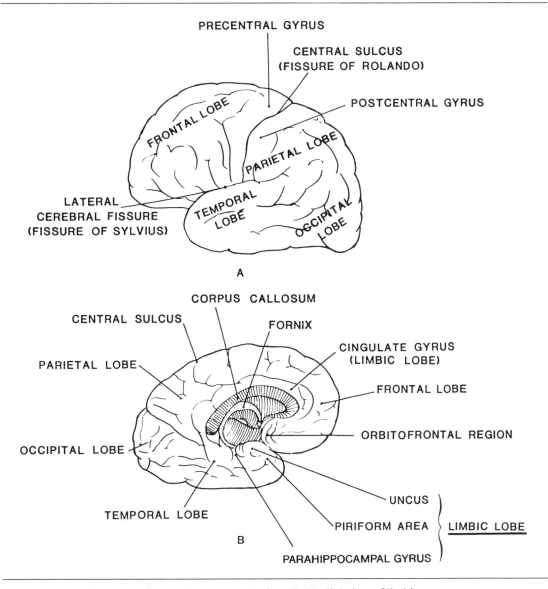

Fig. 16-10. The five lobes of the brain. A. Lateral view. B. Medial view of limbic lobe structures.

Short association fibers connecting adjacent gyri are known as *arcuate fibers* (Fig. 16-9A).

Cerebral Cortex

The cerebral cortex includes the limbic cortex, paralimbic cortex, and neocortex. Limbic cortex is the most primitive area and is derived from the inner tube component of the cerebral hemisphere. The neocortex is derived from the outer tube; it is the most differentiated area and consists of the primary sensory and motor areas and the association areas. The paralimbic cortex is intermediate between limbic cortex and neocortex.

Limbic Cortex

Limbic cortex consists of a group of interconnected structures located on the medial portion of the cerebral hemispheres (Fig. 16-10). It includes the hippocampal formation, entorhinal cortex, other perihippocampal structures, a portion of the cingulate gyrus, and the primary olfactory cortex. The hippocampal

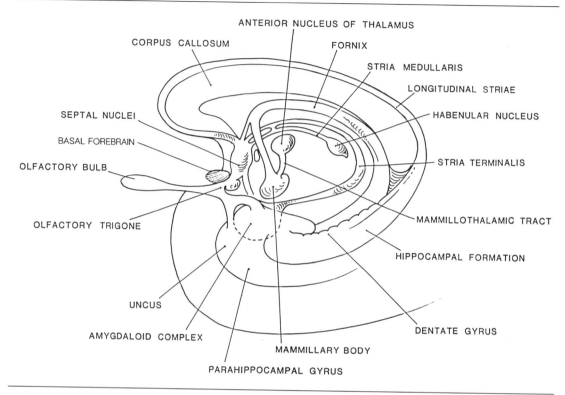

ANTERIOR NUCLEUS OF THALAMUS

CORPUS CALLOSUM

FORNIX

STRIA MEDULLARIS

LONGITUDINAL STRIAE

SEPTAL NUCLEI

HABENULAR NUCLEUS

BASAL FOREBRAIN

OLFACTORY BULB

STRIA TERMINALIS

OLFACTORY TRIGONE

MAMMILLOTHALAMIC TRACT

HIPPOCAMPAL FORMATION

UNCUS

DENTATE GYRUS

AMYGDALOID COMPLEX

MAMMILLARY BODY

PARAHIPPOCAMPAL GYRUS

Fig. 16-11. Medial aspect of temporal lobe and interconnections with limbic lobe and diencephalic structures in the limbic system. The cortex of the temporal lobe has been removed to expose the deep fiber pathways. (Modified from R. C. Truex and M. B. Carpenter. *Strong and Elwyn's Human Neuroanatomy* [5th ed.]. Baltimore: Williams & Wilkins, 1964. P. 446.)

formation includes the dentate gyrus, Ammon's horn, and the subiculum. The entorhinal cortex is the main region that connects the hippocampal formation with the rest of the cerebral cortex. The main output system of the hippocampal formation is the fornix. The fornix projects from the hippocampus to the septal region, the cingulate gyrus, and the mammillary bodies (Fig. 16-11). The mammillary bodies project to the anterior nucleus of the thalamus, and this nucleus projects to the cingulate gyrus, which in turn projects to the hippocampus. The interconnections between the hippocampal formation, mammillary bodies, anterior nuclei of the thalamus, cingulate gyrus, and subiculum are known as the circuit of Papez.

Paralimbic Cortex

The paralimbic cortex is located in the basal portion of the cerebral hemispheres between the frontal and temporal lobes and connects limbic and neocortical regions. The paralimbic regions include the parahippocampal gyrus, most of the cingulate gyrus, the orbitofrontal cortex, and the insula. These areas have an intermediate level of differentiation between the limbic cortex and the neocortex and have reciprocal connections with both. Limbic cortex is connected with other supratentorial components of the inner tube (amygdala, hypothalamus, ventral striatum) and via the paralimbic areas with association areas of the neocortex.

Neocortex

The neocortex occupies the convexity of the cerebral hemispheres. It is a relatively thin mantle of gray matter covering the outer surface of the cerebral hemispheres; it forms the gyri of the brain. Two main sulci, the central sulcus and sylvian fissure, divide each cerebral hemisphere into five lobes: frontal, parietal,

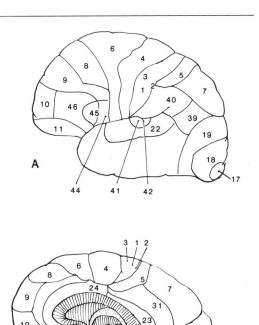

Fig. 16-12. Brodmann's areas of the cerebral cortex. A. Lateral view. B. Medial view. (44 = Broca's motor speech; 11 = orbitofrontal; 6 = premotor; 4 = primary motor; 1, 2, and 3 = primary somatosensory; 5 and 7 = somatosensory association; 18 and 19 = visual association; 17 = primary visual; 41 and 42 = auditory; 22 = Wernicke's speech; 23 and 24 = cingulate.)

occipital, temporal, and limbic lobes (see Fig. 16-10). The frontal lobe is anterior to the central sulcus, and the parietal and occipital lobes are posterior to it. The sylvian fissure separates the temporal lobe from the frontal and parietal lobes. The limbic lobe includes the medial portions of the frontal and temporal lobes: the cingulum, the hippocampus, and the parahippocampal region. The lobes have been subdivided into histologically and functionally distinct areas by the German anatomist Brodmann (Fig. 16-12).

The neocortex includes the primary motor and sensory areas and the association areas (Fig. 16-13). The primary areas include the primary visual area located in the banks of the calcarine fissure of the occipital lobe (Brodmann's area 17), the primary somatosensory area in the postcentral gyrus of the parietal lobe (areas 3, 1, 2), and the primary auditory area in the superior temporal gyrus (Heschl's gyrus, or areas 41 and 42). The primary motor area is located in the precentral gyrus of the frontal lobe (area 4). Surrounding these primary areas are association areas. The association areas occupy most of the external surface of the hemispheres and can be divided into (1) *unimodal*, or modality-specific, *association areas* that surround the primary areas and are intimately related to each sensory modality and (2) *heteromodal association areas* that receive input from the unimodal association areas. The association areas also serve as a connection between the sensory and motor areas of the brain and the components of the limbic cortex. Heteromodal association areas include the parietotemporal regions, the prefrontal cortex, and the paralimbic association areas on the medial surface of the hemisphere.

Histology

The cerebral cortex contains large numbers of cells intermingled with axons, dendrites, neuroglia, and blood vessels. There are two main types of cortical neurons: projection neurons, represented by *pyramidal cells*, and interneurons, represented by the *granule*, or *stellate*, *cells* (Fig. 16-14). The cells are organized into horizontal layers and vertical columns. The arrangement of these layers and columns varies with the function of each area; thus differences in function in the lobes of the brain can be correlated with histologic and topographic differences.

The pyramidal cell is triangular in shape, with its upper end giving off an apical dendrite that extends to the surface of the cortex. The base of the cell gives rise to a long axon that projects to other cortical areas or to subcortical structures. These projections are excitatory and are mediated by L-glutamate.

Stellate cells are small multipolar neurons with a dark-staining nucleus, scanty cytoplasm, and a number of dendrites and axons passing in all directions to synapse with other neurons in the cortex. Generally, they are local inhibitory interneurons and use GABA as their neurotransmitter.

In limbic cortex, the neurons are organized

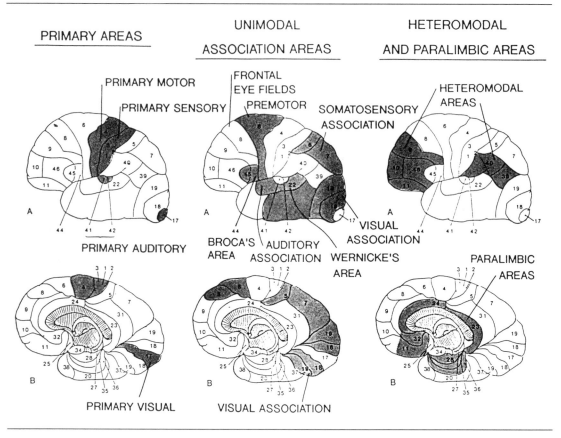

Fig. 16-13. The primary motor and sensory areas, paralimbic areas, and association areas of the cortex. A. Lateral view. B. Medial view.

into one or two cell layers, whereas in the neocortex they form six layers (Fig. 16-15). The six layers of the neocortex are as follows:

1. The molecular (plexiform) layer is the superficial layer. It contains the apical dendrites of pyramidal cells and receives several fiber systems, including projections from structures of the consciousness system.
2. The external (outer) granular layer contains many granule (stellate) cells, whose axons synapse in deeper cortical layers, and pyramidal cells, whose axons (commissural fibers) project to contralateral cerebral cortex.
3. The external (outer) pyramidal layer contains mainly pyramidal cells, whose axons are commissural or association fibers.
4. The internal (inner) granular layer has closely packed granule (stellate) cells and is

the main site for termination of thalamocortical fibers. This layer is well-developed in primary sensory and association areas.
5. The internal (inner) pyramidal layer contains the large pyramidal cells that project to the brain stem and spinal cord. Some of the pyramidal cells give rise to commissural fibers.
6. The multiform layer contains pyramidal neurons that project back to the same areas of the thalamus that give rise to the thalamocortical projections; others project to layer 4.

Physiology

Axons in the cortex run vertically and horizontally, mediating both projectional and associational activity. An important feature of the neocortex is its organization into functional modules, or columns. A *column* is a

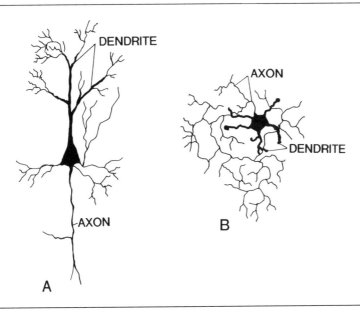

Fig. 16-14. Cells of the cerebral cortex. A. Pyramidal cell. B. Stellate (granule) cell.

vertical cylinder of cortical tissue that includes all six layers and that represents the functional unit of cortex. For example, all the neurons in a column respond to the same sensory modality. Cortical neurons in each column receive input from (1) other columns, (2) local interneurons, (3) the specific thalamic nuclei, and (4) structures of the consciousness system. In general, activation of a column is associated with inhibition of the surrounding columns. This is important for sensory discrimination and for fine motor control. Columns distributed over wide areas of the cortex can be activated simultaneously, a critical feature of cortical function.

The function of the cerebral cortex is characterized by (1) hierarchical, or sequential, processing of information, (2) reciprocal connections between different cortical areas, (3) parallel processing, (4) cortical plasticity, and (5) corticosubcortical interactions. There are close interactions between cognitive processes of the neocortex (outer tube) and the emotional and motivational processes of the limbic cortex (inner tube).

1. *Hierarchical organization.* An important aspect of cortical function is its activity patterns, that is, what regions of the cortex connect directly with other areas. Cells in a primary sensory area project to their own unimodal, or modality-specific, association areas. For example, primary visual cortex projects almost exclusively to visual association cortex. Individual cells in this region respond to visual stimuli only. The cells in unimodal association areas react to specific modalities and project to heteromodal association areas, in which inputs from various sensory modalities converge. The heteromodal association areas also project to the paralimbic structures that, in turn, relay the information to the limbic system. The prefrontal association areas send input to the premotor association areas that project to primary motor cortex.

2. *Reciprocal interactions.* Another important feature of cortical function is the reciprocal flow of information between primary and association sensory and motor areas of the neocortex and between neocortical association areas and the limbic system. This allows continuous monitoring of cortical activity in the different areas of the hemisphere.

Association cortex and paralimbic cortex form a bridge between the primary sensory areas in neocortex and the limbic sys-

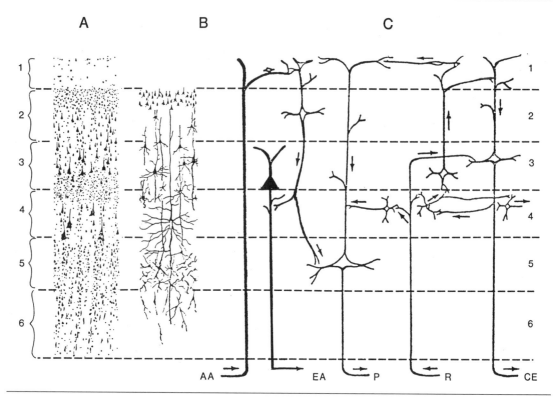

Fig. 16-15. The six layers of the cerebral cortex: molecular layer (1), external granular layer (2), external pyramidal layer (3), internal granular layer (4), internal pyramidal layer (5), and multiform cell layer (6). A. Cells stained by Nissl stain. B. Selected cells stained by Golgi stain. C. Vertical and horizontal connections of cortical neurons. (*AA* = afferent association fiber; *EA* = efferent association fiber; *P* = efferent projection fiber; *R* = afferent radiation fiber; *CE* = commissural efferent fiber.)

tem. Through the reciprocal connections that form this bridge, the external world communicates with the internal world, and the internal world can affect the processing of external stimuli. For example, an object in the external environment stimulates the retina and produces excitation in primary visual cortex. The information is next transmitted to the visual association cortex, where certain features of the stimulus (such as shape, contour, and color) are abstracted. This information is then transferred to the heteromodal association areas, where the visual information about the object is processed in combination with information from other sensory modalities to produce a more complex perception. This multimodal information is transferred to paralimbic and limbic system structures, where emotional or affective features of the stimulus may be added and where processing of the information for memory storage takes place. This whole process is dynamic, and the processing that occurs in the limbic system is fed back to the association cortex, thus influencing subsequent processing of incoming stimuli.

3. *Parallel organization.* An important feature of cortical organization is that every cortical function depends on the parallel and simultaneous processing of information by anatomically separate networks that involve different areas of neocortex, limbic cortex, and paralimbic cortex and their respective connections with the basal ganglia and thalamus. For example, processes such as language involve structures in the posterior and anterior regions of ne-

ocortex, the caudate nucleus, and the thalamus. Processes such as memory and directed attention involve parallel processing in neocortical, limbic, and paralimbic regions. Therefore, even though a lesion in a specific area of the hemisphere produces a specific deficit, this does not mean that this area is necessarily the seat of the function that is affected. Instead, the area may be part of a more complex network involved in that function.

4. *Cortical plasticity.* Cortical plasticity is the ability of the cerebral cortex to undergo anatomical and functional changes in response to environmental circumstances. This phenomenon occurs even in the cerebral cortex of adults. The cortical representations of sensory and motor maps may change in size and distribution in response to peripheral injury or to effects of training. Cortical plasticity may explain recovery of function after a large hemispheric lesion. Functional plasticity includes long-term increase in efficacy of synaptic transmission in response to repetitive activity in a circuit. This phenomenon, called *long-term potentiation*, occurs in the hippocampus and neocortex and is important for learning and memory.

5. *Corticosubcortical interactions.* The function of the cortex depends not only on intracortical connections but also on corticosubcortical circuits that involve the thalamus and basal ganglia.

Pathophysiology

The anatomical and histologic characteristics and functional organization of the cortex make it particularly susceptible to the development of excessive paroxysmal synchronized activity that is manifested as seizures.

A *seizure* is a transient disturbance that occurs as a result of an abnormal, excessive discharge of cortical neurons. It represents a specific pathophysiologic expression of abnormality at the supratentorial level.

The two primary factors that produce seizures are (1) increased excitability of cortical neurons and (2) synchronization of neuronal populations. Mechanisms that may cause these processes include (1) alteration of intrinsic membrane properties, (2) impairment of local inhibitory mechanisms, (3) local changes in neuronal environment, and (4) increased recruitment and recurrent excitation of neuronal populations via synaptic input or electrical coupling. Seizures can become generalized as a result of synchronizing mechanisms between the two hemispheres, recruitment of synchronizing thalamocortical circuits, or involvement of subcortical structures. Repeated activation of a neuronal population may produce a persistent increase in neuronal excitability via long-term potentiation, including long-term changes in cytoarchitecture and genetic expression.

Seizures may be manifested in different ways with involvement of different cortical areas. They may be partial (focal) or generalized in distribution. Partial seizures occur with focal lesions such as vascular disorders, neoplasms, abscess, and trauma. Generalized seizures usually occur with metabolic, toxic, degenerative, and traumatic disorders but may also develop from focal seizures.

Generalized Seizures

Both cerebral hemispheres are involved with abnormal feedback between the cortex and the thalamus to produce widespread discharges in generalized seizures. These seizures involve the consciousness system and are therefore associated with an alteration of consciousness. This may be brief in *absence seizures* or prolonged in *tonic-clonic seizures*. In a *generalized tonic-clonic* (grand mal) *seizure*, the patient abruptly loses consciousness and falls as the body stiffens in a tonic contraction. This is followed by symmetric, clonic jerking of the extremities and head, urinary incontinence, tongue biting, and apnea. After the seizure, the patient is flaccid and unresponsive, with slow return of consciousness through periods of confusion, drowsiness, and headache. The seizure usually lasts 1 to 2 minutes, and the period of altered consciousness after the seizure may last for 10 to 30 minutes. During the seizure, an electroencephalogram shows generalized, repetitive spike discharges in the tonic phase, spike and wave discharges during the clonic phase, and depression of activity followed by slow waves after the seizure (Fig. 16-16). Repeated seizures are called *status epilepticus*.

Brief generalized seizures lasting 5 to 30

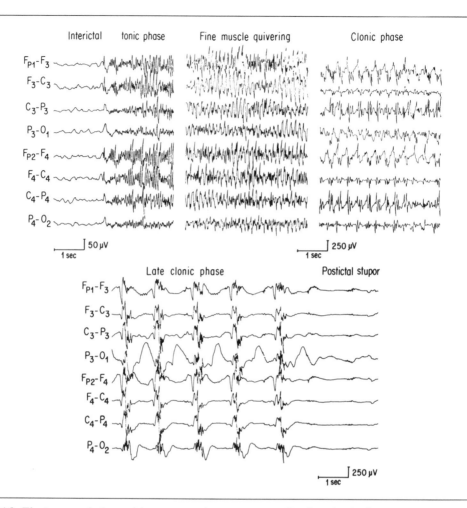

Fig. 16-16. Electroencephalographic accompaniment to generalized tonic-clonic seizure. Segments of the recording during different phases of the seizure are shown. Interictal is before seizure; tonic phase (body stiff) shows repetitive spikes; clonic phase (body jerking) shows spike and wave discharges; postictal (after seizure) shows suppression of activity.

seconds with impaired consciousness but minimal movements are called *absence* (petit mal) *seizures*. Usually, the patient abruptly ceases activity, is unresponsive, and stares, sometimes with mild clonic movements of the face or extremities. These seizures usually occur in children and can be induced by hyperventilation. They are associated with a characteristic bilateral, synchronous, generalized 3-Hz spike-and-wave pattern on the electroencephalogram (Fig. 16-17).

Partial Seizures
Seizures arising from a localized area of the cortex are called *partial* seizures and are clas-

sified as *complex partial seizures* when associated with an alteration of consciousness and as *simple partial seizures* if consciousness is preserved. Partial seizures are often due to a focal pathologic process. The symptoms of partial seizures depend on the site of the discharge. Observation of symptoms can localize the pathologic process. Seizures in the precentral gyrus are associated with clonic movements of the contralateral side of the face or the contralateral arm or leg. Postcentral gyrus seizures are accompanied by paresthesias or dysesthesias of the contralateral side of the face or of the contralateral extremities. Occipital lobe seizures produce unformed visual

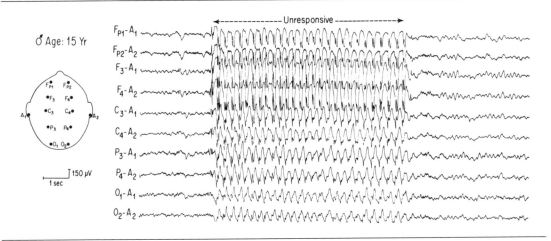

Fig. 16-17. Electroencephalographic accompaniment during absence seizure consisting of 3-Hz spike-and-wave pattern during which the patient was unresponsive.

images or impaired vision. Seizures arising from the temporal and limbic lobes are the most common partial seizures. Symptoms are varied and may include strange odors or tastes, formed auditory or visual hallucinations, fear, unusual sensations, mouthing movements, or automatic behavior. Because there is often an alteration of consciousness, these are complex partial seizures.

A partial seizure may remain localized in a single area or may spread to other areas. It may spread sequentially along a gyrus via arcuate fibers and thereby involve the face, arm, or leg sequentially in a so-called jacksonian march. It may spread from one lobe to another or from one hemisphere to another via association or commissural fibers. Or it may spread via projectional fibers to the thalamus and thereby become generalized. If focal symptoms precede a generalized seizure, the focal symptoms are called an *aura* and provide evidence of the site of seizure origin.

Functional Organization of the Telencephalon

Cortex

The cortex is the site of the highest order of integration of activities of the sensory, motor, internal regulation, and consciousness sys-

tems. In addition to these systems, the limbic, olfactory, and visual systems are located at the supratentorial level. The sensory structures of the cortex are involved with higher order processing of somatosensory, visual, auditory, olfactory, and vestibular sensory functions. The motor system is involved with cortical motor control, motor planning, and ocular motor control. The internal regulation system controls autonomic functions, homeostasis, and emotions. The consciousness system integrates inputs from the brain stem structures involved with cortical arousal and the sleep-wake cycle. The sensory, motor, and visual systems are part of the neocortex. The internal regulation, consciousness, and olfactory systems are components of the limbic system.

Functions that are unique to the telencephalon are attention, control of behavior, language, and memory. Attention, control of behavior, and language are functions of the neocortex, and memory is a function of both the neocortex and the limbic system.

Limbic System

The limbic components of the telencephalon include the basal forebrain (amygdala, ventral striatum, and the cholinergic neurons projecting diffusely to the cerebral cortex), the limbic cortex (hippocampus and adjacent structures), and the septal region. These regions are closely interconnected with limbic components of the diencephalon (dorsomedial and midline thalamic nuclei and hypothalamus) and the structures of the brain stem that correspond to the internal regulation and consciousness systems.

The functions of the limbic system are higher order control of autonomic function, homeostasis, reproduction, emotion, cortical arousal, motivated behavior, and learning. The amygdala provides emotional significance for external or internal sensory stimuli and generates autonomic and motor responses associated with emotion and conditioned responses. The amygdala receives information from sensory areas of the cortex and from the internal regulation system. It projects to the hypothalamus, basal ganglia, and brain stem for initiation of autonomic and motor responses and to the cerebral cortex for emotional experience. It is closely connected with the hippocampus and other regions involved in memory function.

The cholinergic neurons in the nucleus basalis of the basal forebrain project to the neocortex and amygdala, and those in the septal region project to the hippocampus. These projections are involved in arousal and memory mechanisms. The ventral striatum includes the nucleus accumbens, which receives input from the amygdala and the limbic cortex. Through projections to the ventral portion of the globus pallidus, the ventral striatum is important in locomotion and motivational aspects of behavior.

The limbic cortex of the temporal lobe, including the hippocampal formation and entorhinal cortex, is critical for learning and transient storage of memory. The limbic cortex is part of several reverberatory circuits, which allow formation of persistent associations necessary for learning. Important characteristics of limbic circuits are synaptic plasticity and long-term potentiation. Destruction of components of the circuits results in the inability to learn new information.

The main function of the paralimbic cortex is to transmit highly processed sensory information from the neocortical association areas to the limbic cortex and vice versa. Connections of the hippocampal formation with the entorhinal cortex are important for the inter- actions of limbic cortex with neocortical association areas. These interactions are important for the process of long-term memory storage and retrieval. Input from the cholinergic neurons in the basal forebrain facilitates plastic changes, or long-term potentiation, in hippocampal and neocortical circuits and is important in learning and memory.

Two paralimbic regions, the orbitofrontal cortex and anterior cingulate gyrus, are connected with the amygdala and are important in motivation and regulation of emotional behavior. Disorders of these regions can produce either decreased psychomotor activity (akinetic mutism) or inappropriate social behavior.

Olfactory System

An important sensory system of the inner tube at the supratentorial level is the olfactory system. The receptors for cranial nerve I lie in the superior nasal mucosa and respond to the chemical structures of many agents that are perceived as smells. The *olfactory nerve* is composed of multiple small fibers from the receptor cells. The axons penetrate the skull through the cribriform plate to end in the olfactory bulb (Fig. 16-18A). The *olfactory bulb* is a small ovoid structure that lies in the anterior end of the olfactory sulcus on the orbital surface of the frontal lobe. Fibers from the olfactory bulb form the olfactory tract, which passes posteriorly and divides into medial and lateral olfactory striae at the end of the olfactory sulcus. The lateral olfactory stria passes into the medial part of the temporal lobe known as the piriform area and ends in the uncus and amygdala (Fig. 16-18B). The medial olfactory stria terminates in the anterior perforated substance and terminal gyri of the medial basal frontal lobe. Most olfactory fibers end in the anterior uncus, the chief cortical olfactory area. (Seizures arising in this area are called *uncinate seizures* and may present with an aura of an abnormal odor.) These connections and those with the amygdala and adjacent hippocampal gyrus link the olfactory structures with the ring of structures forming the rest of the limbic system.

Neocortex

Important functions of the neocortex and associated regions include (1) control of behav-

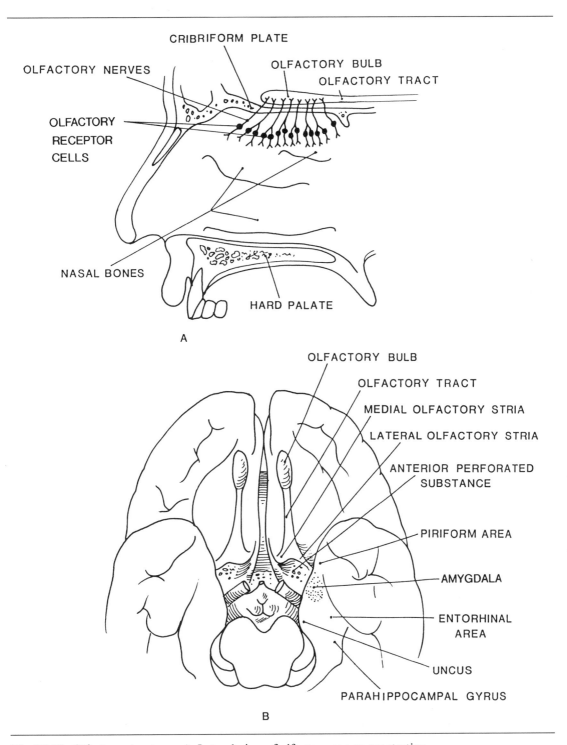

Fig. 16-18. Olfactory structures. A. Lateral view of olfactory nerves penetrating skull through cribriform plate. B. Basal view of brain showing termination of lateral olfactory fibers in piriform area of temporal lobe and medial olfactory fibers in the anterior perforated substance.

ior and motivation, (2) motor programming and execution, (3) processing of somatosensory, visual, and auditory information, (4) directed visual attention to personal and extrapersonal space, (5) oculomotor control, (6) language, and (7) memory. Higher cortical functions depend on synchronized activity in parallel networks of the cerebral cortex and its connections with the thalamus, basal ganglia, and limbic system. Although damage to a specific area of cortex produces a particular deficit, the networks involved in the affected function are more widespread.

High-order Control of Behavior

The *prefrontal region* of the frontal lobe is anterior to the motor and premotor areas and is a heteromodal association area critical for attention, motivation, and problem-solving ability. Its functions include short-term, or "working," memory, motor planning, and control of planned behavior. The prefrontal cortex includes two functionally different regions: the dorsolateral convexity and the orbitofrontal and medial frontal regions. Lesions of prefrontal cortex produce two main syndromes. Lesions of the dorsolateral prefrontal cortex produce psychomotor retardation, hypokinesia, and lack of initiative and spontaneity, a condition called *abulia*. Lesions of the orbitofrontal cortex produce behavioral disinhibition, with hyperkinesia, disruption of social behavior, and inappropriate behavior in response to external stimuli.

Cortical Motor Control

Regions of the frontal and parietal lobe are involved in motor control. The motor regions of the frontal lobe include the primary motor area in the precentral gyrus (area 4), the lateral premotor area (area 6), the supplementary motor area on the medial aspect of the hemisphere (also area 6), and regions of the cingulate gyrus. These regions have several characteristics in common: they receive input from the ventral anterior or ventral lateral nuclei of the thalamus (relay nuclei for the basal ganglia and cerebellum, respectively), they contain a somatotopic representation of the contralateral body, they project to the spinal cord via the corticospinal tract, and they participate in parallel cortical–basal ganglia–thalamic–

cortical circuits that control different aspects of motor behavior. The primary and secondary somatosensory areas of the parietal lobe are also involved in motor control by providing somatosensory information to premotor and motor regions and contributing fibers to the corticospinal tract for control of sensory processing in the dorsal horn.

The *primary motor area* (area 4) contributes approximately 40 percent of the fibers of the corticospinal tract. This area integrates cortical and subcortical inputs and then sends signals to spinal motor neurons and interneurons. This area also provides feed-forward information to motor-controlling circuits and mediates long-loop reflexes, which contribute to postural adjustment in response to sensory feedback. The *premotor area* (area 6) is involved in control of proximal limb muscles, inhibition of transcortical long-loop reflexes, and mediation of visually guided movements via connections with posterior parietal cortex. The *supplementary motor area* corresponds to the medial aspect of area 6 and is critical in planning voluntary movements and in performing tactilely guided exploratory movements of the limbs. The premotor and supplementary motor areas also contribute axons to the corticospinal tract. The anterior cingulate region is important for motivational aspects of motor behavior.

The corticospinal tract is the direct motor pathway of the outer tube and ends on the opposite side of the spinal cord, mainly on spinal interneurons and motor neurons that innervate distal limb muscles. It is important in producing highly fractionated and independent finger movements and in recruiting motor units for increasing force of contraction. The axon of a single cortical pyramidal neuron innervates motor neurons at different segmental levels, and a spinal motor neuron receives input from different cortical motor fields. Thus, individual pyramidal cells can simultaneously activate several groups of synergistic motor units and, through interneurons, inhibit antagonistic motor units. The corticospinal neurons that affect a specific muscle tend to be clustered together in a cortical column.

A specific disorder of motor control at the supratentorial level is apraxia. *Apraxia* is the inability to perform learned, skilled movements in the absence of an attentional disorder, weakness, sensory abnormality, or incoordination. It is caused by lesions in the supplementary motor area, corpus callosum, or dominant parietal lobe. Testing for apraxia may involve asking the patient to pretend he or she has a hammer in the hand and to pound a nail. A patient with limb apraxia is unable to perform this act yet is able to understand the instruction and has normal strength, sensation, and coordination.

Processing of Somatosensory Information
Neurons in ventral posterolateral and posteromedial nuclei of the thalamus receive tactile and proprioceptive information via the lemniscal, spinothalamic, and trigeminal pathways and project to the primary sensory cortex. The primary somatosensory cortex corresponds to the postcentral gyrus and consists of at least four areas (3a, 3b, 2, and 1). Each of these areas contains a complete somatotopic map of the contralateral body and responds to a specific somatosensory modality (touch or proprioception). For the initial stage of information processing in primary somatosensory cortex, neurons in a cortical column have identical, small receptive fields and respond to a specific submodality. For later stages, the neurons have larger receptive fields and respond to convergent stimulus modalities. Tactile information in combination with proprioceptive information from the fingers during the process of "active touch" is important for recognition of shapes of objects; this is called *stereognosis*. Information from primary somatosensory cortex is processed further in the secondary somatosensory area (in the region of the insula), the supplementary sensory area (on the dorsomedial surface of the hemisphere), and the somatosensory association areas (in the posterior region of the parietal lobe). The posterior parietal region includes area 5, important in tactile guidance of limb movement, and area 7, important in integration of somatosensory and visual information. Area 7 is also important in directed visual attention and visual control of hand and eye movements.

A disorder of sensory function that is specific to the supratentorial level is agnosia. *Agnosia* is the inability to identify the meaning of a stimulus despite being able to perceive it. The patient is alert, attentive, not aphasic, and has intact sensation but is unable to tell what the object is. Agnosias can involve any of the sensory modalities. With tactile agnosia, called *astereognosia*, a patient is unable to tell what the object is by palpating it. With visual agnosia, a patient is unable to recognize an object presented visually yet is able to describe its properties. For example, if shown a toothbrush, such a patient is able to describe its length, texture, and color but is not able to name it or to describe its use. With auditory agnosia, a patient can hear the sound but is unable to describe it. Sensory agnosias occur with lesions in the unimodal sensory association areas.

Other types of cortical sensory disorders include loss of two-point discrimination, right-left disorientation, inability to recognize letters or numbers written on the palm of the hand (agraphesthesia), inability to localize touch (atopognosia), loss of ability to discriminate weights (abarognosia), finger-naming difficulty (finger agnosia), and neglect of a body part or one side of the body. The loss of these cortical sensory functions occurs with lesions of unimodal or heteromodal association areas.

Processing of Visual Information
Most of the visual cortex is devoted to analysis of central vision. Information about form and color, on one hand, and movement, on the other, is transmitted via parallel channels throughout the visual pathway. The cells involved with visual processing in the visual cortex break the image into components, such as form, color, and movement, that are encoded by specific neurons in visual association areas.

The visual association areas that are involved in further processing of visual information include areas 18 and 19 in the occipital lobe and areas of the posterolateral and inferior temporal lobe. Analysis of form and color occurs in visual association areas in the temporal lobe; analysis of movement is performed in areas in the parietal lobe.

Oculomotor Control
The major function of the extraocular muscles is to move the eyes in such a way that the images of objects in the binocular visual fields

always fall on corresponding points in the retinas and to direct the eyes to such images. This requires the coordinated contraction of the muscles of the eyes to produce voluntary and reflex conjugate ocular movements. These movements are under the control of several different regions of the brain, including the brain stem (see Chapter 15, The Posterior Fossa Level) and the frontal and occipital eye fields in the cortex (see The Visual System).

Directed Attention

The network for directed attention to extrapersonal space is complex and includes the posterior parietal lobe, frontal eye fields, cingulate gyrus, pulvinar, and caudate nucleus. The posterior region of the parietal lobe directs visual attention; the frontal eye fields are involved in motor exploration; and the cingulate gyrus is involved in motivational components of exploratory behavior. The right hemisphere, particularly the posterior region of the parietal lobe, is dominant for selected attention to extrapersonal or interpersonal space. It controls visual attention to both left and right extrapersonal space or side of the body. The left hemisphere contributes to control of attention to the right side.

Lesions of the right hemisphere produce severe left-side hemineglect, including contralateral visual neglect, anosognosia (lack of awareness of the affected side of the body), dressing apraxia, and constructional apraxia (inability to draw figures). Less severe degrees of right posterior parietal dysfunction can be detected by the phenomenon of extinction, which is elicited by double simultaneous stimulation of visual, auditory, or somatic modalities.

Language

The critical components of language circuits are located in the left cerebral hemisphere. The left cerebral hemisphere is dominant for language in almost all right-handed and in more than two-thirds of left-handed persons. Several regions of the left hemisphere are critical for comprehension, production, repetition, or assembly of words into sentences, for naming, writing, reading, and for sign language. The region of cortex around the left sylvian fissure, the *perisylvian region*, includes Broca's area (areas 44 and 45) in the inferior portion of the left frontal gyrus and the underlying white matter and associated basal ganglia, Wernicke's area (area 22) in the posterior aspect of the auditory association area in the superior temporal gyrus, and neocortical regions interconnecting Broca's area and Wernicke's area, particularly the supramarginal gyrus. Coordinated activity of these regions and their subcortical connections is critical for assembling words.

Homologous regions in the right hemisphere are involved in other aspects of language, including production of automatic idioms, prosody (melody and inflexion of speech), and musical recognition and expression.

Disturbances of language and speech are divided into three types: disorders of central language processing produce aphasia, disorders of motor programming of language symbols produce apraxia of speech, and disorders of the mechanism of speech produce dysarthrias. Dysarthria occurs with disorders of the direct and indirect motor pathways, the motor control circuits, and the lower motor neuron system.

Aphasia is a disturbance in the dominant hemisphere that produces a defect in the expression or comprehension of any of the forms of language. The different types of aphasia are described below (Table 16-6).

Broca's aphasia typically occurs with lesions involving Broca's area, the underlying white matter, and basal ganglia. Specific features include loss of speech fluency, agrammatism (inability to organize words into sentences, "telegraphic speech"), and distorted production of speech sounds. Although the patients have normal reception of language, they *cannot convert thoughts into meaningful language.* These patients may also have hemiparesis of the contralateral face and upper extremity.

Wernicke's aphasia occurs with lesions involving Wernicke's area and is characterized by fluent speech that is unintelligible because of errors in phoneme and word choice, causing paraphasia and jargon speech. Patients with this type of aphasia have *impaired comprehension* of verbal and written language but no focal motor deficit.

Table 16-6. Main Types of Aphasia

Type	Clinical correlate	Area involved
Broca's aphasia	Unable to convert thoughts into meaningful language, nonfluent speech, agrammatism, impaired repetition	Broca's area (frontal lobe areas 44 and 45)
Wernicke's aphasia	Impaired comprehension of language, fluent speech, paraphasia, jargon speech, impaired repetition	Wernicke's area (superior temporal gyrus, area 22)
Conduction aphasia	Impaired repetition only	Connections between Broca's and Wernicke's areas
Transcortical aphasia	Impaired expression or reception of speech but repetition spared	Arterial border zones
Global aphasia	Impaired comprehension and expression	Perisylvian or central regions
Anomia	Inability to name objects	Left anterior temporal cortex

Conduction aphasia is due to lesions that interrupt the connections between Broca's area and Wernicke's area. It is characterized by impaired repetition. However, patients with this type of aphasia can produce intelligible speech and can comprehend sentences.

Global aphasias combine features of Wernicke's aphasia and Broca's aphasia and are commonly associated with a dense contralateral hemiplegia. The perisylvian or central aphasias are commonly due to infarctions in the territory of the left middle cerebral artery, but they may also be an early manifestation of a neoplastic, inflammatory, or degenerative disorder.

Transcortical aphasias result from infarctions in the arterial border zones. These lesions interrupt the connections between the perisylvian language areas and either the anterior (motor) or posterior (sensory) regions of neocortex. With transcortical aphasias, unlike perisylvian aphasias, repetition is spared.

All aphasias are associated with difficulty naming objects, a deficit called *anomia*. Pure anomia occurs with lesions of the left anterior temporal cortex, including the temporal pole. These lesions may impair access to words because of interruption of connections between language and memory areas. Lesions of the left caudate nucleus or the left thalamus may produce subcortical aphasia, characterized by fluent dysarthric speech and hemiparesis.

Aphasia should be distinguished from other disorders of speech production, including speech apraxia, mutism, and dysarthria.

Motor speech apraxia, also called *apraxia of speech*, is a manifestation of lesions restricted to Broca's area (areas 44 and 45). This consists of the partial or complete inability to form the articulatory movements of the lips, tongue, and lower jaw for producing individual sounds that make up words. The patient knows what he or she wants to say but is unable to *execute* the *motor aspects of speech*.

Mutism is the lack of speech production caused by lesions of the prefrontal areas and the cingulate gyrus.

Dysarthrias, unlike aphasias, are difficulties with speech but not with language. There are several different neuroanatomical subtypes of dysarthria. The most common types are the following. *Flaccid dysarthria* results from lesions of the final common pathways of cranial nerves V, VII, IX, X, and XII; breathy voice quality, hypernasality, and articulatory imprecision occur when these cranial nerves are damaged. *Spastic dysarthria* is the result of bilateral upper motor neuron lesions and is characterized by a strained hoarseness, hypernasality, and slow articulatory rate. *Ataxic dysarthria* occurs with lesions of the cerebellum and produces irregular articulatory breakdowns during connected speech and, less frequently, voice tremor and loss of loudness control of the voice. *Hypokinetic (parkinsonian) dysarthria* occurs with lesions of the basal ganglia and is characterized by reduced voice volume, monopitch, and accelerated and indistinct articulation. *Hyperkinetic dysarthrias* are exemplified by dystonias and choreas in which there are uncontrolled and unpredictable movements of laryngeal, pharngeal, lingual, and facial muscles that interrupt and distort phonation, resonation, and articulation.

Memory

Memory is a complex process that involves several structures, including diencephalic and telencephalic components of both the inner tube ("limbic") and outer tube systems. The term *memory* encompasses several different processes, including the ability to learn, store, and retrieve information about events and facts (*declarative memory*), the ability to hold information to be used for actions planned for a relatively short period in the near future (*working memory*), and the learning of habits and skills (*procedural memory*).

Declarative memory involves encoding, learning, storage, and retrieval of information and includes processes of primary and secondary memory. *Primary memory*, also called immediate or short-term memory, refers to the processing done over a brief period during which there is encoding of information for further storage. It depends on distributed and coordinated activity of neocortical association areas. Primary memory has a limited capacity and is generally of short duration; it relies heavily on attentional processes and is disrupted in disorders of attention. For example, primary memory is assessed by asking a patient to remember a short series of digits.

Secondary memory refers to the processing of information for longer retention intervals and involves the processes of learning and storage of information. This is the memory function that most people consider as true memory. There is a temporal gradient of information in secondary memory in that more recently learned events are more labile and subject to disruption. Structures of the medial temporal lobe, including the hippocampus and surrounding regions, diencephalic structures such as the mammillary bodies and the dorsomedial nucleus of the thalamus, and cholinergic neurons of the basal forebrain are involved in the learning of new information before it is transformed into stable long-term memory.

The hippocampus in particular is critical for the process of learning and transient storage before establishment of long-term memory. The hippocampus includes an excitatory circuit organized into several parallel loops that allow reverberatory activity. This circuit is characterized by *long-term potentiation*, which increases the efficacy of excitatory transmission in the hippocampal circuits as a consequence of repetitive activation. Cholinergic input from the basal forebrain also facilitates the establishment of long-term memory.

As memory engrams become more firmly consolidated, more of the processing is transferred from the limbic system to the association areas of neocortex. Well-established and old memories (remote memory) are relatively resistant to disruption. This type of information is often of a personal nature and is quite meaningful to the person. Remote memories can be largely preserved even after damage to the hippocampus and limbic system. These memories are also preserved in more general degenerative processes such as Alzheimer's disease.

Memory also includes working memory and procedural memory. *Working memory* is retaining information for a short time, for example, looking up a telephone number and remembering it briefly before dialing it. It is a function of the prefrontal lobe and depends mainly on attention and ability to prevent interference from other stimuli. Working memory is impaired by lesions of prefrontal cortex. *Procedural memory* (habits and motor skills) involves corticosubcortical circuits that include the caudate and cerebellum. Working and procedural memory are spared in disorders causing classical memory dysfunction (*amnesia*).

Different clinical conditions selectively affect different aspects of memory. Primary memory is compromised in acute confusional states in which there is impaired attention. Secondary memory, learning, and transient storage of information are selectively affected by lesions of the hippocampus and its diencephalic connections.

Bilateral damage of the hippocampus or the entorhinal cortex and other perihippocampal regions impairs the ability to learn new information. A memory disorder can also occur in patients with midline lesions of the diencephalon, including the dorsomedial nuclei of the thalamus; this is called *diencephalic amnesia*. Korsakoff's syndrome occurs in chronic alcoholics who are often nutritionally deprived and is manifested as a profound inability to learn new information. The pathologic lesions in this condition primarily involve the dorsomedial thalamic nucleus and the mammillary bodies, which are part of the limbic circuits connecting the hippocampus and amygdala with the cortex.

Lesions of lateral temporal association neocortex, including pathways connecting the hippocampus with other neocortical regions, produce not only severe difficulty with learning but also the inability to recall remote events.

In Alzheimer's disease, memory dysfunction reflects inability to learn because of involvement of the hippocampus, inability of the hippocampus to transmit information to the neocortical areas due to involvement of the parahippocampal structures, and impaired cholinergic activation of limbic and neocortical circuits due to loss of neurons in the nucleus basalis.

Acute memory disturbances can also be classified on a temporal dimension if they are caused by an abrupt event. *Anterograde amnesia* is the inability to lay down new memories or to learn new information beginning at the time of the injury. For example, a person who has a head injury may have difficulty remembering events that occur after the injury (this may last for up to several days). Anterograde amnesia usually results from damage to medial temporal lobe structures, medial thalamus, or other limbic system structures. These are the structures involved in the establishment of new memories and of transferring information from primary to secondary memory. They are often affected in head injuries.

In contrast, *retrograde amnesia* is the inability to recall events that occurred before an injury. Typically, there is a temporal gradient to retrograde amnesia, with information learned immediately before the injury being more susceptible to disruption because it is less well established.

Clinical Correlates

Disorders of the cerebral hemispheres may be *diffuse* or *focal* and may be manifested as either *loss of function* (*or deficit*) or *excessive activity* (seizures). Diffuse disorders may con-

sist of an alternation in mentation or consciousness, bilateral motor abnormalities, or generalized seizures. Focal disorders of the cerebral hemispheres produce disturbances that are unique to the supratentorial level. These include apraxia, agnosia, aphasia, disorders of directed attention, visual field defects, motor and sensory disturbances affecting the contralateral body and face, and focal seizures. In addition, lesions of the left hemisphere may affect language-related functions, and lesions of the right hemisphere may affect visuospatial-related functions.

Diffuse Disorders

Diffuse movement disorders include hypokinetic disorders such as parkinsonism and hyperkinetic disorders such as chorea or myoclonus. Generalized seizures may consist of absence or generalized tonic-clonic seizures. Disorders of consciousness or mentation consist of confusional states, dementia, and mental retardation.

Confusional State
Confusional state, or *delirium*, is a decrease in awareness of the environment; it typically produces deficits in attention and thus impairs primary memory. In addition to impaired attention, confusional states may be associated with perceptual disturbances (illusions or hallucinations), increased or decreased psychomotor activity, incoherent speech, and disturbances of the sleep-wake cycle. This clinical syndrome commonly develops over a period of hours to days, tends to fluctuate during the day, and may be reversed if caused by a treatable condition. Causes of confusional state include metabolic encephalopathies, drug intoxication or withdrawal states, dementia, infectious processes, head injury, diffuse vascular disease, and nonconvulsive status epilepticus. Generalized motor phenomena such as tremor, myoclonus, or seizures may also be present.

Dementia
Dementia is an acquired condition involving a change in cognitive function from a prior level of performance to the point that social and possibly occupational functions are altered in

Fig. 16-19. Magnetic resonance image showing atrophy of the brain of a patient with Alzheimer's disease. A. Coronal view. B. Sagittal view.

an alert person. The many causes of dementia include degenerative diseases, vascular insults, toxic or metabolic factors, subdural hematoma, neoplasms, and infections. The most common form of dementia, however, is *Alzheimer's disease.* Typically, the initial finding of patients with Alzheimer's disease is a memory loss that over time progresses to a profound difficulty in learning new information. Often, as the disease progresses, difficulties with language and visuospatial skills develop, and the patient tends to get lost easily, cannot perform household tasks, cannot carry out financial activities, and no longer drives an automobile. In later stages of the illness, the patient no longer recognizes family members and may become mute. The patient usually dies of a complicating illness, such as pneumonia or another type of infection.

The incidence and prevalence of Alzheimer's disease increase with age, and 15 to 20 percent of people over the age of 80 are likely to have this disorder. The pathologic features of Alzheimer's disease include cerebral atrophy with cell loss, particularly in the hippocampus, parahippocampus, and heteromodal association areas (Fig. 16-19). The motor and

sensory areas of cortex are relatively spared. The pathologic hallmarks are neurofibrillary tangles and senile plaques in the cortex, as well as granulovacuolar degeneration, amyloid deposition, and loss of cholinergic neurons in the nucleus basalis (Fig. 16-20). Several neurotransmitters are depleted in Alzheimer's disease, especially acetylcholine.

Recently, the human immunodeficiency virus (HIV-1) has become an important cause of dementia, for example, in *HIV encephalopathy* or the *AIDS dementia complex.*

Mental Retardation

Mental retardation is the failure to develop normal intelligence. It is not a single disease but a group of disorders in which the development of normal intellectual functioning is arrested. Retardation may result from a congenital nonprogressive process, an acquired nonprogressive process, or a progressive disease with onset in infancy or childhood. There are many exogenous causes of mental retardation, such as trauma, anoxia, drugs, toxins, and infections. Three specific examples of endogenous causes are the genetic biochemical defects of Tay-Sachs disease, phenylketonu-

Fig. 16-20. Alzheimer's disease. A. Computerized tomogram (CT scan) showing atrophy of brain with widening of cerebral sulci and ventricular dilatation. B. Corresponding horizontal section of brain. C. Histologic section of cortex showing dense neurofibrillary tangles in neurons. (Bodian stain; ×400.)

ria, and the chromosomal abnormality of Down's syndrome.

Tay-Sachs disease is an inherited autosomal recessive disorder characterized by an excessive accumulation of the lipid ganglioside in the neurons of the central nervous system (Fig. 16-21). There is also retinal involvement that produces blindness. Infants with this disorder have normal development during the first few months but then begin to lose previously acquired abilities. The child becomes listless and dull, with weakness, spasticity, and hyperactive reflexes. In the terminal months, there is decerebrate posturing. Death is usually caused by infection.

Phenylketonuria is an inherited autosomal recessive disorder in which an enzymatic defect is associated with inability to convert phenylalanine to tyrosine; the increased levels of phenylalanine produce demyelination in the white matter and ultimately neuronal loss, resulting in retardation and seizures. Fortunately, in contrast to Tay-Sachs disease, the biochemical abnormality of phenylketonuria can be detected in the blood or urine and treated with a diet low in phenylalanine to prevent mental retardation. If untreated, severe mental retardation occurs.

Down's syndrome (*mongolism*), a chromosomal defect with triplication of chromosome 21, is characterized by mental retardation,

Fig. 16-21. Tay-Sachs disease. Histologic section of cerebral cortex showing massive "ballooning" of neurons due to lipid accumulation. (Bodian stain; ×400.)

heart and bladder defects, and a typical physical appearance of a round face, epicanthal folds, a short neck, and a simian crease on the palms of the hands. Children with this syndrome may survive into adulthood and continue to show moderate to severe retardation.

Focal Disorders

Focal disorders occur as a result of a focal process or lesion involving the cerebral hemispheres; the specific type of deficit or seizure indicates the region or lobe of the brain involved (see Figs. 16-10 and 16-12). The following describes the lobes of the brain and the types of dysfunction associated with each.

Frontal Lobe

The frontal lobe includes the primary motor cortex, premotor area, supplementary motor area, medial motor area, frontal eye fields, Broca's area, dorsolateral prefrontal cortex, and orbitofrontal cortex.

The primary motor cortex contributes most of the fibers in the corticospinal tract. Lesions restricted to this area produce the inability to perform fine finger movements. Acute lesions produce flaccid hyporeflexic paralysis. Seizures in this region consist of focal tonic and/or clonic movements of the contralateral face, arm, or leg.

The premotor area controls proximal limb muscles and transmits activity in other cortical regions to primary motor cortex. Lesions on the left side produce bilateral limb apraxia (inability to perform visuomotor tasks) and forced grasping. Lesions involving this area and area 4 result in a spastic, hyperreflexic paralysis.

The supplementary motor area is involved in motor planning and execution. Lesions of the region produce akinetic mutism, limb apraxia, and forced grasping. Seizures in this area produce a characteristic posturing, with elevation of the arm and deviation of the head and eyes toward the elevated arm.

Involvement of the medial motor area (area 4), which contains the representation of the leg, may produce leg weakness. Bilateral involvement may affect corticoreticulospinal input to motor neurons and cingulate input to pontine micturition centers. Such lesions cause bilateral leg spasticity and an uninhibited bladder, with incontinence.

The frontal eye fields contain neurons controlling voluntary and visually guided saccadic eye movements to the opposite side. Lesion produce transient conjugate deviation of the eyes toward the affected hemisphere and inability to move the eyes past the midline. Partial seizures in this region produce deviation of the eyes to the opposite side.

The motor speech (Broca's) area (areas 44 and 45) is located in the inferior frontal gyrus of the dominant (usually left) cerebral hemisphere; it controls the programming of speech. Lesions in this area (Broca's area) produce a motor speech apraxia.

The dorsolateral prefrontal cortex (areas 9, 10, and 46) is involved in attention, working memory, and motor planning. Lesions produce lack of spontaneity and psychomotor retardation, hypokinesia, diminished spontaneity of speech, lack of attention and concentration, and impaired motor planning.

The orbitofrontal and medial prefrontal regions are involved in emotional behavior. Lesions produce behavioral disinhibition and antisocial behavior. Involvement of the olfactory structures in this area produces anosmia (loss of smell). Seizures produce complex automatisms and vocalizations.

Parietal Lobe

The parietal lobe is involved in higher order processing of somatosensory and visual information and in directed attention to interpersonal and extrapersonal space. It includes primary and association somatosensory cortices.

The primary somatosensory cortex is in the postcentral gyrus. Lesions of this area abolish the basic discriminative somatosensory functions such as touch localization (topognosis), two-point discrimination, weight discrimination (barognosis), joint position sense, the highly discriminative functions of "active touch," and recognition of a number written in the hand (graphesthesia). Seizures in primary somatosensory cortex present with transient symptoms of numbness or tingling sensation of the contralateral face or body.

The unimodal somatosensory association area includes area 5 and part of area 7 in the posterior parietal lobe. Lesions here cause inability to identify objects held in the hand (astereognosis) despite the ability to perceive the objects and disturbance of perception of body image.

The heteromodal association area in the parietal lobe (area 7) processes somatosensory and visual inputs important for directed attention to the interpersonal or extrapersonal space. Lesions on the right side produce severe sensory neglect of the left hemibody or extrapersonal space, resulting in dressing apraxia and constructional apraxia. Lesions in the left inferior parietal lobe may produce a combination of deficits, including *agraphia* (difficulty in writing) with or without alexia; *acalculia* (inability to do arithmetical calculations), *finger agnosia* (finger naming difficulties), and *right/left disorientation*; this combination is called *Gerstmann's syndrome*.

Lesions involving the posterior portion of the superior temporal auditory association area and surrounding parietal lobe produce receptive (Wernicke's) aphasia and conduction aphasia. Bilateral superior parietooccipital lesions produce severe spatial disorientation, with *ocular apraxia* (inability to voluntarily control the gaze to an object of interest), *simultanagnosia* (inability to integrate the separate components of a complex visual scene), and *optic ataxia* (inability to accurately reach for an object under visual guidance). This constitutes *Balint's syndrome*.

Occipital Lobe

The occipital lobe includes the primary visual area in the banks of the calcarine fissure on the medial aspect of the occipital lobe (area 17) and the visual association areas 18 and 19 (peristriate cortex). Peristriate cortex is involved in visuospatial processing, discrimination of movement, and color discrimination. Lesions of the occipital lobe produce visual field defects and scotomas. These are discussed in more detail under The Visual System.

Temporal Lobe

The temporal lobe includes primary auditory cortex, unimodal auditory and visual association cortices, and limbic cortex. The primary auditory cortex (areas 41 and 42), in the superior temporal gyrus (Heschl's gyrus), receives auditory fibers from the medial geniculate body. Sounds coming into either ear reach the auditory cortex bilaterally. Therefore, unilateral lesions of the auditory cortex cause some difficulty in sound localization, but there is no significant hearing deficit. Bilateral ablation of the auditory cortex does not prevent reaction to sounds but does greatly reduce or abolish the ability to discriminate different patterns of sound.

The superior temporal gyrus (area 22) contains the auditory unimodal association area. Bilateral lesions of this area produce *pure word deafness*; patients react to environmental noise (thus, they are not deaf) and recognize written language but cannot understand or repeat spoken language. Wernicke's area, in the posterior part of the auditory association cortex of the dominant hemisphere, is involved in the processing of written and spoken language. Damage of this area produces Wernicke's aphasia, characterized by comprehension deficit for all modalities. Lesions of the temporal pole or the inferior temporal cortex disconnect the language areas from the limbic structures and produce anomia.

The temporal visual association areas are located in middle and inferior temporal gyri and receive input from the peristriate visual association areas. They project to heteromodal areas involved in language and limbic functions. Lesions of temporal visual association areas may produce achromatopsia, visual agnosia, prosopagnosia, visual anomia, and pure alexia. *Achromatopsia* is the inability to recognize colors. *Visual agnosia* is the inability to recognize an object by sight. *Prosopagnosia* is the inability to recognize familiar faces. *Visual anomia* is the inability to name normally recognized objects. *Pure alexia* is a deficit of visual recognition confined to words and letters and is a visual agnosia for verbal material.

Seizures in the posterolateral part of the temporal lobe are characterized by auditory or visual hallucinations and language disorders and are often associated with automatisms and amnesia.

Limbic Lobe

The limbic lobe consists of the limbic and paralimbic cortices, portions of the temporal lobe (hippocampal formation), and portions of the frontal lobe (anterior cingulate and medial orbitofrontal regions). Bilateral lesions of the hippocampal formation, particularly those involving the entorhinal and perihippocampal regions, produce severe deficits of learning and memory. Other functions and disorders involving the limbic lobe are described under Limbic System. Seizures arising in this region are complex partial seizures and are associated with impairment of consciousness and various symptoms (altered sensory perceptions, hallucinations, illusions, affective or emotional symptoms, cognitive disturbances, automatisms, and speech disturbances).

Focal Lesions

The most common focal lesions are vascular lesions and mass lesions. One of the most frequent focal lesions is an infarct. The presence of a mass lesion, however, must always be considered and is suggested by a focal, progressive course, with evidence of increased intracranial pressure or distortion of surrounding tissue or both. Neoplasms, intracerebral hemorrhage, subdural hematoma, and abscess are examples of supratentorial mass lesions.

Neoplasms in the cerebral hemispheres seldom metastasize to other body tissues and can be categorized into benign or malignant on the basis of their pathologic characteristics and invasiveness. However, whether they are benign or malignant, intracranial neoplasms are a major threat to life because they enlarge within the confined space of the closed cranial cavity and increase intracranial pressure as well as produce local tissue compression. Although any cell type in the nervous system may undergo neoplastic change, three major groups account for most brain tumors.

Gliomas

Neoplasms arising from the glial cells constitute the most common primary neoplasm of

Fig. 16-22. Astrocytoma. Histologic section of an astrocytoma. Note resemblance of cells to reactive astrocytes but with much more irregularity of size, shape, and nuclear morphology. (H & E; ×200.)

the brain. These neoplasms are usually derived from astrocytes and are called *astrocytomas*. Astrocytomas vary in malignancy and may arise anywhere in the nervous system. Low-grade astrocytomas are accumulations of astrocytes with some anaplastic features (Fig. 16-22). Invasion of surrounding tissue by an astrocytoma damages adjacent axons or neurons to produce focal neurologic deficit. As size increases, pressure increases. Compared with low-grade astrocytomas, high-grade astrocytomas evolve more rapidly and show more invasiveness, anaplasia, and areas of hemorrhage (Fig. 16-23). Vascularity and surrounding edema in high-grade lesions further increase the size of the tumor.

Meningiomas

The neoplastic proliferation of meningothelial cells, the lining cells of the leptomeninges, results in meningiomas. These tumors are al-

most always histologically benign, slow growing, and produce their clinical effects by compression of the brain and neighboring structures (Fig. 16-24A). Although they have many different histologic appearances, they typically have whorls of cells, which may degenerate and calcify to form psammoma bodies (Fig. 16-24B).

Metastatic Neoplasms

Focal accumulations of anaplastic cells within the brain parenchyma may arise from tumors originating elsewhere (Fig. 16-25). Metastatic tumors invade locally and exert a mass effect on the surrounding tissue. The histologic features resemble those of the primary neoplasm, the most common being lung and breast lesions. Frequently surrounding the tumor cells is a large area of cerebral edema, which increases the mass effect of the lesion (Fig. 16-26).

Fig. 16-23. High-grade astrocytoma. Horizontal section of cerebrum showing massive hemorrhagic-necrotic tumor of left hemisphere.

The Visual System

The visual system is a sensory system that transforms visual representations of the external world into a pattern of neural activity that the person can use. It has peripheral receptive structures in the eye and central pathways in the diencephalon and telencephalon. The eye is a peripheral receptor organ specialized to respond to visual stimuli. It has nonneural components whose function is the transmission of the light stimuli to the neural receptors and neural structures that respond to the light. The supratentorial level contains the central neural pathways in the diencephalon and telencephalon, which process and synthesize the visual information.

Nonneural Peripheral Structures

Most of the nonneural structures of the eyeball are derivatives of embryonic ectoderm, although the muscles that control the eye are mesodermal in origin. These nonneural structures include the cornea, sclera, anterior chamber, iris, lens, and vitreous humor (Fig. 16-27).

The eyeball is located in a bony orbit that supports and protects the eye. The six muscles responsible for eye movement and their actions are described in Chapter 15 (The Posterior Fossa Level).

The *cornea* is a transparent membrane that covers the anterior part of the eye and joins the opaque white sclera at the limbus. The *sclera* is a supporting tissue that covers the rest of the eyeball and to which the extraocular muscles are attached. The *iris* is a circular diaphragm with a central aperture, the *pupil*, through which the light projects to the posterior part of the eye. The ciliary body supports the *lens*, a biconvex, transparent, elastic structure that accommodates for vision at varying distances. The *vitreous humor* is a transparent gelatinous material separating the lens and retina and serving to hold both in place. The *choroid* lies between the sclera and the retina and functions to decrease the scatter of light inside the eye.

These nonneural structures transmit light rays and focus them on the neural structures in the back of the eye. The iris opens or closes in response to varying intensity of light to control the illumination of the retina. The lens inverts the image. The lens also changes its configuration in order to focus the light rays from near or distant objects on the retina.

The Retina

The retina is an extension of the brain and performs the first stages of visual processing. In higher visual centers, coded signals from the retina undergo further processing for perception of contours, colors, textures, and movement of objects.

The embryonic optic vesicle is derived from an evagination of the embryonic diencephalon (see Fig. 2-3C and D) and forms a two-layered cup as it grows. The outer layer becomes the retinal pigment epithelium, and the inner layer becomes the neurosensory retina.

Histology

Cells of the neurosensory retina are stratified in well-demarcated layers (Fig. 16-28). From the outer to inner layers, they are the receptor

A

cell layer, outer nuclear layer, outer plexiform layer, inner nuclear layer, inner plexiform layer, and ganglion cell layer. The ganglion cell layer, the innermost layer, lies adjacent to the vitreous humor. The nerve fiber layer lies just inside the ganglion cell layer and is bounded by the internal limiting membrane. Nuclear layers contain cell bodies, and plexiform layers contain dendrites and synapses. The receptor cell layer is bounded by retinal pigment epithelium and Bruch's membrane. Light has to travel across the inner layers before reaching the receptor cells in the outer layer.

The retina contains five types of nerve cells that interact to convert and encode the image focused on the retina. The photoreceptor cells, the rods and cones, are in the outer nuclear layer and are the first-order neurons. They convert light to a transmembrane electrical response. Synaptic terminals of receptor cells contact the second-order neurons, the bipolar

B

Fig. 16-24. Meningioma. A. Ventral view of brain showing large meningioma between the frontal lobes. B. Histologic section showing typical whorl formation of elongated tumor cells. (H & E; ×250.)

Fig. 16-25. Metastatic melanoma. Horizontal section of cerebrum showing multiple pigmented metastatic tumors.

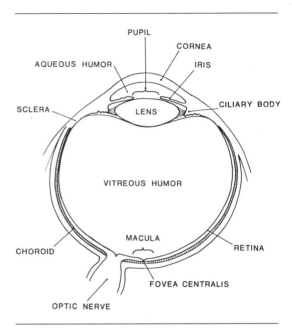

Fig. 16-27. Nonneural structures of the eye form the anterior portion and the outer coats. The retina and optic nerve are the neural components.

cells, in the inner nuclear layer. These cells convey information to the ganglion cells (ganglion cell layer), the output cells of the retina. Ganglion cell axons collectively form the optic nerve. Two types of interneurons, horizontal cells and amacrine cells, modify activity of the receptor-bipolar-ganglion cell pathway and provide lateral integration of information.

The thickness of the retina and its cell density vary from the central visual axis to the peripheral regions. The maximum density of cones is in the *macula lutea*, a specialized region of the posterior pole of the eye. The center of the macula, the *fovea centralis*, is responsible for sharpest visual acuity. Unlike peripheral retina, the overlying structures (bipolar cells, ganglion cells, and blood vessels) are swept to the side so light has an uninterrupted path to the receptor cells. In addition, receptor cells are tightly packed and have nearly a one-to-one ratio to ganglion cells.

Fig. 16-26. Magnetic resonance imaging of metastatic adenocarcinoma of the brain with mass effect.

Physiology

Rods and cones have different functions. Rods have low thresholds for light stimulation and mediate vision under dim light, *scotopic vision*.

Fig. 16-28. The retina has three cell layers from outside to inside: rods and cones, the receptor cells (1); the bipolar cells (2); and the ganglion cells (3). Note that the light rays have to pass through the inner layers to reach the receptor cells in the outer layer.

The visual pigment of the rods is rhodopsin, which contains retinene formed from vitamin A. A deficiency of vitamin A causes a deficiency of retinene and rhodopsin, which results in a condition known as *night blindness*, the inability to see in the dark.

Cones, on the other hand, are specialized for color vision, *photopic vision*, and have a high threshold for light stimulation. There are three types of cones, each with different visual pigments that absorb maximally at the blue, green, or red region of the spectrum. Visual acuity is greatest in the central fovea, where the density of the cones is greatest, and decreases in the peripheral regions. Photopic vi-

sion is important; without cones a person is legally blind.

The outer segment of rods and cones contains high concentrations of visual pigments. Rhodopsin and other visual pigments are a complex of 11-*cis* retinal (vitamin A aldehyde) bound to opsin, a protein. Light isomerizes 11-*cis* retinal to all-*trans* retinal and initiates a series of conformational changes in the protein. This goes through a series of intermediate steps and initiates visual excitation. After it is released, all-*trans* retinal has to be reisomerized to 11-*cis* retinal before rhodopsin is reconstituted.

Photoreceptors are normally depolarized in

the dark, because of persistent opening of their sodium channels; this is called *dark current*. Dark current is turned off by light; illumination activates transducin, which initiates a series of biochemical events leading to closure of light-sensitive cation channels and hyperpolarization of the photoreceptors. Because bright light blocks the regeneration of rhodopsin, vision is reduced for 10 to 15 minutes after entering a dark room. As rhodopsin in the rods regenerates, the eyes become adapted to the dark.

Rods and cones code the location and color of objects in the visual fields. These receptors also undergo adaptation in response to a constant stimulus. Because of adaptation, images stabilized (immobilized) on the retina rapidly fade. Normally, the eyes make continuous, small, rapid, irregular oscillations (microsaccades) when gaze is fixed on an object. Therefore, no retinal image remains immobile. The retina reports on what is changing in the visual field, thereby avoiding the effects of adaptation.

The outer plexiform layer processes the spatial aspects of visual information. The inner plexiform layer processes the temporal aspects of visual information.

Central Neural Structures

The visual structures within the cranial cavity at the supratentorial level include the optic nerve and optic chiasm, the optic tracts and lateral geniculate bodies in the diencephalon, and the optic radiations and occipital cortex in the telencephalon.

Diencephalic Structures

The optic nerve consists of axons arising from ganglion cells in the retina. These axons converge at the optic disk, become myelinated, and then leave the back of the eye via the lamina cribrosa. The optic nerve leaves the orbit and enters the cranial cavity via the optic foramen. Although the optic nerve is considered one of the cranial nerves (cranial nerve II), it is actually a nerve tract similar to tracts in the central nervous system and consists of axons with myelin sheaths formed by oligodendroglia cells rather than by Schwann cells. Thus, disease processes such as multiple scle-

rosis that affect myelin of the central nervous system produce similar lesions in the optic nerve.

After passing through the optic foramen, the optic nerves unite to form the *optic chiasm*, beyond which the axons continue as the *optic tracts*. Within the chiasm, a partial decussation occurs; the fibers from the nasal half of each retina cross to the opposite side; those from the temporal halves of the retina remain uncrossed. As the fibers from the inferior nasal retina cross, they loop forward for a short distance into the opposite optic nerve.

In binocular vision, each visual field, right and left, is projected upon one-half of both right and left retinas. Thus, the images of objects in the right field of vision are projected on the right nasal and the left temporal halves of the two retinas. In the chiasm, the fibers from these two retinal segments are combined to form the left optic tract, which then represents the complete right field of vision. By this arrangement, the whole right visual field is projected upon the left hemisphere, and the left visual field is projected upon the right hemisphere (Fig. 16-29).

After the partial decussation in the optic chiasm, the visual pathways, which are now known as the optic tracts, course laterally and posteriorly to terminate in the lateral geniculate bodies. A few fibers leave the optic tract before it reaches the lateral geniculate body to go to the pretectal area. These fibers constitute the afferent limb of the light reflex. The *lateral geniculate body* receives the fibers from the optic tract and gives rise to the *geniculocalcarine tract*, which forms the last relay of the visual pathway.

Telencephalic Structures

The geniculocalcarine tract arises from the lateral geniculate body, passes through the retrolenticular portion of the internal capsule, and forms the *optic radiations*. The upper or dorsal fibers of the optic radiations run posteriorly in the parietal lobe and terminate in the superior part of the calcarine cortex of the occipital lobe. The lower or ventral fibers loop anteriorly and laterally around the temporal horn in the temporal lobe (Meyer's loop) before turning posteriorly to end in the inferior calcarine cortex (Fig. 16-30).

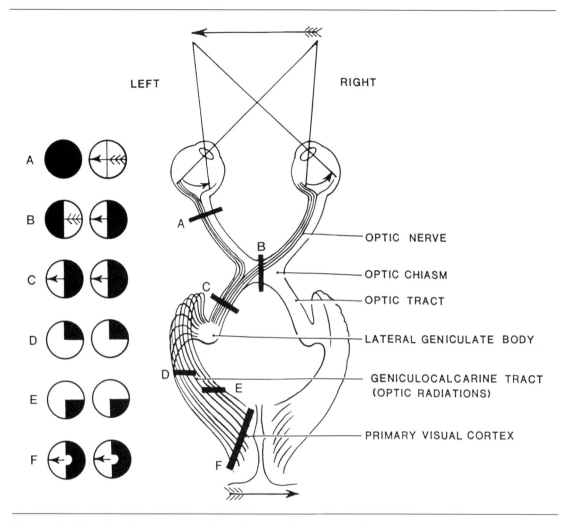

Fig. 16-29. Visual pathways as seen from the base of the brain. The visual impulses from the right half of the visual field project to the left half of each retina and to the left occipital lobe. On the left are the visual field defects (*black areas*) produced by lesions affecting optic nerve (*A*), optic chiasm (*B*), optic tract (*C*), optic radiation in temporal lobe (*D*), optic radiation in parietal lobe (*E*), and occipital cortex (*F*).

The primary visual (calcarine) cortex is organized into columns of cells running from the surface to the white matter. These columns function as units that respond to specific patterns of visual stimuli, such as moving lines or bars. Each column is activated by a particular pattern or array of cells in the lateral geniculate body, which, in turn, is activated by retinal ganglion cells.

The visual images impinging on the retina are inverted so that the superior part of the visual field projects to the inferior part of the retina and the inferior visual field projects to the superior part of the retina. Fibers from the upper part of the retina form the superior part of the optic radiations, which run in the parietal lobe and terminate in the superior calcarine cortex. Fibers from the lower part of the retina form the inferior optic radiations, which run in the temporal lobe to terminate in the inferior calcarine cortex (see Fig. 16-30).

The calcarine cortex thus has a topographic organization such that the superior part of the visual field terminates in the inferior calcarine cortex and the inferior visual field terminates in the superior calcarine cortex (Figs. 16-30

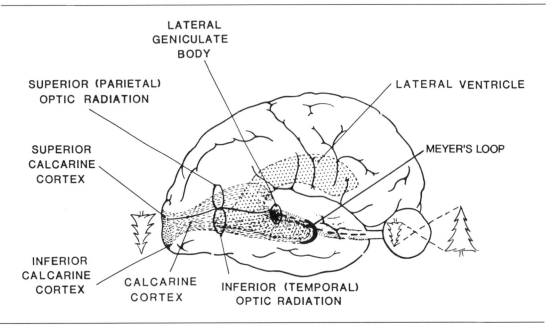

Fig. 16-30. Course of superior and inferior optic radiations. Fibers from the upper part of the retina (which receive impulses from the inferior visual field) form the superior optic radiations (located in the parietal lobe) and terminate in the superior calcarine cortex. Fibers from the inferior half of the retina (which receive impulses from the superior visual field) form the inferior optic radiations (located in the temporal lobe) and terminate in the inferior calcarine cortex.

and 16-31). In addition, the posterior portion of the occipital pole is primarily concerned with macular (central) vision, and the more anterior parts of the visual cortex are concerned with peripheral vision. Throughout the visual pathway, different aspects of the visual image are analyzed by different types of neurons that respond selectively to shape, color, movement, and direction of movement. The final processing of the visual image occurs in the primary and visual association areas of the cerebral cortex (see Fig. 16-31).

The primary visual cortex (area 17) is located in the walls of the calcarine fissure and receives the primary visual stimuli. The visual association areas (areas 18 and 19) are lateral to the primary visual area and are called the peristriate cortex. Other visual association areas are located in the posterolateral and inferior regions of the temporal lobes. The peristriate cortex has two outflow pathways: a dorsal outflow pathway directed to the parietal lobe is predominantly involved in visual spatial processing, and a ventral outflow pathway directed to the temporal visual associa-

tion areas is involved in the discrimination and identification of colors and visual-limbic interactions.

The visual association areas synthesize visual impressions, integrate visual impressions with other sensory modalities, and help form visual memory traces. The visual association areas are also responsible for eye movements induced by visual stimuli.

The *frontal eye fields* are responsible for voluntary control of conjugate gaze. One such center is located in the posterior portion of the middle frontal gyrus (area 8 [see Fig. 16-12]) of each frontal lobe immediately rostral to the precentral gyrus. Stimulation of this center causes the eyes to move conjugately to the opposite side; that is, if the right frontal field is stimulated, the eyes turn to the left. If one center is acutely destroyed, the unbalanced activity of the other center will cause the eyes to deviate to the side of the lesion; that is, if the right side is destroyed, the eyes will deviate to the right.

The *parietooccipital centers* are responsible for involuntary visual pursuit. These centers are located in each hemisphere in the visual

Fig. 16-31. Medial aspect of occipital lobe showing superior and inferior calcarine cortices separated by the calcarine fissure, the location of the primary visual area (17), and the visual association areas (18 and 19).

association area (area 19 [see Fig. 16-12]) at the parietooccipital junction. Stimulation of this area causes contralateral deviation of the eyes in a similar fashion to that outlined for the frontal fields. The involuntary visual pursuit center is responsible for fixing the eyes on an object in the visual field and maintaining that visual fixation as the object moves through the visual field. Because of the action of this center, the eyes of a person casually looking out the window of a moving car will automatically fix on some point in the environment and follow the object involuntarily until it approaches the limits of the person's visual fields. Then visual fixation is broken, and the eyes make a quick conjugate movement in the opposite direction to fix on a new point of interest. Such involuntary visual pursuit of a moving target is the basis for the optokinetic nystagmus produced by a rotating drum containing dark bands alternating with white bands (optokinetic nystagmus is the nystagmus produced by looking at a moving object).

Voluntary movement of the eyes to a point of interest in the visual fields occurs via the frontal eye centers. The parietooccipital centers help keep the eyes fixed on an object after it has been located.

Clinical Correlations

Disorders of the visual system produce specific, readily identifiable visual defects that depend on the part of the visual system damaged. Knowledge of these defects permits precise localization of many lesions involving the visual system. Damage may occur at any site along the visual pathways and will be considered in terms of the observed differences between lesions at each site.

Eye Disease

Most visual system disorders are due to abnormalities in the nonneural structures of the eye and are seen as abnormalities in visual acuity due to inability to focus visual images properly. Common examples are nearsightedness or farsightedness, distortion of light rays by diseases of the cornea or lens such as a cataract, and glaucoma, in which there is increased pressure within the eye. Each of these causes monocular visual loss (unless both eyes are involved) and can be identified by tests of visual acuity and direct inspection of the eye.

Retinal Disease

Disorders of the retina also cause monocular visual loss, often with reduced visual acuity. Retinal detachment and retinal degenerations are associated with progressive loss of vision. A focal lesion of the retina causes a *scotoma*, or blind spot. Vascular diseases involving the retina also are reflected in visible changes in the retinal arteries with arteriosclerosis, small emboli, or hemorrhages. *Amaurosis fugax* is a transient loss of vision in one eye due to reduced blood supply (see Chapter 11, The Vascular System). In elderly persons, it is most often the result of atherosclerotic disease in the ipsilateral internal carotid artery.

Optic Nerve

Focal lesions may involve a single optic nerve to produce a *negative scotoma*, in which part of the visual world is missing. Some disorders of the optic nerve head may be seen with the ophthalmoscope. *Optic atrophy* is seen as a pale disk and occurs with degenerative diseases of the retina or nerve. *Optic neuritis* is an inflammation of the optic nerve and may be associated with blurring of the disk margin and decreased visual acuity. *Papilledema*, a sign of increased intracranial pressure, is seen as swelling and elevation of the disk, with blurring of the disk margin (see Chapter 6, The Cerebrospinal Fluid System).

Optic Chiasm

Lesions of the chiasm cause several kinds of defects. Most commonly, the crossing fibers from the nasal portions of the retina are involved, with consequent loss of the two temporal fields of vision (bitemporal hemianopia) (see Fig. 16-29). Rarely, both lateral angles of the chiasm are compressed; in such cases, the nondecussating fibers from the temporal retinas are affected, and the result is loss of the nasal visual fields (binasal hemianopia).

Optic Tract and Optic Radiations

Lesions affecting the optic tract, the lateral geniculate body, or optic radiations on one side produce homonymous defects in the opposite visual field (see Fig. 16-29). For example, a lesion affecting the optic tract or radiations on the right side results in a homonymous field defect in the left visual field of both eyes. Complete destruction of the optic tract or radiation on one side produces a complete *homonymous hemianopia*, that is, a complete loss of vision in the opposite half of the visual field of each eye. A lesion in the temporal lobe on one side destroys the fibers running in the lower portion of the optic radiation and thus results in a *superior quadrantic field defect*, that is, a loss of vision in the superior portion of the visual fields of the opposite side. A lesion in the parietal lobe destroys the superior optic radiations and thus results in an *inferior quadrantic field defect*, that is, a loss of vision in the inferior visual fields of the opposite side.

Axons mediating the pupillary light reflexes and other visual reflexes leave the optic tract at or before the lateral geniculate to terminate in the pretectal area. Therefore, optic radiation lesions differ from optic tract lesions in that the pupillary light reflex is preserved in the former.

Occipital Lobe

Lesions affecting the visual cortex in the occipital lobe on one side also cause homonymous loss of vision in the contralateral visual field (see Fig. 16-29). Because the visual fibers are topographically ordered in the occipital lobe, lesions here cause congruent visual field defects, that is, exactly the same loss in the fields of the two eyes. Bilateral destruction of the occipital lobes produces a form of blindness in which the visual loss is often denied. Disorders of occipital cortex can be associated with subjective transient anomalies of vision such as scintillating scotomata, visual hallucinations, and illusions. *Scintillating scotomata* are sensations of flashing lights in a field of vision. This condition commonly accompanies migraine headache. *Visual hallucinations* are perceptions of visual images for which there is no external stimulus. These may be unformed in nature and consist of flashing or twinkling lights, or they may be formed visual hallucinations in which an actual scene or picture is visualized. Such hallucinations may occur as part of a seizure involving the posterior temporal lobes or as an imagined phenomenon in psychotic states. *Visual illusions* are distorted perceptions of external visual stimuli; they include macropsia (objects appear larger than normal), micropsia (objects appear smaller), achromatopsia (objects lack color), and erythropsia (objects appear abnormally colored).

Neurologic Examination

Assessment of functions specific to the supratentorial level includes tests of cranial nerves I and II; evaluation of intellectual function, particularly memory and language; and tests of cortical motor and sensory functions.

In addition, the distribution of findings with involvement of longitudinal systems can aid in the localization of supratentorial damage. For example, the presence of weakness in the face, arm, and leg on one side is evidence of a unilateral cerebral lesion.

Cranial Nerve I (Olfactory)

Olfaction is tested by having the patient sniff a substance that has an odor (camphor, coffee, wintergreen) with each nostril separately while the other nostril is held closed. Because it is not possible to quantitate this sensation, the appreciation of the odor is sufficient to exclude anosmia. Intranasal disease is a common cause of impaired olfactory sensation and must be excluded before a diagnosis of neurogenic anosmia is made.

Cranial Nerve II (Optic)

Visual system testing requires attention to four aspects of visual function: the appearance of the nonneural components of the eye, visual acuity, visual field, and ophthalmoscopic examination of the optic fundus. The nonneural structures are examined by direct inspection of the external appearance and by visualization of internal features, such as the lens, with the ophthalmoscope. Tests of the extraocular muscles are described in Chapter 15 (The Posterior Fossa Level).

Visual Acuity
The resolving power of vision depends on the ability of the retina to distinguish a separation between two images, and it is measured as acuity. Visual acuity is tested separately in each eye for near and distant vision. A patient who wears glasses should be tested with and without the glasses. Eye charts (Snellen's chart) are available that are read at fixed distances. The smallest size of print the patient can read is compared with what a person with normal vision can read at the same distance, and acuity is reported as a comparison of these numbers. For example, visual acuity of 20/200 means that the patient can read at 20 feet what a person with normal vision can read at 200 feet. With major visual loss, acuity can be tested with large objects such as fingers or hands.

Visual Field
Localized loss of vision in one area of the field of vision is tested by confrontation in which the examiner faces the patient and compares his or her visual field with the patient's. Each eye is tested separately by having the patient look straight ahead at the examiner's nose while a target (usually a finger) is moved in the field of vision. Two methods of testing can be used. In one, a finger is wiggled and gradually brought in from the periphery in all four quadrants of the visual field to determine where it is first seen. In the second, one to four fingers are briefly extended in each of the four quadrants, and the patient is asked to identify the number of fingers shown. With uncooperative patients or those who cannot respond directly, the field can be tested grossly by swiftly moving the hand toward the eye from one direction and looking for defensive blinking. Very precise plots of the visual field can be obtained with a perimeter or tangent screen.

Funduscopic Examination
Both optic fundi should routinely be examined with an ophthalmoscope as part of a neurologic examination. The optic disk, blood vessels, and retina should be examined. The disk should be examined for variation from its usual yellow color and for flat appearance with distinct margins. In papilledema, the margins are blurred and elevated; in optic atrophy, the disk is pale. The arteriolar caliber and appearance and the venous pulsation should be examined. Areas of exudates, hemorrhage, and abnormal pigmentation may be seen in the retina.

Visual Evoked Potentials
A low-amplitude, surface-positive electrical potential can be recorded over the occipital areas in response to a visual stimulus. The best stimulus for eliciting a consistent visual evoked response is a black and white checkerboard pattern with rapid reversal of the black and white checks. With amplification and computer averaging of a hundred or more successive responses, the evoked response is clearly distinguished from random background electroencephalographic activity (Fig. 16-32). The major surface-positive potential occurs approximately 100 milliseconds after

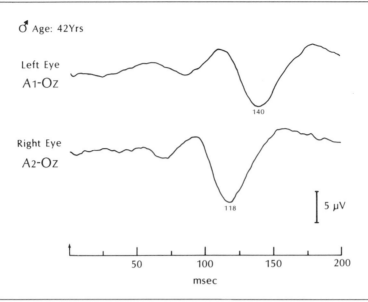

Fig. 16-32. Visual evoked responses to television pattern reversal stimuli in a 42-year-old man with multiple sclerosis. Stimulation of the left eye (*top segment*) shows an abnormal peak-positive response of 140 msec secondary to demyelination of the left optic nerve. Stimulation of the right eye (*bottom segment*) shows a normal response of 118 msec. Responses represent an average of 128 responses. (Recording electrodes: *A1* = left ear; *A2* = right ear; *Oz* = midline occipital.)

the stimulus. A latency of the response prolonged beyond the upper limit of normal is suggestive of delayed conduction in the visual pathway of that eye.

Cortical Functions

The specific functions mediated by the cerebral cortex are tested as a group in the *mental status examination*. The mental status examination is an essential component of the neurologic examination and includes assessment of the level of consciousness, cognitive functions, cortical motor and sensory functions, and language.

Level of Consciousness

Evaluation of the level of consciousness is performed by testing the patient's awareness of (or response to) the external environment, by stimulating him or her with verbal, visual, tactile, and painful stimuli. The responses allow the patient to be characterized as alert, confused, somnolent, stuporous, or comatose (see Chapter 10, The Consciousness System). As part of the assessment of the level of con-

sciousness, the patient's orientation and affect also should be noted. Does the patient know who he or she is, where he or she is, and what the date is? Is his or her emotional state one of anger, hostility, fear, suspicion, or depression?

Cognitive Functions

The patient's intellectual functions are tested with a series of specific tests, most of which depend on diffuse cortical processes. The tests can be helpful in determining the extent of dementia or retardation or in distinguishing organic intellectual impairment from psychiatric diseases. The evaluation should include memory, fund of knowledge, calculation, ability to think abstractly, and judgment. *Memory function* should be tested in the three memory modes of short-term, recent, and long-term memory. Short-term memory is tested by having the patient repeat a sequence of digits of increasing length and recall the names of items after 5 minutes. Normal subjects can readily repeat up to six digits immediately and can recall the names of three cities or objects after 5 minutes. Recent memory is tested by having the patient recall events of the past few days, such as where he or she has been, whom he or she has seen, or what he or she has eaten. Long-term memory is tested by asking about events, such as date of birth and marriage, or overlearned material, such as the alphabet or names of the months.

The *general fund of information* should be tested in the light of the patient's intellectual level, cultural background, and geographic origin. Inquiry can be made into knowledge of the presidents, other public figures, dates of major events such as world wars, or knowledge of geographic features such as rivers, lakes, and distances. Ability to *calculate* is usually tested by serial 7s, in which the patient is asked to subtract 7 from 100 and then from each subsequent answer. For some patients, simpler tasks such as simple addition or serial 3s may be more appropriate for their level of education. The *ability to abstract* is tested by determining the patient's ability to detect similarities such as those between gold and silver or a book and a newspaper. It also may be tested by asking for an interpretation of a well-known proverb such as "People who live in glass houses shouldn't throw stones." A patient's *judgment* is tested by asking such questions as "Why are laws needed?" or "What would you do if there were a fire in a theater?"

Cortical Sensory Function

The general tests for agnosias include assessment of stereognosis, graphesthesia, two-point discrimination, tactile localization, and visual or auditory agnosia. These tests might include tests of ability to recognize visual objects, to identify sounds, to recognize parts of the body, or to know right from left. The last may be tested with commands such as "Show me your thumb" or "Touch your left ear with your right thumb."

Cortical Motor Function

The general tests of motor function have been described in Chapter 8 (The Motor System), but additional special tests may be needed if disease in the frontal association areas and a resultant apraxia are suspected, particularly if the results of standard tests of strength and coordination are normal. The patient's motor activities during the entire examination should be observed, and comparisons should be made between facility in performing automatic acts and facility in performing voluntary acts. In addition, asking the patient to demonstrate how to drink a cup of water or light a match may reveal apraxia that is not apparent on routine testing.

Language

The four modalities of central language processing are listening, speaking, reading, and writing. Each should be tested in a patient if a language disorder is suspected. Listening is evaluated by judging a patient's ability to recognize and respond appropriately to verbal input. The patient may be asked to perform acts, point to objects, move part of the body, and so forth. If there is a defect of speaking, the patient should be asked to respond in ways other than with language. Speaking is evaluated through conducting an ordinary conversation, but it also may be specifically tested by having the patient repeat certain phrases or name objects.

Reading should be evaluated by having the patient either read a paragraph silently and explain what was in the paragraph or, if speech is significantly impaired, to ask the patient to point to words and sentences on the printed page spoken by the examiner. Writing can be tested by having the patient write something from dictation or copy a written message.

Additional Tests of Cortical Function

Additional tests of cortical functions include neuropsychologic testing, electroencephalography, and functional imaging studies. *Neuropsychologic* assessment involves psychometric testing of cortical functions with procedures that have a standardized administration and normative references. In general, neuropsychologic testing is used to detect impairment of cognitive abilities, including learning, memory, attention, language, visuospatial skills, and executive or reasoning functions. Neurocognitive testing is commonly used in evaluating such central nervous system disorders as diffuse encephalopathies, dementia, vascular disorders, stroke, epilepsy, and head injury.

The *electroencephalogram* (EEG) records the electrical activity of the cerebral cortex and can be used to detect abnormalities of cerebral function and indicate whether the disturbance is focal or generalized. The EEG is particularly helpful in evaluating patients with seizures, altered states of consciousness, and focal cortical lesions. It is described in more detail in Chapter 10 (The Consciousness System).

Activity in specific brain regions in humans performing specific sensory, motor, or verbal tasks can be studied with *noninvasive imaging techniques*. These techniques include positron emission tomography (PET), single-photon emission computed tomography (SPECT), and dynamic magnetic resonance imaging (MRI). The principle underlying these techniques is that increased neuronal activity in a particular brain region is coupled with a local increase in cerebral blood flow, oxygen consumption, and glucose metabolism. Thus, changes in blood flow or metabolism detected with PET, SPECT, or MRI reflect activation of cortical regions during specific tasks. PET depends on the use of short-lived isotopes that contain an extra proton and that label biologically relevant molecules such as carbon dioxide, oxygen, 2-deoxyglucose, or drugs that bind to specific membrane receptors. The isotopes are administered to the subject within a few minutes of performance of the task and allow measurement of blood flow (carbon dioxide), oxygen consumption (oxygen), or glucose metabolism (2-deoxyglucose). For example, motor tasks in response to visual commands increase activity in the posterior parietal cortex, cortical motor areas, basal ganglia, and contralateral cerebellum. Tasks involving language increase cerebral blood flow predominantly in the left hemisphere; hearing words produces increased activity in Wernicke's area.

Dynamic MRI detects changes in signal intensity in specific brain regions during performance of a task. The changes reflect either local changes in blood volume or in oxygen concentration in cerebral veins, both of which are proportional to the degree of neuronal activation and oxygen consumption.

Objectives

Diencephalon

1. Name the divisions of the diencephalon, list the components of each division, and localize the structures on a diagram or brain model.
2. List the functional subgroups of the thalamic nuclei and their connections and projections to other parts of the central nervous system.
3. List the regulatory functions of the hypothalamic nuclei.
4. Describe the clinical significance of the pituitary gland, and list the neurohormones secreted by the anterior and posterior lobes and their functions.
5. Describe how a mass lesion in the region of the hypothalamus may affect vision and endocrine function.
6. Describe the clinical significance of the pineal gland.

Telencephalon

1. List the components of the basal ganglia, and identify them on a brain model or diagram.
2. Define projectional fibers, commissural fibers, and association fibers.
3. Locate the internal capsule on a gross specimen, and describe what occurs with a lesion involving the internal capsule.
4. Locate on a diagram and describe the functions of the primary motor and premotor areas, frontal eye fields, motor speech area, primary sensory area, primary visual cortex, primary auditory cortex, Broca's area, and Wernicke's area.
5. Define agnosia, and describe its various types.
6. Define apraxia.
7. Define aphasia and its types, and be able to localize the lesion that produces each type. Define motor speech apraxia.
8. List the types of lesions that may produce dysarthria.
9. List the various types of cortical sensory deficit, and describe how the type of deficit is useful as a localizing sign.
10. Describe the various types of memory, amnesia, dementia, and mental retardation.
11. Differentiate partial from generalized seizures.
12. Describe absence and generalized tonic-clonic seizures.

13. Given the clinical manifestations of a partial seizure, localize the site of origin of the seizure; given the site of origin of a partial seizure, describe the clinical manifestations of the seizure.

Limbic System

1. List the structures of the limbic system.
2. List the functions of the limbic system.
3. List the structures involved with olfaction.

Visual System

1. Describe the anatomy of the optic pathways.
2. Describe what effect a lesion has on the visual fields at the level of the optic nerve, optic chiasm, optic tract, optic radiations, and occipital cortex.
3. Given a visual field defect, localize the lesion.
4. Define and describe the significance of papilledema.
5. Describe the function of the rods and cones.
6. Locate on a diagram: cornea, sclera, iris, ciliary body, lens, vitreous humor, retina, and choroid.
7. Define hemianopia, quadrantanopia, homonymous, macular sparing, scotoma, and visual hallucination.

Clinical Problems

1. A 30-year-old woman noted the onset of amenorrhea 1 year ago. In the past 6 months, she noted that she tired very easily, could not tolerate stress or cold weather, and had lost weight. Physical examination revealed a dull, apathetic, thin woman with low blood pressure, slow pulse, bitemporal hemianopia, and deep tendon reflexes with a slow relaxation phase.
   a. Where is the primary lesion?
   b. What structures are affected by the lesion?
   c. What are the two lobes of the pituitary gland?
   d. Which lobe of the pituitary gland is involved?

e. What hormones are secreted by this lobe? What regulates the release of these hormones?
   f. Which hormones are affected in this patient?
   g. How do you explain the visual symptoms?
   h. What might you expect a radiograph to show?
   i. What structures are near the pituitary gland?
   j. What is the lesion?

2. A 10-year-old boy had become fat and listless during the past year. He also drank water and urinated excessively. For the past several months, he had complained of headaches and had experienced nausea and vomiting on arising in the morning. Neurologic examination revealed an obese boy with papilledema and bitemporal hemianopia.
   a. Where is the primary lesion?
   b. What regulates the release of the hormones?
   c. Which hormone is affected in this patient?
   d. What are the functions of the hypothalamic nuclei?
   e. What is the lesion?

3. A 65-year-old man had the sudden onset of numbness of the right side of his face and body, and he noted difficulty in seeing in his right visual field. Neurologic examination performed 2 hours later revealed that he could not identify objects or written numbers in his right hand, or localize sensory stimuli on the right side, or distinguish right from left. Further testing revealed that he had difficulty with arithmetic calculations and writing his name.
   a. Where is the lesion?
   b. What is the lesion?
   c. What kinds of agnosia are manifested by this patient?
   d. What are the other types of agnosia, and where would the lesion be located to produce these?
   e. What type of visual field defect might be expected in this patient?

4. A 50-year-old woman had the gradual onset of memory loss 3 years ago. This loss has become progressively worse, so that

now she cannot remember from one minute to the next what she has been doing. She also has had difficulty in carrying out various household activities such as sewing, cooking, and washing dishes, even though she denies being weak or having trouble with coordination. Neurologic examination revealed that she could not recall numbers just presented to her, what she had had for breakfast, or even where she was born. She was unable to perform activities such as pretending to light a cigarette or showing how a key would work.

    a. Where is the lesion?

    b. What is the disease process?

    c. What types of memory functioning were affected in this patient?

    d. What is the difference between dementia and mental retardation?

    e. What is the name given to the inability to perform learned complex motor activities in the absence of weakness?

    f. Name three other types of neurologic dysfunction that signify a lesion or disease process affecting cortical structures.

5. Three years ago, a 28-year-old man had onset of transient spells lasting 1 to 2 minutes in which he experienced an unpleasant odor. Immediately after the odor, he felt as if he were in a dream state in which he saw and heard things that he had experienced before. He also was aware that he was unable to understand what other people were saying to him during these episodes. In the past year, the spells have changed somewhat, in that now he hears the sound of a bell and at the same time experiences a mental picture of a country scene from his childhood. In the past 3 months, he has been bothered by increasingly severe headaches, nausea, and vomiting. He has difficulty understanding what people are saying to him even when he is not having his spells. Neurologic examination showed bilateral blurring of the disk margins, a visual field defect, aphasia, and Babinski's reflex on the right.

    a. Where is the lesion?

    b. What is the lesion?

    c. What visual field defect would you expect this patient to show?

    d. What do the transient spells represent?

    e. What was the initial site of origin for the spells?

    f. What clues are present that show progression of the underlying process?

    g. What tests would be most helpful for this patient?

    h. What might these tests show?

    i. What type of language problem did the patient have?

    j. The olfactory structures are part of what system? Name the other structures that are associated with this system. What are the functions of this system?

6. What type of visual field defect might be expected in each of the following clinical situations?

    a. A 47-year-old woman with a large tumor protruding from the pituitary fossa and pushing the optic chiasm forward.

    b. An 81-year-old man who sustained an occlusive vascular event involving the right posterior cerebral artery.

    c. A 44-year-old woman with a right parietal lobe tumor.

    d. A 14-year-old boy with an abscess of the left temporal lobe after a chronic infection of the left middle ear.

Additional Reading

Alexander, G. E., and DeLong, M. R. Central Mechanisms of Initiation and Control of Movement. In A. K. Asbury, G. McKhann, and W. I. McDonald (eds.), *Diseases of the Nervous System: Clinical Neurobiology* (2nd ed.). Philadelphia: Saunders, 1992. Vol. 1, pp. 285-308.

Aronson, A. E. *Clinical Voice Disorders: An Interdisciplinary Approach.* New York: Thieme, 1990.

Becker, K. L. Principles and Practice of Endocrinology and Metabolism. In G. L. Robertson (ed.), *The Endocrine Brain and Pituitary Gland.* Philadelphia: Lippincott, 1990. pp. 92–261.

Berne, R. M., and Levy, M. N. (eds.). *Principles of Physiology.* St. Louis: Mosby, 1990. pp. 529–545.

Department of Neurology, Mayo Clinic and Mayo Foundation. *Clinical Examinations in Neurology* (6th ed.). St. Louis: Mosby, 1991.

Engel, J., Jr. *Seizures and Epilepsy.* Philadelphia: Davis, 1989.

Kandel, E. R., Schwartz, J. H., and Jessel, T. M. *Principles of Neural Science* (3rd ed.). New York: Elsevier, 1991.

Mesulam, M.-M. *Principles of Behavioral Neurology*. Philadelphia: Davis, 1985.

Warwick, R. *Eugene Wolff's Anatomy of the Eye and Orbit* (7th ed.). Philadelphia: Saunders, 1976.

Answers to Clinical Problems

Chapter 1
Integrated Neuroscience for the Clinician
Questions 1 and 2 are both "thought questions," and the "correct" answers will differ for each individual. As you review your answers ask yourself: What type of reasoning did I use to generate hypotheses? Was there any difference between the way I approached question 1 and question 2? What past experiences helped me to understand the problems? What background knowledge did I use? What additional knowledge do I need to understand this problem? Where can I obtain that knowledge?

Chapter 2
Developmental Organization of the Nervous System: Neuroembryology
1. a. Fusion of neural tube, posterior neuropore.
   b. Neural tube at 4 weeks of development.
   c. Motor, sensory, and visceral.
   d. Neural tube and somites (myotome, sclerotome, dermatome).
   e. Ependymal, mantle, and marginal.
   f. Myelomeningocele.
2. a. Tumor formation in ectodermal derivatives: skin, eye, brain.
   b. Ectoderm and diencephalon.
   c. Neuroblast and spongioblast.
   d. Special somatic afferent.
   e. Tuberous sclerosis.

Chapter 3
Diagnosis of Neurologic Disorders: Anatomical Localization
1. Supratentorial, focal-left.
2. Supratentorial, focal-left.
3. Posterior fossa, focal-left.
4. Posterior fossa, focal-right.
5. Spinal, focal-midline.
6. Peripheral, focal-right.
7. Spinal, focal-left.

Chapter 4
Diagnosis of Neurologic Disorders: Neurocytology and the Pathologic Reactions of the Nervous System
1. Supratentorial, focal-right, nonmass, vascular.
2. Supratentorial, focal-right, mass, inflammatory.
3. Supratentorial, focal-left, mass, neoplastic.
4. Multiple levels, nonfocal-diffuse, nonmass, vascular.
5. Multiple levels, nonfocal-diffuse, nonmass, inflammatory.
6. Supratentorial, nonfocal-diffuse, nonmass, degenerative.
7. Posterior fossa, focal-left, nonmass, vascular.
8. Multiple levels, nonfocal-diffuse, nonmass, degenerative.
9. Spinal, focal-right, nonmass, vascular.
10. Peripheral, focal-right, mass, neoplastic.

Chapter 5
Diagnosis of Neurologic Disorders: Transient Disorders and Neurophysiology
1. Anoxia produces block of sodium pump, with accumulation of extracellular potassium. Reduction in ionic concentration gradient reduces resting potential and makes cells inexcitable. Recovery occurs with opening of collateral vessels or restoration of blood flow.

2. a. Both reduced with possible block of action potential conduction.
   b. Reduced.
3. Slow or block conduction in axons with reduction in visual acuity.
4. a. The resting membrane potential moves closer to threshold.
   c. Increased extracellular potassium concentration.
5. a. Decreased.
   b. None.
   c. Decreased.
   d. None.
6. None.
7. a. Equilibrium.
   b. Steady state.
   c. Active transport.

Chapter 6
The Cerebrospinal Fluid System

1. a. By comparison with standardized tables of normal head circumference, 50 cm at 10 months is more than 2 standard deviations above the norm.
   b. An increase in the volume of any of the constituents of the skull. At this age, subdural hematomas and hydrocephalus due to several causes are common.
   c. Computerized tomography and magnetic resonance imaging are safe, noninvasive procedures. This patient had aqueductal stenosis.
   d. Noncommunicating hydrocephalus.
   e. (1) Enlargement of lateral and third ventricles with obstruction at the aqueduct. The fourth ventricle would not be visualized.
      (2) Uniform dilatation of the ventricular system proximal to the blockage (of the lateral and third ventricles, aqueduct, and fourth ventricle), with no extraventricular air present.
      (3) Uniform dilatation of the entire ventricular system, with some air escaping into the basal extraventricular cisterns.
      (4) Usually no changes (but the cerebrospinal fluid would probably be bloody).
2. In the infant, intracranial volume can be increased by modest expansion of the su-

tures, which increases the head size and results in a less significant rise in intracranial pressure. In the adult, such compensation is impossible, and intracranial pressure increases.
3. a. Spinal, focal-midline, mass, neoplastic.
   b. Assuming that the lesion is at the midthoracic level, producing near complete blockage of cerebrospinal fluid pathways, then the opening pressure in the lumbar sac would be low normal; some respiratory pulsations transmitted via the abdomen would be seen but cardiac pulsations would not; compression of abdominal contents would result in an increase in pressure transmitted to the lumbar sac below the blockage, while jugular compression, which increases intracranial pressure, would not result in a pronounced pressure increase because compression-induced pressure would not be fully transmitted beyond the blockage to the lumbar sac.
   c. Skin, subcutaneous tissues, intraspinous ligaments, epidural space, dura mater, subdural space, and arachnoid and subarachnoid spaces.
   d. Myelography.
4. a. Multiple levels, diffuse, nonmass, an unidentified inflammation.
   b. An inflammatory process and a traumatic tap.
   c. Possibly bacteria; growth of the offending organism.
   d. In the presence of bacterial meningitis, the cerebrospinal fluid glucose level is often significantly lowered.
   e. No. It is indicated only in cases of suspected intraspinal lesions.

Chapter 7
The Sensory System

1. a. Peripheral, focal-right, nonmass, traumatic or vascular.
   b. The lateral femoral cutaneous nerve (refer to Fig. 7-12).
   c. Refer to Figure 7-12.
2. a. Spinal, focal-midline and bilateral, mass, neoplastic.
   b. Dorsal roots or spinal nerves of the C-2 segment.

c. Structures listed in 2b and dorsal columns (fasciculus cuneatus and fasciculus gracilis) bilaterally.

d. The segmental loss at C-2 suggests that this is the level of the lesion.

e. Meningioma, neurofibroma.

f. The segmental sensory loss would be at the level of the nipples, and the dorsal column deficit would spare the upper extremities and be present mainly in the lower extremities.

3. a. Spinal, focal-midline, mass, neoplastic.

b. The second-order axons transmitting pain and temperature impulses (bound for the spinothalamic tracts bilaterally), as they decussate in the ventral white commissure at the involved levels.

c. Syringomyelia; but the same clinical pattern could be produced by an intramedullary neoplasm at that level.

4. a. Spinal, focal-left, nonmass, traumatic.

b. T-10 (refer to Fig. 7-13).

c. Brown-Séquard's syndrome.

d. The lesion involves only the left side of the spinal cord; the sensation of touch ascends bilaterally.

e. Wallerian degeneration occurs in the distal axon when it is severed from its cell body of origin. Above the level of the lesion, the left spinothalamic tract would show degeneration up to the level of the thalamus. The left fasciculus gracilis would show degeneration only to the level of its second-order neuron — the nucleus gracilis. The left corticospinal tract would show degeneration below the lesion.

5. a. Supratentorial, focal-right, nonmass, vascular.

b. Thalamus (ventral posterolateral nucleus).

c. In the right thalamocortical radiations.

6. a. Supratentorial, focal-right, mass, neoplastic.

b. Focal sensory seizures.

c. The lesion is suprathalamic, producing a cortical sensory loss. Crude perceptions of touch, pain, temperature, and vibration occur at the thalamic level, while discriminative sensations require intact thalamocortical pathways for perception.

Chapter 8
The Motor System

1. a. Supratentorial, focal-right, mass, neoplastic.

b. Corticospinal.

c. It is higher than normal.

d. Focal clonic seizures secondary to local ionic changes in the area of the tumor.

e. No. It would be dangerous and perhaps fatal to the patient.

2. a. Multiple levels, diffuse, nonmass, degenerative.

b. Basal ganglia control, cerebellar control.

c. It is degenerative according to temporal profile, so toxic and metabolic causes must be considered. This is a case of hepatolenticular degeneration, or Wilson's disease, a genetic error in copper metabolism.

d. Basal ganglia — caudate nucleus, putamen, globus pallidus, thalamus, and cortex; cerebellum — dentate nucleus, red nucleus, thalamus, cortex, and pons.

e. Hypokinesia, hyperkinesia, athetosis, dystonia, tremor, and rigidity.

3. a. Multiple levels, diffuse, nonmass, vascular.

b. Traumatic and toxic. This is an example of carbon monoxide poisoning.

c. Indirect and direct activation pathways.

d. By damage at midbrain level with release of vestibulospinal and excitatory reticulospinal activation of lower motor neurons.

e. Type II (secondary) muscle spindle endings.

4. a. Multiple levels, diffuse, nonmass, inflammatory.

b. Yes, typical of viral infection — in this case, poliomyelitis.

c. Final common pathway.

d. Weakness, atrophy, hypotonia, hyporeflexia, and fasciculations.

e. Sensory from peripheral afferents, corticospinal, vestibulospinal, reticulospinal, rubrospinal, tectospinal, and input from other cord levels.

5. a. Supratentorial, left, nonmass, vascular.

b. Direct activation, precentral gyrus inferiorly on the left, including Broca's area.

c. Babinski's sign present, abdominal reflexes absent.

d. Speech apraxia or aphasia.

e. Lower motor neurons to upper facial muscles receive bilateral cortical innervation.

6. a. Posterior fossa, right, mass, inflammatory.

b. Cerebrospinal fluid pressure might be increased, and cerebellar tonsil herniation might occur.

c. Cerebellar control.

d. Superior cerebellar peduncle in the midbrain, pontocerebellar fibers entering the middle cerebellar peduncle, olivocerebellar fibers entering the inferior cerebellar peduncle.

e. Equilibration in the flocculonodular lobe, posture and gait in the anterior lobe, skilled extremity movements in the posterior lobes, speech in the vermis.

Chapter 9
The Internal Regulation System

1. a. Multiple levels, diffuse.

b. Nonmass, degenerative.

c. Blackouts, impotence, lack of sweating.

d. It would produce sweating.

e. All four.

2. a. Spinal, focal-midline.

b. Mass, neoplastic.

c. Nonreflex, autonomous neurogenic bladder dysfunction.

d. Impotence.

3. a. Peripheral, focal-left.

b. Mass, neoplastic.

c. Superior cervical ganglion or sympathetic trunk.

d. Sympathetic.

e. Midbrain, pons, medulla, cervical cord, T-1 spinal nerve, sympathetic trunk, carotid plexus.

f. Postganglionic or ganglionic lesion.

g. Preganglionic lesion.

4. a. Peripheral, diffuse.

b. Nonmass, other (toxic).

c. Parasympathetic.

d. Mushroom poisoning (muscarine).

e. It would enlarge the pupils.

f. (1), (2), (3), (4) altered by fear; (4) by blushing; (5) by crying.

5. a. Supratentorial, focal-midline.

b. Mass, neoplastic.

c. Hypothalamus and optic chiasm.

d. Osmoreceptors, temperature receptors.

e. Blocking of regulatory hormones that control the pituitary gland, and optic chiasm compression, producing visual loss.

Chapter 10
The Consciousness System

1. a. Multiple levels (supratentorial and posterior fossa), nonfocal and diffuse, nonmass, metabolic.

b. Widespread areas of cerebral cortex and portions of the ascending reticular activating system in the cerebrum, thalamus, and brain stem.

c. Hypoglycemia.

d. Diffuse slow-wave abnormality.

2. a. Supratentorial, focal-right, mass, vascular.

b. Intracerebral hemorrhage.

c. Although unilateral cerebral lesions do not ordinarily cause a loss of consciousness, a mass lesion (such as is present in this case) may compress diencephalic structures bilaterally or produce herniation of the supratentorial structures (or do both) with secondary involvement of diencephalic and brain stem structures bilaterally.

d. In addition to the focal slow-wave abnormality present over the right cerebral hemisphere, a more diffuse slow-wave disturbance may be seen.

3. a. Supratentorial, nonfocal-diffuse, indeterminate. The only abnormalities present were transient symptoms. As noted in Chapter 5, transient symptoms alone may be associated with various disorders and do not allow a pathologic diagnosis to be established.

b. Epileptiform abnormalities generalized in distribution, occurring in repetitive and rhythmic fashion (see Fig. 10-18).

c. Inflammatory (encephalitis), vascular, neoplastic, degenerative, toxic-metabolic, traumatic.

d. The presence of focal seizures would increase the likelihood of an underlying structural lesion involving one cerebral hemisphere. In a patient of this age, a neoplasm should be suspected.

Chapter 11
The Vascular System

1. a. Supratentorial, focal-right, nonmass, vascular.
   b. Vertebrobasilar system. The complete loss of vision suggests involvement of both posterior cerebral arteries; with resolution, only the distribution of the right posterior cerebral artery was involved.
   c. Infarction (right occipital lobe).
   d. Embolization from the heart.
   e. Decrease in PaO_2, increase in $PaCO_2$, increase in lactic acid, decrease in pH.
2. a. Supratentorial, focal-right, nonmass, vascular.
   b. Right carotid system — middle cerebral artery distribution.
   c. Infarction.
   d. May be related to extracranial carotid artery disease: thrombosis or embolization.
   e. True.
3. a. Supratentorial, focal-left, mass, vascular initially. (The loss of consciousness and bilateral Babinski's signs suggest secondary bilateral involvement at supratentorial or posterior fossa levels.)
   b. Intracerebral hemorrhage (with secondary early herniation).
   c. Hypertension, rupture of a vascular anomaly (arteriovenous malformation, aneurysm), trauma.
   d. Focal signs, headache, alteration in consciousness.
   e. Computerized tomography or magnetic resonance imaging.
4. a. Posterior fossa, focal-left, nonmass, vascular.
   b. Vertebrobasilar system, left posterior inferior cerebellar artery distribution.
   c. Infarction (in the left lateral medulla).
   d. Mechanism indeterminate; many patients have thrombotic occlusion of the vertebral artery.
   e. Vertigo — vestibular nucleus involvement; dysarthria, dysphagia, and left palatal weakness — left cranial nerves IX and X; loss of pain sensibility over left face — left descending tract and nucleus of cranial nerve V; loss of pain sensibility of the right limbs and trunk

— left spinothalamic tract; left Horner's syndrome — left descending sympathetic fibers.
5. a. Multiple levels, diffuse, nonmass, vascular. There are no focal abnormalities. The loss of consciousness suggests diffuse involvement of supratentorial and posterior fossa levels. Full recovery suggests no pathologic change in the central nervous system.
   b. Diffuse ischemia (syncope) — secondary to decreased cardiac output.
   c. The ability of an organ to maintain a constant blood supply in spite of variations in blood pressure. This regulation applies for all but the widest extremes in pressure.
   d. Only inhalation of carbon dioxide.
   e. Transient ischemic attacks are episodes of focal neurologic dysfunction; syncope is diffuse ischemia.
6. a. Multiple levels (supratentorial, posterior fossa, and spinal), diffuse, nonmass, vascular. The diffuse involvement, meningeal signs, and bloody cerebrospinal fluid suggest subarachnoid hemorrhage.
   b. At this age, rupture of an intracranial aneurysm is suspected.
   c. Immediate centrifugation of the specimen. The presence of a xanthochromic supernatant would suggest that it was not a traumatic puncture.

Chapter 12
The Neurochemical Systems

1. a. Diffuse.
   b. Nonmass, metabolic (hypoxia, global ischemia).
   c. Excitatory amino acid (glutamate).
   d. Excitotoxicity, mediated by calcium-triggered cascades: phospholipases, proteases, nitric oxide.
   e. Layers 3 to 5 of the cortex, hippocampus, cerebellum, striatum. These areas have "selective vulnerability" to injury.
   f. Blockade of excitatory amino acid receptors and calcium ion channels.
2. a. Supratentorial.
   b. Nonmass, toxic-metabolic.
   c. GABA.
   d. Withdrawal of GABA inhibition in set-

ting of down-regulation of receptors due to chronic exposure.

3. a. Supratentorial.
   b. Nonmass, degenerative, toxic-metabolic.
   c. Acetylcholine.
   d. Decreased memory and learning due to blockade of cortical muscarinic cholinergic receptors.
4. a. Supratentorial — basal ganglia.
   b. Nonmass, toxic-metabolic.
   c. Dopamine.
   d. Parkinson-like features due to blockade of dopaminergic receptors in the striatum.
   e. Chorea-like features, called "tardive dyskinesia," due to supersensitivity of striatal dopaminergic receptors caused by chronic pharmacologic blockade by the antipsychotic drug.
   f. Neuroleptic malignant syndrome, with hyperthermia, rigidity, and autonomic hyperactivity, due to dopaminergic blockade in the hypothalamus and basal ganglia.
5. a. Diffuse.
   b. Toxic-metabolic.
   c. Opioids.
   d. An opioid antagonist.

Chapter 13
The Peripheral Level

1. a. Peripheral (motor, sensory, and visceral), diffuse, nonmass, degenerative (metabolic).
   b. Peripheral neuropathy.
   c. They indicate loss of nerve or muscle fibers.
   d. It indicates loss of innervation of muscle fibers.
   e. Fibrillation is repetitive, rhythmic discharge of single muscle fiber. Fasciculation is single, spontaneous discharge of a motor unit.
2. a. Size of quanta and number of quanta.
   b. Number of quanta released.
   c. 11.
   d. EPP below action potential threshold; no muscle fiber contraction.
   e. Myasthenic syndrome associated with carcinoma.
3. a. Myositis.

b. Peripheral, diffuse, nonmass, inflammatory.
c. Muscle and nerve.
d. Increased rate of firing, recruitment of more motor units.
e. By making them of lower amplitude and shorter duration.
f. Inflammatory cells, fiber degeneration, central nuclei.
g. No.
h. Neurogenic atrophy.
i. As a result of collateral sprouting of intact axons.
j. They all mediate excitation-contraction coupling.
k. Because of leakage of enzyme from damaged muscle fibers.

Chapter 14
The Spinal Level

1. a. Spinal, midline, nonmass, vascular.
   b. L-1 to L-3, all of spinal cord except dorsal columns.
   c. No.
   d. Reflex (automatic) bladder, nonreflex (autonomous) bladder.
   e. Anterior spinal artery occlusion.
2. a. Spinal, midline, mass, neoplastic.
   b. Motor: final common pathway, direct and indirect activation pathways. Sensory: spinothalamic.
   c. C-4 to T-1; central gray matter affecting commissural fibers, ventral horn cells, and corticospinal tracts.
   d. Spinal cord mass — tumor or syrinx (possibly syringomyelia).
3. a. Multiple levels, diffuse, nonmass, degenerative.
   b. Dorsal columns.
   c. Peripheral and spinal cord involvement.
   d. Biochemical (vitamin B_{12} deficiency in this patient).
4. a. Spinal, right mass, traumatic.
   b. Right L-5 spinal nerve.
   c. Peroneal nerve, sciatic nerve, sacral plexus, L-5 spinal nerve, L-5 ventral roots, and lumbar spinal cord.
   d. Traction on sacral spinal nerves.

Chapter 15
The Posterior Fossa Level

1. a. Posterior fossa, left, nonmass, vascular.
   b. Left lateral medulla.
   c. Left posterior inferior cerebellar artery — a branch of the left vertebral artery (which is often the site of occlusion in this syndrome).
   d. The left descending tract of cranial nerve V, the left spinothalamic tract.
   e. Involvement of the descending sympathetic pathways en route to the spinal cord (producing Horner's syndrome).

2. a. Posterior fossa, right, mass, neoplastic.
   b. Cranial nerves IX, X, and XI on the right.
   c. Jugular foramen.
   d. Jugular vein.
   e. Chemodectoma.

3. a. Posterior fossa, left, nonmass, vascular.
   b. Left medullary pyramid (weakness), left medial lemniscus (decreased proprioception), left hypoglossal nerve (tongue weakness).
   c. Infarction of left medial medulla in the paramedian zone.

4. a. Posterior fossa, left, nonmass, vascular.
   b. Special visceral afferent fibers of the facial nerve supply taste to the anterior two-thirds of the tongue.
   c. General visceral efferent fibers of the facial nerve supply the lacrimal gland.
   d. Bell's palsy.

5. a. Posterior fossa, right, mass, neoplastic.
   b. Auditory division of cranial nerve VIII (decreased hearing, tinnitus), vestibular division of cranial nerve VIII (absent caloric response, disequilibrium), facial nerve (weakness of muscles of facial expression), cerebellar control circuit (decreased coordination).
   c. Cerebellopontine angle.
   d. Acoustic neuroma.
   e. Skull roentgenogram and petrous tomograms (enlargement of the internal auditory meatus), computerized tomography, magnetic resonance imaging.

6. a. Posterior fossa, left, nonmass, vascular.
   b. Cranial nerve VI (lateral rectus weakness), cranial nerve VII (facial weakness), medial lemniscus (loss of joint position and vibratory sense), descending (direct and indirect activation) motor pathways (hemiparesis).
   c. Infarction, left paramedian region of the pons.

7. a. Posterior fossa, right, nonmass, vascular.
   b. Cranial nerve III on right (diplopia, ptosis, mydriasis), right cerebral peduncle (left hemiparesis).
   c. Right medial and superior rectus muscles.
   d. The efferent limb of the pupillary light reflex travels via general visceral efferent fibers contained in cranial nerve III.
   e. Infarction, right paramedian region of the mesencephalon.

8. a. Posterior fossa, left, mass, neoplasm.
   b. The left cerebellar hemisphere (ataxia).
   c. Headache, nausea, vomiting, papilledema.
   d. Cerebellar astrocytoma. (These tumors are often cystic and have an excellent prognosis.)

9. a. Multiple levels, diffuse, nonmass, degenerative.
   b. Motor system only, at the posterior fossa and spinal levels.
   c. Final common pathway (weakness, fasciculations), direct activation pathways (bilateral Babinski's signs).
   d. Motor neuron disease (amyotrophic lateral sclerosis).

10. a. Supratentorial, left, mass, inflammatory (abscess).
    b. Secondary involvement of the consciousness system by the expanding mass lesion causing herniation.
    c. Compression of cranial nerve III on the left by an expanding temporal lobe mass.
    d. With increasing herniation, there is also secondary compression of the cerebral peduncle.
    e. Uncal herniation.
    f. Mesencephalon.
    g. Decerebrate rigidity.
    h. Transtentorial or central herniation.

Chapter 16
The Supratentorial Level
1. a. Supratentorial, midline (region of pituitary gland).
   b. Pituitary gland and optic chiasm.
   c. Anterior lobe and posterior lobe.
   d. Anterior lobe.
   e. TSH, GH, ACTH, gonadotropins (FSH, LH), and prolactin; regulatory hormones from the hypothalamus, which descend to the anterior lobe via a portal circulation.
   f. TSH, ACTH, and gonadotropin.
   g. Compression of the optic chiasm by the lesion.
   h. Enlarged sella.
   i. Optic chiasm; internal carotid artery; cavernous sinus with cranial nerves III, IV, V, and VI.
   j. Mass, neoplastic (chromophobe adenoma).
2. a. Supratentorial, midline (in the region of the hypothalamus).
   b. Hypothalamus via nerve fibers.
   c. Vasopressin.
   d. Regulate visceral functions, regulate releasing factors for the anterior pituitary lobe, regulate water metabolism, regulate food intake, regulate body temperature, regulate sleep, regulate the cardiovascular system, regulate emotion.
   e. Mass, neoplastic (craniopharyngioma).
3. a. Supratentorial, left (left parietal cortex).
   b. Nonmass, vascular (infarct).
   c. Astereognosia, graphesthesia, atopognosia, right-left disorientation.
   d. Visual agnosia, occipital lobe. Auditory agnosia, temporal lobe.
   e. A right inferior homonymous quadrantanopia.
4. a. Supratentorial, diffuse (cerebral cortex).
   b. Nonmass, degenerative (Alzheimer's disease).
   c. Short-term, recent, and long-term memory.
   d. Mental retardation is the failure to develop normal intelligence; dementia is the loss of cognitive processes after these have developed.
   e. Apraxia.
   f. Seizures, aphasia, agnosia.
5. a. Supratentorial, left (left temporal lobe).
   b. Mass, neoplastic (glioma).
   c. Right superior homonymous quadrantanopia.
   d. Complex partial seizures arising from the temporal lobe.
   e. Uncus.
   f. Change in the seizures with involvement of more posterior portions of the temporal lobe, the development of aphasia, increasingly severe headaches, and nausea and vomiting.
   g. EEG, magnetic resonance imaging, computerized tomographic scan, and arteriogram.
   h. EEG: focal slowing and spike discharges over the left temporal region. Magnetic resonance imaging and computerized tomographic scan: mass lesion, left temporal lobe. Arteriogram: mass lesion, left temporal lobe.
   i. Receptive aphasia.
   j. Limbic system. Anatomical structures: telencephalic structures — hippocampus, amygdala, part of the cingulate gyrus, basal forebrain, septal region, fornix; diencephalic structures — hypothalamus and anterior, dorsomedial, midline thalamic nuclei. Functions: learning, memory, emotion, affective behavior, control of autonomic function and homeostasis, cortical arousal, motivated behavior, olfaction.
6. a. Bitemporal hemianopia.
   b. Left homonymous hemianopia with macular sparing.
   c. Left inferior homonymous quadrantanopia.
   d. Right superior homonymous quadrantanopia.

Index

Index